SELECTED PAPERS IN PHYSICS

SELECTED PAPERS IN PHYSICS

IN HONOUR OF C. J. GORTER

On the occasion of his retirement
from the State University of Leyden

Editor:

J. VAN DEN HANDEL

Kamerlingh Onnes Laboratory
Leyden, The Netherlands

NORTH-HOLLAND PUBLISHING COMPANY AMSTERDAM

Library of Congress Catalog Card Number 73-92660
NORTH-HOLLAND ISBN: 0 7204 0289
American Elsevier ISBN: 0444 1061 62

Reprinted from PHYSICA volume 69 no. 1

Printed in The Netherlands

Prof. Dr. C. J. Gorter

PREFACE

This volume being originally an issue of the journal Physica is dedicated to Professor Gorter on the occasion of his retirement from the university on the 1st November 1973.

Professor Gorter studied at Leiden University from 1924 until 1930 and obtained his doctorate in 1932. His thesis, entitled "Paramagnetische Eigenschaften von Salzen", revitalized the Leiden research on paramagnetism at low temperatures, initiated bij Kamerlingh Onnes and his collaborators, and was especially stimulated by the work of Van Vleck, who published the first of his famous articles in 1927. The close contacts between Van Vleck and Gorter originate from this time. In the thirties he started his work on paramagnetic relaxation, a subject which became one of his specialities, on which many of his students obtained their degrees and on which he wrote, during the war, a monograph entitled "Paramagnetic Relaxation".

In 1933 Gorter was the first to apply thermodynamics to the transition from the normal to the superconducting state. After the discovery of the Meissner effect (1933), he developed in 1934, together with Casimir, the thermodynamics of the two-fluid model for superconductivity and introduced an internal-order parameter. At about the same time F. and H. London developed the electrodynamics of the two-fluid model. Furthermore, in this connection we mention Gorter's contributions to the understanding of second-order phase transitions and, later, together with Mellink, to the description of the mutual friction between both fluids of the two-fluid model for liquid helium II.

In 1938 Gorter published an explanation of the influence of a magnetic field on the transport properties in paramagnetic gases, the Senftleben effect.

After the war in 1946 he succeeded W. H. Keesom as professor in physics in Leiden and as director of the Kamerlingh Onnes Laboratory. Because of the war activities the scientific work in this laboratory had gradually diminished and come more or less to a standstill. Moreover, academic contacts with the outer world had been virtually severed.

Thanks to Gorter's great energy, intellectual faculties and organizing ability the standard of research in the laboratory was soon restored and it could again play a significant role in the international physics world. During the war new methods, e.g. microwave techniques, had been developed and in the subsequent years Gorter actively persued and encouraged the field of magnetic resonance. The diversity of methods used in the Kamerlingh Onnes Laboratory also made it possible to study special subjects from different points of view. A good example of this was the study of $CuCl_2 \cdot 2H_2O$ *which gave detailed insight into antiferromagnetism which was still further elucidated by his theoretical research with Haantjes.*

Contact with nuclear physicists made it possible to use low-temperature techniques in nuclear physics. From this cooperation work on the orientational dependence of the radiation of radioactive magnetic nuclei was persued. This led in 1957 to the discovery of an asymmetry in the emission of positons by polarized ^{58}Co *nuclei. This supported the work by Wu et al., which had been published a few weeks earlier, on the emission of electrons, indicating the non-validity of the law of parity conservation for weak interactions.*

We have tried to reflect in this volume the many interests of Professor Gorter. When asking physicists in various fields of interest, in The Netherlands as well as abroad, to send a short contribution for this volume we were pleased with the many positive reactions. Not every-one who should have liked to send a note was able to do so in the rather short time available but still many papers were received. In a few cases we asked specifically for a contribution in connection with the special place the author had in the development of Gorter's work. From these contributions those of Van Vleck and Kronig have a more historical character. De Boer who has had in the course of the years very close contact with Gorter on the subject of the two-fluid model was asked to give a review on the present state of research in this field. Finally Wheatley gives a review of the latest spectacular developments in the field of the millidegrees. But in the other cases we asked for a short contribution from current research.

This volume represents the gratitude and admiration of very many physicists, some of whom find their names here as authors. On behalf of all of them I thank Professor Gorter for his contributions to the understanding of physics and for his many stimulating activities.

J. van den Handel
Editor of Physica
Professor of Physics in Leiden and
member of the farewell committee.

LIST OF CONTRIBUTORS

CONTENTS

Physica **69** (1973) 1–4 © *North-Holland Publishing Co.*

MAGNETIC RELAXATION IN RETROSPECT

R. KRONIG

Feldstrasse 3, Erlenbach ZH, Schweiz

Received 16 April 1973

Synopsis

In a brief survey the conditions are described under which the early studies of the interaction between alternating magnetic fields and matter were carried out.

1. *Introduction.* It is not only of historical interest but often also instructive as regards salient features of scientific research to review the development of a branch of science from small beginnings to a full-fledged state. Questions then arise as to why this branch made its appearance at such and such a time in such and such a place, why its progress was slow or rapid, as the case may be, and why the relevant initiatives were taken by such and such persons.

The field of magnetic relaxation is one where considerations of this kind are very profitable. The fact that C. J. Gorter contributed in so large a measure to our knowledge of it, makes it appropriate to include a summary of its essential aspects in this volume.

The interaction of matter with alternating electric fields has had the attention of physicists over a long period. Indeed, visible light as well as radiation in the near-infrared, ultraviolet or X-ray region affects matter primarily through its electric vector because the quantum jumps of atoms and molecules, associated with frequencies in that range, are preponderantly electric-dipole transitions. If we turn our attention to radiofrequencies, we find that even there electric effects predominate when we are dealing with substances composed of molecules with a permanent dipole moment. From the theoretical and experimental work of Debye one had already become familiar with the phenomenon of dielectric relaxation early in this century.

The problem of investigating the influence of alternating magnetic fields on matter naturally arose after this stage had been reached. We shall look one by one at the conditions for carrying out such an investigation as they presented themselves when this subject was first attacked seriously in the middle thirties.

2. *Frequency.* According to what was said above regarding electric-dipole transitions, clear-cut information could be hoped for only in the region of radiowaves. Radiowaves meant at that time waves with wavelengths of the order of magnitude of metres or larger, such as could be generated with the help of ordinary LRC-circuits and old-fashioned electron tubes. Waves in the centimetre and millimetre range of reasonable intensity first became available during the second world war through the development of radar in England and the United States. The new techniques penetrated to the Netherlands only after the war. This circumstance restricted the early work of Gorter and his collaborators to the study of magnetic relaxation and handicapped them, compared to physicists in the countries mentioned, in extending their research immediately to the problems of magnetic resonance.

3. *Materials.* In order to obtain an interaction of an alternating magnetic field with matter, it is necessary that at least a part of the atomic systems present possess magnetic moments. Since the relaxation experiments have to be performed on matter in bulk, in general at or below room temperature, the atomic systems will be occupying the ground state of their electronic configuration. A majority of atoms and molecules in this state have vanishing magnetic moments, the substances composed of them being diamagnetic. Atoms or ions with nonvanishing magnetic moments are encountered in the transiton groups of the periodic system of the elements, where internal shells are being completed. They may either be bound in crystals or occur by dissociation of salts in aqueous solutions. Magnetic relaxation in aqueous solutions, however, will be completely masked by the dielectric relaxation to which the strongly polar molecules of water give rise as well as by the effects of electric conductivity. For practical purposes, one hence was confined to the use of crystals, containing magnetic atoms or ions.

One of the subjects to which much attention had been given at the Kamerlingh Onnes Laboratory in Leiden in the first decennia of the present century was the static magnetic susceptibility of just such magnetic crystals, in particular those containing the ions of the transition elements Ti, V, Cr, Mn and Fe, in which the shell of 3d-electrons is completed. Among these crystals the so-called alums had received special attention since they belong to the cubic system, while their lattice structure was known in full detail. It lay in the nature ot things that Gorter, having had his training as a physicist at Leiden University, directed his attention primarily to these substances. They had the additional advantage that the magnetic ions can be replaced to a greater or lesser extent by non-magnetic ions of the same valency, and that relaxation could thus be studied in terms of an extra variable factor, the degree of dilution.

4. *Temperature.* When comparing magnetic with dielectric relaxation, there is one quantitative feature in which the two differ markedly. When employing the

gaussian system of electric and magnetic units, the electric and magnetic vectors of a plane electromagnetic wave *in vacuo* are equal in strength, while in fields of less simple geometry they are at least of comparable magnitude. On the other hand, in the same system of units the magnetic moments of paramagnetic atoms or ions, of the order of one or a few Bohr magnetons, are by a factor of about 100 smaller than the electric-dipole moments of polar molecules. As a consequence, magnetic relaxation effects, notably the heat developed in paramagnetic crystals by magnetic fields of radiofrequencies, were much more difficult to detect and measure than the analogous dielectric effects, previously investigated by Debye. Steps had therefore to be taken to enhance as much as possible their manifestation.

Since what is measured in relaxation experiments is not so much the heat produced as the temperature rise, which for a given amount of heat is inversely proportional to the specific heat of the sample, it is advantageous to work at low temperatures, where the specific heat may drop far below its classical value as given by the law of Dulong and Petit. Much more cogent reasons, however, for varying the temperature down to low values arise from the fact that the mechanisms of relaxation which determine the speed of establishing thermal equilibrium depend strongly on the temperature. Here again the extensive experience available at Leiden regarding cryogenic procedures came in good stead. Gorter had become thoroughly familiarized with them during his university course and hence was not afraid to employ them.

5. *Constant magnetic fields*. The energy values of the magnetic sublevels which the ions in paramagnetic crystals may occupy can be markedly influenced by an external constant magnetic field that acts on the magnetic moments of these ions at the same time as the alternating magnetic field. In this way another variable parameter, the strength of the constant field, can be disposed of in order to enrich the information regarding relaxation phenomena.

6. *Theoretical basis*. Pioneer work in physics, as in any other science, will always be effectively promoted if besides the necessary experimental equipment and techniques a reasonably clear theoretical picture of the underlying situation is at hand. Otherwise all that can be achieved is an accumulation of empirical data, an example of this being spectroscopy in the second half of last century.

Fortunately theory in the early thirties had sufficiently advanced to provide the necessary background for relaxation studies in paramagnetic crystals. From spectroscopic evidence Hund had been able as early as in 1925 to deduce the nature of the ground states of the ions concerned when in an isolated condition. By using the methods of group theory, Bethe in about 1930 could predict how electric fields of various symmetries, such as arise from the neighbouring atoms in crystals, further resolve the levels for the isolated ions into sublevels. As mentioned previously, X-ray analysis had furnished the necessary geometrical data on the crystallographic structure in the case of the paramagnetic alums.

After successful measurements had been carried out, the theoretical problem arose of calculating the magnitude of the alternating magnetization arising in the crystal when subjected to an alternating magnetic field, as well as the phase relation between the two quantities. This problem is a statistical one. The answer depends on whether the individual magnetic moments of the ions are directly coupled to the vibrations of the crystal lattice; or whether by mutual coupling they form a system which in turn at each moment strives for thermal equilibrium with the lattice. The first situation prevails in crystals diluted by diamagnetic atoms, while the second, first investigated by Casimir and others, may be expected to hold in undiluted ones.

Each of these cases is characterized by a relaxation time, which increases as some negative power of the temperature, the details of the dependence being governed by the type of ground state of the magnetic ion involved.

7. *The personal angle*. The developments referred to in the preceding pages took place when Gorter and I both were affiliated, as lecturers, with the physics institute at the University of Groningen. In more than one way this provided an ideal milieu. At that time, between 1935 and 1939, the university had about 1400 students. Our teaching duties were not exorbitant so that plenty of time was available for research. In a formal sense we were not members of the faculty so that we were free from all the administration inherent in professorships. On the other hand the faculty in Groningen had the pleasant custom of treating the lecturers socially as belonging to their midst by inviting them to the annual faculty dinner and the monthly evening meetings of the professorial circle, where tea, wine and Groninger koek accompanied animating discussions.

At the physics institute the director Professor Coster had created an atmosphere highly conducive to active research. Even in the years of severest economic crisis he succeeded in securing sufficient funds for the purchase of new equipment, and protected the younger functionaries against dismissal for reasons of economic retrenchment. About a dozen advanced students, usually working for the doctorate, were integrated into the research activities of the laboratory; some were attached to the experimental group of Gorter on magnetic relaxation, while others assisted me in the attendant theoretical studies. Thus a very fruitful symbiosis came about. I am afraid that such ideal intimate conditions have become rare at present and will be scarcer still in the future.

REFERENCE

Those interested in the details of the developments sketched here summarily are referred to the issues of Physica from 1935 to 1940 and to Gorter's book "Paramagnetic Relaxation", Elsevier (Amsterdam, 1947).

Physica **69** (1973) 5–11 © *North-Holland Publishing Co.*

WAVE PACKETS OF RELATIVISTIC ELECTRONS

F. BAKKE and H. WERGELAND

Seminar of Theoretical Physics, The University of Trondheim, NTH, N-7034 Trondheim, Norway

Received 2 April 1973

Professor Cornelis Gorter has an old stake in the Dirac electron, particularly in the experimental manifestations of its magnetic moment. Although his designing upon that latter elusive object probably culminated in the polarization experiments with aligned nuclei 1956–58, we hope that the following considerations will not be out of key with the celebration of a great experimentalist who has also a deep understanding for the theoretical models.

Synopsis

It is shown that wave packets of the δ-function type can be constructed without invoking negative energies. The position uncertainty is computed for a typical packet. Unlike the purely diffusive spreading known from nonrelativistic quantum mechanics, the relativistic wave packets always have a wave-like precursor on the light cone.

1. *Introduction.* It is commonly known that the relativistic electron considered as a one-particle system is problematic; less so perhaps, that the difficulties can be resolved by recourse to the full positron theory. These problems are certainly connected to the general question of locality and causality showing up in the vacuum expectation values of products of field operators at different space–time points. As this question still does not seem to be fully clarified[1]) a very limited aim may be justified, namely to inspect how far it is possible to use the solution Ψ of Dirac's equation in the simple-minded way as a probability amplitude. Strictly speaking the c-number function one is then talking about is the transition element of the field operator from a one-electron state to the vacuum. But that is not peculiar to relativistic quantum mechanics. And this physical meaning of Ψ should not need to be explicitly recalled in phenomena where the particle numbers stay constant.

A very beautiful insight into the possibilities here was opened through the transformation discovered by Foldy and Wouthuysen[2]). This transformation, to be sure, makes the position operator a nonlocal one. Recently, however, Jensen and collaborators[3]), in a vigourous revival of the Klein paradox, went even considerably further in ascribing consistency to the Dirac equation as a one-particle theory.

Like Jensen we shall adhere to Dirac's original representation where the position operator is local, but mixes positive and negative energy states. We shall elsewhere try to amplify Jensen's remarks on the Klein paradox. Here we would in the first place like to discuss a convenient type of relativistic wave packets. While analytical expressions for this purpose are abundant in nonrelativistic wave mechanics, we have not in the current books been able to find anything similar for the relativistic domain.

2. *Cauchy problem of the Dirac equation.* Limiting ourselves to one dimension and choosing units such that $\hbar = 1$, $c = 1$, $m = 1$, a general solution of Dirac's equation can be expanded in plane waves as

$$\Psi(x, t) = \int_{-\infty}^{\infty} \mathrm{d}p(a^+u^+\mathrm{e}^{-\mathrm{i}Et} + a^-u^-\mathrm{e}^{\mathrm{i}Et})\mathrm{e}^{\mathrm{i}px}, \tag{1}$$

where $u^{\pm}(p, E)$ are the positive- and negative-energy spinors given by

$$(\boldsymbol{\alpha p} + \beta \mp E)u^{\pm} = 0, \qquad E = (p^2 + 1)^{\frac{1}{2}}. \tag{2}$$

Since the spin operator σ_x commutes with the hamiltonian $H = \boldsymbol{\alpha p} + \beta$, a constant spin amplitude, corresponding to the eigenvalue $\sigma_x' = 1$ say, can be separated out. It will never change in the free motion and therefore it can be omitted. We have thus only to deal with two-component spinors which we shall take in the form

$$u^+ = [2(E+1)]^{-\frac{1}{2}}\begin{pmatrix} E+1 \\ p \end{pmatrix}, \quad u^- = [2(E+1)]^{-\frac{1}{2}}\begin{pmatrix} -p \\ E+1 \end{pmatrix}, \tag{3}$$

i.e., with the invariant normalization $|u|^2 = E$.

While the complete expansion (1) involving negative- as well as positive-energy components is necessary for a general solution of the Cauchy problem, the possible eigenvalues for the energy of a free electron must be positive. It is therefore of interest in connection with the question of localizability of electrons to see how far wave packets can be constructed out of positive energy components only. A widespread belief holds that this must inevitably give the electron a minimum extension of about one Compton wavelength*. However, this is not quite so. As we shall see, the localization by means of positive-energy wave packets can be made just as sharp as in nonrelativistic wave mechanics.

* We have seen that a well-localized state contains, in general, plane-wave components of negative energies. Conversely, we may ask how well localized a state will be which we can form using only plane-wave components of positive energies. A rather careful analysis by Newton and Wigner indicates that the best-localized state we can construct in this way is one in which the characteristic linear dimension of the wave packet is $\approx h/mc$ but not smaller [5]).

3. *Construction of a positive energy wave packet.* If an initial state

$$\Psi(x, 0) = \int \mathrm{d}p \begin{pmatrix} c_1(p) \\ c_2(p) \end{pmatrix} \mathrm{e}^{\mathrm{i}px}, \tag{4}$$

does not imply negative-energy components during its evolution in time, it follows from eqs. (3) that the ratio of c_1 to c_2 must be: $(E + 1)/p = [(E + 1)/(E - 1)]^{\frac{1}{2}} \times \operatorname{sgn} p$. This still leaves us a wide class of initial conditions which can be imposed upon strictly positive-energy solutions:

$$\Psi(x, t) = \int_{-\infty}^{\infty} \mathrm{d}p\, c(p) u^{+} \mathrm{e}^{\mathrm{i}(px - Et)}, \tag{5}$$

by a suitable choice of the expansion coefficients $c(p)$. An especially simple case is

$$c(p) = \mathrm{e}^{-aE}/E, \tag{6}$$

which we shall work out in closed form. In the form (6) of $c(p)$ the parameter a is related to the position uncertainty in the nonrelativistic limiting case by

$$a = 2\Delta x^2 = 1/2\Delta p^2, \tag{7}$$

since then

$$\mathrm{e}^{-aE}/E \to \text{const.}\ \mathrm{e}^{-\frac{1}{2}ap^2},$$

which means a gaussian wave packet with $\Delta p^2 = 1/2a$. Although some other types are also tractable, it will be sufficient for our purpose to consider this one. The integral (5) can then be written in the closed form

$$\Psi(x, t) = N \frac{\mathrm{e}^{-\mathrm{i}(\tau^2 - x^2)^{\frac{1}{2}}}}{(\tau^2 - x^2)^{\frac{1}{4}}} \begin{pmatrix} \operatorname{Cos} \frac{1}{2}\chi \\ \operatorname{Sin} \frac{1}{2}\chi \end{pmatrix}, \tag{8}$$

where $\chi = \arctan(x/\tau)$, $\tau = t - \mathrm{i}a$.

The probability density will be governed both by the exponential and the spinor factor in the expression (8)

$$\Psi^{\dagger}\Psi = N^2 \frac{\mathrm{e}^{2\,\mathrm{Im}\,(\tau^2 - x^2)^{\frac{1}{2}}}}{|\tau^2 - x^2|^{\frac{1}{2}}} \operatorname{Cos}(\operatorname{Re}\chi), \tag{9}$$

where the norm of the spinor

$$\operatorname{Cos}(\operatorname{Re}\chi) = \frac{1}{2}\left[\left(\frac{(t + x)^2 + a^2}{(t - x)^2 + a^2}\right)^{\frac{1}{4}} + \left(\frac{(t - x)^2 + a^2}{(t + x)^2 + a^2}\right)^{\frac{1}{4}}\right]$$

$$\begin{cases} = 1 & \text{for } t = 0, \\ \approx 1 & \text{far from the light cone,} \end{cases}$$

but it should be noted that this factor may be considerable for $x \approx \pm t$ if a is small.

For $t = 0$ one has simply

$$\Psi^\dagger\Psi = N^2 \frac{\mathrm{e}^{-2(x^2+a^2)^{\frac{1}{2}}}}{(x^2+a^2)^{\frac{1}{2}}}, \tag{10}$$

which is the initial distribution corresponding to our present choice of $c(p)$, eq. (6). The normalization factor is

$$N = [2K_0(2a)]^{-\frac{1}{2}}, \tag{11}$$

where K is related to the Hankel functions of imaginary argument by: $K_0(z) = \frac{1}{2}\pi \mathrm{i} H_0^{(1)}(\mathrm{i}z)$.

As we observed in eq. (7) a is closely related to the uncertainty in position

$$a \approx 2\Delta x^2 \quad \text{at} \quad t = 0 \quad \text{if} \quad a \gg 1. \tag{12}$$

When a is large formula (10) for $\Psi^\dagger\Psi$ approaches a normalized gaussian distribution. Like the latter it can also be peaked with *arbitrary* sharpness: $a \to 0$, $K_0(2a) \sim -\log a \to \infty$, and normalization being preserved it can thus be made a δ-function.

Well inside the light cone $x = \pm t$ the behaviour is also simple. Then $\Psi^\dagger\Psi$ is practically determined by the exponential only:

$$\begin{aligned}(\tau^2 - x^2)^{\frac{1}{2}} &= t - \mathrm{i}a - \frac{1}{2}\frac{x^2}{t - \mathrm{i}a} + \cdots \\ &= \text{Real part } -\mathrm{i}a\left(1 + \frac{x^2}{2(t^2+a^2)}\right) + \cdots, \end{aligned} \tag{13}$$

$$2\,\mathrm{Im}\,(\tau^2 - x^2)^{\frac{1}{2}} = -\frac{x^2}{[a + (1/a)t^2]} + \cdots .$$

In this region $|x| \ll t$, the distribution is therefore a gaussian whose diffusion with time is given by

$$2\Delta x^2(t) \approx a + (1/a)t^2. \tag{14}$$

In view of the relation (12) between a and Δx, this is closely similar to the non-relativistic relation

$$\Delta x^2(t) = \Delta x^2(0) + \Delta v^2 t^2, \tag{15}$$

where

$$\Delta v^2 = (\Delta p/m)^2 = (1/2m\Delta x)^2.$$

In nonrelativistic quantum mechanics two statements can be made about localization: 1) a particle can be localized as sharply as we wish, *i.e.*, the wave packet can be made a δ function in space; 2) in the limit $\Delta x \to 0$, however, the wave packet [according to eq. (15)] diffuses with infinite velocity.

The last statement is evidently in conflict with relativity but it cannot be drawn as a conclusion from the similitude of the approximate relation (14) with eq. (15) because the former is by no means generally valid. As we shall see from an exact expression of $\Delta x^2(t)$, however, the statement 1) remains correct in Dirac's theory: *even with exclusively positive energies an electron can be localized sharply*: $\Delta x \to 0$. As before the wave packets will fly apart faster when Δx is decreased, but in contrast to the nonrelativistic case a limit to this appears clearly: the diffusion velocity does indeed not exceed the velocity of light.

4. *Exact computation of the diffusion velocity*. It is convenient to proceed with the packet (7) which is at rest $\langle x \rangle = 0$, since the case of uniform translation can most simply be obtained from this one by a Lorentz transformation. Thus $\Delta x^2(t)$ is given by

$$\Delta x^2 = \langle \Psi | x^2 | \Psi \rangle. \tag{16}$$

It is perhaps interesting to note that in the alternative way of computation

$$\Delta x^2 = \| x\Psi \|^2, \tag{16a}$$

negative-energy components are essential for obtaining the correct result, while in eq. (16) of course they do not appear. By a direct calculation one finds either way an expression of the form

$$\Delta x^2(t) = \Delta x^2(0) + U^2 t^2, \tag{17}$$

where

$$\Delta x^2(0) = \tfrac{1}{2} a K_1(2a)/K_0(2a),$$

$$U^2 = \left[K_0(2a) - 2a \left(K_1(2a) - \int_{2a}^{\infty} K_0(z)\,\mathrm{d}z \right) \right] \Big/ K_0(2a).$$

From the asymptotic properties of the Macdonald–Bessel functions K_0 and K_1 one finds

$$\Delta x^2(0) \approx \begin{cases} 1/|4 \log a| & a \to 0, \\ \tfrac{1}{2} a & a \gg 1, \end{cases}$$
$$U^2 \approx \begin{cases} 1 - 1/|\log a| & a \to 0, \\ 1/a & a \gg 1. \end{cases} \tag{18}$$

Thus one sees that there is a limiting velocity of diffusion

$$U(a \to 0) = 1 (= c), \tag{19}$$

so that at least in this respect the positive-energy wave packets do not show an acausal behaviour.

5. "*Lorentz boost*". So far we have used the simplifications which are special for the "proper system" in which the centre of the wave packet is at rest. Let it henceforth be indicated by a superscript 0: $\langle x^0 \rangle = 0$ for all t^0. Connecting this with a "laboratory system" (x, t) by means of the Lorentz transformation:

$$\Psi^0 \to \Psi(x, t) = e^{\frac{1}{2}\rho\Phi}\Psi^0(x^0, t^0), \quad \rho = \begin{pmatrix} 0 & 1 \\ 1 & 0 \end{pmatrix}, \quad \Phi = \text{artan}\, v, \tag{20}$$

we obtain a wave packet in uniform translation with velocity v.

Since we have tacitly treated the normalization integral as our hermitean scalar product, a word on its transformation may be in place.

The scalar product in Dirac's theory is actually

$$\int_\sigma d\sigma_\mu \bar{\Psi}\gamma^\mu\Psi = \text{invariant}, \tag{21}$$

where σ is any space-like surface. Since in the comoving system we may choose $\sigma \equiv t^0 = \text{const.}$ and in the laboratory system $\sigma \equiv t = \text{const.}$, while the integrand is invariant we have $\int_{-\infty}^{\infty} |\Psi^0|^2 dx^0 = \int_{-\infty}^{\infty} |\Psi|^2 dx$. Thus, even though $|\Psi^0|^2(t_0) \neq |\Psi|^2(t)$, we can, by virtue of the conservation equation (21) consider Ψ^0 and Ψ as the probability densities in the respective systems, provided that the wave functions are correctly transformed according to eq. (20).

Carrying out the transformation (20) one obtains now

$$\Psi^\dagger\Psi = N^2 \frac{\exp(2\,\text{Im}\,\{[(\tau^0)^2 - (x^0)^2]^{\frac{1}{2}}\})}{|(\tau^0)^2 - (x^0)^2|^{\frac{1}{2}}} \text{Cos}\,[\text{Re}\,(\chi + \Phi)],$$

where $x^0 = \gamma(x - vt)$, $\tau^0 = \gamma(t - vx) - ia$. Well inside the light cone the probability density is again dominated by the exponential as in eq. (13)

$$2\,\text{Im}\,\{[(\tau^0)^2 - (x^0)^2]^{\frac{1}{2}}\} = \frac{\gamma^2(x - vt)^2}{a + (1/a)\gamma^2(t - vx)^2},$$

and in the neighbourhood of the classical orbit $x \approx vt$ we have

$$\Psi^\dagger\Psi \approx \exp\{-\gamma^2(x - vt)^2/[a + (1/a)t^2]\},$$

a Lorentz-contracted gaussian packet: $\Delta x^2 = (1/\gamma^2)(\Delta x^0)^2$.

This picture, however, is rather inaccurate. In the first place the spinor factor must also be taken into account. Specifically it is now given by

$$\text{Cos}\,[\text{Re}\,(\chi + \Phi)] = \frac{1}{2}\left[\left(\frac{(1 - v)(t + x)^2 + (1 + v)a^2}{(1 + v)(t - x)^2 + (1 - v)a^2}\right)^{\frac{1}{4}} + \left(\frac{(1 + v)(t - x)^2 + (1 - v)a^2}{(1 - v)(t + x)^2 + (1 + v)a^2}\right)^{\frac{1}{4}}\right].$$

It will supply the packet with a precursor at $x = t$ and a somewhat smaller "postcursor" at $x = -t$. This is perhaps the most striking difference from the purely diffusive spreading of wave packets which is so typical of non-relativistic quantum mechanics.

REFERENCES

1) Shirokov, M. I., Preprint E 1252 Dubna (1963), with extensive references.
2) Foldy, L. L. and Wouthuysen, S. A., Phys. Rev. **78** (1950) 29.
3) Dosch, H. G., Jensen, J. H. D. and Müller, V. F., Phys. Norveg. **5** (1971) 151.
4) Fierz, M., Helv. phys. Acta **23** (1950) 731.
5) Sakurai, J. J., Advanced Quantum Mechanics, Addison Wesley Publ. Co (Reading, 1967), p. 119.

Physica **69** (1973) 12–20 © *North-Holland Publishing Co.*

TRANSPORT COEFFICIENTS IN SPECIAL RELATIVITY

S. R. de GROOT

Instituut voor Theoretische Fysica, Universiteit van Amsterdam, Amsterdam, Nederland

Received 27 April 1973

This paper is dedicated to Cornelis J. Gorter as a token of gratitude and admiration. As my teacher he introduced me to experimental and theoretical molecular physics in Amsterdam, during dark times, and to the nuclear physicists in France, after the Liberation. Our contacts, both as friends and as colleagues, were resumed in this country and were of great value to me. His scientific spirit reminds one of *Condillac*'s words: "*Il est donc certain qu'on ne fait des progrès dans la recherche de la vérité qu'autant que l'art de composer et celui de décomposer se réunissent dans une même méthode. Il faut les connaître tous deux également, et faire continuellement usage de l'un et de l'autre.*" (From: *Art de penser.*)

Synopsis

Results are presented on relativistic values of the heat conductivity, the viscosities and related properties, both for systems of massive particles and of neutrinos. The calculations are based on a method recently devised to obtain the transport coefficients for systems of particles with *arbitrary* cross sections.

1. *Introduction.* In the first phase of non-relativistic theory of transport processes one could only handle the special model of the "Maxwell particles", repelling each other with a negative fifth-power law. Later Chapman and Enskog achieved a break-through by finding a method capable to treat systems of particles with arbitrary interactions.

Similarly in the relativistic extension of the theory at first only particles with a suited special cross section could be treated. An eigenvalue method allowed to find the heat conductivity, the volume viscosity[1]) and – later – the shear viscosity[2]) for systems of such particles, eventually dubbed "Israel particles"[3]). The handling of particles with arbitrary cross sections had again to wait the devising of a new method. This "orthogonal-functions method"[4]) enables one to calculate the transport coefficients as well as the absorption and dispersion of sound waves.

After a sketch of the method of calculation (section 2), values of the heat conductivity, the viscosities, the diffusion constant and the propagation of sound are given for systems of massive particles with various cross sections. The results are presented as the first terms of series expansions in kT/mc^2, with k Boltzmann's constant, T the temperature, m the particle mass and c the speed of light. They are thus valid in the weakly relativistic regime (section 3). Systems of massless particles, like the neutrinos, however, find themselves in the extremely relativistic regime, since the velocities of these particles are always equal to c. For this case of weak interaction the heat conductivity and the viscosity have been calculated (section 4).

2. *The method of calculation.* 2.1. Transport equations and linear laws. The basis of the calculations is the covariant transport equation[5]) of relativistic kinetic theory:

$$p^\alpha \partial_\alpha f = \int\int (f'f'_1 - ff_1)\sigma F \,\mathrm{d}\Omega\, \mathrm{d}^3 p_1/p_1^0, \tag{1}$$

where $f(x, p)$ is the distribution function, with x the time-space four-vector $x = (ct, \boldsymbol{r})$ and p the energy-momentum four-vector $p = (E/c, \boldsymbol{p})$. Furthermore ∂_α is $\partial/\partial x^\alpha$, while σ is the differential cross section of the collision $p + p_1 \to p' + p'_1$. The other distribution functions, which appear in the collision term are $f' \equiv f(x, p'), f_1 \equiv f(x, p_1)$ and $f'_1 \equiv f(x, p'_1)$. The scalar F is equal to $\{(p_\alpha p_1^\alpha)^2 - (mc)^4\}^{\frac{1}{2}}$ and Ω is the collision solid angle. All quantities are defined in the centre-of-mass system of the colliding particles. With (1) one may derive the macroscopic conservation laws of mass and energy-momentum from their microscopic counterparts[1, 6]).

More properties are derived from the linearized (covariant) transport equation. This equation has as a solution a function $\varphi^{(1)}$, which is an approximation to a function φ defined by the following connexion with f:

$$f = f^{(0)}(1 + \varphi). \tag{2}$$

Here $f^{(0)}$ is the equilibrium distribution function, which is the solution of (1) with vanishing right-hand side. The linearized equation reads

$$p^\alpha \partial_\alpha f^{(0)} = -f^{(0)} \int\int f_1^{(0)}(\varphi^{(1)} + \varphi_1^{(1)} - \varphi^{(1)\prime} - \varphi_1^{(1)\prime})\sigma F \,\mathrm{d}\Omega\, \mathrm{d}^3 p_1/p_1^0. \tag{3}$$

With the help of the relativistic definition of entropy, the entropy law (Gibbs relation) and the entropy-balance equation have been derived[6]) from (3). The linear laws between the thermodynamic forces and flows are also obtained[6]) with (3). They read for simple systems:

$$\Pi = -\eta_v \partial_\alpha U^\alpha, \tag{4}$$

$$I_q^\alpha = -\lambda \Delta^{\alpha\beta}(\partial_\beta T - c^{-2} T D U_\beta), \tag{5}$$

$$\mathring{\Pi}^{\alpha\beta} = -2\eta \langle \partial^\alpha U^\beta \rangle. \tag{6}$$

The driving thermodynamic forces are $\partial_\alpha U^\alpha$, the divergence of the hydrodynamic four-velocity, $\partial_\beta T$, the temperature gradient with added to it the relativistic Eckart term (which contains the total time differentiation $D \equiv U^\alpha \partial_\alpha$) and finally $\langle \partial^\alpha U^\beta \rangle$, the traceless velocity gradient. The corresponding flows are Π, the trace of the pressure gradient, I_q^α, the heat four-flow and $\mathring{\Pi}^{\alpha\beta}$, the traceless part of the pressure tensor. The linear laws contain the three transport coefficients η_v, the volume viscosity, λ, the heat conductivity and η, the shear viscosity.

In mixtures more phenomena arise: diffusion and cross-phenomena between heat conduction and diffusion[7]). Moreover, chemical or nuclear reactions may be present[8, 9]). Some irreversible processes are then coupled and reciprocal relations, which are relativistic generalizations of the Onsager relations, are then valid between some of the transport coefficients. These relations stem from the time reversal invariance of the microscopic laws. The role of the reciprocal relations is especially important if external fields are present[10]).

Another general symmetry law, the Curie principle, is also derived[3]). It states for isotropic systems that thermodynamic forces and fluxes of vectorial character are coupled by a scalar, and that thermodynamic forces and fluxes of different tensorial character do not couple [*cf. e.g.* the laws (4)–(6)].

2.2. Transport coefficients: the orthogonal functions method. The values of the transport coefficients have been obtained from the linearized transport equation (3) by means of our "orthogonal-functions method"[4]), which allows to calculate these coefficients for systems of particles with arbitrary differential cross section σ. The first step is to transform the integro-differential equation (3) into a set of algebraic equations. To this end one multiplies (3) by a factor, containing an associated Laguerre polynomial and then integrates the result over the momentum p. Furthermore the function $\varphi^{(1)}$ is also written as a series in Laguerre polynomials. One obtains – for the case of heat conduction – the set

$$\rho^{-1}\beta_n = \sum_{m=1}^{\infty} b_m b_{mn} \quad (n = 1, 2, \ldots) \tag{7}$$

with ρ the density, the β_n known functions of the temperature and the b_{mn} "bracket" expressions involving associated Laguerre polynomials and the cross section σ. If the latter is given for a particular model, one can in principle calculate the brackets b_{mn}. Finally one may solve the b_m from (7); they occur in the transport coefficients, for instance the heat conduction λ, which is given by

$$\lambda = \rho \frac{k^2 T}{3m} \sum_{m=1}^{\infty} b_m \beta_m . \tag{8}$$

Successive approximations of order r are obtained for the b_m if the set (7) is truncated by writing r instead of ∞. One obtains thus also successive approximations to the expression (8) for the heat conductivity. The first ($r = 1$) and the second ($r = 2$) read

$$[\lambda]_1 = \frac{k^2 T}{3m} \frac{\beta_1^2}{b_{11}}, \tag{9}$$

$$[\lambda]_2 = \frac{k^2 T}{3m} \frac{\beta_1^2 b_{22} - 2\beta_1 \beta_2 b_{12} + \beta_2^2 b_{11}}{b_{11} b_{22} - b_{12}^2}, \tag{10}$$

expressed in terms of the coefficients β_m and b_{mn}.

3. *Massive particles* ($m \neq 0$). 3.1. Transport coefficients: values for various systems. For a number of particle models, *i.e.*, for different expressions of the cross section σ, transport coefficients have been calculated, the method being capable of handling arbitrary particle interactions. Four cases have been treated analytically[4]). Some results are listed below. They are given as series expansions in c^{-2}, of which the first two terms are given. At first simple systems are considered.

3.1.1. Rigid spherical particles. By definition one then has for the cross section

$$\sigma = \tfrac{1}{4}\pi a^2 \tag{11}$$

with a a constant. The results for the volume viscosity η_v, the heat conductivity λ and the shear viscosity η are in first and second approximation:

$$[\eta_v]_1 = \frac{25}{64} \frac{1}{a^2} \left(\frac{mkT}{\pi}\right)^{\frac{1}{2}} \left(\frac{kT}{mc^2}\right)^2 \left(1 - \frac{183}{16} \frac{kT}{mc^2}\right) + \mathcal{O}(c^{-8}), \tag{12}$$

$$[\eta_v]_2 = \frac{31}{30} [\eta_v]_1 \left(1 + \frac{259}{930} \frac{kT}{mc^2}\right) + \mathcal{O}(c^{-8}), \tag{13}$$

$$[\lambda]_1 = \frac{75}{64} \frac{1}{a^2} \left(\frac{k^3 T}{\pi m}\right)^{\frac{1}{2}} \left(1 + \frac{13}{16} \frac{kT}{mc^2}\right) + \mathcal{O}(c^{-4}), \tag{14}$$

$$[\lambda]_2 = \frac{45}{44} [\lambda]_1 \left(1 + \frac{763}{3960} \frac{kT}{mc^2}\right) + \mathcal{O}(c^{-4}), \tag{15}$$

$$[\eta]_1 = \frac{5}{16} \frac{1}{a^2} \left(\frac{mkT}{\pi}\right)^{\frac{1}{2}} \left(1 + \frac{25}{16} \frac{kT}{mc^2}\right) + \mathcal{O}(c^{-4}), \tag{16}$$

$$[\eta]_2 = \frac{205}{202} [\eta]_1 \left(1 + \frac{539}{8282} \frac{kT}{mc^2}\right) + \mathcal{O}(c^{-4}). \tag{17}$$

The volume viscosity starts off with terms in c^{-4}, while the heat conductivity and the shear viscosity start with c^0-terms: the well-known non-relativistic expressions[11]). The third approximations have also been calculated. It turns out that the relativistic terms show the same rapid convergence as is known to be the case for the non-relativistic terms.

3.1.2. Particles with inverse power-law interaction. For particles with a force law of the form

$$F = \kappa r^{-\nu} \tag{18}$$

with distance r, a positive constant κ and an exponent $\nu \geqq 5$, the transport coefficients become functions of a quantity

$$\Omega_i^{(s)}(\nu) \equiv \left(\frac{\pi kT}{m}\right)^{\frac{1}{2}} \left(\frac{\kappa}{2kT}\right)^{2/(\nu-1)} A_s(\nu)\Gamma\left(i + 2 - \frac{2}{\nu-1}\right) \tag{19}$$

with $A_s(\nu)$ a known function of s and ν. With the abbreviation $q \equiv (\nu - 5)/(\nu - 1)$ the results may be written as:

$$[\eta_v]_1 = \frac{25}{32} \frac{kT}{\Omega_2^{(2)}(\nu)} \left(\frac{kT}{mc^2}\right)^2 \left\{1 + \frac{1}{4} \frac{kT}{mc^2}(-43 - \tfrac{5}{2}q - \tfrac{1}{4}q^2)\right\} + \mathcal{O}(c^{-8}), \tag{20}$$

$$[\eta_v]_2 = [\eta_v]_1 \left[1 + \frac{1}{2} \frac{q}{14 + q} \left\{q + \frac{7}{14 + q} \frac{kT}{mc^2}(14 + 4q + \tfrac{1}{2}q^2)\right\}\right] + \mathcal{O}(c^{-8}), \tag{21}$$

$$[\lambda]_1 = \frac{75}{32} \frac{k^2T}{m\Omega_2^{(2)}(\nu)} \left\{1 + \frac{1}{4} \frac{kT}{mc^2}(7 - \tfrac{7}{2}q - \tfrac{1}{4}q^2)\right\} + \mathcal{O}(c^{-4}), \tag{22}$$

$$[\lambda]_2 = [\lambda]_1 \left[1 + \frac{1}{2} \frac{q}{21 + q} \left\{q + \frac{7}{21 + q} \frac{kT}{mc^2}(21 + \tfrac{11}{2}q + \tfrac{3}{4}q^2)\right\}\right] + \mathcal{O}(c^{-4}), \tag{23}$$

$$[\eta]_1 = \frac{5}{8} \frac{kT}{\Omega_2^{(2)}(\nu)} \left\{1 + \frac{1}{4} \frac{kT}{mc^2}(11 - \tfrac{9}{2}q - \tfrac{1}{4}q^2)\right\} + \mathcal{O}(c^{-4}), \tag{24}$$

$$[\eta]_2 = [\eta]_1 \left[1 + \frac{1}{2} \frac{q}{98 + 3q} \left\{3q + \frac{98}{98 + 3q} \frac{kT}{mc^2}(7 + 6q + \tfrac{3}{4}q^2)\right\}\right] + \mathcal{O}(c^{-4}). \tag{25}$$

As ν runs from 5 to ∞, the parameter q ranges from 0 to 1. The case $\nu = \infty$ ($q = 1$) corresponds to the rigid sphere. The case $\nu = 5$ ($q = 0$) represents the "Maxwell particle", which will now be considered separately.

3.1.3. Maxwell particles. Their cross section is given by

$$\sigma(g, \Theta) = m\Gamma(\Theta)/2g \tag{26}$$

with $2g$ the relative momentum of the colliding particles in the centre-of-mass system and $\Gamma(\Theta)$ a certain function of the scattering angle Θ. The results will be expressed with the help of a quantity

$$\varepsilon_2 \equiv 2\pi \int_0^\infty (1 - \sin^4 \tfrac{1}{2}\Theta - \cos^4 \tfrac{1}{2}\Theta)\Gamma(\Theta) \sin \Theta \, d\Theta, \tag{27}$$

which is related to (19). The expressions for the transport coefficients obtained are

$$\eta_v = \frac{5}{6} \frac{kT}{\varepsilon_2} \left(\frac{kT}{mc^2}\right)^2 \left(1 - \frac{43}{4} \frac{kT}{mc^2}\right) + \mathcal{O}(c^{-8}), \tag{28}$$

$$\lambda = \frac{5}{2} \frac{k^2T}{m\varepsilon_2} \left(1 + \frac{7}{4} \frac{kT}{mc^2}\right) + \mathcal{O}(c^{-4}), \tag{29}$$

$$\eta = \frac{2}{3} \frac{kT}{\varepsilon_2} \left(1 + \frac{11}{4} \frac{kT}{mc^2}\right) + \mathcal{O}(c^{-4}). \tag{30}$$

The connexion between (19) for $\nu = 5$ and (27) is such that their quotient is equal to 15/16.

3.1.4. Israel particles. Their cross section is

$$\sigma(g, \Theta) = m\Gamma(\Theta)/2g\{1 + (g/mc)^2\}. \tag{31}$$

The three transport quantities become then:

$$\eta_v = \frac{5}{6} \frac{kT}{\varepsilon_2} \left(\frac{kT}{mc^2}\right)^2 \left(1 - \frac{29}{4} \frac{kT}{mc^2}\right) + \mathcal{O}(c^{-8}), \tag{32}$$

$$\lambda = \frac{5}{2} \frac{k^2T}{m\varepsilon_2} \left(1 + \frac{21}{4} \frac{kT}{mc^2}\right) + \mathcal{O}(c^{-4}), \tag{33}$$

$$\eta = \frac{2}{3} \frac{kT}{\varepsilon_2} \left(1 + \frac{25}{4} \frac{kT}{mc^2}\right) + \mathcal{O}(c^{-4}). \tag{34}$$

These results agree with those obtained by means of the eigenvalue method (*v.* introduction).

All results given above were valid for simple systems. In mixtures more processes take place, for instance diffusion. For the models, employed above, the transport coefficients have been calculated[7]). To give an idea of their structure the first approximations to the diffusion constant for mixtures of isobaric gases with particles of mass m are given here for three of the models. Firstly *rigid spherical particles* with diameters a_1 and a_2. With $a_{12} \equiv \frac{1}{2}(a_1 + a_2)$ one obtains

$$[D]_1 = \frac{3}{8} \frac{1}{n} \frac{1}{a_{12}^2} \left(\frac{kT}{\pi m}\right)^{\frac{1}{2}} \left(1 - \frac{11}{16} \frac{kT}{mc^2}\right), \tag{35}$$

where n is the particle density. For *Maxwell particles* the result is

$$[D]_1 = \frac{3}{8} \frac{kT}{nm} \frac{1}{\Omega_1^{(1)}(5)} \left(1 + \frac{1}{4} \frac{kT}{mc^2}\right), \tag{36}$$

while finally for *Israel particles* the expression

$$[D]_1 = \frac{3}{8}\frac{kT}{nm}\frac{1}{\Omega_1^{(1)}(5)}\left(1 + \frac{11}{4}\frac{kT}{mc^2}\right) \tag{37}$$

has been found. The diffusion and thermal diffusion constants have also been calculated for mixtures of gases with different masses, again for the models mentioned[7]).

3.2. Sound propagation: absorption and dispersion. The relativistic theory of sound has also been studied. The absorption of sound in a simple gas is due to the irreversible phenomena of heat conduction and viscosity[12]). The calculation of the absorption coefficient yields the result:

$$\alpha = \frac{\omega^2}{2\rho c_{s0}^3}\left\{\lambda\frac{k}{mc_p c_v}\left(1 - \frac{c_p T}{h}\right)^2 + \left(\tfrac{4}{3}\eta + \eta_v\right)\frac{c^2}{h}\right\}. \tag{38}$$

The terms are proportional to the transport coefficients λ, η and η_v. Furthermore ω is the frequency of the sound wave, c_p and c_v the specific heats and h the specific enthalpy, which contains a rest mass contribution c^2. The two heat-conduction terms with h in the denominator represent thus purely relativistic contributions. Moreover, the transport coefficients have their relativistic values and the viscosity term contains the factor c^2/h which also involves a relativistic contribution. Finally the expression includes a factor with c_{s0}, which is the speed of sound in first approximation:

$$c_{s0} = \left(\frac{c_p}{c_v}\frac{kT}{m}\frac{1}{\hat{h}}\right)^{\frac{1}{2}}, \tag{39}$$

where $\hat{h}$ stands for h/c^2. In contrast to the absorption the speed of sound (39) shows no dispersion in first approximation. However, in second approximation the speed of sound is found to be:

$$c_{s1} = c_{s0}\left[1 + \left(\frac{\omega}{\rho c_{s0}^2}\right)^2\left\{\left(\frac{\lambda}{c_v}\right)^2(\varepsilon_1 + \zeta_1) + \frac{\eta\lambda}{\hat{h}c_v}(\varepsilon_2 + \zeta_2)\right.\right.$$
$$\left.\left. + \left(\frac{\eta}{\hat{h}}\right)^2(\varepsilon_3 + \zeta_3) + \frac{\eta\eta_v}{\hat{h}^2}\zeta_4 + \frac{\eta_v\lambda}{\hat{h}c_v}(\varepsilon_5 + \zeta_5) + \left(\frac{\eta_v}{\hat{h}}\right)^2(\varepsilon_6 + \zeta_6)\right\}\right], \tag{40}$$

which does show a dependency on the frequency. The quantities ε_i ($i = 1, 2, \ldots, 6$) are transport coefficients of higher order than λ, η and η_v. Furthermore the ζ_i ($i = 1, 2, \ldots, 6$) are simple functions of the temperature. (The sound propagation in mixtures[13]) has also been investigated.)

4. *Neutrinos*[14]). 4.1. Weak interaction: differential cross section. The neutrinos are supposed to interact by means of a weak interaction, described

by an interaction hamiltonian, which is the product of two neutral currents:

$$H = 2^{-\frac{1}{2}} G \bar{\psi}_\nu \gamma_\alpha (1 - \gamma_5) \psi_\nu \bar{\psi}_\nu \gamma^\alpha (1 - \gamma_5) \psi_\nu \tag{41}$$

with G the weak coupling constant, ψ_ν the neutrino field operators and $\gamma_1, \gamma_2, \gamma_3, \gamma_4$ and γ_5 the Dirac matrices. The differential cross section for the (elastic) neutrino collision which one gets from (41) is

$$\sigma = G^2 P^2 / 4\pi^2 \hbar^4 c^2, \tag{42}$$

where P is the total momentum in the centre-of-mass system.

4.2. Transport coefficients: their values. The transport equations (1) and (3) remain valid. The function F simplifies to $2g^2$ (with g the length of the three-momentum of a neutrino) owing to the vanishing of the mass. The calculations, in which use is made of a different set of orthogonal functions as employed for the case of massive particles, yield finally linear laws of the forms (5) and (6), while no law (4) is found, because it turns out that the volume viscosity vanishes. The first approximations to the heat conductivity and the shear viscosity are obtained to be

$$[\lambda]_1 = \frac{3\pi}{80} \frac{\hbar^4 c^5}{G^2} \frac{1}{kT^2}, \tag{43}$$

$$[\eta]_1 = \frac{3\pi}{184} \frac{\hbar^4 c^3}{G^2} \frac{1}{kT}. \tag{44}$$

These expressions show the magnitudes of the transport coefficients as well as the way in which they depend on the weak coupling constant and the temperature.

4.3. An "Eucken relation". From the last two expressions one finds the quotient

$$[\lambda]_1 T / [\eta]_1 c^2 = \tfrac{23}{10}, \tag{45}$$

a constant quantity (as might already be expected on dimensional grounds). In non-relativistic theory of massive particles one has the well-known Eucken relation $\lambda/\eta c_v = \frac{5}{2}$. Since then the specific heat c_v is equal to $3k/2m$ and the mean square velocity v^2 of the particles to $3kT/m$, one may cast the Eucken relation into the alternative form

$$\lambda T / \eta v^2 = \tfrac{5}{4}. \tag{46}$$

It has thus the same general structure as the formula (45), valid for the neutrino gas, since for neutrinos the velocity v is always equal to the speed of light c.

5. *Final remark.* Transport coefficients could be calculated in the framework of special relativity for systems of particles with arbitrary interaction. At very high

temperatures processes like ionization, radiation and particle production may also take place. In the present relativistic kinetic theory of transport processes their influence has hardly been taken into account.

Acknowledgements. I would like to express my gratitude to Professors T. D. Lee and M. A. Ruderman of Columbia University, New York, who stressed the importance of finding transport coefficients for a neutrino gas to me. Their stimulation led to the work of which the results are reported in section 4.

This work is a result of investigations, which form part of the research programme of the "Stichting voor fundamenteel onderzoek der materie (F.O.M.)", which is financially supported by the "Nederlandse organisatie voor zuiver-wetenschappelijk onderzoek (Z.W.O.)".

REFERENCES

1) Israel, W., J. math. Phys. **4** (1963) 1163.
2) van Leeuwen, W. A. and de Groot, S. R., Physica **51** (1971) 1, 16, 32 (articles IV, V, VI); van Leeuwen, W. A., Proc. K. Ned. Akad. Wetensch. B **74** (1971) 122, 134, 150, 269, 276 (thesis, Amsterdam).
3) de Groot, S. R., Acta Physica Austriaca, Suppl. **10** (1973) 529: "The Boltzmann Equation", ed. E. G. D. Cohen and W. Thirring.
4) van Leeuwen, W. A., Polak, P. H., de Groot, S. R., Phys. Letters A **37** (1971) 323; CR Acad. Sci. A **274** (1972) 431; Physica **63** (1973) 65 (art. IX); Polak, P. H., van Leeuwen, W. A. and de Groot, S. R., Physica **66** (1973) 455 (art. X).
5) Lichnerowicz, A. and Marrot, R., CR Acad. Sci. **210** (1940) 1957.
6) de Groot, S. R., van Weert, C. G., Hermens, W. Th. and van Leeuwen, W. A., Phys. Letters A **26** (1968) 345, 439; Physica **40** (1968–1969) 257, 581; **42** (1969) 309 (art. I, II, III).
7) Kox, A. J., *et al.*, Physica, in preparation (art. XIII, XIV).
8) Hermens, W. Th., Proc. K. Ned. Akad. Wetensch. B **74** (1971) 376, 387, 461, 478 (thesis, Amsterdam); Hermens, W. Th., van Leeuwen, W. A., van Weert, Ch. G. and de Groot, S. R., Physica **60** (1972) 472 (art. VIII).
9) van Weert, Ch. G., de Jagher, P. C. and de Groot, S. R., Physica **66** (1973) 474 (art. XI).
10) van Weert, Ch. G., Proc. K. Ned. Akad. Wetensch. B **73** (1971) 381, 397, 500, 517 (thesis, Amsterdam).
11) Chapman, S. and Cowling, T. G., The Mathematical Theory of Non-uniform Gases, University Press (Cambridge, 1939 *v.* also 1952).
12) Guichelaar, J., van Leeuwen, W. A. and de Groot, S. R., Physica **59** (1972) 97 (art. VII); Phys. Letters A **43** (1973) 323; Physica, to be published (art. XII).
13) Guichelaar, J., *et al.*, Physica, in preparation (art. XV, XVI).
14) van Leeuwen, W. A. and de Groot, S. R., Lettere al Nuovo Cimento **6** (1973) 470; van Leeuwen, W. A., Meltzer, P. H. and de Groot, S. R., Physica (1973), in preparation (art. XVII).

Physica **69** (1973) 21–26 © *North-Holland Publishing Co.*

PARAELECTRIC RELAXATION AND PARAELECTRIC RESONANCE (PER) IN SOLIDS

J. VOLGER and J. KERSSEN

Fysisch Laboratorium der Rijksuniversiteit Utrecht,
Utrecht, Nederland

Received 3 May 1973

Synopsis

As a tribute to C. J. Gorter a few examples of relaxation and resonance of paraelectric centres are discussed, emphasis being placed upon the many similarities to the paramagnetic case. Mainly electronic transitions are being considered, including recent observations of electronic PER in rutile.

1. *Introduction. Paraelectric relaxation.* Paraelectric relaxation has been known for a long time. Interesting experiments on polar liquids were published as early as in the 1920's and it was probably the famous book of Peter Debye, which caused the most effective spread of knowledge in this field[1]). The knowledge of paramagnetic relaxation is of about the same age. Kamerlingh Onnes and Ehrenfest[2]) had already been aware of the possible after-effects in paramagnetics; Gorter's well-known monograph[3]) gave the first survey of the basic experimental and theoretical investigations into paramagnetic relaxation which had been carried out from the 1930's on, much of these in Gorter's school. These investigations were, and still are, pretty much restricted to paramagnetic solids and did not readily find their paraelectric counterpart in solid dielectrics*. Indeed, only after the rise of interest in lattice defects was it understood that solids may contain distinct paraelectric impurities, exhibiting paraelectric relaxation phenomena[4]). For instance, when in NaCl an Na^+ ion is replaced by Ba^{++} and electro-neutrality is preserved by the simultaneous presence of a cation vacancy, and when at moderate temperatures these two lattice defects are associated, an electric dipole is formed. This dipole changes its direction when by appropriate jumps of Na ions the vacancy moves over a set of equivalent sites around the attractive Ba^{++} ions (Breckenridge[5]), Haven[6])). The corresponding paraelectric relaxation is governed by a temperature-dependent relaxation time

* The first author remembers that in his student days he tried under the guidance of J. v. d. Handel to detect dielectric relaxation in organic substances at low temperatures.

$$\tau = \tau_0 \exp (Q/kT), \tag{1}$$

and the phenomenon bears much resemblance to other atomic diffusion processes. τ_0 is of the order of the dominant lattice frequency, about $10^{13}\ s^{-1}$ and the activation energy Q is usually of the order of 0.5 eV. Also cases of ionic displacements over much smaller distances are found, especially when dipolar diatomic ions or "off-centre" ions are brought into the host lattices as diluted impurities (refs. 4, 7, 8 and 9).

In our opinion a particularly interesting case of paraelectric relaxation is found when the dipolar reorientation is caused by electronic rather than ionic jumps. Arising from Stevels's pioneering research on glass structures, it has been found to occur with certain colour centres in α-quartz[10]), and also in a number of sub-

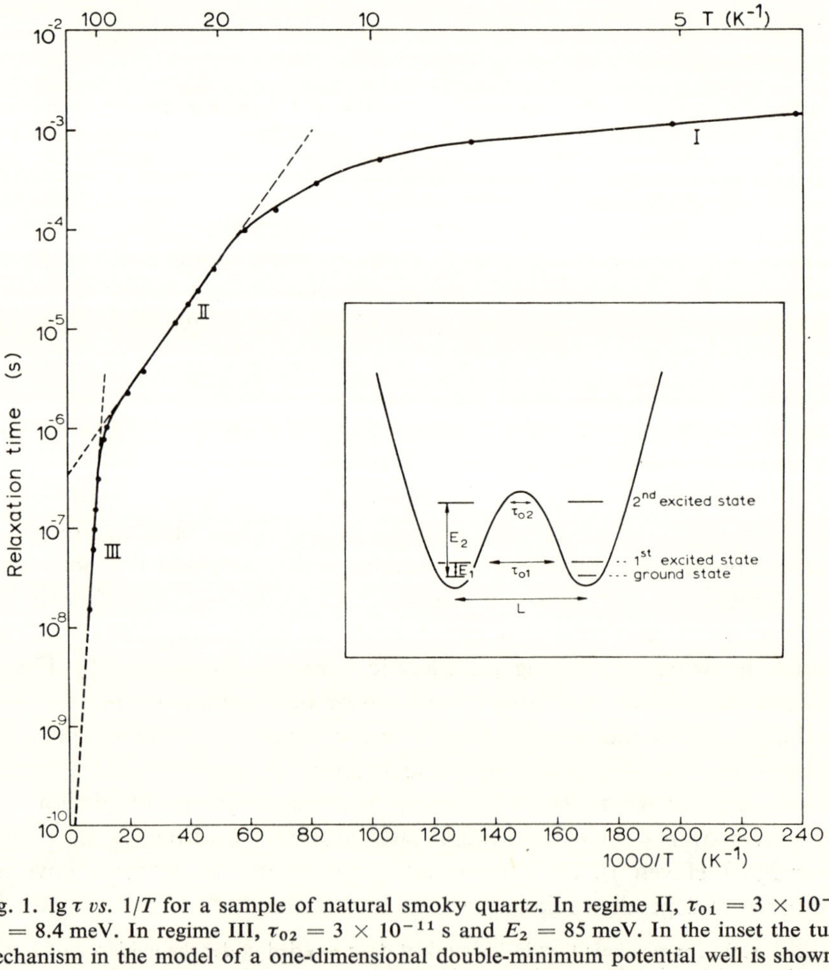

Fig. 1. lg τ *vs.* $1/T$ for a sample of natural smoky quartz. In regime II, $\tau_{01} = 3 \times 10^{-7}$ s and $E_1 = 8.4$ meV. In regime III, $\tau_{02} = 3 \times 10^{-11}$ s and $E_2 = 85$ meV. In the inset the tunnelling mechanism in the model of a one-dimensional double-minimum potential well is shown. There are excited states acting as intermediates for tunnelling at higher temperature.

stances like Fe_2O_3 and NiO in which the cations easily change their valency, *i.e.*, easily accommodate one electron more or less[11,12]). One could regard the latter case as an embryonic onset of the hopping model of electronic conduction.

The paraelectric relaxation phenomenon in smoky quartz has been reinvestigated by De Vos and Volger[13]) and it is striking that many of its characteristics are quite similar to what is found in paramagnetic relaxation. In fig. 1 the experimental relaxation time τ of a certain sample of natural smoky quartz is plotted as a function of temperature. τ was derived from experimental r.f. dielectric loss curves which were very nearly Debye-shaped. The data can be understood on the basis of a multiple-minimum potential-well model, substantiated by the nature of the colour centre, *i.e.*, a hole trapped at an oxygen tetrahedron around a substitutional aluminium ion in such a way that the hole may "tunnel" between certain oxygen-ion sites. With perfect symmetry, localization would not occur (the dipole moment would have no diagonal matrix elements) but an electric field causes Stark splitting and then localization does occur. In the paramagnetic case transitions between Zeeman levels are considered, whereby the electronic system experiences a rearrangement in angular momentum, whereas in our paraelectric case the transitions are between Stark levels whereby the electronic system experiences a firm rearrangement in real space, *i.e.*, in charge distribution. Even a double-well model brings out the essentials of the phenomenon quite adequately. It is, in fact, surely applicable since in quartz the oxygen tetrahedron mentioned is slightly distorted, two oxygen-ion sites forming a preferred set indeed.

As is clear from the plot, we can distinguish three different regimes and their characteristics may be summarized as follows[13]). Regime I: at very low temperatures an adiabatic phonon-assisted tunnelling transition in the ground state is the only relaxation path. Sussmann[14]) and others[15]) have studied the quantum mechanics of barrier crossing in detail and it appears that at the lowest temperature a single-phonon process is the most probable, leading to

$$\tau_{(\text{phonon})} = A/T, \tag{2}$$

A being a measure for the coupling between the phonon field and the dipole system. The experimental behaviour of τ in regime I is in excellent agreement with (2). A static electric field should reduce $\tau_{(\text{phonon})}$, which has indeed been found experimentally. At higher temperatures theory predicts the appearance of Raman scattering of phonons and $\tau_{(\text{phonon})}$ should then depend more strongly on T. However, in the case of smoky quartz it appears that we enter sooner into the second regime. Regime II: here the relaxation process is similar to the paramagnetic Orbach process. Thermal activation brings the system into a first excited state, allowing for easier tunnelling. Now obviously

$$\tau_1 = \tau_{01} \exp(E_1/kT), \tag{3}$$

where $1/\tau_{01}$ is the tunnelling rate at that first excited state. τ_{01} can be, and in fact is found to be, very different from the usual 10^{-13} s, for instance 10^{-7} s. Owing to internal strain and also by the application of a static electric field τ_{01} increases. A statistical treatment of the asymmetries in the multiple-well potentials in the real crystal is possible. In favourable cases all such "internal fields" (inhomogeneities) can be overruled by a strong external d.c. field. In this limit theory predicts a linear increase

$$\tau_{01}(f)/\tau_{01}(0) \cong 2pf/[\hbar/\tau_{01}(0)], \tag{4}$$

in which p is the dipole strength and $2pf$ the induced Stark splitting. Eq. (4) has been confirmed completely. Regime III: at still higher temperatures a second excited state may be reached, forming the intermediate state for a still more favourable relaxation path. τ_{02} is found to be smaller than τ_{01}, as it should, and $E_2 > E_1$.

2. *Paraelectric resonance* (*PER*). Paraelectric resonance in samples with paraelectric impurities has also been detected. Most investigations deal with ionic PER, *i.e.*, resonance on the Stark levels of tunnelling dipolar diatomic ions (hindered rotation) or tunnelling off-centre ions[16]). However, we should also expect PER in the situation discussed above, where electrons or holes are trapped near an attractive centre in such a way that they may be more or less localized at a number of neighbouring sites[17]). A small overlap between the site states introduces a zero-field splitting of the energy of the system and the possibility of transitions between the site states. Electronic PER may be detectable when the levels are sufficiently split by the application of an electric field (local field strength f) and when

$$f = h\nu/2p. \tag{5}$$

Transitions can be regarded as electric-dipole flips due to electron jumps. Probably the first case of electronic PER was observed in smoky quartz[18]). The resonance curve, taken at X band, was smeared out considerably owing to inhomogeneous broadening, which, however, was understood quantitatively on the basis of the same distribution function describing local asymmetries that governed paraelectric relaxation of the sample. Generally speaking, in PER spectroscopy narrow lines seem much harder to obtain than in EPR spectroscopy, the reason being that electric dipoles are much more vulnerable to disturbing effects such as interaction and lattice defects than magnetic dipoles. In passing we might mention the anomalous saturation of PER intensity in smoky quartz, probably due to the existence of a phonon bottleneck[19]); the effect is so dramatic because of the direct piezoelectric conversion of microwave energy into resonant phonons, such that at a higher microwave-power level mainly acoustic paraelectric resonance occurs.

We now want to report recent PER measurements in slightly reduced aluminiumdoped rutile single crystals[20]). In properly treated crystals interstitial Ti^{3+} is present as has been inferred from EPR data[21]). From dielectric-loss measurements[22]) it is very plausible that electron hopping may occur between adjacent Ti ions near the interstitial ion. At helium temperatures well-resolved PER was detected in very neat crystals with very low dipole concentration, using high microwave frequency (Q band). In view of the high dielectric constant we used a suitably dimensioned crystal as a dielectric cavity resonator[23, 24]). The sample was provided with electrodes by vacuum deposition of a thin layer of Au or Ag. Proper coupling of the microwaves to the sample was accomplished by tapering the waveguide to the thickness of the rutile platelet. The static field was applied parallel to the microwave electric field. The part of the waveguide wall that made contact with the electrode on the sample was isolated from the rest of the wall and connected to a variable d.c. source *via* a choked construction. The microwave absorption was measured in transmission, as a derivative, using a small 10 kHz modulation. The sample was about $1 \times 4 \times 4$ mm^3 with f as well as the c axis parallel to the short dimension. The resonant f-values were proportional to ν in the region 32–37 GHz. Saturation effects were not found. Fig. 2 shows a measuring curve.

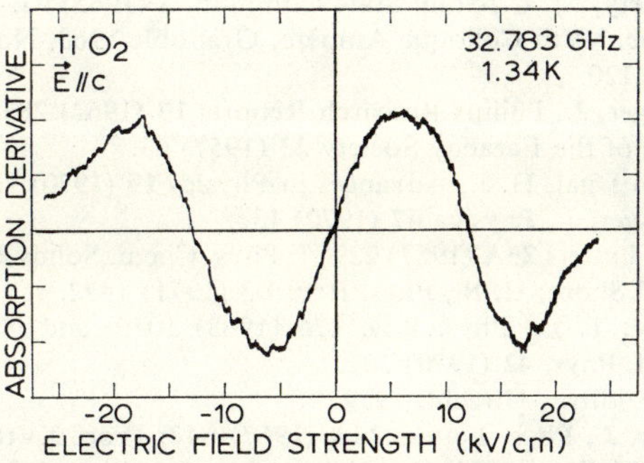

Fig. 2. The derivative of the microwave absorption in TiO_2 (slightly reduced) at 1.34 K, plotted as a function of the applied electric-field strength // c axis. Frequency 32.783 GHz.

Inserting into (5) the mean field, as calculated from the applied voltage and the sample thickness, we find an uncorrected dipole moment $p = 2.66$ debye for the centre of the resonance line. When p is written as $p = \frac{1}{2}eL$, in which L is the distance between the potential minima for the electron, we find $L = 1.1$ Å. This is of the order of the interatomic distance and therefore in qualitative agreement with the electron-hop model for adjacent Ti ions along the c axis. However, f is really an effective (or local) field and may be somewhat different from the mean field for two reasons. The first reason is that a thin space-charge region at the electrodes could reduce the mean field in the bulk, but there are arguments[20]) which consider this as a correction of limited importance. The second reason is that lattice distortion and polarization, due to the presence of the interstitial Ti^{3+} ion and polarization of this ion under the influence of the applied field and of the charge distribution in the paraelectric system under consideration, influence the effective field. The classical dielectric internal-field correction factors of Lorentz, Clausius Mossotti and Onsager are not applicable, since the electron jumps should occur between almost identical lattice sites. We feel that a correction factor of about 0.4, which would bring our PER data in quantitative agreement with the model of the multiply localized electron, is acceptable. However, further study of this problem is needed.

REFERENCES

1) Debye, P., Polare Molekeln, Hirzel Leipzig, 1929.
2) Ehrenfest, P., Z. Phys. **5** (1921) 35; Verslag. Kon. Akad. Wetensch. Amsterdam **29** (1920) 793; Comm. Phys. Lab. Univ. Leyden 44*b*.
3) Gorter, C. J., Paramagnetic Relaxation, Elsevier (Amsterdam, 1947).
4) For older work *cf.* Volger, J., Progress in Semiconductors, Heywood Company London **4** (1959) 205.
5) Breckenridge, R. G., J. chem. Phys. **16** (1948) 959.
6) Haven, Y., J. chem. Phys. **21** (1953) 171.
7) Känzig, W., Phys. Rev. Letters **13** (1964) 543.
8) Sack, H. S. and Moriarty, M. C., Solid State Commun. **3** (1965) 93.
9) Smoluchowski, R., Proc. XVth Colloque Ampère, Grenoble 1968, North-Holland Publ. Co. (Amsterdam, 1969), p. 120.
10) Stevels, J. M. and Volger, J., Philips Research Reports **17** (1962) 283.
11) Volger, J., Discussions of the Faraday Society **23** (1957) 63.
12) Bosman, A. J. and Van Daal, H. J., Advances in Physics **19** (1970) 1.
13) De Vos, W. J. and Volger, J., Physica **47** (1970) 13.
14) Sussmann, J. A., Phys. Letters **25A** (1967) 227; J. Phys. Chem. Solids **28** (1967) 1643.
15) *E.g.* Sander, L. M. and Shore, H. B., Phys. Rev. **B3** (1971) 1472.
16) See, for instance, Estle, T. L., Phys. Rev. **176** (1968) 1056; and Narayanamurti, V. and Pohl, R. O., Rev. Mod. Phys. **42** (1970) 201.
17) Volger, J., Inaugural Address, Utrecht, 1959.
18) Kerssen, J. and Volger, J., Phys. Letters **24A** (1967) 647; Proc. XVth Colloque Ampère, Grenoble 1968, North-Holland Publ. Co. (Amsterdam, 1969), p. 313.
19) Kerssen, J. and Volger, J., to be published.
20) Kerssen, J. and Volger, J., Phys. Letters, **44A** (1973) 368.
21) Kerssen, J. and Volger, J., Physica, to be published.
22) Rowan, L. G., Phys. Rev. **B5** (1972) 1675; Dominik, L. A. K. and MacCrone, R. K., Phys. Rev. **163** (1967) 757.
23) Okaya, A., Proc. I.R.E. **48** (1960) 1921.
24) Bethe, K., Philips Res. Reports Suppl. 1970, no. 2, p. 125.

Physica **69** (1973) 27–37 © *North-Holland Publishing Co.*

ON THE THEORY OF SPIN–LATTICE RELAXATION, WITH SPECIAL REFERENCE TO F-CENTERS

J. KORRINGA and A. YOSHIMORI *

Department of Physics, The Ohio State University, Columbus, Ohio, USA

Received 10 May 1973

Synopsis

The theory of spin–lattice relaxation is extended to the case that electronic excitation is associated with appreciable lattice distortions. The formulation is entirely in terms of the Born–Oppenheimer approximation sometimes called the adiabatic approximation. This has the advantage that the electron–lattice coupling is simply related to the lattice kinetic-energy operator. With a suitable transformation, the transition matrix elements of first and second order are obtained in full generality. With use of the time-reversal operator, results equivalent with the "Van Vleck cancellations" are obtained. It is shown that, as long as the Born–Oppenheimer approximation can be used as basis for a perturbation expansion, the direct- and Raman-type relaxation rates can be calculated on the basis of the Franck–Condon principle, using only the electronic states for the ground-state lattice configuration and their derivatives with respect to the nuclear cartesian coordinates. The application of this method to the spin relaxation of F-centers in strong magnetic fields is discussed.

1. *Introduction.* The theory of spin–lattice relaxation of a Kramers doublet has been studied by many since Kronig's and Van Vleck's pioneering papers[1,2]) were published. Two recent reviews of the subject can be found in ref. 3. While the subject contains few mysteries to insiders, the theory is far from quantitative in many applications. One of the simplest cases, that of F-centers in alkali halides, has long been the stepchild of the theorists. Its basic relaxation process is somewhat atypical, being due, as originally indicated by Portis[4,5]), to the hyperfine interaction of the F-center electron with the neighboring alkali and halide nuclei. Recently, Panepucci and Mollenauer[6]) reported measurements of the relaxation time at a low temperature as a function of the magnetic field B. They also gave the first detailed calculation of the hyperfine relaxation mechanism, obtaining reasonable accuracy, and showed that at the highest fields, the Kronig–Van Vleck type mechanism is important. Experimentally, this can be inferred from the B^5 term in the relaxation rate, adding to the B^3 law prevalent at lower fields. The

* Permanent address: Institute for Solid State Physics, University of Tokyo, Tokyo, Japan.

authors gave only an order of magnitude estimate of the coefficient of the B^5 term, which was off by a factor of 25. The F-center is atypical also in that electronic excitation leads to large lattice distortions, which are well known from the study of optical properties. Such distortions are usually disregarded in calculations of the relaxation time, although the excited states are involved in the perturbation theory, in particular for the Raman-type process.

The question of the influence of these distortions on the spin relaxation has led us to reformulate the general theory in terms of the "adiabatic" Born–Oppenheimer approximation. The merits of this method are compared with those of the static B–O approximation in a review article by Markham[7]). The disadvantage of the static method, which is the one habitually used in relaxation theory, is that it uses a set of basic wave functions which are nonorthogonal due to the abovementioned distortions. In the following, we hope to show that the adiabatic approximation yields an elegant formulation from which known results can easily be derived and insight into the effect of distortions can be obtained.

2. *The Born–Oppenheimer approximation.* The B–O approximation defines a complete orthonormal set of states of the form

$$|\alpha n\rangle = \psi_\alpha(x, X)v_{\alpha n}(X). \qquad (1)$$

Here, x stands for all electronic coordinates, including spin, and X stands for all nuclear cartesian coordinates, $\{X_\lambda\}$. We neglect all effects of nuclear spins. ψ_α are the eigenfunctions of an electronic hamiltonian, defined by $\mathscr{H}_e = \mathscr{H} - \mathscr{J}_L$, where $\mathscr{H}$ is the total hamiltonian, and $\mathscr{J}_L$ the nuclear kinetic energy

$$\mathscr{J}_L = -\frac{\hbar^2}{2}\sum\frac{1}{M_\lambda}\frac{\partial^2}{\partial X_\lambda^2}. \qquad (2)$$

In other words, ψ_α are eigenfunctions for fixed but arbitrary nuclear configuration:

$$\mathscr{H}_e\psi_\alpha(x, X) = E_\alpha(X)\psi_\alpha(x, X). \qquad (3)$$

The functions $v_{\alpha n}(X)$ are the eigenfunctions of the nuclear hamiltonian

$$\mathscr{H}_{L\alpha} = \mathscr{J}_L + E_\alpha(X), \qquad (4)$$

in which $E_\alpha(X)$ serves as potential energy. It includes, of course, in unmodified form, all nuclear interactions from $\mathscr{H}$. The energy in the B–O approximation is $E_{\alpha n}$ given by

$$\mathscr{H}_{L\alpha}v_{\alpha n} = E_{\alpha n}v_{\alpha n}. \qquad (5)$$

One often uses (3) in the Hartree–Fock approximation, and (5) in the harmonic approximation. If the equilibrium lattice configuration belonging to the electronic state α is denoted by $\{X_{\lambda\alpha}\}$, we write the harmonic approximation for $\mathscr{H}_{L\alpha}$ as

$$\mathscr{H}_{L\alpha} \approx E_{\alpha n}(X_{\lambda\alpha}) + \sum_k \hbar\omega_{\alpha k} a^\dagger_{\alpha k} a_{\alpha k}, \tag{6}$$

where the label k describes all states of all the branches of the lattice excitation spectrum. We are, of course, interested in the accoustical branches.

If we denote by $\mathscr{H}_0$ the hamiltonian of which the B–O wave functions are the eigenfunctions, one has

$$\mathscr{H} = \mathscr{H}_0 + \mathscr{H}_1, \quad \mathscr{H}_1\psi v = -\hbar^2 \sum_\lambda \frac{1}{M_\lambda}\left(\frac{\partial\psi}{\partial X_\lambda}\frac{\partial v}{\partial X_\lambda} + \frac{1}{2}\frac{\partial^2\psi}{\partial X_\lambda^2} v\right). \tag{7}$$

$\mathscr{H}_1$ is of central interest in relaxation theory. We have found it very helpful to cast it in a different form which we have not seen in the literature, although it is obtained in a trivial manner as follows.

For eq. (7), one can write

$$\mathscr{H}_1\psi_\alpha v_{\alpha n} = \mathscr{J}_L\psi_\alpha v_{\alpha n} - \psi_\alpha \mathscr{J}_L v_{\alpha n} \tag{8}$$

and therefore, because $E_\alpha(X)$ commutes with ψ, one gets with (4)

$$\mathscr{H}_1\psi_\alpha v_{\alpha n} = [\mathscr{H}_{L\alpha}\psi_\alpha]_- v_{\alpha n}. \tag{9}$$

The commutator in the right-hand side is simply $\hbar/\mathrm{i}$ times the rate of change of ψ_α due to nuclear motion. Writing

$$[\mathscr{H}_{L\alpha}\psi_\alpha]_- = \sum_\lambda \frac{\partial\psi_\alpha}{\partial X_\lambda}[\mathscr{H}_{L\alpha}, X_\lambda - X_{\lambda\alpha}]_-, \tag{10}$$

one can now express $X_\lambda - X_{\lambda\alpha}$ in normal coordinates $q_{\alpha k}$:

$$X_\lambda - X_{\lambda\alpha} = \sum \zeta_{\lambda\alpha k} q_{\alpha k}, \tag{11}$$

where

$$q_{\alpha k} = \mathrm{i}(\hbar/2\omega_{\alpha k})^{\frac{1}{2}}(a_{\alpha k} - a^\dagger_{\alpha k}), \tag{12}$$

and therefore, in the harmonic approximation,

$$[\mathscr{H}_{L\alpha} q_{\alpha k}]_- = -\mathrm{i}(\tfrac{1}{2}\hbar\omega_{\alpha k})^{\frac{1}{2}}(a_{\alpha k} + a^\dagger_{\alpha k}). \tag{13}$$

The constants $\zeta_{\lambda\alpha k}$ will be written in the form

$$\zeta_{\lambda\alpha k} = \zeta_{\lambda\alpha 0} + (\kappa/\kappa_\mathrm{D})\eta_{\lambda\alpha k}, \tag{14}$$

where κ is the magnitude of the vector k, and κ_D is the Debye wave number. The advantage is, that upon substitution into eq. (10), the term $\zeta_{\lambda\alpha o}$ cancels, because it corresponds to a uniform translation, *i.e.*, it is constant as a function of particle label. For the accoustical branches, κ is proportional to the frequency $\omega_{\alpha k}$. Substitution in eq. (10) finally gives:

$$\mathscr{H}_1\psi_\alpha v_{\alpha n} = -\mathrm{i}\hbar \sum_{\alpha k} \frac{\partial\psi_\alpha}{\partial X_\lambda}\frac{\kappa}{\kappa_\mathrm{D}}\eta_{\lambda\alpha k}(\tfrac{1}{2}\hbar\omega_{\alpha k})^{\frac{1}{2}}(a_{\alpha k} + a^\dagger_{\alpha k})v_{\alpha n}. \tag{15}$$

In this equation, the factor $\partial\psi_\alpha/\partial X_\lambda$ is still a function of $\{X_\lambda\}$, *i.e.*, an operator.

3. *The transition matrix.* The rate of spontaneous transition from a state $|\alpha n\rangle$ to a state $|\beta n'\rangle$ is obtained with the "golden rule",

$$\mathscr{R}_{\alpha n\to\beta n'} = (2\pi/\hbar)\delta(E_{\alpha n} - E_{\beta n'})|T_{\alpha n,\beta n'}|^2, \tag{16}$$

where the transition matrix T is, in perturbation expansion,

$$T_{\alpha n,\beta n'} = \langle\beta n'|\mathscr{H}_1|\alpha n\rangle + \langle\beta n'|\mathscr{H}_1 \frac{1 - P_{\alpha n}}{E_{\alpha n} - \mathscr{H}_0} \mathscr{H}_1|\alpha n\rangle + \cdots. \tag{17}$$

$P_{\alpha n}$ is the projection operator onto $|\alpha n\rangle$.

When ψ_α and ψ_β are different electronic spin states, the first term in (17) gives the transitions for the Kronig–Van Vleck direct effect, while the important contributions to the Raman-type process come from the second term. This term also contributes to the direct effect, but normally this is negligible. Likewise, the first term contains Raman-type elements, which are normally negligible compared to the dominant contributions from the second term.

4. *The first-order term.* Substitution of (17) in the first term of eq. (15) gives

$$\langle\beta n'|\mathscr{H}_1|\alpha n\rangle = \sum_{\lambda k} A_{\lambda\alpha k}\langle v_{\beta n'}| \left(\psi_\beta, \frac{\partial\psi_\alpha}{\partial X_\lambda}\right) (a_{\alpha k} + a^\dagger_{\alpha k})|v_{\alpha n}\rangle, \tag{18}$$

where

$$A_{\lambda\alpha k} = -i\hbar(\kappa/\kappa_D)\eta_{\lambda\alpha k}(\tfrac{1}{2}\hbar\omega_{\alpha k})^{\frac{1}{2}}. \tag{19}$$

The brackets around the factor involving ψ denote electron-space integration. We are interested in the case that the lattice equilibrium configurations belonging to states α and β are identical, and that the phonon states can also be considered the same. This is so for a Kramers doublet as well as for a non-Kramers doublet.

Expansion of the electronic factor in powers of X_λ-$X_{\lambda\alpha}$ yields with the help of (11) and (12) one-, two- and multiple-phonon terms. The lowest-order term is obtained by substituting $X_{\lambda\alpha}$ for X_λ, to be indicated by the subscript α. One has

$$\langle\beta n'|\mathscr{H}_1|\alpha n\rangle_1 = i\hbar \sum_{\lambda k} \eta_{\lambda\alpha k} \frac{\kappa}{\kappa_D} \left(\frac{\hbar\omega_{\alpha k}}{2}\right)^{\frac{1}{2}} \left(\psi_\beta, \frac{\partial\psi_\alpha}{\partial X_\lambda}\right)_\alpha \langle v_{\beta n'}|a_{\alpha k} + a^\dagger_{\alpha k}|v_{\alpha n}\rangle. \tag{20}$$

This gives the direct effect, $v_{\alpha n}$ and $v_{\beta n'}$ must differ by one phonon of wavenumber k. On the energy shell, the sum over k is restricted to phonons with

$$\hbar\omega_{\alpha k} = E_\beta(X_{\lambda\alpha}) - E_\alpha(X_{\lambda\alpha}). \tag{21}$$

Eq. (20) is explicitly proportional to the $\frac{3}{2}$ power of this energy difference, one power coming from κ.

For a Kramers doublet, the splitting is the Zeeman energy

$$\hbar\omega = 2\mu B \tag{22}$$

and the states ψ_α and ψ_β are related by the time-reversal operator[8,9]). Therefore, $(\psi_\beta, \partial\psi_\alpha/\partial X_\lambda)$ is an even function of B. This can be seen as follows. One can choose the phase of ψ_β in such a way that

$$\psi_\beta(B) = \theta\psi_\alpha(-B), \tag{23}$$

where θ is the time-reversal operator. Thus, as for a Kramers doublet

$$\theta^2\psi = -\psi, \tag{24}$$

one has

$$\theta\psi_\beta(B) = -\psi_\alpha(-B). \tag{25}$$

Furthermore, as θ is anti-unitary, one has for any ψ_1, ψ_2:

$$(\theta\psi_1, \theta\psi_2) = (\psi_2, \psi_1). \tag{26}$$

Therefore, defining $\partial\psi_\alpha/\partial X_\lambda = \psi'_\alpha$:

$$\begin{aligned}(\psi_\beta(B), \psi'_\alpha(B)) &= (\theta\psi'_\alpha(B), \theta\psi_\beta(B)) = -(\psi'_\beta(-B), \psi_\alpha(-B)) \\ &= (\psi_\beta(-B), \psi'_\alpha(-B)), \quad \textit{q.e.d.}\end{aligned} \tag{27}$$

The last line follows from $\partial(\psi_\beta, \psi_\alpha)/\partial X_\lambda = 0$. As a consequence, the electronic factor can be approximated by a constant independent of B, and so the matrix element for the direct effect is proportional to $B^{\frac{3}{2}}$, leading to the familiar B^5 dependence of the relaxation rate for a Kramers doublet.

For a non-Kramers doublet, one finds that in fields for which the Zeeman energy is large compared with the zero-field splitting, $(\psi_\beta, \psi'_\alpha) \approx B^{-1}$. This is seen, for example, as follows. In $B = 0$, the doublet consists of non-magnetic states $\psi_+ \pm \psi_-$ with Jahn–Teller splitting a. In a strong magnetic field, the states are $\psi_\pm \pm (a/2\mu B)\psi_\mp$. Hence, with these states as ψ_α and ψ_β, one has

$$(\psi_\beta, \psi'_\alpha) = \pm \frac{1}{2\mu B} \frac{\partial a}{\partial X_\lambda}. \tag{28}$$

As a consequence, the relaxation rate is proportional to B^3.

The Raman-type term in first order is easily obtained from eqs. (18), (11) and (12). One has

$$\begin{aligned}\langle\beta n'|\mathscr{H}_1|\alpha n\rangle_1 = \frac{\hbar^2}{2} \sum_{\lambda\mu kk'} \frac{\kappa\kappa'}{\kappa_D^2} \left(\frac{\omega_{\alpha k}}{\omega_{\alpha k'}}\right)^{\frac{1}{2}} \eta_{\lambda\alpha k}\eta_{\mu\alpha k'} \\ \times \left[\frac{\partial}{\partial X_\mu}\left(\psi_\beta, \frac{\partial\psi_\alpha}{\partial X_\lambda}\right)\right]_\alpha \langle v_{n'}|(a_{k'} - a^\dagger_{k'})(a_k + a^\dagger_k)|v_n\rangle.\end{aligned} \tag{29}$$

On the energy shell, one has

$$\hbar(\omega_{\alpha k} - \omega_{\alpha k'}) = E_\beta(X_{\lambda\alpha}) - E_\alpha(X_{\lambda\alpha}). \tag{30}$$

For a Kramers doublet, this difference is $2\mu B$, and assuming $\mu B \ll kT$, each of the terms $\hbar\omega_k$ is large compared with this difference. When neglecting the difference between k and k' in the factors multiplying the phonon matrix element, the terms of (29) related by interchange of k and k' cancel. As a consequence of this and of the fact that, for a Kramers doublet, the electronic factor is even in B, one obtains the result that this matrix element is proportional to B, and its contribution to the relaxation rate proportional to B^2.

5. *The second-order term.* Writing (17) in terms of an intermediate state, one has

$$(T_{\alpha n,\beta n'})_2 = \sum_{\gamma n''}{}' \langle \beta n'|\mathscr{H}_1|\gamma n''\rangle \frac{1}{E_{\alpha n} - E_{\gamma n''}} \langle \gamma n''|\mathscr{H}_1|\alpha n\rangle. \tag{31}$$

Before expanding this expression with use of eq. (15), it is important to note that the terms with $\gamma = \alpha$ and $\gamma = \beta$ very nearly cancel, so that, as these terms are small anyway, the sum in (31) for all practical purposes can be restricted to $\gamma \neq \alpha$, $\gamma \neq \beta$. As a consequence, the energy denominator always contains an electronic excitation. This result is derived in the appendix.

We now substitute eq. (15) in the second factor of (31) and likewise, with α changed to β, in the first factor, using the hermitian property of $\mathscr{H}$. This gives

$$(T_{\alpha n,\beta n'})_2 = \sum_{\lambda\mu kk'} A_{\lambda\alpha k} A^*_{\mu\beta k'} \sum_{\gamma n''}{}' \langle v_{\beta n'}|(a_{\beta k'} + a^\dagger_{\beta k'}) \left(\psi_\gamma, \frac{\partial\psi_\beta}{\partial X_\mu}\right)^* |v_{\gamma n''}\rangle$$
$$\times \frac{1}{E_{\alpha n} - E_{\gamma n''}} \langle v_{\gamma n''}| \left(\psi_\gamma, \frac{\partial\psi_\alpha}{\partial X_\lambda}\right) (a_{\alpha k} + a^\dagger_{\alpha k})|v_{\alpha n}\rangle. \tag{32}$$

Unlike in the first-order term, the electronic factors can, in general, not be expanded, because the equilibrium configurations for the phonon states $v_{\alpha n}$ and $v_{\gamma n''}$ are in general different due to the excited-state distortions. Still, the approximation used by Kronig comes through as usual. Although it is well known[2]) that, for $\mu B \ll kT$, this leaves out the dominant term, it is instructive to see how this comes about in the present formulation. Our argument is similar to Orbach's[10]).

In the energy denominator, $E_{\gamma n''}$ is replaced by the constant $E_\gamma(X_{\lambda\gamma})$. Then summation over n'' can be performed, yielding the unit operator. The resulting matrix is proportional to

$$\sum_\gamma \frac{1}{E_{\alpha n} - E_\gamma(X_{\lambda\gamma})}$$
$$\times \langle v_{\beta n'}|(a_{\beta k'} + a^\dagger_{\beta k'}) \left(\psi_\gamma, \frac{\partial\psi_\beta}{\partial X_\mu}\right)^* \left(\psi_\gamma, \frac{\partial\psi_\alpha}{\partial X_\lambda}\right) (a_{\alpha k} + a^\dagger_{\alpha k})|v_{\alpha n}\rangle. \tag{33}$$

The time-reversed expression for $B \to 0$ is similar but has the opposite sign, λ and μ interchanged and ψ_γ replaced by $\theta\psi_\gamma$. As excited states also exist as Kramers doublets, this term cancels against another term in the sum (32), apart from terms of the order $\mu B/(E_\alpha - E_\gamma)$.

Thus, as in the undistorted case, the important contributions of (32) come from the dependence of the denominator on the phonon energy in the intermediate state. It seems that here, finally, the distortions are of essential influence. But once more they elude us in the usual approximation which includes excited-state phonons to first order only. Writing

$$1/(E_{\alpha n} - E_{\gamma n''}) \approx [E_{\alpha n} - E_\gamma(X_{\lambda\gamma})]^{-2}[E_{\gamma n''} - E_\gamma(X_{\lambda\gamma})], \tag{34}$$

the last factor is, apart from a constant, the matrix element of $\mathscr{H}_{L\gamma}$. Summing over n'', therefore, gives

$$\sum_{n''} |v_{\gamma n''}\rangle \frac{1}{E_{\alpha n} - E_{\gamma n''}} \langle v_{\gamma n''}| \approx [E_{\alpha n} - E_\gamma(X_{\lambda\gamma})]^{-2}\mathscr{H}_{L\gamma}. \tag{35}$$

However, upon substitution into (32) one can replace $\mathscr{H}_{L\gamma}$ with $\mathscr{H}_{L\alpha}$. The difference between these hamiltonians is the difference in potentials, which is a function of X_λ only. This commutes with the electronic factors, and thus gives terms which cancel in zero field, as explained above. With this substitution, all reference to the distorted equilibrium state disappears and one can expand the electronic factors around the ground-state equilibrium configuration $X_{\lambda\alpha}$. This gives to lowest order:

$$(T_{\alpha n,\beta n'})_2 \approx \sum_{\lambda\mu kk'} A_{\lambda\alpha k} A^*_{\mu\beta k'} \sum_\gamma{}' \left(\psi_\gamma, \frac{\partial\psi_\beta}{\partial X_\mu}\right)^*_\alpha \left(\psi_\gamma, \frac{\partial\psi_\alpha}{\partial X_\lambda}\right)_\alpha [E_{\alpha n} - E_\gamma(X_{\lambda\gamma})]^{-2}$$
$$\times \langle v_{\beta n'}|(a_{\beta k'} + a^\dagger_{\beta k'})(\sum \hbar\omega_{\alpha k''} a^\dagger_{\alpha k''} a_{\alpha k''})(a_{\alpha k} + a^\dagger_{\alpha k})|v_{\alpha n}\rangle.$$

This is the familiar Raman-type term which, at higher temperatures, contributes an extra factor T^2 to the relaxation rate. The only reference to the distortion is through the energy $E_\gamma(X_{\lambda\gamma})$ in the denominator, but that is not significant because, in order that the relevant intermediate states have small phonon energies, the difference in $E_\gamma(X_{\lambda\gamma})$ and $E_\gamma(X_{\lambda\alpha})$ must be small also.

Eq. (36) also shows that, if this approximation is valid, the second-order elements of the T matrix give negligible contributions to the direct effect. One has, namely, to expand the electronic factor to first order to get a one-phonon term. So, if the present approximation is valid, the original perturbation expansion of the T matrix is justified.

The above argument obviously does not apply to second- and higher-order terms of the expansion in intermediate-state phonon energy. These depend essentially on the dynamic properties of the lattice in the excited state. One can even expect cases in which the distortion is so large that the non-orthogonality between ground- and excited-state phonons causes so high intermediate-state phonon energies that this expansion does not converge. In that case, the expansion of the T matrix is also in doubt, and there could be a "short ciicuit" between the two spin states leading to short relaxation times. In fact, the Born–Oppenheimer approximation breaks down. There is, of course, another case in which the phonon expansion is not possible, namely when the electronic-state energy E_γ is close to E_α. This is well known[11]) and leads to important changes in the relaxation process.

6. *Application to F-centers.* The results of section 4, in particular eq. (20), can be used to calculate the direct effect for F-centers which, as shown in ref. 6, begins to compete with the mechanism due to hyperfine coupling at fields near 10 tesla. Two separate quantities, $\eta_{\lambda\alpha k}$ and $(\psi_\beta, \partial\psi_\alpha/\partial X_\lambda)_\alpha$, have to be found. We do not attempt to calculate them in this paper, but only give a qualitative discussion.

To obtain the coefficient $\eta_{\lambda\alpha k}$ of the expansion of lattice displacements in terms of normal coordinates is difficult because we deal with an impurity center, in the vicinity of which the normal modes of the crystal are strongly distorted. In a case like this, one uses approximate normal coordinates which are localized near the center (configuration coordinates) and obtains the coupling of these with phonons in a perfect crystal.

As the electronic factor contains only the wave functions at the ground-state equilibrium configuration and its derivative, the lattice distortions in electronic excited states do not appear in this order. To get a nonzero matrix element $\mathscr{H}_e$ must, of course, include the spin–orbit coupling. This small interaction is used in first-order perturbation only, which must be applied with fixed nuclear configuration, as in the Franck–Condon principle, at and near lattice equilibrium.

The unperturbed electron wave functions for F-centers are often approximated by linear combinations of spherical harmonics times smooth radial functions, which are orthogonalized to the core functions of the first, second and sometimes further neighbor ions[6, 12]). Thus, the functions are linear combinations of smooth functions and neighbor-ion core functions. Excited states have a different smooth part and therefore different overlap integrals that multiply the core functions. As a consequence, the spin–orbit interaction is expressed in terms of the angular-momentum operators of the neighbor ions, and the principal problem is to calculate the overlap integrals at and near the equilibrium configuration, adjusting, of course, the smooth function with each change of position, using the variational method.

Calculations of this type have not been performed, to our knowledge, but they are not too much different from those used to obtain the ground and excited stationary states[12]).

The calculation of the Raman term, to first order in the intermediate-state phonon energy, involves similar problems, though the coefficients $\eta_{\lambda\alpha k}$ must now be obtained for any finite wave number, and not just for very small k as in the direct effect. Again, the calculation must follow the Franck–Condon principle. However, such a calculation is fairly academic, because the spin–lattice coupling based on the modulation of the hyperfine interaction contains Raman-type terms of much greater magnitude[13]). There is no B dependence that could allow the Van Vleck terms to compete. The temperature dependence would be T^7, but by the time the T^9 law of Van Vleck takes over, the Born–Oppenheimer approximation is probably no longer valid.

7. *Conclusions.* We set out to trace the effect of lattice distortions, associated with electron excitation of a paramagnetic center, on the electron-spin relaxation rate. As the theory involves perturbations by the spin–orbit interaction as well as the orbit–lattice interaction, which explicitly introduce the excited states, we initially thought that the magnetic field or the temperature dependence of the relaxation rate, as established originally by Van Vleck, might be altered. Our conclusion is that no such effect can be expected as long as the electron–lattice coupling can be obtained from a perturbation scheme based on the Born–Oppenheimer approximation. In fact, one can strictly adhere to the Franck–Condon principle in perturbation theory, in which the electronic excited states and their first derivative with respect to the lattice coordinates appear only at the ground-state equilibrium configuration.

In studying this problem, we found it very convenient to use systematically the so-called adiabatic form of the B–O approximation, which is the form in which no further approximations are explicitly introduced. This has the advantage that the perturbation representing the electron–phonon coupling is expressed in terms of the nuclear kinetic energy. We found a way to present this in a form which is at once mathematically simple and physically transparent. This does, of course, not solve the real difficulties of an actual calculation, but it gives a clear separation between the calculation of the electron states in a static lattice on the one hand, and of the effect of the lattice dynamics on the other.

While we could verify, for a Kramers doublet, the validity of the B^5 law for the direct effect, the T^7B^2 law for the Kronig-type Raman terms and the T^9B^0 law of the Van Vleck–Raman terms, the interpretation of our formulas leading to these results differs markedly from those in the static approximation. For example, the B^5 law does not appear as the consequence of any "cancellation", but on the contrary, the B^3 law for a non-Kramers doublet is caused by a B^{-1} dependence of the matrix element.

We expect that our formalism will be useful to the calculation of the direct effect for F-centers, for which the lattice states are strongly coupled to the electron states.

APPENDIX

In order to show that the terms with $\gamma = \alpha$ and $\gamma = \beta$ in eq. (31) nearly cancel, we write them in a form similar to eq. (32). We will discuss only the Raman effect, for which the electronic factors can be taken at lattice equilibrium. The terms in question then are, omitting superfluous indices on v and a:

$$\sum A_{\lambda\alpha k} A^*_{\mu\beta k'} \left[\left(\psi_\alpha, \frac{\partial\psi_\beta}{\partial X_\mu}\right)^*_\alpha \left(\psi_\alpha, \frac{\partial\psi_\alpha}{\partial X_\lambda}\right)_\alpha \times \langle v_{n'}|a_{k'} + a^\dagger_{k'}|v_{n''}\rangle (E_{\alpha n} - E_{\alpha n''})^{-1} \langle v_{n''}|a_k + a^\dagger_k|v_n\rangle + \left(\psi_\beta, \frac{\partial\psi_\beta}{\partial X_\mu}\right)^*_\alpha \left(\psi_\beta, \frac{\partial\psi_\alpha}{\partial X_\lambda}\right)_\alpha \langle v_{n'}|a_{k'} + a^\dagger_{k'}|v_{n''}\rangle (E_{\alpha n} - E_{\beta n''})^{-1} \langle v_{n''}|a_k + a^\dagger_k|v_n\rangle \right]. \tag{A.1}$$

From eqs. (23)–(26) it follows that, for $B \approx 0$

$$\left(\psi_\alpha, \frac{\partial\psi_\alpha}{\partial X_\lambda}\right) = \left(\psi_\beta, \frac{\partial\psi_\beta}{\partial X_\lambda}\right)^*, \tag{A.2}$$

while from the orthogonality of ψ_α and ψ_β one has

$$-\left(\psi_\beta, \frac{\partial\psi_\alpha}{\partial X_\lambda}\right) = \left(\psi_\alpha, \frac{\partial\psi_\beta}{\partial X_\lambda}\right)^*. \tag{A.3}$$

As k and k' are nearly equal (the corresponding energies differ by $2\mu B$) one has

$$A_{\lambda\alpha k} A^*_{\mu\beta k'} \approx A_{\mu\alpha k} A^*_{\lambda\beta k'}. \tag{A.4}$$

If finally the Zeeman energy is neglected,

$$E_{\alpha n''} \approx E_{\beta n''}, \tag{A.5}$$

one sees that the two terms cancel.

This argument shows that near-cancellation produces an extra factor $\mu B/kT$. On top of this, to get a nonzero value for $(\psi_\alpha, \partial\psi_\alpha/\partial X_\lambda)$, ψ_α must be complex. This means that in the perturbation expansion of ψ_α one must include either the spin–orbit or the Zeeman interaction. This produces an extra factor λ/Δ or $\mu B/\Delta$, where λ is the strength of the spin–orbit coupling and Δ the energy difference between an excited state and the ground state. We conclude that these terms of the expansion of the transition matrix are negligible.

Acknowledgment. One of the authors (A.Y.) would like to express his deep thanks to Professor E. L. Jossem and other members of the Physics Department of The Ohio State University for their hospitality extended to him during his stay in the academic year of 1972–73.

REFERENCES

1) Kronig, R. de L., Physica **6** (1939) 33.
2) Van Vleck, J. H., Phys. Rev. **57** (1940) 426.

3) Stevens, K. W. H., Rep. Progr. Phys. **30** (1967) 189.
Abragam, A. and Bleany, B., Electron Paramagnetic Resonance of Transition Ions, Clarendon Press (Oxford, 1971).
4) Portis, A. M., Phys. Rev. **91** (1953) 1071.
5) Deigen, M. F. and Zevin, V. Ya., Zh. eksper. teor. Fiz. **39** (1960) 1126; Engl. Transl., Soviet Physics JETP **12** (1961) 785.
6) Panepucci, H. and Mollenauer, L. F., Phys. Rev. **178** (1969) 589.
7) Markham, J. J., Rev. mod. Phys. **31** (1959) 956.
8) Wigner, E., Göttinger Nachrichten **32** (1932) 546.
9) Merzbacher, E., Quantum Mechanics, John Wiley and Sons (New York, 1970).
10) Orbach, R., Proc. Roy. Soc. **A264** (1961) 458.
11) Finn, C. B. P., Orbach, R. and Wolf, W. P., Proc. Phys. Soc. **77** (1961) 261.
12) Wood, R. F. and Öpik, U., Phys. Rev. **179** (1969) 783.
13) Zevin, V. Ya., Soviet Physics – Solid State **3** (1961) 439.

Physica **69** (1973) 38–48 © *North-Holland Publishing Co.*

THE ROLE OF GORTER–MELLINK MUTUAL FRICTION IN COOLING BY FORCED SUPERFLUID FLOW

J. F. OLIJHOEK, H. VAN BEELEN, R. DE BRUYN OUBOTER and K. W. TACONIS

Kamerlingh Onnes Laboratorium der Rijksuniversiteit,
Leiden, Nederland

(communication No. 403*b*)

Received 11 May 1973

Synopsis

Experiments on the flow of He II under high overall pressure through a thermally isolated system consisting of a superleak, a chamber and a capillary in series are reported. Depending on the direction of the flow a cooling or a warming up of the chamber occurs. The Gorter–Mellink mutual friction gives an adequate description of the phenomena observed. The occurrence of a limiting temperature for cooling of about 0.75 K can be ascribed to heat input into the chamber generated by the flow either in the chamber itself or in the capillary.

1. *Introduction.* When liquid He II is forced to flow through a thermally isolated system consisting of a superleak connected *via* a small chamber to a narrow capillary (see fig. 1) a cooling of the chamber temperature T_a occurs[1, 2, 3]). Normal excitations are dragged from the chamber by the flow and are replenished by pure superfluid, which is stripped off its entropy in the superleak. In review, results on T_a as a function of the applied pressure head obtained at different bath temperatures, as published in a previous paper[2]), are shown in fig. 2. Large pressure heads were obtained by heating liquid helium under its own vapour pressure inside a thermally insulated glass vessel, connected *via* a capillary and a heat exchanging bellows to the entrance of the superleak (see fig. 1). The behaviour of T_a as a function of the applied pressure head has been interpreted in the following way[2]).

Since over the superleak the chemical potential difference remains zero, the applied pressure head $\rho g \Delta Z$ appears as a chemical potential difference over the capillary

$$g\Delta Z = -\Delta\mu = -\frac{\Delta P}{\rho} + \int_{T_a}^{T_{\text{bath}}} s\,\mathrm{d}T, \qquad (1)$$

where ρ is the density and s the entropy per gram of liquid helium.

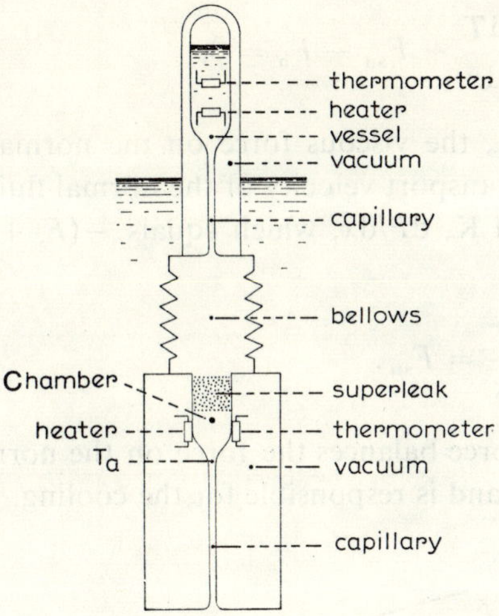

Fig. 1. Schematic diagram of the apparatus used in the experiments with helium at s.v.p. The applied pressure head ΔZ is equal to the difference in vapour pressure between vessel and bath (expressed in cm He) plus the hydrostatic pressure difference. The pressure drop over the upper capillary can be neglected.

The curves in fig. 2 represent this relation when ΔP is taken zero, so that

$$T_a = T_{\mathrm{bath}} - \frac{g\Delta Z}{\bar{s}} \tag{2}$$

with $\bar{s}$ the entropy per gram averaged over the temperature interval $T_a - T_{\mathrm{bath}}$.

These curves fit the data rather well for $T_a > 1$ K, showing that the pressure difference over the capillary can be neglected in this temperature region.

In a two-fluid model, the equation of motion for the transport of the superfluid component can be written as

$$\rho_s \frac{\mathrm{d}\boldsymbol{v}_s}{\mathrm{d}t} = -\rho_s \nabla\mu - \boldsymbol{F}_{sn} - \boldsymbol{F}_s, \tag{3}$$

where $\boldsymbol{v}_s$ is the transport velocity of the superfluid, $\boldsymbol{F}_{sn}$ the momentum transferred from the superfluid transport to the transport of the normal component, $\boldsymbol{F}_s$ the momentum transfer from the superfluid transport eventually to the walls of the system.

For stationary flow, neglecting gradients in v_s^2 and v_n^2, eq. (3) for the transport direction (x) reduces to

$$-\frac{\rho_s}{\rho}\frac{\mathrm{d}P}{\mathrm{d}x} + \rho_s s \frac{\mathrm{d}T}{\mathrm{d}x} - F_{sn} - F_s = 0. \tag{4}$$

For the transport of the normal component one obtains under the same conditions

$$-\frac{\rho_n}{\rho}\frac{dP}{dx} - \rho_s s \frac{dT}{dx} + F_{sn} - F_n = 0, \tag{5}$$

where $-\boldsymbol{F}_n = \eta_n \nabla^2 \boldsymbol{v}_n$, the viscous force on the normal component with η_n the viscosity and $\boldsymbol{v}_n$ the transport velocity of the normal fluid. From the experimental result that for $T_a > 1$ K, dP/dx, which equals $-(F_s + F_n)$, can be neglected, it follows that

$$-\rho_s \frac{d\mu}{dx} = \rho_s s \frac{dT}{dx} = F_{sn}. \tag{6}$$

The mutual-friction force balances the force on the normal component due to the temperature gradient and is responsible for the cooling, at least above 1 K.

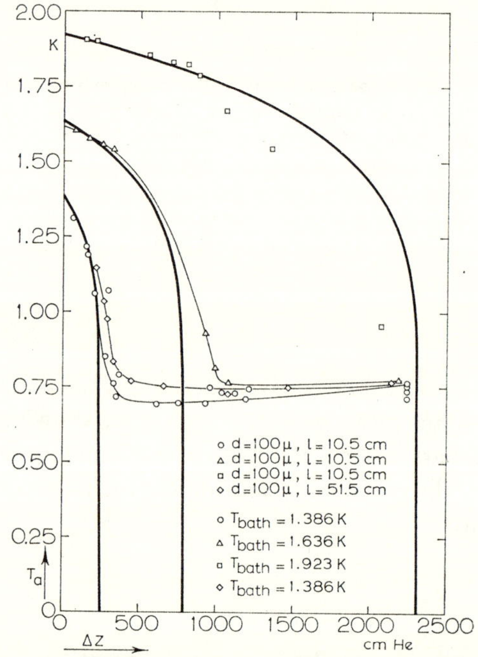

Fig. 2. T_a **as a function of the applied pressure head at different bath temperatures. The heavy full curves correspond to zero pressure difference over the capillary.**

From fig. 2 it appears that for T_a a limit is set at about 0.75 K. It was shown[2]) that this limit is not caused by heat leaks from the bath and it was suggested that it were due to the fact that the mutual-friction force becomes ineffective below 0.75 K due to the decrease of roton density with temperature. Since the roton density increases with overall pressure a lowering of this limit was expected at higher overall pressures. In this paper an experimental method is briefly described which allows to study the pressure dependence of T_a at accurately known flow velocities. An interpretation of the results on T_a in the region above 1 K as a function of the flow velocity will be given in terms of mutual friction. Experiments to reveal the origin of the limiting temperature will be briefly discussed. In a separate paper the present results will be given in more detail[4]).

2. *Experimental method.* The flow phenomena at high overall pressures (up to 25 atm) are studied using a slightly modified form of the apparatus depicted in fig. 1. Instead of using the high-pressure-head generator, the entrance of the superleak is now connected *via* a heat exchanger with the bath, to a storage cylinder with helium under high pressure at room temperature. The exit of the capillary (208 μm i.d., 10.4 cm long) is connected to the outside world, *via* a heat exchanger with the bath, a throttle by which the flow rate can be adjusted and a flow meter at room temperature. The flow direction can be reversed by interchanging the in- and outlet connections. With a heater, mounted to the wall of the chamber, the normal transport velocity can be adjusted independently of v. Unfortunately we did not succeed to measure the pressure difference over the capillary; due to gas vibrations the levels in the differential manometer connected over the flow system were heavily oscillating and even T_a showed large fluctuations.

3. *Experimental results.* 3.1. Interpretation of the results above 1 K in terms of a mutual-friction force of the Gorter–Mellink type. Results of T_a as a function of the flow velocity v for two different bath temperatures (1.152 K and 1.455 K) both at an overall pressure of 10 atm are shown in figs. 3a and 3b.

In these figures data are shown for different values of $\dot{Q}_H$ (in erg s^{-1}), the heat supplied to the chamber by means of the heater H. In the positive v direction, which corresponds to cooling, helium flows from the superleak through the capillary, whereas in the negative direction the flow is directed towards the superleak. The curves in figs. 3a and 3b are drawn smoothly through the individual measuring points.

We succeeded to interpret these results in terms of a mutual friction force of the Gorter–Mellink type, *i.e.*,

$$F_{sn} = A\rho_s\rho_n(v_s - v_n)^3 \tag{7}$$

which proved to be successful for the description of heat-conduction measurements in He II under saturated-vapour pressure. A was found to be a slowly varying function of temperature, of the order of 50 cm s g^{-1}, v_s and v_n are the transport velocities averaged over the cross section of the capillary[5]). In view of the conclusion drawn from the results given in fig. 2, we shall also neglect in the present analysis all pressure effects in the capillary. It then follows from eqs. (6) and (7) that

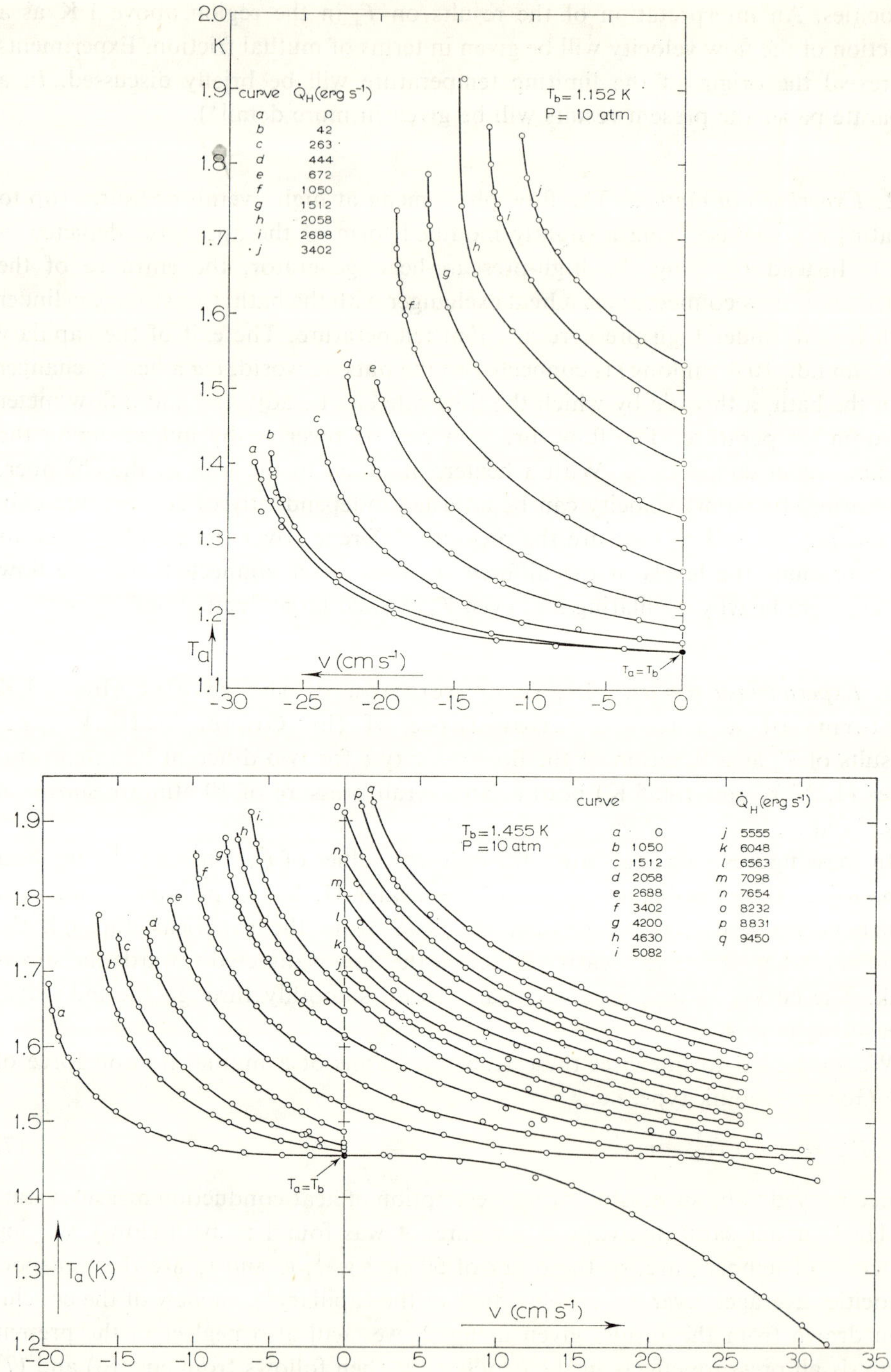

Fig. 3a and 3b. T_a as a function of the net mass flow velocity at various heat inputs.

$$\frac{\mathrm{d}T}{\mathrm{d}x} = \frac{A\rho}{s_\lambda}\left(\frac{\rho}{\rho_\mathrm{s}}\right)^3 (v - v_\mathrm{n})^3, \tag{8}$$

where use is made of the relation $\rho_\mathrm{n}s_\lambda = \rho s$, a simplification allowable in the temperature region considered here.

Imposing the boundary condition $T = T_\mathrm{bath}$ at $x = l$, the exit of the capillary, once $A(T)$ and v_n are known, one can compute the temperature distribution as a function of v along the capillary by numerical integration of eq. (8). From the relation

$$O_\mathrm{c}\rho s T v_\mathrm{n} = \dot{Q}, \tag{9}$$

where $\dot{Q}$ is the heat flow in the capillary, v_n can be obtained as a function of temperature. Due to heat production in the capillary by the flow, given by

$$\mathrm{div}\,\dot{\boldsymbol{q}} = -\rho\boldsymbol{v}\cdot\nabla\mu, \tag{10}$$

where $\dot{\boldsymbol{q}}$ is the heat-flux density, the heat flow is given by

$$\dot{Q}(x) = \dot{Q}_\mathrm{H} - \rho O_\mathrm{c} v \int_0^x \frac{\mathrm{d}\mu}{\mathrm{d}x}\mathrm{d}x = \dot{Q}_\mathrm{H} + \rho O_\mathrm{c} v \int_{T_\mathrm{a}}^{T_x} s\,\mathrm{d}T' = \dot{Q}(T_x), \tag{11}$$

where again we have used the assumption that $\mathrm{d}P/\mathrm{d}x$ can be neglected. Equation (8) can now be written as

$$\mathrm{d}x = \frac{s_\lambda}{A\rho}\left(\frac{\rho_\mathrm{s}}{\rho}\right)^3 \left[v - \frac{\dot{Q}_\mathrm{H}}{O_\mathrm{c}\rho s T} - \frac{v\int_{T_\mathrm{a}}^{T} s\,\mathrm{d}T'}{sT} \right]^{-3} \mathrm{d}T, \tag{12}$$

where we have separated the variables x and T.

As $A(T)$, at an overall pressure of 10 atm, is still an unknown quantity, we used the data of T_a for $\dot{Q}_\mathrm{H} = 0$ as given in figs. 3a and 3b to determine $A(T)$ numerically from eq. (12).

These series of measurements were chosen, since the results given in fig. 2 provide evidence that the boundary condition $T_{x=l} = T_\mathrm{bath}$ is fulfilled for such a flow.

Fig. 4 shows $A(T)$ at 10 atm, calculated from the two curves at two different bath temperatures. For comparison, results of Vinen[6]) of $A(T)$ under saturated vapour pressure are also given in this figure, showing a similar temperature dependence, $A(T)$ being somewhat higher at high pressure. The curve, drawn smoothly through the calculated points, is used to analyse all the results given in figs. 3a and 3b.

Fig. 5 shows again the curves for $\dot{Q}_\mathrm{H} = 0$ computed from eq. (12) using the smoothed values of $A(T)$. It shows that the rather large spread in the calculated

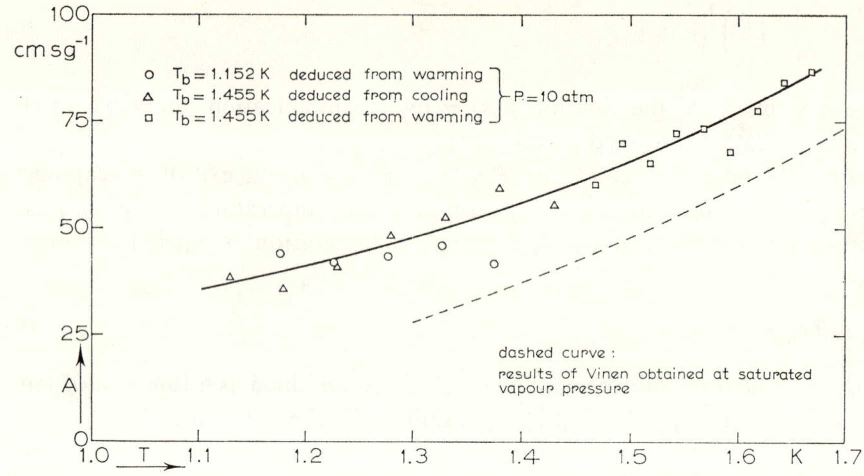

Fig. 4. The mutual friction constant at a pressure of 10 atm. The dashed curve shows the results of Vinen at s.v.p.

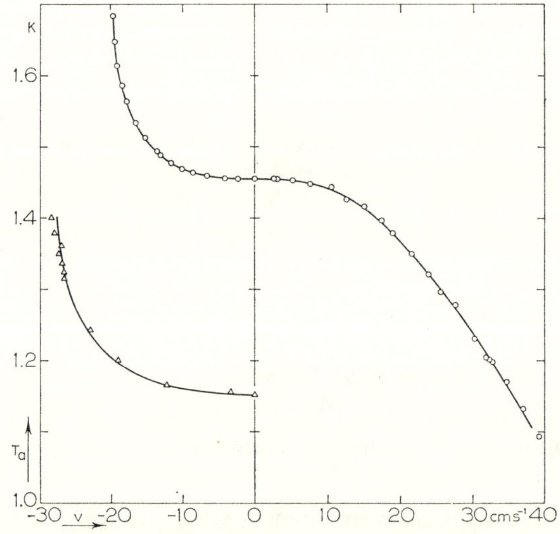

Fig. 5. Comparison between the experimental data points of T_a as a function of the net mass flow velocity with the calculated curve.

points of fig. 4 is only due to the inaccuracy introduced by the numerical method used to determine $A(T)$.

For two different bath temperatures, fig. 6 shows T_a, plotted as a function of the heat supplied to the chamber, $\dot{Q}_H$, in the case that the net flow is zero ($v = 0$). The calculated curves seem to be in fair agreement with the experimental data points. It should be noted, that for rather large values of $\dot{Q}_H$, the experimental data for the two bath temperatures coincide on the same curve, showing that the

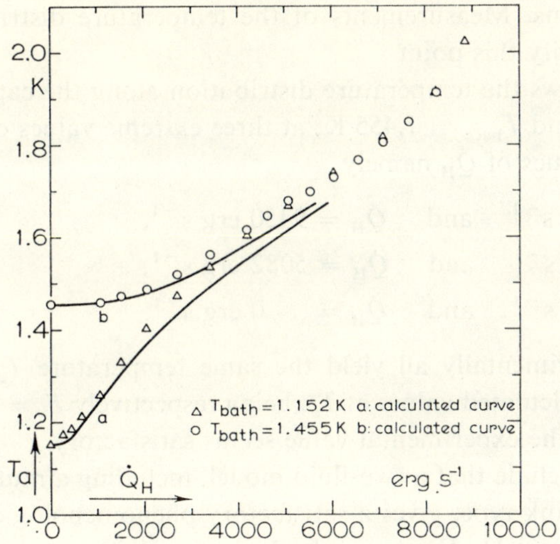

Fig. 6. T_a **as a function of the heat input to the chamber in the case that** $v = 0$**. Open symbols are the experimental data points, the solid curves are calculated by means of numerical integration of eq. (12).**

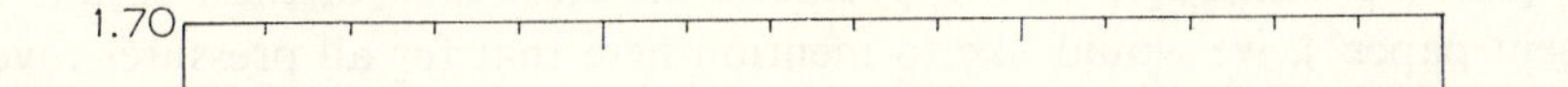

Fig. 7. The calculated temperature distribution along the capillary.

bath temperature becomes irrelevant. In the calculated curves the influence of the bath, though rather small at high $\dot{Q}_H$, remains noticeable. This is due to the necessity of imposing a boundary condition (for which we have chosen $T_{x=l} = T_{\text{bath}}$) in a description of the flow phenomena which considers only flow under stationary conditions. Measurements of the temperature distribution along the capillary could clarify this point.

Finally fig. 7 shows the temperature distribution along the capillary, calculated for $T_a = 1.676$ K and $T_{bath} = 1.455$ K, at three extreme values of v together with the appropriate values of $\dot{Q}_H$ namely

$$v = +15.5 \text{ cm s}^{-1} \quad \text{and} \quad \dot{Q}_H = 9450 \text{ erg s}^{-1},$$

$$v = 0 \text{ cm s}^{-1} \quad \text{and} \quad \dot{Q}_H = 5082 \text{ erg s}^{-1},$$

$$v = -19.6 \text{ cm s}^{-1} \quad \text{and} \quad \dot{Q}_H = 0 \text{ erg s}^{-1}.$$

These values experimentally all yield the same temperature $T_a = 1.676$ K. The agreement of the calculated values of T_a, being respectively $T_a = 1.629$ K, 1.638 K and 1.676 K, with the experimental value seems satisfactory.

We therefore conclude that a two-fluid model, including a mutual friction force of the Gorter–Mellink type, gives a satisfactory phenomenological description of the flow phenomena in He II, also under high overall pressure.

3.2 The behaviour of T_a near the limiting temperature. As expected the limiting temperature of about 0.75 K at s.v.p. is found to decrease with increasing pressure. Although we will postpone the discussion of these results to a subsequent paper[4]), we would like to mention here that for all pressures investigated, this limit is found to correspond to a roton density of 9.8×10^{18} cm^{-3}*.

However, if the limiting lowest temperature is determined only by a fixed roton density at which the mutual friction becomes ineffective, one does not expect this temperature to be affected by a small heat input, $\dot{Q}_H$, to the chamber. It would merely be reached at a somewhat larger flow velocity.

Fig. 8, for instance, shows that this is not true. It throws therefore considerable doubt upon our attempt to explain the origin of the limiting temperature along these lines only, though it does not affect our conclusion that the mutual friction is responsible for the cooling itself.

In order to reveal the information contained in fig. 8, the quantity $O_c\rho s_a T_a v - \dot{Q}_H$ is plotted as a function of the flow velocity in fig. 9. Surprisingly it shows that for all $\dot{Q}_H$ the data join on one curve, which slightly depends on the overall pressure. The most plausible interpretation of this result is, that there occurs a heat input $\dot{Q}_{ch}$ into the chamber and that, as the heat flow from the chamber obeys

$$O_c \rho s_a T_a v_{n,a} = \dot{Q}_H + \dot{Q}_{ch}, \tag{13}$$

* Because recently an unexplained discrepancy between the calibration of the thermometers against CMN and ^{3}He vapour pressure showed up [8]), we investigated the influence of a systematic error in the temperature calibration on the results presented in this section. We found that even when all temperatures are assumed to be as much as 25 mK higher our conclusions remain qualitatively the same. The limit occurs again at a fixed roton density (now of about 1.5×10^{19} cm^{-3}) and $v_{n,a}$ remains still equal to v, as the results of fig. 9 appear to be merely shifted along the ordinate, such that $\dot{Q}_{ch}$ becomes somewhat larger.

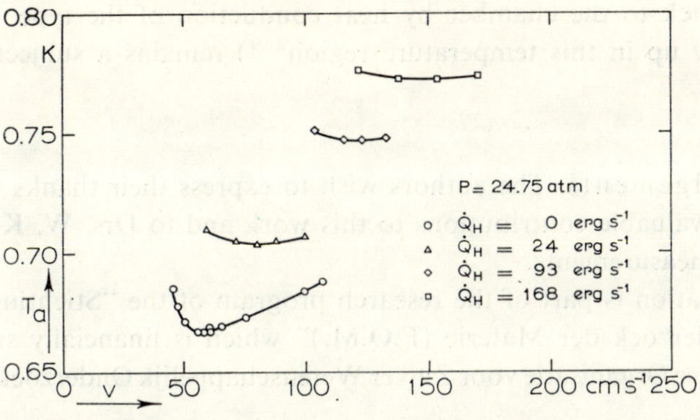

Fig. 8. T_a as a function of the net mass flow velocity for various heat inputs to the chamber at an overall pressure of 24.75 atm.

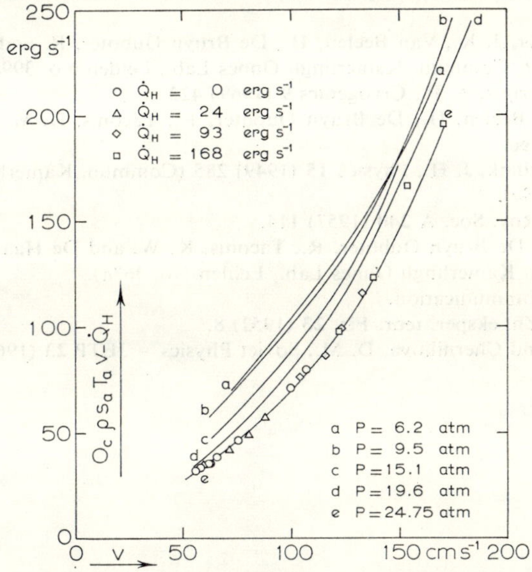

Fig. 9. The heat input into the chamber, $\dot{Q}_{ch}$, as a function of the net mass flow velocity. For the sake of clearness only data points are shown for a pressure of 24.75 atm.

this heat is carried away with the velocity $v_{n,a} = v$, once the maximum cooling is attained. In this picture $\dot{Q}_{ch}$ is unaffected by $\dot{Q}_H$ and the curves in fig. 9 show $\dot{Q}_{ch}$ as a function of v. Since these curves seem to extrapolate to zero at $v = 0$, we conclude that $\dot{Q}_{ch}$ is generated by the flow itself. We therefore hold this heat input into the chamber responsible for the occurrence of a limiting temperature and its pressure dependence. The large values of $\dot{Q}_{ch}$, in the order of 50 erg s^{-1}, as compared to the results of Van Alphen *et al.*[7]), are not understood. Whether $\dot{Q}_c$ corresponds to dissipation in the chamber or to heat dissipated in the capillary which flows back to the chamber by heat conduction of the type $-K\nabla T$, that begins to show up in this temperature region[2, 9]) remains a subject for further study.

Acknowledgements. The authors wish to express their thanks to Dr. J. K. Hoffer for his valuable contributions to this work and to Drs. W. Koops for his help with the measurements.

This investigation is part of the research program of the "Stichting voor Fundamenteel Onderzoek der Materie (F.O.M.)" which is financially supported by the "Nederlandse Organisatie voor Zuiver Wetenschappelijk Onderzoek (Z.W.O.)".

REFERENCES

1) Olijhoek, J. F., Van Alphen, W. M., De Bruyn Ouboter, R. and Taconis, K. W., Physica **35** (1967) 483.
2) Olijhoek, J. F., Hoffer, J. K., Van Beelen, H., De Bruyn Ouboter, R. and Taconis, K. W., Physica **64** (1973) 289 (Commun. Kamerlingh Onnes Lab., Leiden No. 399*b*).
3) Staas, F. A. and Severijns, A. P., Cryogenics **9** (1969) 422.
4) Olijhoek, J. F., Van Beelen, H., De Bruyn Ouboter, R., Taconis, K. W. and Koops, W., Physica to be published.
5) Gorter, C. J. and Mellink, J. H., Physica **15** (1949) 285 (Commun. Kamerlingh Onnes Lab., Leiden, Suppl. No. 98*a*).
6) Vinen, W. F., Proc. Roy. Soc. A **240** (1957) 114.
7) Van Alphen, W. M., De Bruyn Ouboter, R., Taconis, K. W. and De Haas, W., Physica **40** (1969) 469 (Commun. Kamerlingh Onnes Lab., Leiden No. 367*a*).
8) Koops, W., private communication.
9) Khalatnikov, I. M., Zh. éksper. teor. Fiz. **23** (1952) 8.
Khalatnikov, I. M. and Chernikova, D. M., Soviet Physics – JETP **23** (1966) 274.

Physica **69** (1973) 49–53 © *North-Holland Publishing Co.*

THE INFLUENCE OF NUCLEAR SPIN DECOUPLING ON THE TRANSVERSE THERMAL CONDUCTIVITY COEFFICIENT OF HD

J. P. J. HEEMSKERK, H. F. P. KNAAP and J. J. M. BEENAKKER

Kamerlingh Onnes Laboratorium der Rijksuniversiteit, Leiden, Nederland

Received 1 June 1973

Synopsis

Transport properties of diatomic molecules in a magnetic field usually obey an H/p law. Deviations are to be expected for magnetic-field values in the order of the coupling strength between the nuclear spin and the rotational magnetic moment. Experimental evidence for this effect is presented for the transverse thermal conductivity of HD.

1. *Introduction*. In 1938 Gorter[1]) published a note in Naturwissenschaften entitled "Zur Interpretierung des Senftleben-Effektes". In this paper he gave a qualitative explanation for the remarkable behaviour found in the viscosity and thermal conductivity of oxygen gas in a magnetic field which had been puzzling physicists for nearly a decade[2, 3]). According to Gorter the precession of the rotational axis of O_2 in a magnetic field causes an averaging of the nonspherical cross section of the molecules, thus a changing in the transport properties.

This picture led in 1962 to a new development. It was then shown that the influence of a magnetic field on the transport properties of gases is not limited to paramagnetic molecules like O_2, but is a general property of all rotating molecules. Since then these magnetic-field effects have proved to be a valuable tool in the study of nonspherical molecules.

In his second and final paper on this subject (1939), Gorter[4]) indicated some of the limitations of the model he had introduced. He remarked "One has assumed that the oxygen molecule possesses a fixed moment that is rigidly coupled perpendicular to the plane of the molecule. At higher values of the field, however, there will certainly be decoupling .... However, no experimental indications for this effect are available". Only recently has the influence of the decoupling between the electron spin and the rotational angular momentum in O_2 been observed[5, 6]). Furthermore, using the decoupling idea a detailed theory for the transport properties of O_2 has been developed which gives remarkable agreement with the experimental results[7, 8]). A similar phenomenon can occur for diamagnetic gases where in this case the nuclear spins and the angular momenta may be coupled or decoupled in the field. This problem has been studied theoretically by Coope, Sanctuary and Beenakker[9]). We thought a presentation of an experimental confirmation of this effect to be an appropriate contribution on this occasion.

One of the characteristic features of the field effect on transport properties is that it can usually be described as a function of H/p, the ratio of field strength and pressure. This stems from the fact that the field effects in gases originate from a competition between the precession frequency ω and the collision time τ. When ω is proportional to H, an H/p dependence results. Equivalently, the hamiltonian describing the precessional motion of the molecules is linear in H. In general, however, the hamiltonian is a complicated expression containing terms describing the interaction of the external field with the magnetic moments present in the molecule (nuclear, electronic and rotational), and terms arising from the intramolecular interactions. Two extreme cases can be considered: (i) At high fields, *i.e.*, when the influence of the external field is much stronger than the intramolecular interactions, each magnetic moment can be treated as virtually independent (Paschen–Back limit). Retaining only the terms that affect the molecular orientation, an adequate hamiltonian for the molecular precession of molecules in Σ states is:

$$\mathscr{H} = -\gamma \boldsymbol{J} \cdot \boldsymbol{H}, \tag{1}$$

where $\boldsymbol{J}$ is the rotational angular momentum and γ the gyromagnetic ratio. (ii) For low enough fields the various angular momenta are coupled together more strongly than to the magnetic field. Denoting the resultant angular momentum by $\boldsymbol{R}$, the hamiltonian of the rigidly coupled system can be written as

$$\mathscr{H} = -\gamma_{\mathrm{R}} \boldsymbol{R} \cdot \boldsymbol{H}, \tag{2}$$

where γ_{R} is the corresponding gyromagnetic ratio. Since the electron spin is coupled to $\boldsymbol{J}$ by a factor of about a thousand stronger than the nuclear spin, O_2 is usually in the coupled case [eq. (2)], while for diamagnetic molecules the nuclear spin is usually completely decoupled [eq. (1)].

As for diamagnetic molecules the coupling is strong for the hydrogen isotopes, these gases appeared to be most suitable for an experimental study. Although the hamiltonian is more complicated for HD than for H_2, HD was chosen because this asymmetric hydrogen isotope shows an appreciable change of the transport properties in a magnetic field. To observe the transition between coupled and uncoupled nuclear spin, it is necessary to work at fields below 200 Oe. This forces one to work at rather low pressures (< 0.1 torr) in order to reach values for H/p that are large enough to observe the field effect. For an experimental investigation of the transition regime, we studied the behaviour of λ^{tr} of HD between 10 and 600 Oe. The coefficient λ^{tr} describes the transverse heat flow which arises due to a magnetic field (that is, a heat flow perpendicular to both the temperature gradient and the magnetic field).

2. *Results and discussion.* Fig. 1 shows the theoretical results on λ^{tr} as obtained in ref. 9 for HD at 50 K. At that temperature all rotating molecules are in the $J = 1$ state. The dashed line in fig. 1 corresponds to the equation

$$\frac{\lambda^{tr}}{\lambda} = -\psi\left\{\frac{\omega\tau}{1+\omega^2\tau^2} + 2\frac{2\omega\tau}{1+4\omega^2\tau^2}\right\} \quad \text{with} \quad \omega\tau \propto H/p. \tag{3}$$

This equation is valid in the situation where the nuclear spin is completely decoupled. It is seen from fig. 1 that at lower pressures (and corresponding lower fields) strong deviations occur from the dashed curve: not only the heights and positions, but also the shapes of the curves are changed.

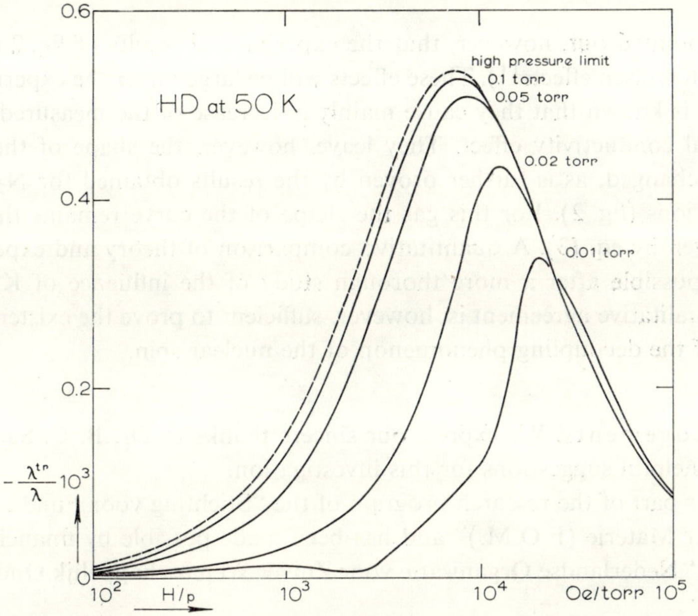

Fig. 1. Theoretical results for λ^{tr} obtained for HD at 50 K at various low pressures, as calculated in ref. 9. The dashed curve is the high-pressure limit as given by eq. (3).

For our experiments the apparatus described in ref. 10 was used. The experiments, carried out for the pressures 0.057, 0.027, 0.020 and 0.018 torr, were performed at 85 K, this being the lowest temperature that could conveniently be reached in our setup. The results are given in fig. 2. From a comparison of figs. 1 and 2 it is seen that qualitiative agreement is obtained between theory and experiment. Note in particular the agreement with respect to the shapes of the curves.

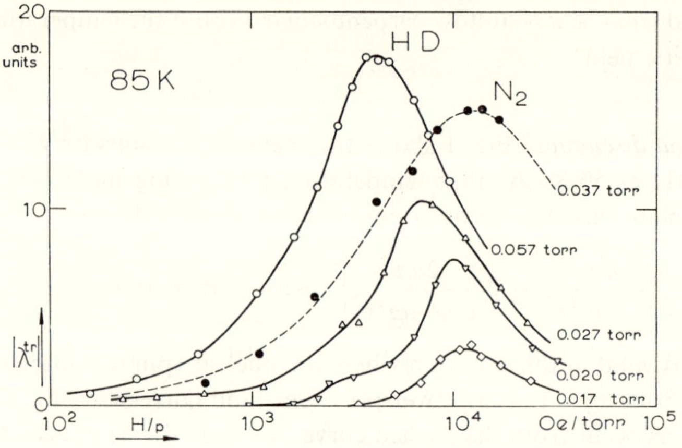

Fig. 2. Experimental results for λ^{tr} obtained for HD at 85 K at various low pressures. The dashed curve, which is fitted to the N_2 results, is given by eq. (3).

It should be pointed out, however, that the experimental results of fig. 2 are not corrected for Knudsen effects[11]). These effects will be large under the experimental conditions. It is known that they cause mainly a decrease of the measured values of the thermal conductivity effect. They leave, however, the shape of the curve essentially unchanged, as is further proven by the results obtained for N_2 under similar conditions (fig. 2). For this gas the shape of the curve remains the same as the one given by eq. (3). A quantitative comparison of theory and experiment will only be possible after a more thorough study of the influence of Knudsen effects. The qualitative agreement is, however, sufficient to prove the existence and importance of the decoupling phenomenon of the nuclear spin.

Acknowledgements. We express our sincere thanks to Dr. B. C. Sanctuary for his many helpful suggestions for this investigation.

This work is part of the research program of the "Stichting voor Fundamenteel Onderzoek der Materie (F.O.M.)" and has been made possible by financial support from the "Nederlandse Organisatie voor Zuiver Wetenschappelijk Onderzoek (Z.W.O.)".

REFERENCES

1) Gorter, C. J., Naturwissenschaften **26** (1938) 140.
2) Senftleben, H., Physik. Z. **31** (1930) 822, 961.
3) Herzfeld, K. F., Handb. Jahrb. chem. Phys. 3/2 IV (1939) 222.
4) Gorter, C. J., Ned. Tijdschr. Natuurk. **7** (1940) 89.
5) Kikoin, I. K., Balashov, K. I., Lasarev, S. D. and Neushtadt, R. E., Phys. Letters **24A** (1967) 165.
6) Hulsman, H., Burgmans, A. L. J., Van Waasdijk, E. J. and Knaap, H. F. P., Physica **50** (1970) 558.

7) Beenakker, J. J. M., Coope, J. A. R. and Snider, R. F., Phys. Rev. **A4** (1971) 788.
8) Maksimov, L. A., Soviet Physics – JETP **34** (1972) 322.
9) Coope, J. A. R., Sanctuary, B. C. and Beenakker, J. J. M., to be published.
10) Hermans, L. J. F., Schutte, A., Knaap, H. F. P. and Beenakker, J. J. M., Physica **46** (1970) 491.
11) Hermans, L. J. F., Koks, J. M., Hengeveld, A. F. and Knaap, H. F. P., Physica **50** (1970) 410.

Physica **69** (1973) 54–56 © *North-Holland Publishing Co.*

CRITERIA FOR SUPERCONDUCTING TRANSITION TEMPERATURES

B. T. MATTHIAS

Department of Physics, University of California, San Diego, La Jolla, California 92037, U.S.A.*

and

Bell Telephone Laboratories, Murray Hill, New Jersey 07974, U.S.A.

Received 2 May 1973

Synopsis

Crystallographic instabilities seem to be a necessary condition for high superconducting transition temperatures in multicomponent phases.

It was almost two decades ago since an empirical criterion for high and low superconducting transition temperatures was first discovered. At that time, the maximum transition temperature was approximately 15 K, today it is 21 K. Depending on one's point of view, this progress can be viewed as poor, modest or promising. In the following, I want to outline what has happened during the last twenty years, and what – in my opinion – the outlook for superconductivity in the future is.

As I described in an earlier article published in one of Professor Gorter's series on low temperature physics (Progress in Low Temperature Physics, Vol. II, (1957) p. 138), the decisive parameter for high transition temperatures in superconducting elements and alloys was the number of valence electrons per atom (e/a). Accordingly, for compounds, the literal or arithmetic average had to be taken. By valence electrons we meant, and still mean, *all* electrons outside the filled shell of an atom or the atoms forming the compound.

For the elements, as long as e/a does not exceed the number that can be accommodated by half-filled shells, as in the middle of the periodic system, this e/a is identical with the conventional chemical valency. For higher values, this identity gradually disappears. Thus, the concept of chemical valency is no longer relevant

* Research in La Jolla sponsored by the Air Force Office of Scientific Research, Contract #AFOSR-F44620-72-C-0017.

for superconductivity. The real meaning behind the e/a dependence is the fact that superconductivity is determined to a large extent by the nature of the isolated atoms, or then, their combinations. Such stark simplifications entirely ignore the importance of crystal structure, chemical bonds and effects originating from lattice dynamics. But then, using e/a to find superconductors was only the first step, and had the added virtue that it relied completely on those data that could be gotten from the periodic system without any further information. All this I have stated before in one way or another.

Today, just as almost twenty years ago, the highest superconducting transition temperatures still occur for $4.5 < e/a < 5$, the optimum value for most cubic crystals such as the (NaCl) and (β–W) structures. $Nb_3(Al_{0.75}Ge_{0.25})$, which has a cubic β–W structure and the highest known superconducting transition temperature to date, again has an e/a about 4.6.

As would have been anticipated, new optimum e/a values have been found for other crystal structures. They are:

$e/a \approx 4$ for (Pu_2C_3) and (MoB_2);
$e/a = 5.7$ for structures such as ($CuAl_2$);
$6.3 < e/a < 6.7$ for many hexagonal structures.

Critical temperatures in all these structure types range from 12 K to 17 K. Obviously, today high temperatures are no longer restricted to cubic structures. Also, it is evident that e/a as defined earlier is no longer a decisive parameter. One is, therefore, forced to find a new or different criterion for the occurrence of superconducting transition temperatures. I think that we have found one, though it is not as simple as e/a was in the past. The criterion now is the metastability of an intrinsically unstable crystallographic phase.

Instabilities associated with high transition temperature superconductors is certainly not a new idea. Long ago, it had become clear that there were some natural obstacles to high-temperature superconductivity. These instabilities are of a very general nature and can show themselves in many different ways:

a) The height of instability is reached when the compound just won't form at all, such as Nb_3Si which usually crystallizes in a tetragonal structure instead of the cubic β–W phase.

b) The proper stoichiometry cannot be reached, for instance Nb_3Ge becomes $Nb_{3.3}Ge$ and VC becomes $VC_{0.87}$.

c) The compound will form, but in a completely disordered fashion. Thus Mo_3Tc crystallizes closer to a ratio of 1 : 1 than 3 : 1 as in β–W, even though the structure is still retained.

d) The compound will not form or then only improperly at atmospheric pressures: such as NbN or Y_2C_3, and high pressures have to be used to make the compound form.

e) The compound forms correctly from every point of view, but at lower temperatures – sometimes as low as 20 K – it suddenly undergoes a polymorphic phase transition. These transitions are usually displacive in nature, and invariably reduce the symmetry of the metal. For instance, Nb_3Sn becomes tetragonal, and HfV_2, again originally cubic, becomes orthorhombic.

While nowhere near all of the high-temperature superconducting binary systems have been explored, it seems probable that the vicinity of 20 K is about as high as we will ever be able to get with binary systems. However, in the maximum transition temperature systems, such as in Nb_3(Al, Ge) or Nb(N, C) one of the ways to proceed in the future is already given. It is by using at least three elements instead of just two, along the same lines as for binary compounds. For pseudo-binary phases, such as the one just mentioned, the rules of the past still work well, since both of the constituent binaries are in themselves already high transition temperature superconductors having optimum e/a values. Ternary compounds, however, are quite different.

Here we are dealing with three elements for which no combination between any of the two constituent elements ever gives comparable high transition temperatures. Recently, we have discovered true ternary compounds with high T_c's of which the two most prominent groups are exemplified by

$Li_{0.3}Ti_{1.2}S_2$ hexagonal

and

$X_{0.5}Mo_3S_4$ rhombohedral, with X = Cu, Ag, Mg, Zn, Cd, Sn and Pb.

Since the range of transition temperatures for all these compounds covers values between 2 and 17 K, here the e/a ratio, as defined in the past, is no longer a decisive parameter. The number of possibilities for new high transition temperature structures has increased considerably with the discovery of these ternary compounds. But, since the conventional e/a is no longer such a good number, the concept of instability may have replaced it. Let me show this by just one example.

Mo_3Se_4 is rhombohedral and superconducting near 6 K. Mo_3S_4 will not crystallize in this structure. However, $Sn_{0.5}Mo_3S_4$ will crystallize in the Mo_3Se_4 structure and is superconducting near 15 K. $Sn_{0.5}Mo_3Se_4$ is superconducting near 3 K. If the ratio would remain constant (!), rhombohedral Mo_3S_4 would become superconducting far above 21 K. It is for this reason that it does not exist. So, it seems for ternary compounds we have slipped back two decades, and are forced once again to find new or different criteria more positive than the pure concept of instability for the occurrence of high superconducting transition temperatures.

From now on, I shall look for systems that should exist, but won't – unless one can persuade them.

Note added in proof. Recently, J. R. Gavaler of Westinghouse Laboratories has succeeded in making almost stiochiometric Nb_3Ge, raising the transition temperature from 18 to 22.3 K.

Physica **69** (1973) 57–66 © *North-Holland Publishing Co.*

ON THE RELATION BETWEEN MACROSCOPIC AND MICROSCOPIC NONLINEAR SUSCEPTIBILITIES

D. BEDEAUX and N. BLOEMBERGEN *

Instituut-Lorentz, Rijksuniversiteit Leiden, Leiden, Nederland

Received 17 May 1973

Synopsis

A general formulation of the relationship between macroscopic and microscopic nonlinear dielectric response functions is presented. The results are in agreement with and justify previous theoretical and experimental data for local field corrections for the nonlinear susceptibilities χ_2 and χ_3, and for a contribution proportional to $\{\chi_2\}^2$ to χ_3^{eff}.

1. *Introduction.* It is a basic concept of electromagnetic theory that from a microscopic point of view one has only the electromagnetic field in vacuo and a microscopic distribution of currents and charges[1]). These are related to the microscopic field by an internal constitutive relationship, which may be of arbitrary form and contain linear as well as nonlinear terms. The microscopic field is the sum of the external (vacuum) field produced by sources outside the medium and the field produced in a small volume element by the currents and charges in all other volume elements of the medium.

In a homogeneous medium it is useful to introduce a macroscopic field. For a linear dielectric the polarization is proportional to this field. The proportionality constant is the (internal) linear susceptibility, or the dielectric constant minus one. The relationship between this quantity and the molecular polarizabilities was already the subject of discussion in 1880 in the papers of Lorentz and Lorenz[2]). The effects of particle density correlations in dense systems have recently been studied[3]).

It is the purpose of this note to extend this formalism to the nonlinear dielectric. Since the nonlinear polarization terms are usually small compared to the external fields and the linear polarization terms, a power series expansion is indicated[4]) and carried out in section 2 of this work. Relations are derived between the internal and the external susceptibilities. In the third section the nonlinear suscep-

* On leave from Harvard University.

tibilities are related to microscopic nonlinear polarizabilities. In the final section the formal results will be given a simple physical interpretation.

The purpose of this note is to provide a more rigorous justification of previous, more intuitive formulations, used in the description of nonlinear optical phenomena.

2. *The relation between external and internal response functions.* The Maxwell equations in a dielectric are

$$\operatorname{curl} \boldsymbol{E} = -\frac{\partial \boldsymbol{B}}{\partial t}, \quad \operatorname{div} \boldsymbol{D} = \rho,$$
$$\operatorname{curl} \boldsymbol{H} = \frac{\partial \boldsymbol{D}}{\partial t} + \boldsymbol{j}, \quad \operatorname{div} \boldsymbol{B} = 0, \tag{2.1}$$

where $\boldsymbol{E}(\boldsymbol{r}, t)$ and $\boldsymbol{B}(\boldsymbol{r}, t)$ are respectively the electric and magnetic fields, $\boldsymbol{D}(\boldsymbol{r}, t)$ and $\boldsymbol{H}(\boldsymbol{r}, t)$ the inductions, and $\boldsymbol{j}(\boldsymbol{r}, t)$ and $\rho(\boldsymbol{r}, t)$ are the externally controlled current and charge densities; units are chosen such that the velocity of light in vacuum is one. Neglecting the magnetic properties we have

$$\boldsymbol{H} = \boldsymbol{B}, \qquad \boldsymbol{D} = \boldsymbol{E} + \boldsymbol{P}, \tag{2.2}$$

with $\boldsymbol{P}$ the polarization.

From eqs. (2.1) and (2.2) we obtain the wave equation governing the electric field.

$$\operatorname{curl}\operatorname{curl} \boldsymbol{E} + \frac{\partial^2}{\partial t^2}\boldsymbol{E} = -\frac{\partial^2}{\partial t^2}\boldsymbol{P} - \frac{\partial}{\partial t}\boldsymbol{j}. \tag{2.3}$$

Defining Fourier transforms with respect to $\boldsymbol{r}$ and t of a field f by

$$f(\boldsymbol{k}, \omega) = \int \mathrm{d}\boldsymbol{r}\,\mathrm{d}t \exp\left[-\mathrm{i}(\boldsymbol{k}\cdot\boldsymbol{r} - \omega t)\right] f(\boldsymbol{r}, t), \tag{2.4}$$

eq. (2.3) becomes

$$\left[\boldsymbol{k}\boldsymbol{k} - k^2 + \omega^2\right]\cdot \boldsymbol{E}(\boldsymbol{k}, \omega) = -\omega^2 \boldsymbol{P}(\boldsymbol{k}, \omega) - \mathrm{i}\omega \boldsymbol{j}(\boldsymbol{k}, \omega). \tag{2.5}$$

The general retarded solution of this equation is

$$\boldsymbol{E}(\boldsymbol{k}, \omega) = \boldsymbol{E}_{\mathrm{V}}(\boldsymbol{k}, \omega) - \mathsf{F}(\boldsymbol{k}, \omega)\cdot \boldsymbol{P}(\boldsymbol{k}, \omega), \tag{2.6}$$

where $\boldsymbol{E}_{\mathrm{V}}$ is a solution of the equation in the absence of the dielectric ($\boldsymbol{P} = 0$) and is therefore the incident radiation field in vacuum plus the fields due to external sources in vacuum. The retarded propagator of the electromagnetic field in vacuum F is given by

$$\begin{aligned} \mathsf{F}(\boldsymbol{k}, \omega) &= [\boldsymbol{kk} - k^2 + (\omega + \mathrm{i}0)^2]^{-1}\omega^2 \\ &= [k^2 - (\omega + \mathrm{i}0)^2]^{-1}(\boldsymbol{kk} - \omega^2) \\ &= \left[\tfrac{1}{2}\mathrm{i}\pi k^{-1}\{\delta(k - \omega) - \delta(k + \omega)\} + \mathscr{P}\left(\frac{1}{k^2 - \omega^2}\right)\right](\boldsymbol{kk} - \omega^2), \end{aligned} \tag{2.7}$$

where i0 is an infinitesimally small positive imaginary number. We will also use eq. (2.6) in the more formal notation

$$\boldsymbol{E} = \boldsymbol{E}_{\mathrm{V}} - \mathsf{F} \cdot \boldsymbol{P}. \tag{2.8}$$

The advantage of this form is that it is valid in both the $\boldsymbol{k},\omega$ and the $\boldsymbol{r},t$ representation, or in fact any other representation. F is to be interpreted as a linear operator which is diagonal in $\boldsymbol{k},\omega$ representation, and of which the diagonal elements are given by eq. (2.7).

In order to close the set of equations governing the fields constitutive relations relating the polarization $\boldsymbol{P}$ to the electric field $\boldsymbol{E}$ must be given

$$\boldsymbol{P} = \boldsymbol{\chi}_1 \cdot \boldsymbol{E} + \boldsymbol{g}(\boldsymbol{E}). \tag{2.9}$$

$\boldsymbol{\chi}$ is the linear susceptibility tensor while $\boldsymbol{g}$ contains the nonlinear effects

$$\boldsymbol{g}(\boldsymbol{E}) = \boldsymbol{\chi}_2 \vdots\!\!: \boldsymbol{EE} + \boldsymbol{\chi}_3 \,\vdots\, \boldsymbol{EEE} + \text{higher order terms.*} \tag{2.10}$$

The $\boldsymbol{\chi}$'s are in their most general form operators so that *e.g.* in the $\boldsymbol{r},t$ representation

$$(\boldsymbol{\chi}_1 \cdot \boldsymbol{E})(\boldsymbol{r}, t) = \int \mathrm{d}\boldsymbol{r}_1\, \mathrm{d}t_1\, \boldsymbol{\chi}_1(\boldsymbol{r}, t|\boldsymbol{r}_1, t_1) \cdot \boldsymbol{E}(\boldsymbol{r}_1, t_1), \tag{2.11}$$

$$(\boldsymbol{\chi}_2 \cdot \boldsymbol{EE})(\boldsymbol{r}, t) = \int \mathrm{d}\boldsymbol{r}_1\, \mathrm{d}t_1 \int \mathrm{d}\boldsymbol{r}_2\, \mathrm{d}t_2\, \boldsymbol{\chi}_2(\boldsymbol{r}, t|\boldsymbol{r}_1, t_1; \boldsymbol{r}_2, t_2) : \boldsymbol{E}(\boldsymbol{r}_1, t_1)\boldsymbol{E}(\boldsymbol{r}_2, t_2) \tag{2.12}$$

and similar for other quantities. The various expressions can of course be simplified using properties like translational invariance, stationarity, *etc.*

Eq. (2.9) relates the polarization to the electric field $\boldsymbol{E}$, it is, however, also possible to express the polarization in terms of the external field $\boldsymbol{E}_{\mathrm{V}}$.

$$\boldsymbol{P} = \boldsymbol{\gamma}_1 \cdot \boldsymbol{E}_{\mathrm{V}} + \boldsymbol{c}(\boldsymbol{E}_{\mathrm{V}}). \tag{2.13}$$

$\boldsymbol{\gamma}_1$ is the linear external susceptibility while $\boldsymbol{c}$ contains the nonlinear effects.

$$\boldsymbol{c}(\boldsymbol{E}_{\mathrm{V}}) = \boldsymbol{\gamma}_2 : \boldsymbol{E}_{\mathrm{V}}\boldsymbol{E}_{\mathrm{V}} + \boldsymbol{\gamma}_3 \,\vdots\, \boldsymbol{E}_{\mathrm{V}}\boldsymbol{E}_{\mathrm{V}}\boldsymbol{E}_{\mathrm{V}} + \text{higher order terms.} \tag{2.14}$$

We will now show that the external and the internal susceptibilities can be expressed in each other in a simple way. Combination of eqs. (2.8) and (2.13) yields

$$\boldsymbol{P} = \boldsymbol{\gamma}_1 \cdot \boldsymbol{E} + \boldsymbol{\gamma}_1 \cdot \mathsf{F} \cdot \boldsymbol{P} + \boldsymbol{c}(\boldsymbol{E} + \mathsf{F} \cdot \boldsymbol{P}). \tag{2.15}$$

* The symbols : and ⋮ indicate, respectively, double and threefold contracted products.

This again gives

$$\boldsymbol{P} = (1 - \gamma_1 \cdot \mathsf{F})^{-1} \cdot \gamma_1 \cdot \boldsymbol{E} + (1 - \gamma_1 \cdot \mathsf{F})^{-1} \cdot \boldsymbol{c}(\boldsymbol{E} + \mathsf{F} \cdot \boldsymbol{P}). \tag{2.16}$$

Using iteration one can now use this equation to derive relations between the external and internal susceptibilities. Because $\boldsymbol{c}$ contains only nonlinear terms it follows that

$$\chi_1 = (1 - \gamma_1 \cdot \mathsf{F})^{-1} \cdot \gamma_1 = \boldsymbol{\epsilon} - 1, \tag{2.17}$$

which is the usual relation[5]) for the linear susceptibilities; and where $\boldsymbol{\epsilon}$ is the dielectric constant of the dielectric.

Inversion of eq. (2.17) yields

$$\gamma_1 = (1 + \chi_1 \cdot \mathsf{F})^{-1} \cdot \chi_1 . \tag{2.18}$$

Substitution of eq. (2.17) into eq. (2.16) yields

$$\begin{aligned}\boldsymbol{P} &= \chi_1 \cdot \boldsymbol{E} + (1 + \chi_1 \cdot \mathsf{F}) \cdot \boldsymbol{c}(\boldsymbol{E} + \mathsf{F} \cdot \boldsymbol{P}) \\ &= \chi_1 \cdot \boldsymbol{E} + (1 + \chi_1 \cdot \mathsf{F}) \cdot \boldsymbol{c}(\{1 + \mathsf{F} \cdot \chi_1\} \cdot \boldsymbol{E} + \mathsf{F} \cdot (1 + \chi_1 \cdot \mathsf{F}) \cdot \boldsymbol{c}(\boldsymbol{E} + \mathsf{F} \cdot \boldsymbol{P})).\end{aligned} \tag{2.19}$$

In terms of the nonlinear susceptibilities this equation becomes

$$\begin{aligned}\boldsymbol{P} = {} & \chi_1 \cdot \boldsymbol{E} + (1 + \chi_1 \cdot \mathsf{F}) \cdot \gamma_2 : \{(1 + \mathsf{F} \cdot \chi_1) \cdot \boldsymbol{E}\}\{(1 + \mathsf{F} \cdot \chi_1) \cdot \boldsymbol{E}\} \\ & + (1 + \chi_1 \cdot \mathsf{F}) \cdot \gamma_3 \,\vdots\, \{(1 + \mathsf{F} \cdot \chi_1) \cdot \boldsymbol{E}\}\{(1 + \mathsf{F} \cdot \chi_1) \cdot \boldsymbol{E}\}\{(1 + \mathsf{F} \cdot \chi_1) \cdot \boldsymbol{E}\} \\ & + (1 + \chi_1 \cdot \mathsf{F}) \cdot \gamma_2 : \{(1 + \mathsf{F} \cdot \chi_1) \cdot \boldsymbol{E}\} \\ & \times [\mathsf{F} \cdot (1 + \chi_1 \cdot \mathsf{F}) \cdot \gamma_2 : \{(1 + \chi_1 \cdot \mathsf{F}) \cdot \boldsymbol{E}\}\{(1 + \chi_1 \cdot \mathsf{F}) \cdot \boldsymbol{E}\}] \\ & + (1 + \chi_1 \cdot \mathsf{F}) \cdot \gamma_2 : [\mathsf{F} \cdot (1 + \chi_1 \cdot \mathsf{F}) \cdot \gamma_2 : \{(1 + \chi_1 \cdot \mathsf{F}) \cdot \boldsymbol{E}\}\{(1 + \chi_1 \cdot \mathsf{F}) \cdot \boldsymbol{E}\}] \\ & \times \{(1 + \mathsf{F} \cdot \chi_1) \cdot \boldsymbol{E}\} + \text{higher order terms.}\end{aligned} \tag{2.20}$$

One therefore finds, comparing with eqs. (2.9) and (2.10), for the nonlinear susceptibilities

$$\chi_2 = (1 + \chi_1 \cdot \mathsf{F}) \cdot \gamma_2 : (1 + \mathsf{F} \cdot \chi_1)(1 + \mathsf{F} \cdot \chi_1), \tag{2.21}$$

$$\begin{aligned}\chi_3 = {} & (1 + \chi_1 \cdot \mathsf{F}) \cdot \gamma_3 \,\vdots\, (1 + \mathsf{F} \cdot \chi_1)(1 + \mathsf{F} \cdot \chi_1)(1 + \mathsf{F} \cdot \chi_1) \\ & + (1 + \chi_1 \cdot \mathsf{F}) \cdot \gamma_2 : (1 + \mathsf{F} \cdot \chi_1)\{\mathsf{F} \cdot (1 + \chi_1 \cdot \mathsf{F}) \cdot \gamma_2 : (1 + \chi_1 \cdot \mathsf{F})(1 + \chi_1 \cdot \mathsf{F})\} \\ & + (1 + \chi_1 \cdot \mathsf{F}) \cdot \gamma_2 : \{\mathsf{F} \cdot (1 + \chi_1 \cdot \mathsf{F}) \cdot \gamma_2 : (1 + \chi_1 \cdot \mathsf{F})(1 + \chi_1 \cdot \mathsf{F})\}(1 + \chi_1 \cdot \mathsf{F}).\end{aligned} \tag{2.22}$$

The expression for χ_3 can be simplified using χ_2 instead of γ_2. Substitution of eq. (2.21) into eq. (2.22) yields

$$\begin{aligned}\chi_3 = {} & (1 + \chi_1 \cdot \mathsf{F}) \cdot \gamma_3 \,\vdots\, (1 + \chi_1 \cdot \mathsf{F})(1 + \chi_1 \cdot \mathsf{F})(1 + \chi_1 \cdot \mathsf{F}) \\ & + \chi_2 \cdot [\{\mathsf{F}_\varepsilon \cdot \chi_2\}_2 + \{\mathsf{F}_\varepsilon \cdot \chi_2\}_1],\end{aligned} \tag{2.23}$$

where $\boldsymbol{F}_\varepsilon$ is the propagator in the linear medium

$$F_\varepsilon(\boldsymbol{k}, \omega) = (\boldsymbol{kk} - k^2 + \omega^2 \boldsymbol{\epsilon})^{-1}\omega^2 = (1 + F \cdot \boldsymbol{\chi}_1)^{-1} \cdot F \tag{2.24}$$

and where the index 2, respectively 1 indicates that it combines with the second or first variable on the right-hand side of the operator $\boldsymbol{\chi}_2$. So is *e.g.*

$$\begin{aligned}(\boldsymbol{\chi}_2 \cdot \{F_\varepsilon \cdot \boldsymbol{\chi}_2\}_2)(\boldsymbol{r}, t|\boldsymbol{r}_1, t_1; \boldsymbol{r}_2, t_2; \boldsymbol{r}_3, t_3) \\ = \int \boldsymbol{\chi}_2(\boldsymbol{r}, t|\boldsymbol{r}_1, t_1; \boldsymbol{r}', t') \cdot F_\varepsilon(\boldsymbol{r}', t'|\boldsymbol{r}'', t'') \\ \cdot \boldsymbol{\chi}_2(\boldsymbol{r}'', t''|\boldsymbol{r}_2, t_2; \boldsymbol{r}_3, t_3) \mathrm{d}\boldsymbol{r}' \mathrm{d}t' \mathrm{d}\boldsymbol{r}'' \mathrm{d}t''.\end{aligned} \tag{2.25}$$

It is convenient to introduce the linear internal field in the dielectric medium $\boldsymbol{E}_\mathrm{L}$ which is defined by

$$\boldsymbol{E}_\mathrm{L} \equiv \boldsymbol{E}_\mathrm{V} - F \cdot \boldsymbol{\chi}_1 \cdot \boldsymbol{E}_\mathrm{L}. \tag{2.26}$$

In the absence of nonlinear contributions $\boldsymbol{E}_\mathrm{L}$ would simply be equal to the internal field $\boldsymbol{E}$. From eqs. (2.8), (2.9) and (2.26) one obtains

$$\boldsymbol{E} = (1 + F \cdot \boldsymbol{\chi}_1) \cdot \boldsymbol{E}_\mathrm{L} - F \cdot \boldsymbol{P} = (1 + F \cdot \boldsymbol{\chi}_1) \cdot \boldsymbol{E}_\mathrm{L} - F \cdot \boldsymbol{\chi}_1 \cdot \boldsymbol{E} - F \cdot \boldsymbol{g}(\boldsymbol{E}). \tag{2.27}$$

Solving the internal field from this relation and using also eq. (2.24) yields

$$\boldsymbol{E} = \boldsymbol{E}_\mathrm{L} - F_\varepsilon \cdot \boldsymbol{g}(\boldsymbol{E}). \tag{2.28}$$

Iteration of this equation leads to an expression for $\boldsymbol{E}$ in terms of $\boldsymbol{E}_\mathrm{L}$

$$\boldsymbol{E} = \boldsymbol{E}_\mathrm{L} - F_\varepsilon \cdot \boldsymbol{\chi}_2 : \boldsymbol{E}_\mathrm{L} \boldsymbol{E}_\mathrm{L} - F_\varepsilon \cdot \boldsymbol{\chi}_3^\mathrm{eff} \vdots \boldsymbol{E}_\mathrm{L} \boldsymbol{E}_\mathrm{L} \boldsymbol{E}_\mathrm{L} + \text{higher-order terms}, \tag{2.29}$$

where

$$\boldsymbol{\chi}_3^\mathrm{eff} = \boldsymbol{\chi}_3 - \boldsymbol{\chi}_2 : [\{F_\varepsilon \cdot \boldsymbol{\chi}_2\}_1 + \{F_\varepsilon \cdot \boldsymbol{\chi}_2\}_2]. \tag{2.30}$$

$\boldsymbol{\chi}_3^\mathrm{eff}$ is a combination of the normal three-mode susceptibility and the two-mode mixing terms.

3. *The relation between the molecular polarizabilities and the macroscopic response functions.* In this section we will give a simple microscopic theory relating the macroscopic response functions to the molecular polarizabilities of the molecules. It is assumed that the fields vary sufficiently slowly over the diameter of the molecules to describe the molecular response by point dipoles. The position of the molecules is assumed to be fixed. Within the context of the model the dipole moment $\boldsymbol{p}_i(t)$ of particle i at time t is given by (see *e.g.* ref. 3 for the linear case).

$$\boldsymbol{p}_i(t) = \boldsymbol{\alpha}_1 \cdot \boldsymbol{E}_\mathrm{e}(\boldsymbol{r}_i, t) + \boldsymbol{a}(\boldsymbol{E}_\mathrm{e}(\boldsymbol{r}_i, t)), \tag{3.1}$$

where $\boldsymbol{\alpha}_1$ is the linear polarizability of the molecules, $\boldsymbol{E}_\mathrm{e}$ is the effective field and $\boldsymbol{a}$ contains the contributions of the nonlinear polarizabilities of the molecule

$$\begin{aligned}\boldsymbol{a}(\boldsymbol{E}_\mathrm{e}(\boldsymbol{r}_i, t)) = \boldsymbol{\alpha}_2 : \boldsymbol{E}_\mathrm{e}(\boldsymbol{r}_i, t)\boldsymbol{E}_\mathrm{e}(\boldsymbol{r}_i, t) + \boldsymbol{\alpha}_3 \vdots \boldsymbol{E}_\mathrm{e}(\boldsymbol{r}_i, t)\boldsymbol{E}_\mathrm{e}(\boldsymbol{r}_i, t)\boldsymbol{E}_\mathrm{e}(\boldsymbol{r}_i, t) \\ + \text{higher-order terms.}\end{aligned} \tag{3.2}$$

The linear and the nonlinear molecular polarizabilities may depend on the frequency in which case they are a convolution operator in time. The effective field is given by

$$E_e(r_i, t) = E_V(r_i, t) - \sum_{j \neq i} \int F(r_i - r_j, t - t') \cdot p_j(t') dt' - \tfrac{1}{2} \int \{F(0, t - t') - F^\dagger(0, t - t')\} \cdot p_i(t') dt'. \tag{3.3}$$

The first contribution is the incident field in vacuum. The second is the field acting on particle i due to the other particles. The third is particle i's own reaction field. $F^\dagger$ is the hermitian conjugate of the operator F and is the advanced propagator. We note that this choice of the effective field is in essence the same as the choice originally made by Dirac[6, 7]) for a system of point charges rather than point dipoles.

If we now define the molecular-particle and dipole-moment densities as

$$\rho(r) \equiv \sum_i \delta(r_i - r), \tag{3.4}$$

$$p(r, t) \equiv \sum_i p_i(t) \delta(r_i - r) \tag{3.5}$$

and furthermore define a "cutoff" propagator by

$$H(r, t|r', t') = \begin{cases} (F - F^\dagger)(r - r', t - t') & \text{if } |r - r'| < a \\ F(r - r', t - t') & \text{if } |r - r'| > a, \end{cases} \tag{3.6}$$

where a is any length between zero and the distance of closest approach of the molecules. In ref. 3 it is shown that the effective field can now be written as

$$E_e(r_i, t) = E_V(r_i, t) - H \cdot p(r_i, t). \tag{3.7}$$

This can be verified by substitution of H as given in eq. (3.6). Substituting eqs. (3.1) and (3.7) into eq. (3.5) yields for the molecular polarizability density

$$\begin{aligned} p(r, t) &= \sum_i \delta(r - r_i)[\alpha_1 \cdot E_e(r, t) + a(E_e(r, t))] \\ &= \rho(r)[\alpha_1 \cdot E_e(r, t) + a(E_e(r, t))] \\ &= \rho(r)\alpha_1 \cdot E_V(r, t) - \rho(r)\alpha_1 \cdot H \cdot p(r, t) \\ &\quad + \rho(r) a(E_V(r, t) - H \cdot p(r, t)). \end{aligned} \tag{3.8}$$

The macroscopic polarization density P can now be found from the molecular polarization density by averaging over an appropriate ensemble in fluids or over *e.g.* the unit cell in crystals. In the rest of this section we will neglect all the density–density correlations and consequently the density–polarization density and polarization density–polarization density correlations. The contributions due to these correlations have been studied in detail for the linear susceptibilities where they are usually not more than a few procent. Similarly one might expect that the corrections to the nonlinear coefficients are of the same order. We intend to investigate this in more detail in a future publication.

Upon averaging eq. (3.8) neglecting all correlations one obtains

$$P(r, t) = \rho_0 \boldsymbol{\alpha}_1 E_V(r, t) - \rho_0 \boldsymbol{\alpha}_1 \cdot H \cdot P(r, t) + \rho_0 a(E_V(r, t) - H \cdot P(r, t)), \tag{3.9}$$

where ρ_0 is the average density. Substituting eq. (2.8) then yields

$$P(r, t) = \rho_0 \boldsymbol{\alpha}_1 \cdot E(r, t) + \rho_0 \boldsymbol{\alpha}_1 \cdot G \cdot P(r, t) + \rho_0 a(E(r, t) + G \cdot P(r, t)), \tag{3.10}$$

where

$$G = F - H. \tag{3.10a}$$

It can now be shown that[3])

$$\lim_{a \downarrow 0} G(r, t|r', t') = \tfrac{1}{3}\delta(r - r'). \tag{3.11}$$

The reason being simply that in this limit G is the singular part of F in $r = r'$. Upon taking this limit in eq. (3.10) we obtain, transforming also to frequency representation,

$$\begin{aligned} P(r, \omega) &= (1 - \tfrac{1}{3}\rho_0 \boldsymbol{\alpha}_1(\omega))^{-1} \cdot \rho_0 \boldsymbol{\alpha}_1(\omega) \cdot E(r, \omega) \\ &\quad + (1 - \tfrac{1}{3}\rho_0 \boldsymbol{\alpha}_1(\omega))^{-1} \cdot \rho_0 a(E(r, \omega) + \tfrac{1}{3}P(r, \omega)). \end{aligned} \tag{3.12}$$

The linear susceptibility can now be identified as

$$\boldsymbol{\chi}_1(\omega) = \boldsymbol{\epsilon}(\omega) - 1 = (1 - \tfrac{1}{3}\rho_0 \boldsymbol{\alpha}_1(\omega))^{-1} \cdot \rho_0 \boldsymbol{\alpha}_1(\omega). \tag{3.13}$$

This is the well-known Clausius–Mossotti formula for the linear case. Using this expression for the dielectric constant, eq. (3.12) can be written as

$$\begin{aligned} P(r, \omega) &= (\boldsymbol{\epsilon} - 1) \cdot E(r, \omega) + \tfrac{1}{3}(\boldsymbol{\epsilon} + 2) \cdot \rho_0 a(E(r, \omega) + \tfrac{1}{3}P(r, \omega)) \\ &= (\boldsymbol{\epsilon} - 1) \cdot E(r, \omega) + \tfrac{1}{3}(\boldsymbol{\epsilon} + 2) \cdot \rho_0 a(\tfrac{1}{3}(\boldsymbol{\epsilon} + 2) \cdot E(r, \omega) \\ &\quad + \tfrac{1}{9}(\boldsymbol{\epsilon} + 2) \cdot \rho_0 a(E(r, \omega) + \tfrac{1}{3}P(r, \omega))). \end{aligned} \tag{3.14}$$

Substitution of a as given in eq. (3.2) into this equation now gives

$$\begin{aligned} P(r, \omega) &= (\boldsymbol{\epsilon} - 1) \cdot E(r, \omega) + \tfrac{1}{3}(\boldsymbol{\epsilon} + 2) \cdot \rho_0 \boldsymbol{\alpha}_2 \\ &\qquad : \{\tfrac{1}{3}(\boldsymbol{\epsilon} + 2) \cdot E(r, \omega)\}\{\tfrac{1}{3}(\boldsymbol{\epsilon} + 2) \cdot E(r, \omega)\} \\ &+ \tfrac{1}{3}(\boldsymbol{\epsilon} + 2) \cdot \rho_0 \boldsymbol{\alpha}_3 \vdots \{\tfrac{1}{3}(\boldsymbol{\epsilon} + 2) \cdot E(r, \omega)\}\{\tfrac{1}{3}(\boldsymbol{\epsilon} + 2) \cdot E(r, \omega)\}\{\tfrac{1}{3}(\boldsymbol{\epsilon} + 2) \cdot E(r, \omega)\} \\ &+ \frac{1}{3}\left(\frac{\boldsymbol{\epsilon} + 2}{3}\right) \cdot \rho_0 \boldsymbol{\alpha}_2 : \{\tfrac{1}{3}(\boldsymbol{\epsilon} + 2) \cdot E(r, \omega)\} \\ &\times \{\tfrac{1}{3}(\boldsymbol{\epsilon} + 2) \cdot \rho_0 \boldsymbol{\alpha}_2 : \{\tfrac{1}{3}(\boldsymbol{\epsilon} + 2) \cdot E(r, \omega)\}\{\tfrac{1}{3}(\boldsymbol{\epsilon} + 2) \cdot E(r, \omega)\}\} \\ &+ \frac{1}{3}\left(\frac{\boldsymbol{\epsilon} + 2}{3}\right) \cdot \rho_0 \boldsymbol{\alpha}_2 : \{\tfrac{1}{3}(\boldsymbol{\epsilon} + 2) \cdot \rho_0 \boldsymbol{\alpha}_2 \\ &: \{\tfrac{1}{3}(\boldsymbol{\epsilon} + 2) \cdot E(r, \omega)\}\{\tfrac{1}{3}(\boldsymbol{\epsilon} + 2) \cdot E(r, \omega)\}\}\{\tfrac{1}{3}(\boldsymbol{\epsilon} + 2) \cdot E(r, \omega)\} \\ &+ \text{higher order terms.} \end{aligned} \tag{3.15}$$

The nonlinear susceptibilities can now be identified as

$$\chi_2 = \tfrac{1}{3}(\epsilon + 2) \cdot \rho_0 \alpha_2 : \tfrac{1}{3}(\epsilon + 2) \tfrac{1}{3}(\epsilon + 2), \tag{3.16}$$

$$\begin{aligned} \chi_3 = {} & \tfrac{1}{3}(\epsilon + 2) \cdot \rho_0 \alpha_3 \,\vdots\, \tfrac{1}{3}(\epsilon + 2) \tfrac{1}{3}(\epsilon + 2) \tfrac{1}{3}(\epsilon + 2) \\ & + \frac{1}{3}\left(\frac{\epsilon + 2}{3}\right) \cdot \rho_0 \alpha_2 : [\tfrac{1}{3}(\epsilon + 2)\{\tfrac{1}{3}(\epsilon + 2) \cdot \rho_0 \alpha_2 : \tfrac{1}{3}(\epsilon + 2) \tfrac{1}{3}(\epsilon + 2)\} \\ & + \{\tfrac{1}{3}(\epsilon + 2) \cdot \rho_0 \alpha_2 : \tfrac{1}{3}(\epsilon + 2) \tfrac{1}{3}(\epsilon + 2)\} \tfrac{1}{3}(\epsilon + 2)]. \end{aligned} \tag{3.17}$$

The trilinear susceptibility can be simplified using the bilinear susceptibilities. This gives

$$\begin{aligned} \chi_3 = {} & \tfrac{1}{3}(\epsilon + 2) \cdot \rho_0 \alpha_3 \,\vdots\, \tfrac{1}{3}(\epsilon + 2) \tfrac{1}{3}(\epsilon + 2) \tfrac{1}{3}(\epsilon + 2) \\ & + \chi_2 \cdot [\{(\epsilon + 2)^{-1} \cdot \chi_2\}_1 + \{(\epsilon + 2)^{-1} \chi_2\}_2]. \end{aligned} \tag{3.18}$$

In the case that the dielectric consists of a number of different molecules or atoms the macroscopic susceptibilities can be shown, neglecting again the correlations, to be equal to

$$\chi_1 = \epsilon - 1 = (1 - \tfrac{1}{3} \sum_l \rho_{0,l} \alpha_{1,l})^{-1} \sum_l \rho_{0,l} \alpha_{1,l}, \tag{3.19}$$

$$\chi_2 = \tfrac{1}{3}(\epsilon + 2) \cdot (\sum_l \rho_{0,l} \alpha_{2,l}) : \tfrac{1}{3}(\epsilon + 2) \tfrac{1}{3}(\epsilon + 2), \tag{3.20}$$

$$\begin{aligned} \chi_3 = {} & \tfrac{1}{3}(\epsilon + 2) \cdot (\sum_l \rho_{0,l} \alpha_{3,l}) \,\vdots\, \tfrac{1}{3}(\epsilon + 2) \tfrac{1}{3}(\epsilon + 2) \tfrac{1}{3}(\epsilon + 2) \\ & + \chi_2 \cdot [\{(\epsilon + 2)^{-1} \cdot \chi_2\}_1 + \{(\epsilon + 2)^{-1} \cdot \chi_2\}_2], \end{aligned} \tag{3.21}$$

where l labels the various constituents of the dielectric. The effective three-mode susceptibility χ_3^{eff} as defined in eq. (2.31) becomes

$$\begin{aligned} \chi_3^{\text{eff}} = {} & \tfrac{1}{3}(\epsilon + 2) \cdot (\sum_l \rho_{0,l} \alpha_{3,l}) \,\vdots\, \tfrac{1}{3}(\epsilon + 2) \tfrac{1}{3}(\epsilon + 2) \tfrac{1}{3}(\epsilon + 2) \\ & - \chi_2 \cdot [\{(F_\varepsilon - (\epsilon + 2)^{-1}) \cdot \chi_2\}_1 + \{(F_\varepsilon - (\epsilon + 2)^{-1}) \cdot \chi_2\}_2]. \end{aligned} \tag{3.22}$$

The correction $(\epsilon + 2)^{-1}$ to F_ε in the mode mixing term is due to the fact that the particles feel the local field rather than the macroscopic fields and has therefore the same origin as the local-field correction factors $\frac{1}{3}(\varepsilon + 2)$ appearing in the other terms.

4. *Discussion*. In section 2 it was shown that the nonlinear polarization may be expressed in terms of the fields external to the medium, *i.e.* the vacuum fields, or in terms of the internal field inside the dielectric. General relationships have been derived for the nonlinear response functions corresponding to these different choices.

In section 3 these nonlinear susceptibilities are related to the nonlinear polarizabilities of the molecular constituents. The linear and nonlinear internal susceptibilities are purely local. One readily recognizes in eqs. (3.20) and (3.21) the same local-field correction factors which were previously derived in section IIIb and the appendix of ref. 8. These susceptibilities are, because of their local nature, independent of the shape of the material specimen and the boundary conditions. They are, therefore, indeed characteristic material properties.

The total field in the dielectric is related to the linear fields in the dielectric by eq. (2.29). It is seen that the effective nonlinear sources for these fields may be written as

$$\boldsymbol{P}_2^{\mathrm{NLS}} = \boldsymbol{\chi}_2 : \boldsymbol{E}_{\mathrm{L}} \boldsymbol{E}_{\mathrm{L}}, \quad \boldsymbol{P}_3^{\mathrm{NLS}} = \boldsymbol{\chi}_3^{\mathrm{eff}} \,\vdots\, \boldsymbol{E}_{\mathrm{L}} \boldsymbol{E}_{\mathrm{L}} \boldsymbol{E}_{\mathrm{L}},$$

where $\boldsymbol{\chi}_3^{\mathrm{eff}}$ is given by eq. (2.30) and eq. (3.22). Thus the previous more intuitive use of the eqs. (2.29), (2.30) and (3.20), (3.21) and (3.22) is completely justified in terms of the present rigorous derivations. It is especially gratifying that the expression for $\boldsymbol{\chi}_3^{\mathrm{eff}}$ contains a term proportional to $\boldsymbol{\chi}_2^2$. A specific example which illustrates the physical meaning of this term is given by a light-wave mixing experiment[9, 10]). Applied light waves at the frequencies ω_1 and ω_2, respectively, create a nonlinear polarization and radiation at the combination frequency $2\omega_1$-ω_2. A two-step contribution to this process has been observed in the crystals GaAs and CuCl. In the first step the wave at ω_1 creates a nonlinear polarization at the frequency $2\omega_1$. This polarization is the nonlinear source for a forced electromagnetic wave at the frequency $2\omega_1$, which may have a transverse and/or a longitudinal character[9−11]). Since the nonlinear source, which is correctly expressed in terms of the macroscopic $\boldsymbol{\chi}_2$, creates the field inside the linear dielectric, this field is appropriately given by the propagator for the linear dielectric acting on the nonlinear polarization source term.

$$\boldsymbol{E}(2\boldsymbol{k}_1, 2\omega_1) = \mathsf{F}_\varepsilon(2\boldsymbol{k}_1, 2\omega_1) \cdot \boldsymbol{\chi}_2 : \boldsymbol{E}(\boldsymbol{k}_1, \omega_1)\boldsymbol{E}(\boldsymbol{k}_1, \omega_1).$$

In the second step this field at $2\omega_1$, in combination with the light-wave field $E(\boldsymbol{k}_2, \omega_2)$ creates a nonlinear polarization at the desired combination frequency

$$\begin{aligned}\boldsymbol{P}(2\boldsymbol{k}_1 - \boldsymbol{k}_2, 2\omega_1 - \omega_2) &= \boldsymbol{\chi}_2 : \boldsymbol{E}(2\boldsymbol{k}_1, 2\omega_1)\boldsymbol{E}^*(k_2, \omega_2)\\ &= \boldsymbol{\chi}_2 \cdot \{\mathsf{F}_\varepsilon(2\boldsymbol{k}_1, \omega_1) \cdot \boldsymbol{\chi}_2\} \,\vdots\, \boldsymbol{E}(\boldsymbol{k}_1, \omega_1)\boldsymbol{E}(\boldsymbol{k}_1, \omega_1)\boldsymbol{E}^*(k_2, \omega_2).\end{aligned}$$

These is another two-step contribution in which a field at the difference frequence $\omega_1 - \omega_2$ is created in the first step. In the second step this field combines with the field $\boldsymbol{E}(\omega_1)$ to give another contribution to $\boldsymbol{P}(2\omega_1 - \omega_2)$ proportional to $\boldsymbol{\chi}_2^2$. In general one has to sum over all possible exitations with their respective frequencies and polarization directions in the intermediate step. These intermediate exitations need not be of electromagnetic character. In a recent experiment[12]) the interference was demonstrated of Raman-type contributions with the non-resonant contributions arising from the electronic nonlinear polarizability.

The authors take pleasure in dedicating this paper to Professor C. J. Gorter, who has contributed so much to theory and experiment of response functions in magnetism.

Acknowledgement. For one of us (D. B.) this work was performed as part of the research program of the "Stichting voor Fundamenteel Onderzoek der Materie" (F.O.M.) with financial support from the "Nederlandse Organisatie voor Zuiver Wetenschappelijk Onderzoek" (Z.W.O.).

REFERENCES

1) See, for example, de Groot, S. R., The Maxwell Equations, North-Holland Publ. Comp. (Amsterdam, 1969).
2) See, for example, Lorentz, H. A., The Theory of Electrons, Teubner, (Leipzig, 1916); or Van Vleck, J. H., Electric and Magnetic Susceptibilities, Oxford University Press (Oxford, 1932).
3) Bedeaux, D. and Mazur, P., Physica **67** (1973) 23.
4) See, for example, Bloembergen, N., Nonlinear Optics, Benjamin (New York, 1965).
5) Martin, P. C., Measurements and Correlation Functions in Many-body-Physics, C. de Witt and R. Balian, eds., Les Houches 1967, Gordon and Breach (New York, 1968).
6) Dirac, P. A. M., Proc. Roy. Soc. London **A167** (1938) 148.
7) Wheeler, J. A. and Feynman, R. P., Rev. mod. Phys. **17** (1945) 157.
8) Armstrong, J., Bloembergen, N., Ducuing, J. and Pershan, P. S., Phys. Rev. **127** (1962) 1918.
9) Yablonovitch, E., Flytzanis, C. and Bloembergen, N., Phys. Rev. Letters **29** (1972) 865.
10) Parsons, F. G., Kramer, S. D. and Bloembergen, N., Bull. Amer. Phys. Soc. II **18** (1973) 74, and to be published.
11) Bloembergen, N. and Pershan, P. S., Phys. Rev. **128** (1962) 606.
12) Levenson, M. D., Flytzanis, C. and Bloembergen, N., Phys. Rev. **B6** (1972) 3962.

Physica **69** (1973) 67–75 © *North-Holland Publishing Co.*

THE MAGNETIC SUSCEPTIBILITIES OF $NiCl_2 \cdot 6H_2O$ *

A. I. HAMBURGER** and S. A. FRIEDBERG

Carnegie-Mellon University, Pittsburgh, Pa. 15213, USA

Received 17 April 1973

Synopsis

The magnetic susceptibilities of monoclinic single crystals of the antiferromagnet $NiCl_2 \cdot 6H_2O$ ($T_N = 5.34$ K) have been measured between 1.2 and 4.2 K and from 14 to 20 K. The preferred spin axis below T_N was found to lie in the *ac* plane at an angle of $10.5 \pm 1.5°$ from the *a* direction. At 1.24 K, $\chi_{\|} \equiv \chi_{a_{\|}} = 0.0012$ cgs/mole and extrapolates nearly to zero as $T \to 0$ K. χ_b and $\chi_{c\perp}$ are nearly equal and only slightly temperature dependent below 4.2 K. They extrapolate to a value of ≈ 0.069 cgs/mole. $\chi_{a_{\|}}, \chi_b, \chi_{c\perp}$ obey Curie–Weiss laws in the H_2 range which can be fitted with a spin hamiltonian for $S = 1$ having an isotropic splitting factor $g = 2.22 \pm 0.01$, $D = -1.5 \pm 0.5\, k$, $E = 0.26 \pm 0.40\, k$ and a molecular field interaction $zJ = 6.0\, k$. Assuming the anisotropy below T_N to be predominantly uniaxial and of the single-ion type, these results yield an anisotropy field $H_{an} = 10$ kOe at $T = 0$ K. $\chi_{\perp}(0)$ then gives a nearest-neighbor interaction $zJ = 6.3\, k$ or an exchange field, $H_E = 85$ kOe. The energy gap in the spin-wave spectrum at $k = 0$ implied by H_{an} and H_E corresponds to $T_{AE} \approx 6$ K.

1. *Introduction.* It has been established through measurements of the specific heat[1]), single-crystal magnetic susceptibility[2, 3]), proton resonance[4, 5]), and antiferromagnetic resonance[6]) that $NiCl_2 \cdot 6H_2O$ becomes antiferromagnetically ordered below a Néel temperature $T_N = 5.34$ K. X-ray studies[7]) of this monoclinic crystal at room temperature show the space group to be C2/m. The unit cell contains two Ni^{++} ions and has the dimensions $a = 10.23$ Å, $b = 7.05$ Å, $c = 6.57$ Å with $\beta = 122°10'$. Each Ni^{++} ion is coordinated with two Cl^- ions and four H_2O molecules, the Cl^- ions occupying opposite vertices of a distorted octahedron. Neutron diffraction[8]) shows that the structure is essentially unchanged down, at least, to 4.2 K and, thus, through T_N.

The original susceptibility data[2, 3]) were obtained along the *b* and *c* axes as well as along a direction in the *ac* plane orthogonal to the *c* axis, the so called *a'* direction. Below T_N, χ_b and χ_c are nearly equal and essentially temperature independent while $\chi_{a'}$ falls with temperature suggesting that the preferred direction

* Work supported by the National Science Foundation and the Office of Naval Research.
** Permanent address: University of São Paulo, São Paulo, Brazil.

of antiferromagnetic spin alignment is close to if not coincident with a'. It was noted[3]), however, that $\chi_{a'}$ does not extrapolate to zero as $T \to 0$ K. When neutron diffraction studies of the ordered spin structure were performed[9]), the preferred direction was found to lie in the ac plane but 22.5° away from the a' direction at (a − 10°). Antiferromagnetic resonance observations[6]) gave similar results, locating the preferred direction at (a − 7°). They also indicated that the dominant source of anisotropy in $NiCl_2 \cdot 6\,H_2O$ was of the single-ion type and provided estimates of the spin-hamiltonian parameters D and E which describe the combined effect of the crystalline field and spin–orbit interaction producing such anisotropy.

In this paper we wish to report new measurements of the single-crystal susceptibilities of $NiCl_2 \cdot 6H_2O$ between 1.2 and 4.2 K and from 14 to 20 K. The objects of this work are 1) to locate independently the preferred direction of spin alignment below T_N; 2) to determine $\chi_{||}$ and $\chi_{\perp}$ and their temperature dependence in the ordered phase; 3) to examine the anisotropy of χ above T_N; and 4) to compare the single-ion anisotropy and exchange constants needed to fit the data above and below T_N.

2. *Experimental details.* Magnetic susceptibilities were measured by an ac mutual inductance method at 275 Hz. The technique and most of the characteristics of the apparatus used in this laboratory for such measurements, have been described elsewhere[10]). The single-crystal specimens of $NiCl_2 \cdot 6H_2O$ weighed between 500 and 1000 mg and were grown from aqueous solutions of the reagent grade salt. They were oriented using the data of Groth[11]). Particular care was taken to insure accurate alignment of the crystal axes with the direction of the oscillatory measuring field. Specimens were attached with GE 7031 lacquer to lucite wedges cut to appropriate angles and their orientation checked with a goniometer. They were then mounted inside cylindrical containers made of C8 resin. Two such cylinders were attached to opposite ends of a rod of C8 resin to form a rigid assembly 122 mm in length and 17 mm in maximum diameter. This holder was connected to a rod which was manipulated from the top of the cryostat so that the specimens could be moved vertically through the mutual inductance coils. A standard sample, suspended beneath the holder, could also be placed within the coils for calibration purposes. Clearances were such as to permit the holder axis and that of a crystal specimen to deviate from the vertical direction by no more than 0.5°. Allowing for errors in the mounting of a crystal, we estimate that orientation of our specimen is accurate to within $\pm 1°$.

Measuring coils and specimens were immersed directly in baths of liquid ^4He, between 1.2 and 4.2 K, and H_2, between 13.8 and 20.2 K. Temperatures were determined from the measured vapor pressure in terms of the 1958 ^4He scale[12]) and the 1951 NBS scale[13]) for equilibrium liquid H_2.

3. *Results and discussion.* Below T_N, the susceptibility was measured along directions in the *ac* plane which make the following angles with the *a* axis; 8°, 9°, 10°, 11°, 12° and 32° (*a'*). The results are shown in fig. 1. The susceptibilities at ($a-32°$) *i.e.* *a'*, agree well with previously reported values[2, 3]) and may be compared with them in fig. 2. The susceptibilities for all other directions between *a'* and the *a* axis

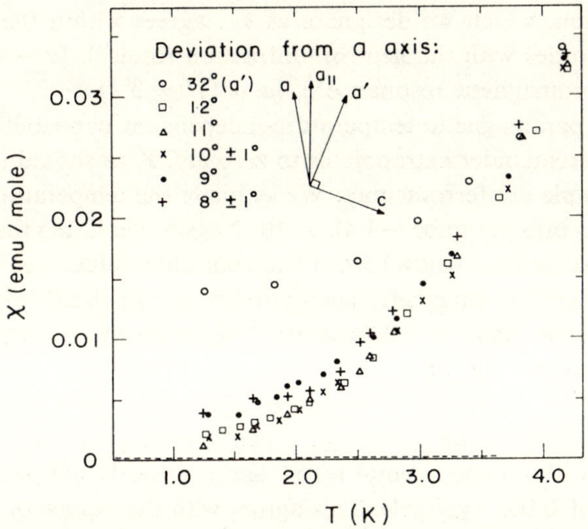

Fig. 1. Magnetic susceptibilities of $NiCl_2 \cdot 6H_2O$ below 4.2 K measured in the *ac* plane at various angles from the *a* axis. The preferred direction of spin alignment is found to be $a-10.5 \pm 1.5° \equiv a_{||}$. The direction $a-32° \equiv a'$ was originally thought to be preferred. The temperature-independent susceptibility is indicated by the dashed line.

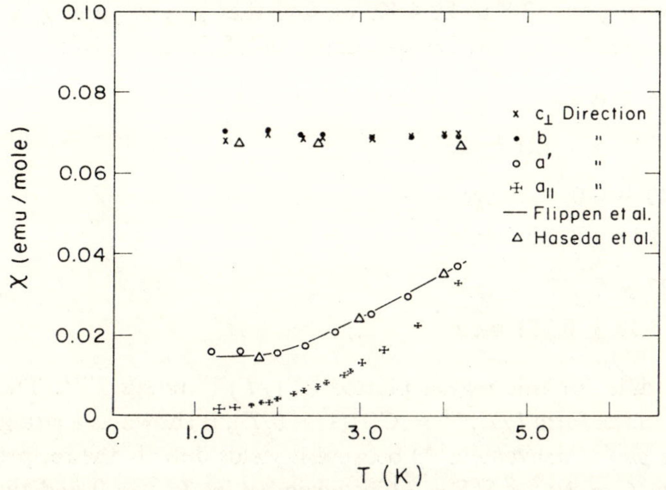

Fig. 2. Magnetic susceptibilities of $NiCl_2 \cdot 6H_2O$ below 4.2 K measured along the principal axes $a_{||}$, *b*, and $c_{\perp}$ as well as *a'*. Typical values from refs. 2 and 3 are shown for comparison. $\chi_{a_{||}}$ is an average over measurements nominally at 10°, 11° and 12° from the *a* axis in the *ac* plane.

are seen in fig. 1 to be much smaller than $\chi_{a'}$ at low temperatures. In the $(a - 11°)$ direction, a value of 0.0012 cgs/mole is reached at 1.24 K. Inspection of the data of fig. 1 suggests that the extremal susceptibility occurs between $(a - 10°)$ and $(a - 11°)$. Noting that the precision of specimen orientation is about $\pm 1°$ and that other uncertainties equivalent to an additional 1° occur in data for $(a - 8°)$ and $(a - 10°)$, we take as the direction of preferred spin alignment $[a-(10.5° \pm 1.5°)]$. This direction, which we designate as $a_{||}$, agrees within the combined experimental uncertainties with the neutron-diffraction result[9]), $[a - (9° \pm 1°)]$, and that from antiferromagnetic resonance[6]), $[a - (7° \pm 3°)]$.

When a small net paramagnetic temperature-independent contribution is subtracted from $\chi_{a_{||}}$, the remainder extrapolates to zero at 0 K as should the parallel susceptibility of a simple antiferromagnet. We estimate the temperature-independent diamagnetic susceptibility to be -1.42×10^{-4} cgs/mole. Using the measured departure of the g-factor (see below) from the spin-only value, the Van Vleck temperature-independent paramagnetic susceptibility is calculated to be $+2.16 \times 10^{-4}$ cgs/mole. The net result is $+0.74 \times 10^{-4}$ cgs/mole which is significant at the lower temperatures (see fig. 1).

In fig. 2 we also show the results of measurements along the b axis as well as along another direction in the ac plane, $c_{\perp}$, which is orthogonal to $a_{||}$ and to b. $\chi_{c\perp}$ and χ_b coincide within experimental error, and are nearly temperature independent at a value of 0.069 cgs/mole. This agrees with the values of χ_b and χ_c reported by Haseda *et al.*[2]), some of which are shown for comparison in fig. 2. The values of χ_b and χ_c found by Flippen and Friedberg[3]) are slightly larger and rise at the lowest temperatures suggesting that their specimens may have contained some paramagnetic impurity.

In the liquid H_2 region, 13.8 to 20.4 K, we find that $\chi_{a_{||}}$, $\chi_{c\perp}$ and χ_b are well described by the Curie–Weiss law. Least-squares fits of the data give:

$$\chi_{a_{||}} = \frac{1.232 \pm 0.012}{T + (7.50 \pm 0.12)} \frac{\text{cgs}}{\text{mole}}, \tag{1}$$

$$\chi_{c\perp} = \frac{1.240 \pm 0.017}{T + (8.11 \pm 0.20)} \frac{\text{cgs}}{\text{mole}}, \tag{2}$$

$$\chi_{b} = \frac{1.227 \pm 0.017}{T + (8.37 \pm 0.35)} \frac{\text{cgs}}{\text{mole}}. \tag{3}$$

Fig. 3 shows the data for this region plotted as $(\chi T)^{-1}$ *versus* T^{-1}. The fitted Curie–Weiss law, in the form $(\chi T)^{-1} = C^{-1}(1 + \theta/T)$, is shown as a straight line in each case. This plot is convenient[14]) because it yields directly the reciprocal of the Curie constant $C = Ng^2\mu_B^2 S(S+1)/3k$ when we let $T^{-1} \to 0$ and thus emphasizes the coincidence of C for the three crystal directions. The splitting factors obtained from C, taking the spin of the Ni^{++} ion to be $S = 1$ are $g_{a_{||}} = 2.219$

$\pm$ 0.008; $g_{c\perp} = 2.227 \pm 0.009$; and $g_b = 2.215 \pm 0.012$. Within the experimental uncertainty, the splitting factor is thus isotropic and equal to $g = 2.22 \pm 0.01$.

In order to analyze further the data taken above T_N we shall assume that each of the equivalent Ni^{++} ions in the crystal can be described by a spin hamiltonian of the form:

$$\mathscr{H} = DS_z^2 + E(S_x^2 - S_y^2) + g\mu_B \boldsymbol{H} \cdot \boldsymbol{S} + 2zJ\boldsymbol{S} \cdot \langle \boldsymbol{S} \rangle, \tag{4}$$

where $S = 1$, $g = 2.22$, and the z axis lies along the $a_{||}$ direction. D and E measure, respectively, the contributions of the axial and rhombic parts of the crystal field to the zero-field splitting of the Ni^{++} ion ground state. The term $2zJ\boldsymbol{S} \cdot \langle \boldsymbol{S} \rangle$ represents the molecular-field approximation to the sum of the exchange interactions, each of strength J, of the given ion with its z equivalent nearest neighbors. The principal susceptibilities of a system of N such interacting ions are given by Watanabe[15]). For $kT \gg |D|, |E|$, and $z|J|$ they approximate the Curie–Weiss law with effective Weiss constants:

$$\theta_{a_{||}} = (D + 4zJ)/3k, \tag{5}$$

$$\theta_b = -(D - 3E - 8zJ)/6k, \tag{6}$$

$$\theta_{c\perp} = -(D + 3E - 8zJ)/6k. \tag{7}$$

A value for zJ is easily calculated using the relation

$$\theta_{AV} = (\theta_{a_{||}} + \theta_b + \theta_{c\perp})/3 = 4zJ/3k. \tag{8}$$

Referring to eqs. (1), (2) and (3) we find that the average of the measured θ's is 8.0 K which agrees reasonably well with a reported powder value[16]) of about 7 K and another value from crystal measurements[2]) of about 10 K. From our result and eq. (8), we find $zJ/k = 6.0 \pm 0.4$ K, where the sign is antiferromagnetic. From the additional relations

$$D/k = -3(\theta_{AV} - \theta_{a_{||}}) \tag{9}$$

and

$$E/k = \theta_b - \theta_{c\perp}, \tag{10}$$

we find $D = -1.5 \pm 0.5\ k$ or $-1.02 \pm 0.33\ cm^{-1}$ and $E = 0.26 \pm 0.40\ k$ or $0.18 \pm 0.27\ cm^{-1}$. These values of D and E agree well with those deduced from antiferromagnetic resonance data[6]) taken below T_N, namely, $D = -1.2 \pm 0.2\ cm^{-1}$ and $E = 0.15 \pm 0.2\ cm^{-1}$.

Let us consider now some properties of the antiferromagnetic phase. The neutron-diffraction work of Kleinberg[9]) shows that the ordered spin structure below T_N belongs to the magnetic space group I_c2/c. Within an (001) plane, each spin is antiferromagnetically aligned with respect to four nearest neighbors. Neighboring spins on adjacent (001) planes are also antiferromagnetically aligned.

Date and Motokawa[6]) have estimated the dipolar contribution to the anisotropy field for this structure and found it to be nearly uniaxial and equal to 0.84 kOe. This is smaller by an order of magnitude than the single-ion effect, as we shall see. From the analysis of their antiferromagnetic resonance results, Date and Motokawa conclude that the magnetocrystalline anisotropy in ordered $NiCl_2 \cdot 6H_2O$ is orthorhombic. The most obvious consequence of this departure from uniaxial symmetry for the low-field susceptibility with which we are concerned might be a difference between those values measured in the two directions perpendicular to the preferred axis. However, above T_N the fitted value of E is smaller than the experimental error and such a difference has not been clearly established. Below T_N we see in fig. 3 that, although there may be some tendency for $\chi_{c\perp}$ to be slightly below χ_b at the lowest temperatures, the difference is small and near the limit set by experimental error. To a good approximation, $\chi_{c\perp}$ and χ_b behave like the perpendicular susceptibilities of a uniaxial antiferromagnet and may be analyzed on that basis.

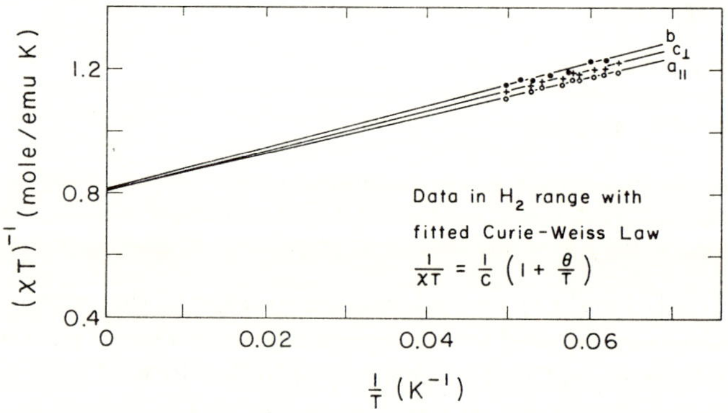

Fig. 3. Magnetic susceptibilities of $NiCl_2 \cdot 6H_2O$ in the liquid H_2 region ($T > T_N = 5.34$ K) measured along the $a_{||}$, b, and $c_\perp$ directions and plotted as $(\chi T)^{-1}$ *versus* T^{-1}.

Assuming the anisotropy energy to vary with the angle ϕ between the sublattice magnetization and the preferred axis as $K(T) \sin^2 \phi$, it may be shown[17]) that at $T = 0$ K the single-ion mechanism gives

$$K(0) = -DNS(S - \tfrac{1}{2}), \tag{11}$$

where N is the number of Ni^{++} ions per unit volume and $S = 1$. Letting $D = -1.5\ k$, the value deduced from our results above T_N, we find $K(0) = 6.3 \times 10^7$ erg/mole. Defining an anisotropy field as $H_{an} = K/M_0$, where $M_0 = 1/2Ng\mu_B S = 6200$ erg/Oe mole, and substituting this value of $K(0)$, we obtain $H_{an} = 10$ kOe. This will outweigh the estimated dipolar contribution, 0.84 kOe, mentioned earlier.

For a uniaxial two-sublattice antiferromagnet, in either the molecular field approximation or the lowest-order spin-wave approximation[18]), one finds

$$\chi_\perp(0) = \frac{1}{A + H_{an}/2M_0}, \tag{12}$$

where $A = 4zJ/Ng^2\mu_B^2$. For antiferromagnets with high Néel points, usually $A \gg H_{an}/2M_0$ and the latter term may be ignored. In the present instance, however, the anisotropy term is not completely negligible and we estimate it using the above value of H_{an}. The dipolar contribution may be roughly compensated by the effects of orthorhombicity and, therefore, has not been included. Extrapolating $\chi_{c\perp}$ to 0 K, we take $\chi_\perp(0) = 0.069$ cgs/mole and find $A = 1/\chi_\perp(0) - H_{an}/2M_0 = 14.49 - 0.83 = 13.66$ Oe^{2}mole/erg. Thus, from the definition of A, we conclude that $zJ = 6.3\,k$ which agrees very closely with the value obtained for $T > T_N$. It should be noted that eq. (12) contains only the nearest-neighbor interaction in spite of the fact that intrasublattice or next-nearest neighbor coupling is explicitly included in the model for which it is derived. On the other hand, the latter interactions are ignored in the derivation of eqs. (5), (6), and (7). The agreement of the values of zJ obtained in these two ways thus suggests that nearest-neighbor exchange is the dominant interaction in $NiCl_2 \cdot 6H_2O$.

An effective exchange field is defined in terms of the quantity A by the relation $H_E = AM_0$. Using the value of A obtained above, one finds $H_E = 85$ kOe, as compared with $H_E = 86 \pm 1$ kOe from antiferromagnetic resonance[6]). The energy gap in the spin-wave spectrum of a two-sublattice antiferromagnet at zero wave vector in the absence of an applied field is expressed in terms of a "gap temperature", T_{AE}. It arises from the presence of anisotropy[18, 19, 20]) and depends on H_E and A_{an} as follows:

$$kT_{AE} = g\mu_B[H_{an}(2H_E + H_{an})]^{\frac{1}{2}}. \tag{13}$$

Substituting values for g, H_{an}, and H_E given above, we find $T_{AE} = 6.4$ K. This gap is measured in antiferromagnetic resonance experiments as a critical field at which the antiferromagnetic phase becomes unstable with respect to the spin-flopped phase. At 0 K, we obtain

$$H_c = [H_{an}(2H_E + H_{an})]^{\frac{1}{2}}. \tag{14}$$

Using our values of H_E and H_{an}, one finds $H_c = 43$ kOe which compares well with the experimental result $H_c = 40 \pm 1$ kOe corresponding to $T_{AE} = 5.8$ K.

Recently Becerra and Paduan[21]) have determined the spin-flop boundary for $NiCl_2 \cdot 6H_2O$ by a direct high-field susceptibility method. At 1.1 K they find a critical field of 39.6 kOe. Anderson and Callen[22]) have pointed out that, because of the first-order character of this phase transition, the critical field measured by many techniques may actually not be that of eq. (14) but rather

$$H_c^0 = [H_{an}(2H_E - H_{an})]^{\frac{1}{2}}. \tag{15}$$

In systems with small exchange fields the difference between H_c and H_c^0 can be significant. With the previously used constants, eq. (15) gives $H_c^0 = 40$ kOe at 0 K which is quite close to the measured value.

It was noted by Robinson and Friedberg[1]) that the heat capacity of $NiCl_2 \cdot 6H_2O$ could be approximated rather well from their lowest temperature, 1.4 K, to about 4.3 K ot 0.8 T_N by spin-wave theory in the weak anisotropy limit. Donaldson and Edmonds[23]) extended the measurements down to 0.7 K, by which point the presence of an energy gap in the spin-wave spectrum had become clearly evident. They fitted the data with a spin-wave model[19]) of a uniaxial two-sublattice antiferromagnet, determining structure-dependent constants in the theory by normalization to measured values at temperatures where the heat capacity is proportional approximately to T^3. The best fit was obtained for $T_{AE} = 4.0 \pm 0.5$ K.

The temperature dependence of the parallel susceptibility should reveal the presence of an energy gap at a higher temperature[19, 20]) than the heat capacity. We have, therefore, fitted our data for $\chi_{a_{\parallel}}$ with the same simplified spin-wave model. While determination of constants by normalization is not practical in this case, the constants are the same as those appearing in the expression for the heat capacity and are thus available. In fig. 4 we show the $\chi_{a_{\parallel}}$ results together with theoretical curves for three different values of T_{AE}. An excellent fit of the data up to about 4 K or 0.75 T_N is obtained with $T_{AE} = 4$ K, the same value needed to fit the heat capacity over a comparable range.

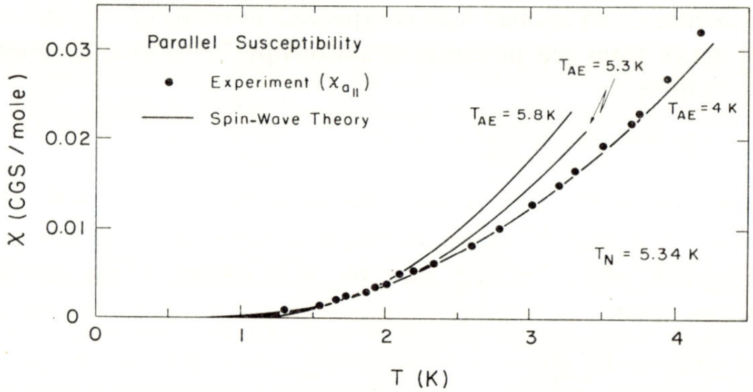

Fig. 4. Parallel susceptibility of $NiCl_2 \cdot 6H_2O$ below T_N together with theoretical curves calculated for a simple spin-wave model with several values of the gap temperature, T_{AE}.

The fact that the spin-wave model gives a consistent description of the heat capacity and parallel susceptibility to such a high temperature is quite striking. It is probably associated with the relatively large energy gap which suppresses the excitation of spin waves and, hence, their interaction until T is close to T_N. The discrepancy between the value $T_{AE} = 4$ K obtained by fitting these temperature-dependent quantities and $T_{AE} = 5.8$–6.4 K found essentially at 0 K by measurements of antiferromagnetic resonance, spin-flopping and $\chi_{\perp}$ appears to be significant. However, it is not nearly so large as that originally suggested by Donaldson and Edmonds whose preliminary antiferromagnetic resonance experiment had indicated that $T_{AE} = 7.7$ K, for reasons now understood[6]). As a possible source of the discrepancy, they considered, qualitatively, the modification of the excitation spectrum produced by spin wave–phonon coupling. We prefer, at this point, however, not to speculate until a more realistic spin-wave model of $NiCl_2 \cdot 6H_2O$ has been developed. Such a model would have to include Brillouin-zone effects, the orthorhombic anisotropy, and the possible two-dimensional character of the spin system resulting from weak exchange interaction between (001) layers of Ni^{++} ions.

Acknowledgements. One of the authors (S. A. F.) wishes to express his deep appreciation to Professor C. J. Gorter for introducing him to the study of low-temperature magnetism. We join our colleagues in honoring Professor Gorter as scientist, teacher, and friend.

Travel expenses for A. I. H. were provided by the Conselho Nacional de Pesquisas of Brazil and are gratefully acknowledged.

REFERENCES

1) Robinson, W. K. and Friedberg, S. A., Phys. Rev. **117** (1960) 402.
2) Haseda, T., Kobayashi, H. and Date, M., J. Phys. Soc. Japan **14** (1959) 1724.
3) Flippen, R. B. and Friedberg, S. A., J. appl. Phys. Suppl. **31** (1960) 338S.
4) Sugawara, T., J. Phys. Soc. Japan **14** (1959) 1248.
5) Spence, R. D., Middents, P., El Saffar, Z. and Kleinberg, R., J. appl. Phys. **35** (1964) 854.
6) Date, M. and Motokawa, M., J. Phys. Soc. Japan **22** (1967) 165.
7) Mizuno, J., J. Phys. Soc. Japan **16** (1961) 1574.
8) Kleinberg, R., J. chem. Phys. **50** (1969) 5690.
9) Kleinberg, R., J. appl. Phys. **38** (1967) 1453.
10) Schriempf, J. T. and Friedberg, S. A., J. chem. Phys. **40** (1964) 296.
11) Groth, P., Chem. Kryst. II (1908) 247.
12) Brickwedde, F. G., Van Dijk, H., Durieux, M., Clement, J. R. and Logan, J. K., J. Res. Nat. Bur. Stand. **64A** (1960) 1.
13) Woolley, H. W., Scott, R. B. and Brickwedde, F. G., J. Res. Nat. Bur. Stand. **41** (1948) 379.
14) Danielian, G., Proc. Phys. Soc. **80** (1962) 981.
15) Watanabe, T., J. Phys. Soc. Japan **17** (1962) 1856.
16) Haseda, T. and Date, M., J. Phys. Soc. Japan **13** (1958) 175.
17) Kanamori, J. and Minatono, H., J. Phys. Soc. Japan **17** (1962) 1759.
18) Kubo, R., Phys. Rev. **87** (1952) 569.
19) Eisele, J. A. and Keffer, F., Phys. Rev. **96** (1954) 929.
20) Keffer, F., *Handbuch der Physik*, S. Flügge, ed., Springer (Berlin, 1966), Vol. 18 Pt. 2, p. 1.
21) Castilla Becerra, C. and Paduan, A., Phys. Letters (to be published) (1973).
22) Anderson, F. B. and Callen, H. B., Phys. Rev. **136** (1964) A1068.
23) Donaldson, R. H. and Edmonds, D. T., Proc. Phys. Soc. **85** (1965) 1209.

Physica **69** (1973) 76–86 © *North-Holland Publishing Co.*

ON THE MAGNETIC STATE OF $CoBr_2 \cdot 6[(1 - x)H_2O \cdot xD_2O]$

J. P. A. M. HIJMANS, W. J. M. DE JONGE, P. VAN DER LEEDEN and M. J. STEENLAND

Technische Hogeschool Eindhoven, Afdeling der Technische Natuurkunde, Eindhoven, Nederland

Received 17 April 1973

Synopsis

Antiferromagnetic resonance, critical-field measurements, proton magnetic resonance and bromine nuclear resonance in $CoBr_2 \cdot 6[(1-x)H_2O \cdot xD_2O]$ are reported for several values of x with emphasis on the completely deuterated case. For $x \geqq 0.55$ both the crystallographic and magnetic space group, for which suggestions are given, differ from those of $CoBr_2 \cdot 6H_2O$.

1. *Introduction.* The magnetic state of $CoCl_2 \cdot 6H_2O$ and $CoBr_2 \cdot 6H_2O$ has been the subject of a considerable number of both experimental and theoretical studies. The majority of these papers deals with $CoCl_2 \cdot 6H_2O$, however, most of the results seem to apply to both substances. The studies include specific-heat measurements[1, 2]), nuclear magnetic resonance[3, 4]), antiferromagnetic resonance[5, 6]), electron-spin resonance[6]), susceptibility measurements[6]) and calculations of the ground state of the Co^{2+} ion[7]). Recently the effect of deuteration of $CoCl_2 \cdot 6H_2O$ was studied[8, 9]) and a rather anomalous magnetic behaviour was observed. In this paper we want to report some data on the magnetic state of $CoBr_2 \cdot 6[(1 - x)H_2O, xD_2O]$ with the emphasis on the completely deuterated salt.

The current interest of our laboratory in this series of Co compounds is motivated by two aspects. The first can be summarized as follows. The symmetry of the cluster as well as its spatial arrangement and the conjectured relative strength of the magnetic interactions makes it attractive to interpret relevant data in terms of a simplified model for the exchange interactions. Specifically we can refer to a combination of preliminary antiferromagnetic-resonance results and high-temperature specific-heat measurements[10]) which, interpreted in terms of a simplified model, give rather promising results. The second reason for our interest in this series of Co salts is given by the excellent quality of the pure quadrupole resonance signals of both the chlorine and bromine nucleus in the paramagnetic state[3]). This enables us to perform a detailed study of the effects on the hyperfine tensor *A* when chlorine is substituted by bromine. In other compounds we found that these studies are usually hampered by the rather poor quality of the bromine signals in the paramagnetic state[11, 12]).

In view of the above-mentioned considerations it seemed worthwhile to verify whether, in spite of the magnetic anomalous behaviour (as we shall see later on), there is any reason to assume that $CoBr_2 \cdot 6D_2O$ cannot be confronted with the same model as the hydrated compounds. When this work was in progress, a brief abstract on the effect of deuteration in $CoBr_2 \cdot 6H_2O$ with emphasis on the change of the ordening temperature and deuterium resonance was published[13]).

2. *Crystallography.* Although the crystal structure of $CoBr_2 \cdot 6D_2O$ is not known one is readily inclined to assume that it is isostructural with $CoBr_2 \cdot 6H_2O$ which is also isostructural with $CoCl_2 \cdot 6H_2O$[14, 15, 16]). The structure can be described by the space group C 2/m and the unit cell with $a = 11.00$ Å, $b = 7.16$ Å, $c = 6.90$ Å and $\beta = 124°$ contains two formula units. The isolated $[CoBr_2O_4]$ clusters show approximate uniaxial symmetry around the Br–Co–Br axis, which coincides within a few degrees with the a^* axis perpendicular to c. The coupling between the clusters in the face-centered *ab* plane involves links like Co^{2+}–Br–Br–Co^{2+} or Co^{2+}–Br–H_2O–Co^{2+}. The coupling between the layers involves links like Co^{2+}–O–H–H_2O–H–O–Co^{2+}. This coupling must be considered as relatively weak[16, 17]), which is also indicated by the perfect cleavage of the crystals along the (001) plane.

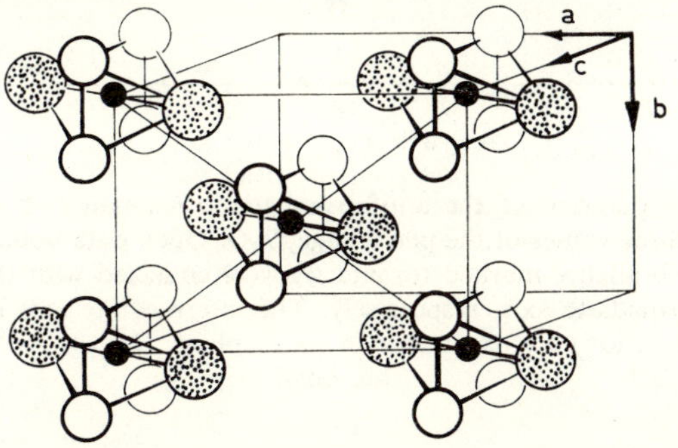

Fig. 1. Part of the crystal structure of $CoBr_2 \cdot 6H_2O$ showing the face-centered arrangement of the $[CoBr_2O_4]$ clusters in the *ab* plane. Cobalt atoms are small and black, bromine atoms are shaded and oxygen atoms are drawn as open circles.

The proposed magnetic structure of $CoBr_2 \cdot 6H_2O$ shows an antiferromagnetic nearest-neighbour interaction between the Co^{2+} ions in the *a–b* layers and between the layers. The schematic spatial arrangement of the clusters is shown in fig. 1.

3. *Experimental.* 3.1. Antiferromagnetic resonance. Antiferromagnetic-resonance (afmr) results on some partially deuterated crystals are shown in fig. 2. The results on purely hydrated $CoBr_2 \cdot 6H_2O$ agree with former measurements by Murray and Wessel[6]). Up till $x = 0.55$ the preferred direction is along the c axis, while both ω_0 and H_{crit} increase with increasing x (see also fig. 3). For $x \geqq 0.55$ the spectrum splits into two components, *i.e.*, resonance originally observed with the field along the c axis will now be observed at angles symmetrically

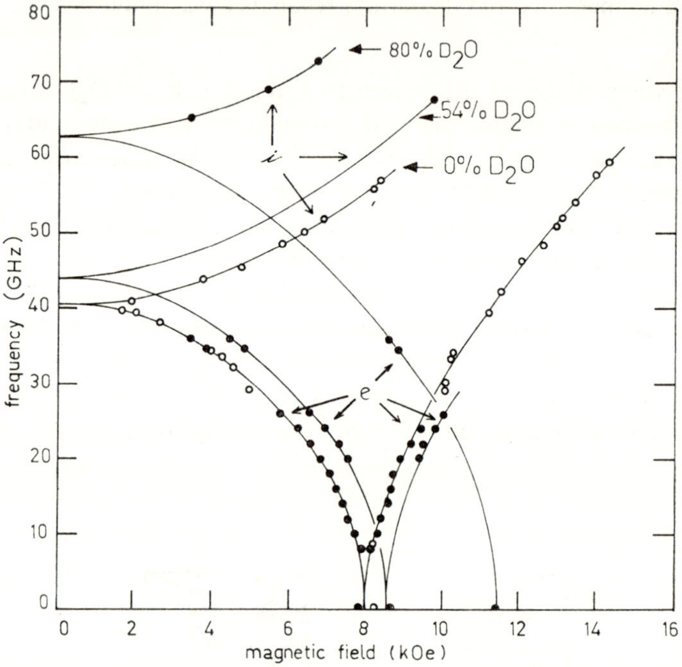

Fig. 2. Frequency-field diagram of the antiferromagnetic resonance in $CoBr_2 \cdot 6[(1-x)H_2O \cdot xD_2O]$ at 1.25 K for three values of the percentage D_2O. Open data points are taken from ref. 6 ($x = 0$). Data on the branches marked (e) and (i) were collected with the magnetic parallel to the easy and the intermediate axis, respectively. The intermediate axis is perpendicular to the easy axis (preferred direction) and is situated in the *bc* plane. Drawn curves are meant for visual aid only.

around the c axis in the bc plane. The angle with the c axis varies with the percentage x till 32 degrees in the completely deuterated sample ($x = 1$). One of the most obvious results of these experiments is that they strongly suggest that above $x = 0.55$ the magnetic moments can be divided into two antiferromagnetic sets each turned away from the c axis in the bc plane but in opposite directions.

3.2. The critical field. We studied the critical field more closely by absorption experiments at nuclear magnetic resonance (NMR) frequencies. The resonance

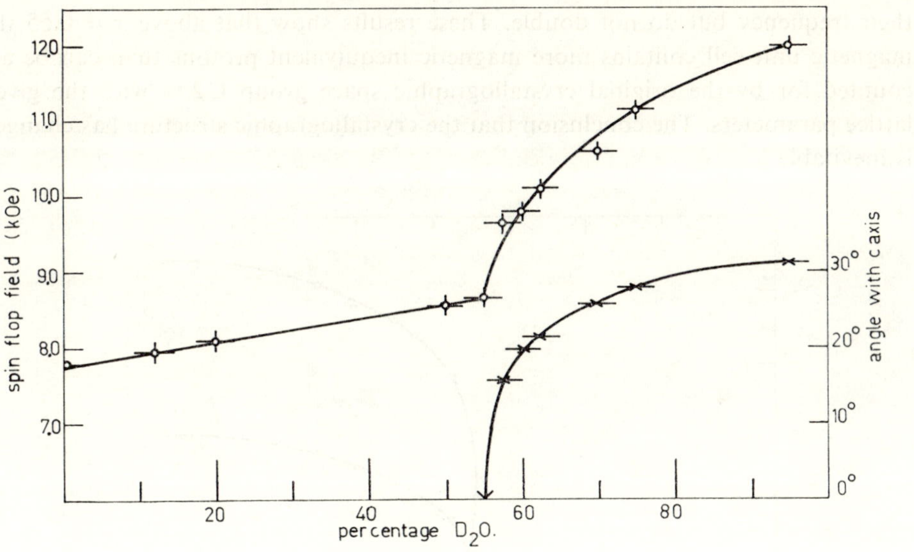

Fig. 3. Spin-flop field parameters in $CoBr_2 \cdot 6[(1-x)H_2O \cdot xD_2O]$ at 1.15 K as a function of the deuterium fraction x.

phenomena we observed with the external field exactly along the sublattice magnetization can be interpreted as essentially zero-frequency afmr. Off axis we assume to be tracing the critical hyperbola[18]). Fig. 3 shows the critical field as function of the deuterium fraction x. At $x > 0.55$ the spin flop, which at lower percentages could only be observed with the external field along c, can now be observed in two directions both in the bc plane but symmetrically spaced around c. In completely deuterated $CoBr_2 \cdot 6D_2O$ the angle with the c axis is 32 degrees, and the spin-flop field has increased by about 50 % compared with the hydrated compound. Off axis the transition could only be seen in planes through a^* and the preferred directions. This is consistent with the antiferromagnetic-resonance results which show the a^* axis to be the hard axis. So the critical hyperbola must lie in the plane through a^* and the preferred direction of the magnetization[18]). Within experimental accuracy the angle dependence of the critical field in the above-mentioned plane can be described by $H_{crit} \cos\theta = H_{crit}(\theta = 0)$, where θ is the angle of the field with the preferred direction. This result shows that the critical curve is a straight line parallel to the a^* axis and that in first approximation the moments are restricted to the bc plane.

3.3. Proton resonance. The proton resonance data as a function of the percentage x are shown in fig. 4. For $x \geqq 0.55$ the number of zero-field resonances changes from 4 to 6. Only those resonances double which arise from protons originally situated at a general position. The proton absorption lines at 4.4 and 6.8 MHz from the H_2O molecule originally situated in the mirror plane just change their frequency but do not double. These results show that above $x = 0.55$ the magnetic unit cell contains more magnetic inequivalent protons than can be accounted for by the original crystallographic space group C2/m with the given lattice parameters. The conclusion that the crystallographic structure has changed is inevitable.

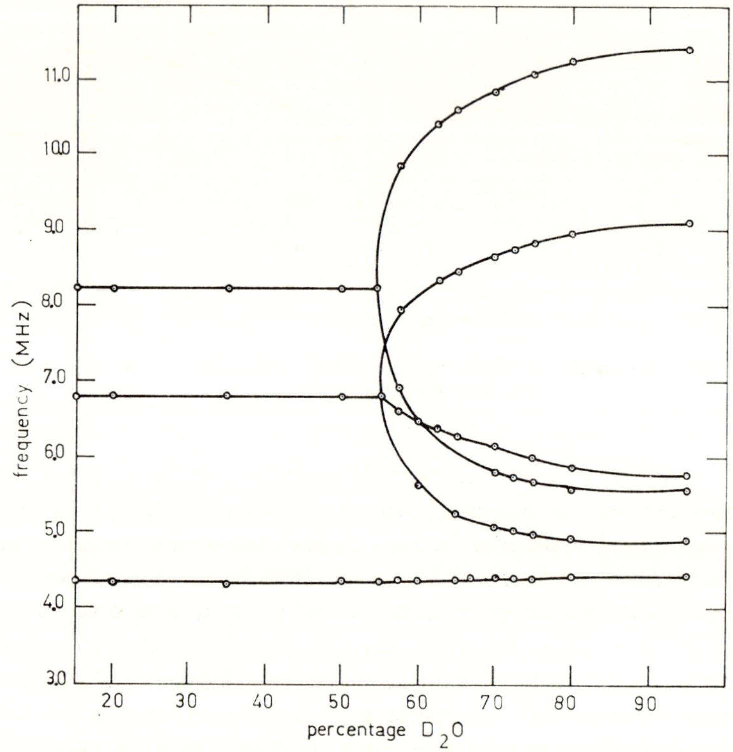

Fig. 4. Proton frequencies in $CoBr_2 \cdot 6[(1-x)H_2O \cdot xD_2O]$ at 1.15 K *versus* the deuterium fraction x.

3.4. Bromine nuclear resonance. Our aim will be to determine the parameters which characterize the electric interaction both above and below the ordening temperature in $CoBr_2 \cdot 6D_2O$ and compare them with $CoBr_2 \cdot 6H_2O$ in order to get some qualitative arguments about the structural change which apparently has taken place. Secondly we want some information about the direction of the individual magnetic moments by means of the direction of the hyperfine field at the bromine nucleus. The analysis of the bromine resonances in $CoBr_2 \cdot 6H_2O$ was already published in a former article[3]).

In the ordered state eight absorptions could be detected in $CoBr_2 \cdot 6D_2O$ which could be assigned to transitions of the ^{79}Br and ^{81}Br nuclei. The frequencies are tabulated in table I and the temperature dependence is shown in fig. 5. In the

TABLE I

Labelling of the frequencies and the interaction parameters for the bromine nuclei in $CoBr_2 \cdot 6D_2O$

Nucleus	ν_i[a]	Label	ν_Q	ν_Z	θ	$\eta\cos 2\Phi$
	13.56	ν_3				
^{79}Br	35.23	ν_2	42.42[b]	24.45	79°30′	0.01
	40.51	ν_1	42.47[c]			
	48.79	$\nu_2 + \nu_3$				
	15.57	ν_3				
^{81}Br	33.13	ν_2	35.44[b]	26.36	79°30′	0.01
	40.95	ν_1	35.48[c]			
	48.69	$\nu_2 + \nu_3$				

[a] In MHz at $T = 1.12$ K.
[b] In MHz at $T = 4.2$ K.
[c] Calculated from ν_1, ν_2 and ν_3.

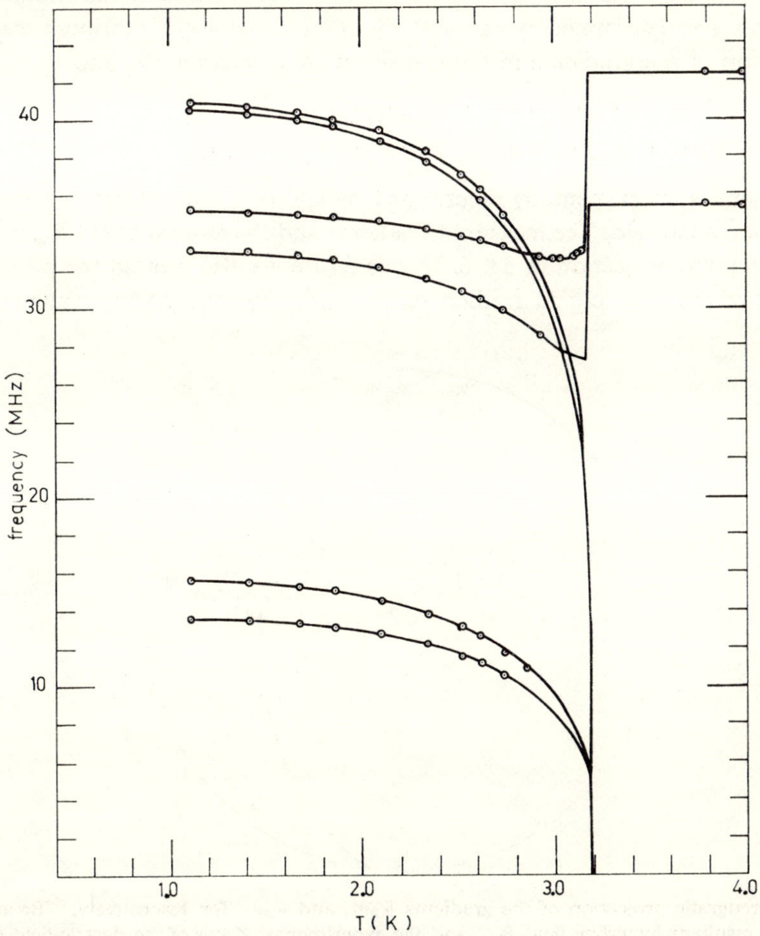

Fig. 5. Temperature dependence of the bromine nuclear-resonance lines. The drawn curves are the theoretical temperature dependencies calculated with the parameters tabulated in table I.

ordered state the bromine nuclei are subjected simultaneously to a Zeeman interaction and a quadrupole interaction ($I = \frac{3}{2}$ for both isotopes). The hamiltonian describing these interactions is:

$$H = H_Z + H_Q = -\gamma_N \hbar \boldsymbol{I} \cdot \boldsymbol{B} + \frac{e^2 qQ}{4I(2I-1)} [3I_z^2 - \boldsymbol{I}^2 + \tfrac{1}{2}\eta(I_+^2 + I_-^2)].$$

The general procedure to interpret the transition frequencies in terms of this hamiltonian, including the selection of the sets arising from ^{79}Br and ^{81}Br, as well as the labelling of the transitions ν_1, ν_2 and ν_3 between successive levels within a set, is outlined in a number of previous papers[3, 11]) and will, because of the restricted length of this article not be repeated here. The resulting parameters are tabulated in table I.

The direction of the internal field at the bromine nucleus in the frame of the crystal axes was determined experimentally in the usual way[19]) through the linear combination of the gradients of the transition frequencies ν_1, ν_2 and ν_3:

$$\boldsymbol{B} = \tfrac{1}{10}(2\pi/\gamma_N)^2[\nabla_B \nu_1(\tfrac{3}{2}\nu_1 + \nu_2 + \tfrac{1}{2}\nu_3) + \nabla_B \nu_2(\nu_1 + 2\nu_2 + \nu_3) + \nabla_B \nu_3(\tfrac{1}{2}\nu_1 + \nu_2 + \tfrac{3}{2}\nu_3)].$$

The gradient is experimentally determined by splitting the absorption line by an external magnetic field. The measured gradients and the resultant field $\boldsymbol{B}_{tot}$ is shown in stereographic projection in fig. 6. In this figure we also plotted the principal Z axis (V_{zz}) of the electric-field gradient as measured by splitting experiments of the

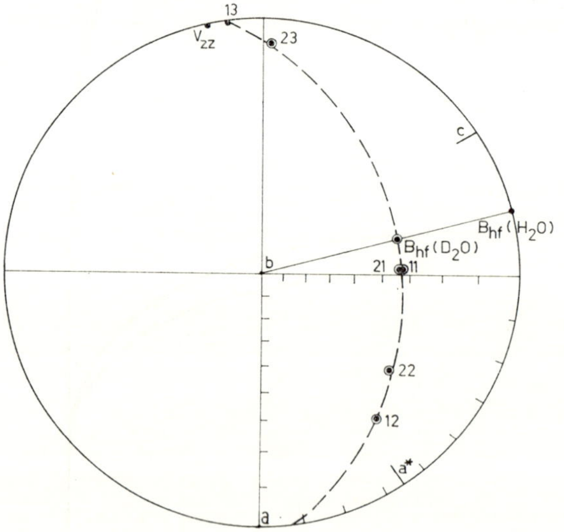

Fig. 6. Stereografic projection of the gradients $\nabla_B \nu_{1i}$ and $\nabla_B \nu_{2i}$ for, respectively, ^{79}Br and ^{81}Br nuclei, the resultant hyperfine field $\boldsymbol{B}_{h.f.}$ and the experimental Z axis of the electric-field gradient tensor. The dotted great circle indicates the plane in which all the gradients and the total field must lie if $\eta = 0$.

pure quadrupole bromine lines in the paramagnetic state at $T = 4.2$ K. The angle θ between V_{zz} and $\boldsymbol{B}_{tot}$ agrees very well with the θ value calculated from the spectrum in the antiferromagnetic state.

The total field at a bromine nucleus in the antiferromagnetic state is a summation of the hyperfine interaction with the Co^{2+} ion in the cluster and a dipole sum to account for the localized moments. Subtracting this last (in general small) contribution, the remaining field can be written as:

$$\boldsymbol{B}_{hf} = -(\gamma_N \hbar)^{-1} \boldsymbol{A} \cdot \boldsymbol{S}.$$

Preliminary experiments on isostructural $CoCl_2 \cdot 6H_2O$ gave as results in the paramagnetic state $A_{a*} = 5.16 \times 10^{-4}$ cm^{-1}, $A_b = 4.98 \times 10^{-4}$ cm^{-1} and $A_c = 4.70 \times 10^{-4}$ cm^{-1}. Determination of the principal values of the hyperfine tensor in $CoBr_2 \cdot 6H_2O$ are in progress. However, the qualitative conclusion that the $\boldsymbol{A}$ tensor is largely isotropic will probably be justified. This means that the direction of the h.f. field at the bromine nucleus closely reflects the spin direction on the central ion. From fig. 6 we see that the field at the bromine nucleus is shifted from the original direction in the *ac* plane towards the $+b$ and $-b$ axis by 33°, thus maintaining the mirror symmetry with respect to the *ac* plane. These directions coincide within experimental accuracy with the directions in which spin-flop transitions can be observed. This leads to the conclusion that the magnetic structure can be described as two apparently independent systems with effectively no interaction.

A further conclusion concerns the crystallographic structure of the hydrated and the deuterated compound which, as we showed before, must be different. A comparison (see table II) between the pure quadrupole resonance frequencies in the paramagnetic state of the two compounds shows that they differ only by 0.3 ‰.

TABLE II

Comparison of the hyperfine field and the quadrupole-interaction parameters for a ^{79}Br nucleus in $CoBr_2 \cdot 6D_2O$ and $CoBr_2 \cdot 6H_2O$ [3])

	B_{hf} (kOe)	Orientation B_{hf} [a] α	β	γ	ν_Q (MHz)	$\eta\cos 2\Phi$
$CoBr_2 \cdot 6D_2O$	24.12	81.5°	56°	35°	42.42	0.01
$CoBr_2 \cdot 6H_2O$	23.73	80°	90°	10°	42.40	0.02

[a] With respect to the orthogonal axes *a**, *b* and *c*.

The calculated ν_Q in the antiferromagnetic state is also very close to this value. Furthermore the asymmetry parameters $\eta\cos 2\Phi$ differ only 0.01 and the directions of the principal *Z* axes of the electric field gradients coincide within the experimental accuracy. Because all these parameters are very sensitive to structure changes we may conclude that in a first approximation neither the cluster symmetry in $CoBr_2 \cdot 6D_2O$ nor their orientation and spatial distribution have changed compared with the hydrated compound.

4. *Discussion.* The difference in magnetic structure between $CoBr_2 \cdot 6H_2O$ and $CoBr_2 \cdot 6D_2O$ cannot be explained without assuming a different crystallographic structure. The 2/m site symmetry of the Co^{2+} ion in the hydrated compound allows only orientations of the magnetic moments parallel to the twofold axis or perpendicular to it. The canted cross-structure in the *bc* plane, as we found it, is strictly forbidden in all the magnetic space groups belonging to the Opechowski[20]) family of C 2/m. The direct evidence for such a structure difference between the two compounds is given by the proton-resonance results reported here. Although this leads to a different group-theoretical description of the crystal structure, bromine nuclear resonance showed that the new space group will have to leave the clusters invariant. Probably we are dealing with a slight rearrangement of one or more water molecules just enough to break down the symmetry as was indicated by quadrupole resonance on the deuterium nuclei[13]).

Now let us try to construct a crystallographic and a magnetic space group which are consistent with the experimental data so far. In order to sort out the different possibilities we shall summarize the conditions set by the experimental data.

1. The twofold axis *and* the mirror plane at the Co^{2+} ion must vanish.
2. The inversion center at the Co site must remain because otherwise the bromine nuclei in one cluster would become inequivalent.
3. Equivalent nuclear sites, originally at a general crystallographic position, must become inequivalent in the new structure as can be concluded from the doubling of the proton absorption lines.
4. The crystallographic space group must admit in one of its magnetic groups the aspect group 2/m as shown by the symmetry of the local fields at proton and bromine sites.
5. We *assume* that the crystallographic space group of $CoBr_2 \cdot 6D_2O$ will be a subgroup of C 2/m. Furthermore we want to draw attention to the fact that the figs. 3 and 4 seem to indicate that the two structures shade off into one another.

Condition 3 requires that one out of two possibilities applies. Either the unit cell becomes twice as large, or one of the generating symmetry elements in the space group C 2/m disappears completely. In view of the fact that successive face-centered *ab* layers are separated in the *c* direction by water molecules which apparently have a large influence on the structural change, we conjecture that the *c* axis becomes twice as large. This is by no means a unique case. It has been reported to occur for instance in $Cu(COOH)_2 \cdot 4H_2O$[21]) and $NiCl_2 \cdot 2H_2O$[22]).

Once this choice is made the construction of the new space group is readily completed. Because the new unit cell contains 8 bromine nuclei which must be equivalent the general position must be eightfold at least. Within the assembly of subgroups of C 2/m this leaves only C 2/c and C 2/m. If it should be C 2/m it would require a general rearrangement of the symmetry elements in the unit cell according to condition 1 which is not in agreement with our assumption 5. So we quote that the space group C 2/c with a = 11.0 Å, b = 7.2 Å, c = 13.8 Å and $\beta = 124°$ qualitatively meets all the conditions set by our experimental data.

According to our experiments the magnetic structure can be described as a cross structure consisting of two simple antiferromagnetic sets, canted with respect to each other and with a very small mutual interaction. Because the interaction between moments in neighbouring *ab* layers in the original structure can be considered as relatively weak, we assume that the moments situated in one *ab* layer belong to one antiferromagnetic set canted with respect to the moments in neighbouring layers. Taking into account the original magnetic space group of $CoBr_2 \cdot 6H_2O$ and condition 5 we arrive at the magnetic space group $C_P\ 2/c$. The resultant magnetic array is sketched in fig. 7.

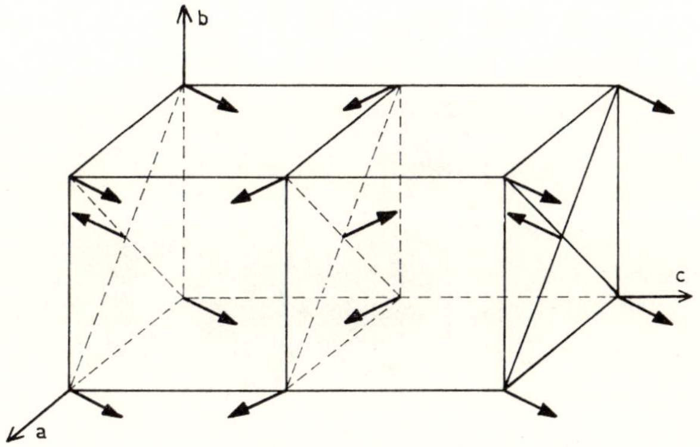

Fig. 7. The proposed magnetic structure C_P2/c of $CoBr_2 \cdot 6D_2O$ with a doubled *c* axis. All the moments are parallel to the *bc* plane.

Acknowledgement. The authors wish to thank C. H. W. Swüste for the stimulating discussions and continuous interest. We are much indebted to A. M. J. Duymelinck for his technical assistance and to J. H. Daemen for his help in collecting the afmr data.

REFERENCES

1) Forstat, H., Taylor, G. and Spence, R. D., Phys. Rev. **116** (1959) 897.
2) Robinson, W. K. and Friedberg, S. A., Phys. Rev. **117** (1960) 402.
3) Rama Rao, K. V. S., de Jonge, W. J. M. and Swüste, C. H. W., Physica **53** (1971) 621.
4) Spence, R. D., Middents, P., Elsaffar, Z. and Kleinberg, R., J. appl. Phys. **35** (1964) 854.
5) Date, M., J. Phys. Soc. Japan **16** (1961) 1337.
6) Murray, T. E. and Wessel, G. K., J. Phys. Soc. Japan **24** (1968) 738.
7) Uryû, N., Skalyo, J. and Friedberg, S. A., Phys. Rev. **144** (1966) 689.

8) Legrand, J. P. and Renard, J. P., CR Acad. Sci. B **266** (1968) 1165.
9) Benoit, H., Legrand, J. P. and Renard, J. P., CR Acad. Sci. B **264** (1967) 1556.
10) Kopinga, K., unpublished.
11) Swüste, C. H. W. and Kopinga, K., Physica **60** (1972) 415.
12) Swüste, C. H. W., De Jonge, W. J. M. and Van Meyel, J. A. G. W., to be published.
13) Legrand, J. P. and Renard, J. P., 17th Congress Ampere, Nuclear Magnetic Resonance (1972) 68.
14) Stroganov, E. V., Andreev, S., Kochina and Soloviev, V., Vestnik Leningradskogo Univ. Fiz Khim. **16** (1961) 114. For a comment on this structure determination see ref. 6.
15) Mizuno, J., J. Phys. Soc. Japan **15** (1960) 1412.
16) Kleinberg, R., J. chem. Phys. **53** (1970) 2660.
17) Haseda, T., J. Phys. Soc. Japan **15** (1960) 483.
18) Gorter, C. J. and Haantjes, J., Physica **18** (1952) 285.
19) Spence, R. D., Casey, J. A. and Nagarajan, V., Phys. Rev. **181** (1969) 488.
20) Opechowski, W. and Guccione, R., Magnetism, Rado and Suhl, eds., Academic Press Inc. (New York, 1965), Vol. 2A, Chap. 3.
21) Soda, G. and Chiba, T., J. Phys. Soc. Japan **26** (1969) 249.
22) Bongaarts, A. L. M., Van Laar, B., Botterman, A. C. and De Jonge, W. J. M., Phys. Letters **41** A (1972) 411.

Physica **69** (1973) 87–96 © *North-Holland Publishing Co.*

A MODEL POTENTIAL FOR A DILUTE ALLOY OF GOLD IN SILVER *

D. W. KNOBLE, W. D. JOSEPHSON and L. D. ROBERTS

University of North Carolina,
Chapel Hill, N. C. 27514, USA

Received 25 April 1973

Synopsis

A brief discussion is given of a phenomenological model potential for a dilute alloy of Au in Ag, the parameters of which were determined from electrical resistivity and Mössbauer-effect measurements. This potential is compared with a model potential for the alloy calculated in a relativistic apw approximation.

1. *Introduction.* In the development of the theory of metals and alloys, studies of alloys of gold with silver have been of much interest. This has been due, in part, to the facts that Au and Ag are noble metals and that the atomic volumes of the pure metals and of their alloys are nearly the same.

In pictorial terms, when a gold impurity atom is dissolved in a silver or other metallic host, a disturbance or shift of the electrical charge within the gold atom and around it in the host will occur. This charge shift, or screening of the gold atom, may be calculated from a suitable model potential, $W(r)$, for the Au atom dissolved in Ag. In the following, we briefly review information about the screening charge distribution and about $W(r)$ which may be drawn from Mössbauer effect and alloy electrical-resistivity measurements[1, 2, 3]) in conjunction with the Friedel sum rule[2]). We then describe a calculation of several aspects of $W(r)$ which are related to these measurements.

One of the earliest systematic studies of the resistivity of binary alloys was made by Linde[4]). These studies included measurements on dilute gold–silver alloys, Ag(Au).

An early theoretical treatment of Ag(Au) alloys was given by Huang[5]). In his treatment, Au, as an impurity in Ag, was described in part by a model potential

* Research jointly sponsored by the U. S. Atomic Energy Commission under contract AT-(40-1)-3897 with the University of North Carolina, by the Materials Research Center of the University of North Carolina under Grant No. GH-33632 from the National Science Foundation and by the University of North Carolina.

of square-well shape. The radius of the well was taken to be equal to the Wigner–Seitz radius, R_{ws}, for Au, and the well depth was estimated from measured values of the sublimation and ionization energies for the pure metals. The electrical resistivity due to the Au impurity in the Ag host and the alloy screening charge distribution were calculated approximately using this model potential. It was possible to compare this calculation of the resistivity due to the gold in the alloy with the corresponding resistivity measurements[4]); but, at that time, there were no measurements of the electron density in the alloys suitable for a comparison with the calculated screening function. With the discovery of the Mössbauer effect[6]), however, a method became available which could give experimental information about the electron density in alloys.

^{197}Au is a suitable nucleus for Mössbauer-effect measurements[6,7]), and measurements of the Mössbauer isomer shift[6]), ΔE, may be interpreted to give information about the electron charge density at the ^{197}Au nucleus[1]). Thus, it became possible to obtain experimental information both about the alloy wave function and the electrical resistivity due to Au in alloys.

The Mössbauer isomer shift[6]) may be described by

$$\Delta E = G[|\Psi_{\text{alloy}}(0)|^2/|\Psi_{\text{Au}}(0)|^2 - 1], \quad G = n|\Psi_{\text{Au}}(0)|^2. \tag{1}$$

In these equations, n is a quantity[6]) which depends on nuclear parameters of ^{197}Au, $|\Psi_{\text{alloy}}(0)|^2$ is the average valence band electron density at ^{197}Au nuclei in the alloy and $|\Psi_{\text{Au}}(0)|^2$ is this density in pure Au metal.

In the dilute Ag(Au) alloy, $|\Psi_{\text{alloy}}(0)|^2$ is related to the scattering of Ag host conduction electrons by a gold impurity atom; and, in particular, this density is related to the phase shift, $\delta_0(k)$, of the $l = 0$ or s partial wave in this scattering process[1]). k is the magnitude of the wave vector of a conduction electron incident on a gold impurity. The isomer shift is seen to be an aspect of the screening of the Au impurity atom by the Ag host conduction electrons.

$\delta_0(k)$ and thus ΔE may be calculated from the model potential, W, which describes Au alloyed in the Ag host; and, conversely, information about this potential may be inferred from measurements of the isomer shift. In a related way, the alloy electrical resistivity due to the Au may be calculated from W, and information about W may be obtained from resistivity measurements.

The resistivity per Au atom will depend on the transport cross section, σ_t, of the Au impurity for the host conduction electrons at the Fermi surface. For a spherical Fermi surface, Huang[5]) showed that in a nonrelativistic treatment,

$$\sigma_t = (4\pi/k_F^2) \sum_l (l + 1) \sin^2 (\delta_l(k_F) - \delta_{l+1}(k_F)). \tag{2}$$

Here $\delta_l(k_F)$ is the scattering phase shift for the partial wave of angular momentum l at the Fermi surface with the wave vector, k_F. When, for example, a dilute alloy of Au in Ag is prepared, the alloy must, of course, remain electrically neutral.

For a nonrelativistic model, this requirement of charge neutrality has been stated by Friedel[2]) in terms of a sum rule over the phase shifts $\delta_l(k_F)$,

$$\Delta Z = (2/\pi) \sum_l (2l + 1)\delta_l(k_F). \tag{3}$$

ΔZ is the valence difference between the impurity and host atoms. The potential W must be such that the $\delta_l(k_F)$ calculated from W will satisfy this sum rule[2]).

The Mössbauer isomer shift, eq. (1), the transport cross section, σ_t, of eq. (2), and the Friedel sum rule, eq. (3), may be correlated through a suitable model potential $W(r)$. An approximate model potential which served to do this was found in the following way[1]).

σ_t for Au in Ag had been measured[4]). Since it *was not* equal to zero, some of the δ_l were also not equal to zero. The valences of Au and Ag, however, were each equal to one and ΔZ thus *was* equal to zero. Thus from eqs. (2) and (3), to make $\Delta Z = 0$ with $|\delta_l| \neq 0$, it was clear that some of the δ_l must be *positive* and some *negative*.

To obtain a model potential which could give δ_l of either sign for different l, a model potential W of operator form was postulated[1]),

$$W = \sum_l V_{l,R} |l\rangle\langle l|. \tag{4}$$

In the application of this potential to the calculation of the isomer shift, ΔE, the partial potentials, $V_{l,R}$, were taken to be square wells of radius R, the Wigner–Seitz radius for Au, and $|l\rangle\langle l|$ is a projection operator for the lth partial wave. Thus a given $V_{l,R}$ can scatter only the lth partial wave. The well depth for each $V_{l,R}$ then has a direct correspondence with each phase shift, δ_l. δ_l will be positive if $V_{l,R}$ is negative and *vice versa.* Heine and Abarenkov[8]) have used a model potential of similar form for the treatment of pure metals.

The above ideas were used in the calculation of the Mössbauer isomer shift for Au alloyed in Ag as follows: It was assumed that only δ_0 and δ_1 were finite, *i.e.*, that all $\delta_l = 0$ for $l \geqq 2$. Then, using the measured σ_t, eqs. (2) and (3) gave two equations in the two unknowns, δ_0 and δ_1, the s and p wave phase shifts for the conduction electrons at the Fermi surface, E_F. We solved these equations in particular for δ_0. Then, from δ_0, we calculated the $V_{s,R}$ in eq. (4) which would produce this δ_0 at E_F. It was found that the depth of the $l = 0$ partial potential $V_{s,R} = -1.1$ eV for Ag(Au).

The charge density at the gold nucleus, $|\psi_{alloy}(0)|^2$, is due only to the $l = 0$ partial wave, *i.e.*, only $V_{s,R}$ of eq. (4) would contribute to ΔE. It was assumed then that this $V_{s,R} = -1.1$ eV, obtained from δ_0 at E_F, was independent of electron energy within the free-electron valence band of the Ag host. This $V_{s,R}$ was used to calculate $|\psi_k(0)|^2$, the charge density at the gold nucleus for each state k throughout the band. $|\psi_k(0)|^2$ was then integrated over the free-electron valence band, from $k = 0$ to k_F, of the Ag host to obtain a value for the $|\psi_{alloy}(0)|^2$ of eq. (1).

In this way we obtained a theoretical estimate of the charge density at the Au nucleus from (i) the Friedel sum rule together with (ii) an electrical-resistance measurement. The calculation was more detailed and complete than our brief discussion here can indicate. We note, however, that exchange effects were omitted in the above calculation[1,9]).

We followed the above procedure for dilute solid solutions of Au alloyed in Ag, Cu, Pd and Pt hosts. We found that the isomer-shift data for these alloys could be fitted together quite well with $G = +(8 \pm 1)$ mm/s, eq. (1).

The form of the operator potential, W, eq. (4), is perhaps the central element in the above correlation[1]) of ΔE with σ_t; and the principal experimental result of this work was the sign and magnitude of G. It was felt that the potential W was basically reasonable and that it would be of value to obtain a check of this model potential. An indirect check of W could be obtained by measuring G by an experimental method which would be quite independent of the above Au-alloy study. The method used was a measurement of the pressure dependence of the gold isomer shift. It was found that the value for G obtained from the high-pressure work was in agreement with the value obtained in the above gold-alloy study[10]).

2. *An approximate model potential for gold in silver.* Because the model potential, W, of eq. (4) gave a reasonable correlation of the above alloy[1]) and high-pressure (ref. [9,10])) Mössbauer measurements with σ_t measurements[4]) and the Friedel sum rule[2]), we have sought to calculate the depths of the partial potentials. In the following we will sketch a calculation of these depths using a relativistic model potential $W_r(r)$ for Au in Ag. The calculation of $W_r(r)$ has been made as a function of energy within the Ag Wigner–Seitz valence band.

We shall suppose that the alloy consists of one atom of gold dissolved in a large amount of silver. For pure silver, the wave equation will be

$$\mathscr{H}^{\mathrm{Ag}}\psi_{\bar{k}}^{\mathrm{Ag}}(\bar{r}) = E_{\bar{k}}^{\mathrm{Ag}}\psi_{\bar{k}}^{\mathrm{Ag}}(\bar{r}). \tag{5}$$

Here $\mathscr{H}^{\mathrm{Ag}}$ is the hamiltonian operator for pure silver. $\psi_{\bar{k}}^{\mathrm{Ag}}$ and $E_{\bar{k}}^{\mathrm{Ag}}$ are the corresponding eigenfunction and eigenvalue for a state of wave vector $\bar{k}$. For the dilute alloy, the wave equation becomes

$$[\mathscr{H}^{\mathrm{Ag}} + W_r(r)]\psi_{\bar{k}}^{\mathrm{alloy}}(\bar{r}) = E_{\bar{k}}^{\mathrm{alloy}}\psi_{\bar{k}}^{\mathrm{alloy}}(\bar{r}). \tag{6}$$

$\psi_{\bar{k}}^{\mathrm{alloy}}(r)$ and $E_{\bar{k}}^{\mathrm{alloy}}$ are the wave function and eigenvalue for a state designated by the quantum numbers $\bar{k}$. The perturbing potential $W_r(r)$ will be given approximately by

$$W_r(r) = W_r^{\mathrm{Au}}(r) - W_r^{\mathrm{Ag}}(r). \tag{7}$$

$W_r^{\mathrm{Au}}(r)$ and $W_r^{\mathrm{Ag}}(r)$ are potentials which would be suitable for the description of the pure gold and silver metals. $W_r(r)$, eq. (7), is taken to be approximately the difference of these. Because we will wish to compare the results of the present calculation with those obtained earlier[1]), W_r^{Au}, W_r^{Ag}, and W_r will be written in operator form as in eq. (4). Thus we have

$$W_r^{Au}(r) = \sum_{l,j} V_{l,j,R}^{Au}(r, E)|l, j\rangle\langle l, j|, \tag{8}$$

$$W_r^{Ag}(r) = \sum_{l,j} V_{l,j,R}^{Ag}(r, E)|l, j\rangle\langle l, j|, \tag{9}$$

$$W_r(r) = \sum_{l,j} V_{l,j,R}(r, E)|l, j\rangle\langle l, j|, \tag{10}$$

where

$$V_{l,j,R}(r, E) = V_{l,j,R}^{Au}(r, E) - V_{l,j,R}^{Ag}(r, E). \tag{11}$$

The present calculation, and thus the above potentials, will be in a relativistic approximation. With the gold impurity at the origin, the angular-momentum operators which will be diagonal are j_z, j^2, l^2 and s^2 where j, l, and s are total, orbital and spin angular momenta. The relativistic partial potentials, for example $V_{l,j,R}$, will be characterized by both l and j, where, in the earlier nonrelativistic model[1]), eq. (4), the orbital angular momentum l gave a sufficient designation of the spin-independent partial potential, $V_{l,R}$. For the purpose of comparison with earlier results, the partial potentials in eqs. (8)–(11) will again be obtained in the form of square wells of radius R. $|l,j\rangle\langle l,j|$ is a projection operator for partial waves of good l^2, s^2, j^2 and j_z in the plane wave incident on the Au atom. $\delta_{l,j}(k)$ will be the phase shift associated with the scattering of the l,jth partial wave on $W_r(r)$.

We shall obtain results here for $V_{s,\frac{1}{2},R}(r, E)$ for Au in Ag for E falling within the Wigner–Seitz free-electron valence band for Ag, and also for $V_{p,\frac{1}{2},R}(r, E_F)$, $V_{p,\frac{3}{2},R}(r, E_F)$, $V_{d,\frac{3}{2},R}(r, E_F)$, $V_{d,\frac{5}{2},R}(r, E_F)$, $V_{f,\frac{5}{2},R}(r, E_F)$, and $V_{f,\frac{7}{2},R}(r, E_F)$ where E_F is the Wigner–Seitz free-electron Fermi energy for Ag. The corresponding phase shifts at E_F will be given. The method used for the calculation of the partial potentials is an approximate application of a relativistic augmented plane-wave model[11]) to the dilute Ag(Au) alloy system.

2.1. Potentials for the pure metals. In an apw model for a metal, each atom is treated in spherical symmetry out to a radius R, the so-called "muffin tin" radius. The potential within this sphere is often taken to be mainly an atomic Hartree or Hartree–Slater potential but with a contribution to it from the neighboring metal atoms. To give it a name we will call this the "true" atomic potential. In the space outside of the "muffin tins," the potential is approximately uniform and we will take it to be constant. Thus within a sphere or "muffin tin" one has atomic-like wave functions and outside one has plane waves.

To obtain the partial potentials for silver, $V_{l,j,R}^{Ag}(r, E)$, one may begin by solving the wave equation within a spherical region, for example, within the "muffin tin" of radius R using the "true" atomic potential described above. Thus one may obtain the logarithmic derivatives of the large component of the relativistic radial wave functions on the surface of the sphere at R as a function of energy. This may be done for the s,p,d, *etc.* states within the sphere for the valence-band energy region of the metal.

These wave functions which describe the internal structure of an atom (Ag, for example) within the "muffin tin" are complex. In spite of this complexity of the atom, the external part of the valence-band wave function is determined in a single-electron treatment simply by the logarithmic derivatives on the surface of the sphere at R as a function of energy for the s,p,d, *etc.* valence states of the atom. Thus, *any* model potential for an atom which gives correctly the logarithmic derivatives at some selected radius R as a function of energy for the s,p,d, *etc.* valence states will be the equivalent of the "true" atomic potential for the calculation of a band structure in an apw model[11]). Eqs. (8) and (9) are such model potentials.

The partial potentials, eq. (4), which we used in our earlier study[1]) of Ag(Au) were square wells of radius R_{ws} and with a depth which was assumed to be independent of the energy of a state within the valence band. Here, for comparison with this earlier study, we have again taken the partial potentials to be square wells, but the well depths have not been assumed to be independent of the energy E.

Each square-well partial potential may be used in the wave equation and the internal wave function within the square well may be calculated. These radial wave functions will be spherical Bessel functions, $j_l(Kr)$. By selecting the energy-dependent depth of each square well $V^{\mathrm{M}}_{l,j,R}(E)$ properly, identically the same behavior for the logarithmic derivatives at R can be obtained for the potentials given in eqs. (8) and (9) and for the "true" atomic potential. These well depths have been selected such that $j_l(Kr)$ has no nodes within the well, $0 \leqq r \leqq R$.

As seen from outside the atom the "true" atomic potential and the model potential are indistinguishable. Inside of R, however, the two potentials and thus the wave functions are very different. The potentials, eqs. (8) and (9), would be useful in a band-structure calculation, and eq. (10) would be useful for a calculation of σ_t of eq. (3), for example. To obtain a calculation of the isomer shift, however, it will be more appropriate to use the wave functions within the Au atom which are obtained from the "true" atomic potential rather than the model wave functions, $j_l(Kr)$.

A computer program[9]) was developed several years ago by which the wave functions $\psi_\eta(r)$ and eigenvalues E_η for an atom may be calculated in a Wigner–Seitz–Hartree–Dirac approximation, with or without Slater exchange. η designates the states, $1s_{\frac{1}{2}}$, $2s_{\frac{1}{2}}$, $2p_{\frac{1}{2}}$, *etc.* We have used a modification of this program. As we have said, we wish to compare the present calculation with our earlier treatment (ref. 1, 9). Thus, for the silver host, we have again omitted exchange, and have obtained the $\psi_\eta(r)$ and the E_η for the 47 silver electrons for a $4d^{10}$ 5s valence configuration and with Wigner–Seitz boundary conditions[9]). The Wigner–Seitz (or "muffin tin") radius was $R = 3.00$ Bohr units. Here $E_{5s} = E_{ws}^{Ag}$ will be an approximate energy for the bottom of the 5s band in silver metal. For silver we find $E_{ws}^{Ag} = E_{5s} = -10.33$ eV. It is this E_{ws}^{Ag} which we take as the zero of energy for the plane-wave states outside of the "muffin tins."

To obtain an approximate "true" atomic potential for Ag, we now hold the Wigner–Seitz $\psi_\eta(r)$ and thus the associated atomic screening potentials constant or invariant for all 46 of the inner-shell Ag electrons. Using a potential which is the sum of the potential due to the Ag nucleus and that due to these 46 inner-shell electrons, we then integrate the Dirac equation from $r = 0$ to R for each of a set of specified energies, E, in the range $E_F^{Ag} \geqq E \geqq E_{ws}^{Ag}$ and obtain a $\psi_{5s}(r)$ at each E. Here we assume the value for E_F^{Ag} to be $(\hbar^2 k_F^2/2m + E_{ws}^{Ag}) = -4.76$ eV. For each E we then calculate the logarithmic derivative $D_{5s}(E)$ at R from the large component of these $\psi_{5s}(r)$. Any potential which gives this same $D_{5s}(E)$ at R will serve (equally as well as the "true" atomic potential) for the $l = 0$ part of the model potential, $V_{s,\frac{1}{2},R}^{Ag}(r, E)$, for pure silver. As we have indicated, a square well is suitable and we have thus obtained a square-well model potential of radius R and energy-dependent depth, $V_{s,\frac{1}{2},R}^{Ag}(E)$.

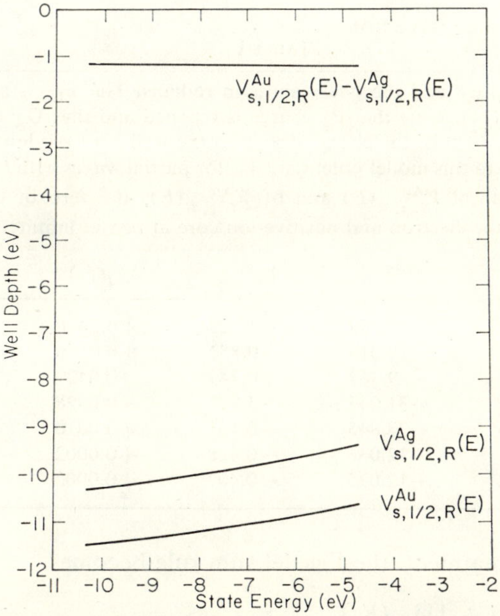

Fig. 1. Depths of approximate square-well s-wave partial potentials for pure silver, $V_{s,\frac{1}{2},R}^{Ag}(E)$, for pure gold, $V_{s,\frac{1}{2},R}^{Au}(E)$, and for a dilute alloy of Au in Ag, $V_{s,\frac{1}{2},R}(E) = V_{s,\frac{1}{2},R}^{Au}(E) - V_{s,\frac{1}{2},R}^{Ag}(E)$. The depths are graphed as a function of energy E where E falls in the Ag Wigner–Seitz free-electron band. See text, eqs. (8)–(11). $V_{s,\frac{1}{2},R}(E)$ has only a weak dependence on energy. Exchange was omitted in the calculation of these potentials. In the calculation of $V_{l,j,R}^{Ag}(E)$ and $V_{l,j,R}^{Au}(E)$, the zero of the potential energy corresponds to the electron and positive-ion core at rest at infinite separation.

We have also carried out the above program for Au to obtain $V^{\mathrm{Au}}_{\mathrm{s},\frac{1}{2},R}(E)$. The results of these two calculations are shown in fig. 1.

2.2. A potential for the alloy. For a dilute solution of Au in Ag, the depth of the $l = 0$ part of the model potential which will produce the Au isomer shift will be approximately $V_{\mathrm{s},\frac{1}{2},R}(E) = V^{\mathrm{Au}}_{\mathrm{s},\frac{1}{2},R}(E) - V^{\mathrm{Ag}}_{\mathrm{s},\frac{1}{2},R}(E)$, eq. (11). The result of the calculation of $V_{\mathrm{s},\frac{1}{2},R}(E)$ is shown in fig. 1. We find $V_{\mathrm{s},\frac{1}{2},R}(E)$ from the above calculation to be about -1.2 eV for $R = 3.00$ Bohr units, the approximate Wigner–Seitz radius for both Au and Ag. $V_{\mathrm{s},\frac{1}{2},R}(E)$ is found to be almost independent of E through the 5.5 eV width of a Ag free electron band. This value for $V_{\mathrm{s},\frac{1}{2},R}(E) = -1.2$ eV is in reasonable agreement with the result $V_{\mathrm{s},R} = -1.1$ eV which we obtained from our more phenomonological treatment earlier[1]). In a manner completely similar to the above calculation of $V_{\mathrm{s},\frac{1}{2},R}(E)$, we have calculated the depths of the partial potentials for several higher l,j values at the free-electron Fermi energy for silver, $E^{\mathrm{Ag}}_{\mathrm{F}} = -4.76$ eV, using the same "true" atomic potential as in the above calculation of $V_{\mathrm{s},\frac{1}{2},R}(E)$. The values for the partial potentials at $E^{\mathrm{Ag}}_{\mathrm{F}}$ and the corresponding phase shifts which we have obtained are given in table I.

TABLE I

The energies are given in eV and the phase shifts in radians. The $V_{l,j,R}$ are the depths of the partial potentials of eq. (11). Note that $\mathrm{P}_{\frac{3}{2}}$ charge is repelled and that $\mathrm{D}_{\frac{5}{2}}$ charge is but weakly attracted by W_{r}. Because of this, the charge drawn to the well is of predominantly s character. The total charge drawn into this model potential, W_{r}, for partial waves with $l \neq 0$ is only $0.0797/\pi$ electron. In the calculation of $V^{\mathrm{Ag}}_{l,j,R}(E)$ and of $V^{\mathrm{Au}}_{l,j,R}(E)$, the zero of the potential energy corresponds to the electron and positive-ion core at rest at infinite separation.

Shell	$V^{\mathrm{Au}}_{l,j,R}$	$V^{\mathrm{Ag}}_{l,j,R}$	$V_{l,j,R}$	$\delta_{l,j}(E_{\mathrm{f}})$	$(2j+1)\delta_{l,j}(E_{\mathrm{F}})/\pi$
$\mathrm{S}_{\frac{1}{2}}$	−10.618	−9.389	−1.229	+0.2466	0.1570
$\mathrm{P}_{\frac{1}{2}}$	−10.869	−10.018	−0.852	+0.0556	0.0354
$\mathrm{P}_{\frac{3}{2}}$	− 8.613	− 9.362	+0.749	−0.0429	−0.0547
$\mathrm{D}_{\frac{3}{2}}$	−34.826	−31.033	−3.793	+0.0328	0.0418
$\mathrm{D}_{\frac{5}{2}}$	−28.986	−28.845	−0.141	+0.0010	0.0020
$\mathrm{F}_{\frac{5}{2}}$	−12.465	−12.036	−0.428	+0.0002	0.0004
$\mathrm{F}_{\frac{7}{2}}$	−12.442	−12.035	−0.407	+0.0002	0.0005

For a relativistic treatment, the Friedel sum rule becomes

$$\Delta Z = (1/\pi) \sum_{j,l} (2j+1)\delta_{l,j}(E_{\mathrm{F}}). \tag{12}$$

The charge displaced into or out of the vicinity of the Au atom in each partial wave $|l,j\rangle$ is given by $(2j+1)\delta_{l,j}(E_{\mathrm{F}})/\pi$. Thus the charge of s character which would be attracted to the Au atom by W_{r} is 0.1570 electron, table I.

The net charge of p character, on the other hand, is found to be repelled. This comes about because the fine-structure splitting of the 6p state for Au is substantially larger than that of the 5p state of Ag, whereas the average binding energy of these valence p electrons in Au and in Ag is about the same[9]). Thus in eqs. (10) and (11) the partial potential $V_{p,\frac{1}{2},R}(E_F)$ is attractive but $V_{p,\frac{3}{2},R}(E_F)$ is repulsive. The net charge of p character repelled is calculated to be 0.0192 electron.

Fine-structure effects also play a role in the displacement of charge of d character. Here, however, the charge of d,5/2 character is attracted, although less strongly than the d,3/2 charge. On balance, a total of 0.025 electron is drawn to W_r by states with $l > 0$. This is but 16 % of the charge of s character attracted by W_r. The total charge attracted is 0.182 electron, table I.

The Friedel sum rule, eq. (12), requires that the net charge displacement for Au in Ag must be zero, not 0.182 electron. Thus the potential, W_r, of eq. (10) and table I does not satisfy this sum rule. It would not be expected to do this. W_r draws electron charge to the Au atom but does not account for the electron repulsion due to this charge. The charge of predominantly s character drawn to the well, W_r, will be repulsive to all partial waves.

We have studied this repulsive contribution to the potential in an approximate way. It was assumed that the repulsive character of the charge attracted by W_r could be described by a repulsive square-well potential V_ρ with a radius ρ equal to or greater than R, but with a height independent of l, j and E. The total potential would then be $W_T = W_r + V_\rho$. The height of V_ρ for a given ρ was selected such that the Friedel sum rule would be satisfied for W_T. One may expect that ρ will be somewhat greater than R. We find that if $\rho = 2R = 6.000$ Bohr units, $V_\rho \approx 0.1$ eV.

The total potential at E_F is then $W_T = W_r + V_{2R}$. This theoretical model potential may be compared with the model potential, W, of eq. (4) which was obtained in a more phenomenological way from ΔE and σ_t measurements[1]). We note that $V_{s,\frac{1}{2},R}(E)$, fig. 1, has only a weak dependence of E. In the more phenomonological treatment earlier[1]), it was assumed that in W of eq. (4), $V_{s,R}(E)$ was independent of the energy E of the valence-band electron incident on the potential. $V_{s,R}$ of eq. (4) was found to have a depth of -1.1 eV. $V_{s,\frac{1}{2},R}(E)$ is calculated to have the value -1.16 eV at the bottom of the band and to decrease to -1.23 eV at E_F^{Ag}. The depth of the total potential, W_T, for s-wave scattering will then be about -1.1 eV. Because of the close agreement of $V_{s,\frac{1}{2},R}(E)$ with the more phenomenological potential, $V_{s,R}$, one may expect that the isomer shift for Au in Ag calculated from W_T would be in reasonable agreement with experiment. This is found to be true[12]). The phase shifts $\delta_{l,j}(k_F)$ calculated from W_T are also similar to those obtained earlier[1]) from W, eq. (4). Thus one may expect the σ_t calculated from W_T to agree reasonably with experiment. This also is found to be the case[12]). We note that the potential given by Huang[5]) gives the sign for the Mössbauer isomer shift which is observed experimentally[1,9,10]), and, to this extent, is in qualitative agreement with the above model potentials, W_r and W_T.

Finally, we recall that exchange has been omitted in the above calculation, and also that the wave functions of the Ag host have been treated in the Wigner–Seitz approximation. It may be expected that the above conclusions as to the charge attracted to the Au atom will be modified somewhat when exchange is included and when the Ag host band wave functions are obtained from a more exact band-theory calculation.

REFERENCES

1) Roberts, L. D., Becker, R. L., Obenshain, F. E. and Thomson, J. O., Phys. Rev. **137** (1965). A895.
2) Friedel, J., Nuovo Cimento **7** (1958) 287.
3) Blandin, A. and Daniel, E., Phys. Chem. Solids **10** (1959) 126. Daniel, E., Phys. Chem. Solids **10** (1959) 174.
4) Linde, J. O., Ann. Physik **15** (1932) 239.
5) Huang, K., Proc. Phys. Soc. London **60** (1948) 161.
6) Frauenfelder, H., The Mössbauer Effect, W. A. Benjamin, Inc. (New York, 1962).
7) Roberts, L. D. and Thomson, J. O., Phys. Rev. **129** (1963) 664.
8) Heine, V. and Abarenkov, I., Phil. Mag. **9** (1964) 451.
9) Tucker, T. C., Roberts, L. D., Nestor, Jr., C. W., Carlson, T. A. and Malik, F. B., Phys. Rev. **178** (1969) 998.
10) Roberts, L. D., Patterson, D. O., Thomson, J. O. and Levey, R. P., Phys. Rev. **179** (1969) 656.
11) Kittel, C., Quantum Theory of Solids, John Wiley and Sons (New York, 1967). Heine, V., Cohen, M. L. and Heine, V., and Heine, V. and Wearie, D., in Solid State Physics, Vol. 24, H. Ehrenreich, F. Seitz and D. Turnbull, eds. Academic Press (New York and London, 1970).
12) Josephson, W. D., Knoble, D. W. and Roberts, L. D., to be published.

Physica 69 (1973) 97–102 © *North-Holland Publishing Co.*

SPECIFIC HEAT OF OSMIUM BETWEEN 0.18 AND 4.2 K *

ALI M. OKAZ and P. H. KEESOM

Department of Physics, Purdue University,
Lafayette, Indiana 47907, USA

Received 29 January 1973

Synopsis

The specific heat of a polycrystalline osmium sample (resistivity ratio 500) has been measured between 0.18 and 4.2 K in zero magnetic field. The transition from superconducting to normal state occurs at $T_0 = 0.638 \pm 0.002$ K. In the normal state, the coefficient of the electronic contribution was found to be 2.050 ± 0.003 mJ/mole deg^2, and the Debye temperature at absolute zero, $\Theta_0 = 467 \pm 6$ K. In the superconducting state, the electronic specific heat was found to agree with $C_{es} = a\gamma T_0 e^{-bT_0/T}$ where $a = 9.8$ and $b = 1.51$. The critical-field parameter H_0 was found to be 77.5 G, and the deviation of the critical-field curve from the parabolic law was 4.3 %. The value of the superconducting energy gap derived from γ, T_0, and H_0 is $3.55\, kT_0$.

1. *Introduction.* In the last 15 years, the specific heat of nearly all elemental superconductors have been reported and compared with the BCS theory of superconductivity[1]). Osmium is one of the few elements which up to now had not been investigated in the superconducting state, probably a consequence of its very high melting point which makes it difficult to produce a suitable crystal. Recently, the Naval Research Laboratory made some crystals of osmium and was kind enough to loan one of them for specific-heat measurements.

Hein and Gibson[2]) used arc-melted pellets of osmium to study the isotope effect and the critical-field curves. They reported values for both the transition temperature and the electronic specific heat in the normal state different from the values which had been published at that time[3–7]).

In the present investigation, the transition temperature and the critical-field curve are both different than previously reported[2–4, 6, 7]). The results agree quite well with the BCS theory and show that osmium is a weak-type superconductor. The coupling strength and the electron–phonon coupling constant are calculated using the theory of McMillan[8]) on the behaviour of the transition metals.

* This work was supported by the Advanced Research Projects Agency (IDL Program DAHC-0213) and the National Science Foundation (Program GH 34403, and MRL Program GH 33574).

2. *Experimental details.* The sample, 0.1426 moles, consisting of several large crystals was used. Its preparation is described by Kamm and Anderson[9]), who used portions cut from it for measurements of the Fermi surface. They reported the resistivity ratio $R_{300}/R_{4.2\,\mathrm{K}}$ of about 500.

A ^{3}He refrigerator was used to produce temperatures down to 0.3 K, and a dilution refrigerator allowed measurements between 0.15 and 0.7 K. The heat-pulse technique for specific heat was employed. A commercial germanium thermometer had been calibrated previously[10]) and recalibrated below 1 K using ^{3}He vapour pressure as secondary thermometer (T_{62}) down to 0.45 K. Below 0.45 K the temperature was based on the extrapolation of an iron-ammonium thermometer in the original calibration. In the recalibration, the temperature was based on the extrapolation of a commercial CMN thermometer, whose magnetization was measured with a SQUID. The two calibrations agreed within the accuracy of 1 mK.

The calibration data were fitted by a least-squares method to a polynomial of the form:

$$\ln T = \sum_{i=0}^{7} A_i (\ln R)^i, \tag{1}$$

wherein the A_i are constants. To check on the calibration, we measured separately the specific heat of a standard copper sample (T 4.2) provided by the Argonne National Laboratory. The results agreed within 2 % down to 0.15 K with the extrapolation of the data reported by Osborne *et al.*[11]).

A co-netic cylinder outside the dewar reduced the magnetic field at the sample to 0.03 G. The heat capacity of the addenda (thermometer, heater wire, glue and thread) had been measured previously. The correction due to the addenda was less than 2 % of the total heat capacity. The measurements were done in the ^{3}He refrigerator as well as in the dilution refrigerator and the results agreed within experimental accuracy. The random error in the heat capacity is estimated to be 1 % above 1 K and increases to 3 % at the lowest temperatures. Systematic errors are probably only due to the temperature scale and the calibration of the thermometer.

3. *Results and discussion.* 3.1. Normal state. In table I are collected a representative set of specific-heat results in the normal state: C_n. At sufficiently low temperatures, the specific heat of a normal metal can be written as:

$$C_n = C_{en} + C_{ln} = \gamma T + \alpha T^3, \tag{2}$$

in which C_{en} and C_{ln} represent, respectively, the electronic and the lattice contribution to the specific heat. A least-squares fit of all the available data gives:

$\alpha = 0.0190 \pm 0.0003$ mJ/mole deg^4, and
$\gamma = 2.050 \pm 0.003$ mJ/mole deg^2.

TABLE I

Specific heat of osmium in normal (C_n) and superconducting (C_s) state (C is in mJ/mole deg)

T (K)	C_n	T (K)	C_s
0.6419	1.343	0.1813	0.057
0.6591	1.359	0.1895	0.073
0.7071	1.464	0.1963	0.085
0.7502	1.551	0.2043	0.101
0.8065	1.669	0.2213	0.145
0.8460	1.760	0.2383	0.204
0.9059	1.865	0.2595	0.312
0.9710	2.003	0.2956	0.501
1.068	2.211	0.3277	0.702
1.170	2.439	0.3617	0.917
1.299	2.714	0.3884	1.111
1.403	2.934	0.4197	1.330
1.555	3.268	0.4396	1.467
1.693	3.584	0.4749	1.745
1.816	3.858	0.4979	1.929
2.043	4.356	0.5139	2.043
2.147	4.583	0.5378	2.261
2.395	5.097	0.5596	2.445
2.630	5.751	0.5832	2.654
2.902	6.395	0.6050	2.841
3.359	7.658	0.6193	2.958
3.654	8.392	0.6314	3.062
3.919	9.151		
4.137	9.851		

From the value of α follows the Debye temperature at 0 K: $\Theta_0 = 467 \pm 6$ K.

The only other specific-heat measurements on osmium, by Wolcott[5]), gave: $\gamma = 2.35$ mJ/mole deg^2 and $\Theta_0 = 500$ K. As the electronic contribution is dominant below 4 K, Wolcott's results are 15 % higher than found in this research. His sample is probably slightly less pure than the sample used in this investigation, but it is doubtful that a slight difference in purity could account for the difference in specific heat. Wolcott published at the same time results on 15 other elements. From a review article by Phillips[1]), it can be seen that Wolcott's results are nearly always higher than the results of other investigators, and on the average the difference is 12 %. It is then not surprising that the newer result differs from Wolcott's by 15 %.

3.2. Superconducting state. The results of the measurements in the superconducting state are also given in table I and plotted in fig. 1. The entries in the table are suitable averages over many data points. The transition temperature T_0 in a residual field of 0.03 G can be deduced from these specific-heat results. The transition temperature T_0 was also obtained by allowing the sample to drift slowly

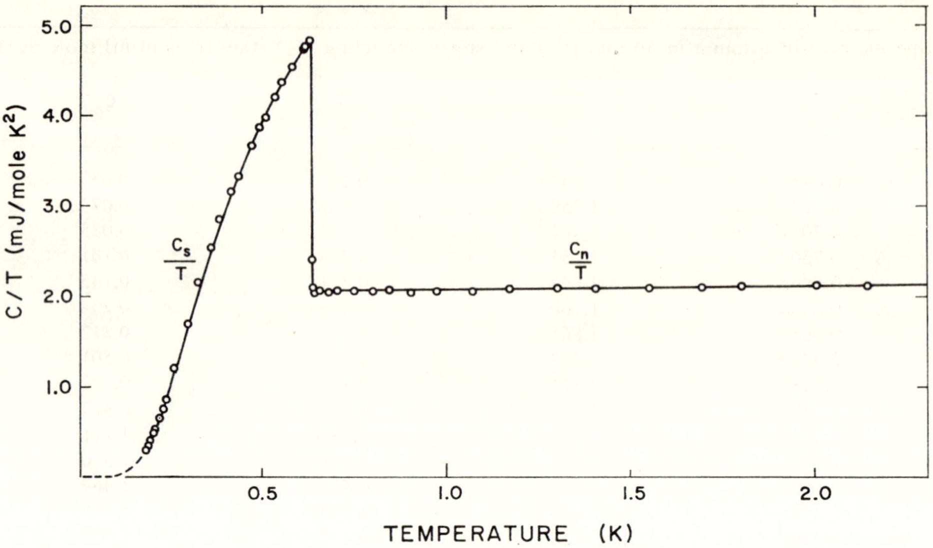

Fig. 1. Specific heat of osmium in the superconducting (C_s) and normal (C_n) states, plotted as C/T *vs.* T. The dashed part of the curve is an extrapolation to 0 K.

through the transition and noting the sudden change in the drift. Both methods indicate a sharp transition, within 1 mK, and give: $T_0 = 0.638 \pm 0.002$ K.

The superconducting-state specific heat can be written as:

$$C_s = C_{es} + C_{ls}, \tag{3}$$

in which C_{ls} is the lattice specific heat and is assumed to be independent of the state. For $T_0/T > 2$, the BCS theory approximates the electronic contribution by:

$$C_{es} = a\gamma T_0 \, e^{-bT_0/T}, \tag{4}$$

in which a and b are constants. In fig. 2 is plotted ln $(C_{es}/\gamma T_0)$ *vs.* T_0/T. A straight line represents the data very well for $T_0/T > 2$. From this line follows: $a = 9.8 \pm 0.5$ and $b = 1.51 \pm 0.03$ to be compared with the BCS values: $a = 8.5$ and $b = 1.44$.

Making use of the well-known thermodynamic formulae, the critical-field curve can be derived from the specific heat. For the molar volume, the value $V = 8.4$ cm^3 was used; this was calculated from the X-ray density at room temperature, correcting for a 0.5% increase in density on cooling to the lowest temperatures. Below 0.18 K, the electronic specific heat C_{es} was extrapolated using eq. (4) and the values of the constants given above. The entropy in the superconducting state was obtained numerically and at T_0 was 0.7% higher than the calculated entropy in the normal state at T_0. This is within the experimental accuracy. For thermodynamic consistency, the value of γ was adjusted to 2.065 mj/mole deg^2. From the calculations follows the value of the critical field at 0 K: $H_0 = 77.5$ G. The devia-

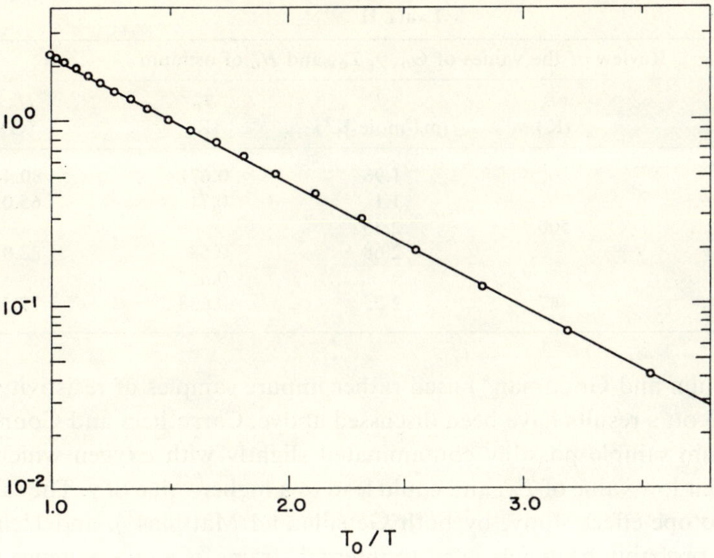

Fig. 2. Electronic specific heat of osmium in the superconducting state, plotted as $C_{es}/\gamma T_0$ *vs.* T_0/T.

tion from the parabolic law: $D(T) = H/H_0 - [1 - (T/T_0)^2]$ is plotted in fig. 3. The maximum deviation is 4.3 % compared to about 4 % for the BCS theory. Also in fig. 3 is plotted a curve obtained from the calculations of Mühlschlegel[12]) for weak-coupling superconductors. From the specific-heat jump at T_0 follows the slope of the critical-field curve: $dH/dT|_{T_0} = -208.0 \pm 5.0$ G/deg.

In table II are collected values of γ, Θ_0, T_0, and H_0. Goodman[3]) did not specify

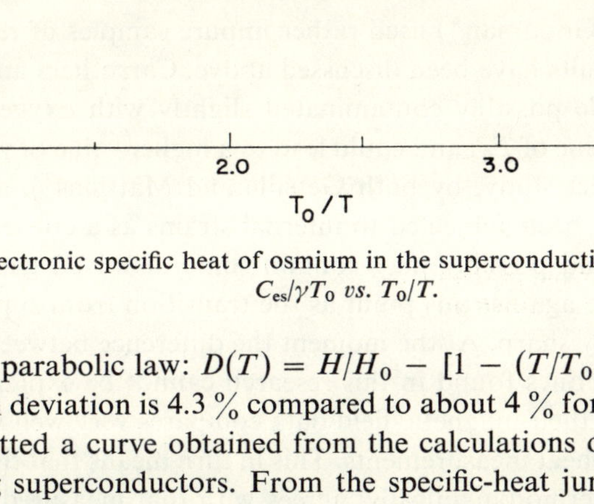

Fig. 3. Deviation of the critical field of osmium from parabolic dependence on the reduced temperature ($t = T/T_0$); the dashed curve is obtained from the calculations of Mühlschlegel.

TABLE II

Review of the values of Θ_0, γ, T_0, and H_0 of osmium

	Θ_0 (K)	γ (mJ/mole K^2)	T_0 (K)	H_0 (G)
Ref. 2		1.98	0.671	80.4
Ref. 3, 4		1.1	0.71	65.0
Ref. 5	500	2.35		
Ref. 6		2.68	0.58	82.0
Ref. 7			0.655	
This work	467	2.05	0.638	77.5

his sample; Hulm and Goodman[4]) used rather impure samples of resistivity ratio about 25. Wolcott's results have been discussed above. Carruthers and Connelly[6]) used an osmium sample possibly contaminated slightly with oxygen which may account for their low value of T_0, and could lead to a higher value of γ. The samples used in the isotope-effect study, by both Geballe and Matthias[7]), and Hein and Gibson[2]) had probably been subjected to internal strains as a consequence of the arcmelting technique and possibly may contain some dissolved gases. Hein and Gibson, however, argue against this point as the transition from superconducting to normal state was very sharp. At the moment the difference between their values of H_0 and T_0, and the ones found in this research cannot be explained. The calculated value of γ from their magnetic-field data compares very well with the value obtained in the specific-heat measurements. This in turn means that the dependence of H on T^2, derived thermodynamically, agrees with that measured by Hein and Gibson.

According to the BCS theory, the energy gap at 0 K: $2\Delta_d(0)$, neglecting the effect of the "s" electrons, can be estimated from the free-energy consideration by the relation

$$\frac{2\Delta_d(0)}{kT_0} = \frac{4\pi}{\sqrt{3}} \left[\frac{H_0^2 V}{8\pi\gamma T_0^2}\right]^{\frac{1}{2}}. \tag{5}$$

Using the values of γ, T_0, and H_0 found above gives: $2\Delta_d(0)/(kT_0) = 3.55$. This value is very close to the value calculated in the BCS theory, which is to be expected for this weak-type superconductor. McMillan[8]) found an empirical formula which expresses the electron–phonon coupling constant λ in terms of T_0, Θ_0, and the Coulomb pseudopotential μ^*. This formula can be written as:

$$\lambda = \frac{1.04 + \mu^* \ln(\Theta_0/1.45T_0)}{[(1 - 0.62\mu^*)\ln(\Theta_0/1.45T_0)] - 1.04}, \tag{6}$$

in which $(\lambda - \mu^*)$ plays the same role as the coupling strength $N_0 V$ in the BCS theory for weak-coupling superconductors. μ^* can be written in terms of the isotope effect α as:

$$\mu^* = (1 - 2\alpha)^{\frac{1}{2}}/\ln(\Theta_0/1.45T_0). \qquad (7)$$

Using $\alpha = 0.21$, found by Hein and Gibson, gives: $\mu^* = 0.122$ which can be compared with the theoretical estimate of 0.13 for most of the transition metals, and the value 0.12 reported by McMillan. Equation (6) gives: $\lambda = 0.382$ compared to the reported value 0.39. The coupling strength is then estimated to be: $N_0 V = 0.26$ while the original version of the BCS theory gave 0.17.

Acknowledgments. We are grateful to Dr. G. N. Kamm and the Naval Research Laboratory for providing the sample, and to Dr. R. A. Hein for helpful discussion.

REFERENCES

1) Phillips, N. E., CRC Critical Reviews in Solid State Sciences **2** (1971) 467.
2) Hein, R. A. and Gibson, J. W., Phys. Rev. **131** (1963) 1105.
3) Goodman, B. B., Nature **167** (1951) 111.
4) Hulm, J. K. and Goodman, B. B., Phys. Rev. **106** (1957) 659.
5) Wolcott, N. M., Conférence de Physique des Basses Températures, Paris, Supplément au Bulletin de l'Institut International du Froid **3** (1955) 286.
6) Carruthers, J. A. and Connelly, A., Proc. of the 5th International Conference on Low Temperature Physics and Chemistry (1957), Wisconsin Univ. Press (1958) 276.
7) Geballe, T. H. and Matthias, B. T., IBM J. Res. Developm. **6** (1962) 256.
8) McMillan, W. L., Phys. Rev. **167** (1968) 331.
9) Kamm, G. N. and Anderson, J. R., Phys. Rev. B **2** (1970) 2944.
10) Sjöstrand, M. E., Ph.D. Thesis (unpublished), Purdue Univ. (1972).
11) Osborne, D. W., Flatow, H. E. and Schreiner, F., Rev. Sci. Instr. **38** (1967) 159.
12) Mühlschlegel, B., Z. Phys. **155** (1959) 313.

Physica **69** (1973) 104–110 © *North-Holland Publishing Co.*

THE SPECIFIC HEATS OF ADSORBED HELIUM SUBMONOLAYERS

I. ON COPPER *

J. G. DAUNT and P. MAHADEV

Cryogenics Center, Stevens Institute of Technology,
Hoboken, New Jersey, USA

Received 25 May 1973

Synopsis

Specific heats of submonolayer ^{4}He films adsorbed on copper have been measured between 0.75 K and 4.0 K. Near monolayer coverages the film shows a two-dimensional (2-D) solid-like Debye behavior with the addition, at the higher temperatures, of a term due to desorption from the film into the three-dimensional (3-D) vapor above it. At lower coverages down to 0.18 monolayers, the specific heat per atom is anomalous and can be explained by a theory proposed by Roy and Halsey.

1. *Introduction.* This paper describes the results of experimental observations of the specific heats of submonolayer ^{4}He films adsorbed on bare sintered copper. Interest in these substrates followed earlier work by Dash and his coworkers[1,2]) and by Princehouse[3]), all of which stemmed from the initial use of sintered copper by Dash *et al.*[4]) as a medium which provided a large surface to volume ratio desirable for submonolayer film work. Sintered copper moreover has been previously used by Daunt and Lerner[5]) and by Wallace and Goodstein[6]) in desorption isotherm work on ^{4}He and ^{3}He films and a considerable amount of thermodynamic data has been accumulated for it.

A brief previous report on our work has been made[7]). This paper serves to provide more complete information on our experimental data and on tentative interpretations.

2. *Experimental arrangements and procedures.* The measurements were carried out in the temperature range 0.75 K to 4.0 K using an adiabatic calorimeter cooled by a ^{3}He cryostat. The calorimeter was cooled to below 0.75 K, prior to starting the heat-capacity measurements, through a superconducting Pb thermal valve[8]) which was thermally attached to the ^{3}He chamber of the cryostat.

* Work supported by a grant from the National Science Foundation and by contracts with the Office of Naval Research and the Department of Defense (Themis Program).

Temperature measurements were made using a germanium resistance thermometer, connected to a sensitive ac bridge. Calibrations of the thermometer were carried out in separate runs using a helium vapor-pressure thermometer, which was in the form of a small copper bulb attached to the calorimeter itself. Both ^{3}He and ^{4}He were used in the vapor-pressure calibrations and it was found that, even at the lowest temperatures, the thermomolecular corrections[9]) never exceeded 1.5 % of the observed pressure. The calibration data were found to fit a three-constant formula, as proposed by Antcliffe[10]).

A large copper surface was provided within the copper calorimeter by a stack of thirteen sintered copper discs, approximately 5 cm diameter and 0.63 cm thick, thermally connected to the calorimeter body. Each disc was made by sintering compressed carefully cleaned copper powder[11]), of particle size approximately 2 microns on edge by 0.2 microns thick, in hydrogen at 650 °C for 30 min. The resultant discs were found to have a density of 47 % that of bulk copper and a surface area, as determined by adsorption-isotherm measurements[5, 12]) of 0.374 m^2/g. The total mass of the sintered copper in the calorimeter was 695 g, giving a surface area of 260 m^2.

Just prior to the measurements, the calorimeter was baked out and simultaneously pumped out to high vacuum through its filler tube for a period of approximately five days in order to remove impurities from the surface of the sintered copper.

Measurements were made of the heat capacities of ^{4}He adsorbed on the bare sintered-copper surface. Measurements were also made of the heat capacity of the empty calorimeter, these data being subtracted from each heat-capacity determination of the calorimeter with its charge of ^{4}He, in order to arrive at the heat capacity of the adsorbed ^{4}He.

The ^{4}He measurements were made using the following amounts of ^{4}He in the calorimeter: 15 cm^3 (STP), 30 cm^3 (STP), 50 cm^3 (STP), 60 cm^3 (STP), 70 cm^3 (STP), 87.5 cm^3 (STP). Using the monolayer coverage data obtained previously[5, 12]) by us for ^{4}He adsorbed on copper, we have interpreted these coverages to be characterized by fractional monolayer coverages, x, as follows: $x = 0.18, 0.37, 0.61, 0.73, 0.85$ and 1.07.

3. *The results and some interpretations.* Figs. 1 to 5 give our results, indicated by open circles plotted as the specific heat per ^{4}He atom (C/nR, where n is the number of moles of ^{4}He in the calorimeter) against temperature, for calorimeter fillings of ^{4}He in amounts 30, 50, 60, 70, and 87.5 cm^3 (STP). The full lines in each figure represent the following function:

$$C/nR = a + bT + cT^2, \tag{1}$$

where a, b, c are constants which vary with ^{4}He coverage. At the highest coverages ($x = 0.85$, and 1.07) there is in addition a contribution associated with desorption

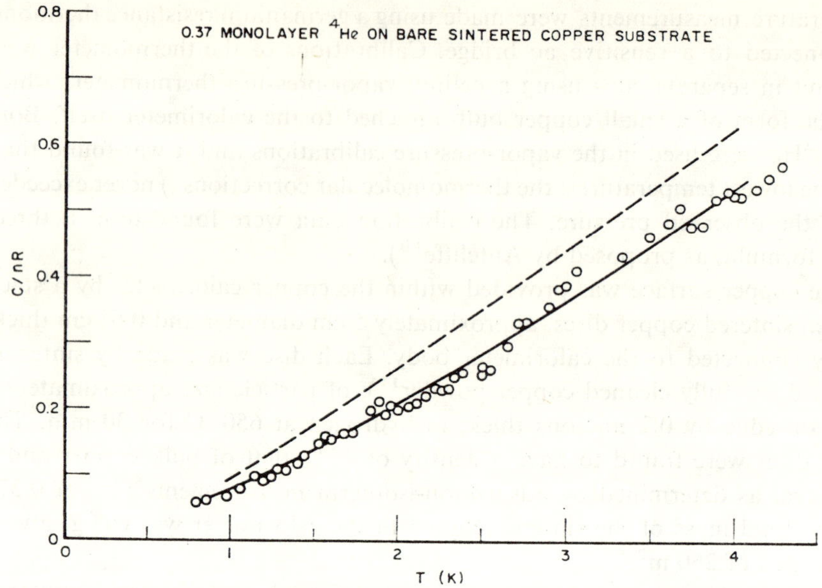

Fig. 1. Plot of specific heat per ^{4}He atom against temperature for a coverage of 0.37 monolayers on bare sintered copper. The open circles give our experimental results. The full curve gives eq. (1), with the values of the constants given in table I. The dashed curve gives the results of Princehouse [3]) for a coverage, $x = 0.4$.

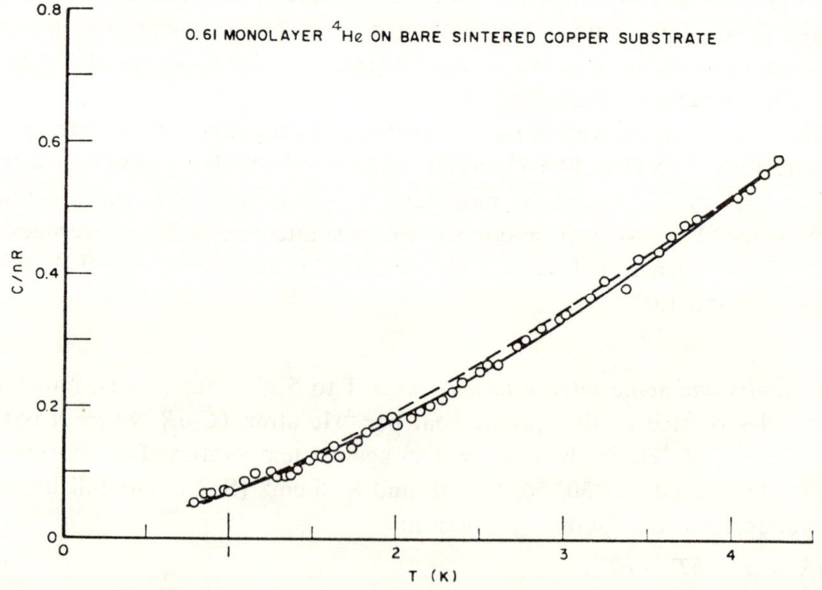

Fig. 2. The same as in fig. 1, for a coverage of 0.61 monolayers. The dashed curve gives results of Princehouse [3]) for $x = 0.75$.

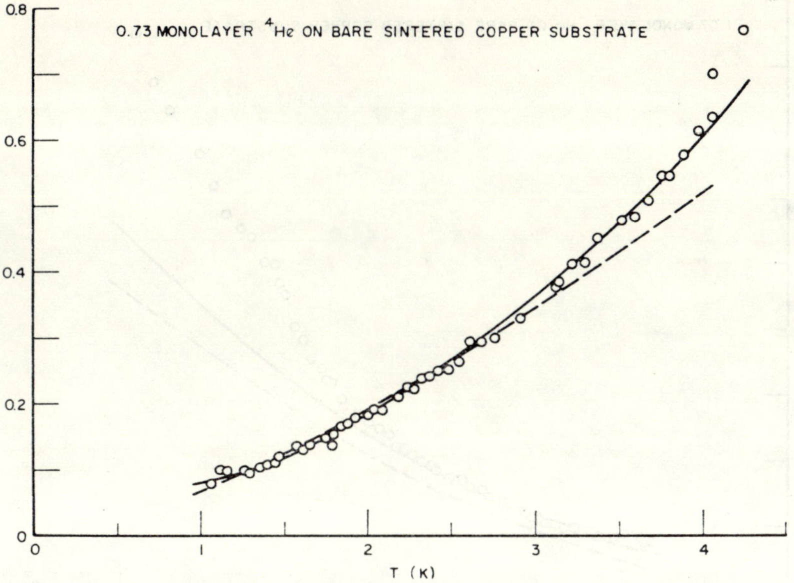

Fig. 3. The same as in fig. 1, for a coverage of 0.73 monolayers. The dashed curve gives results of Princehouse [3]) for $x = 0.75$.

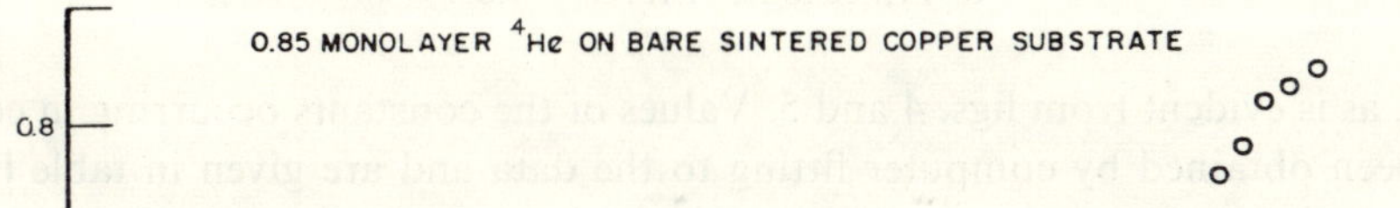

Fig. 4. The same as in fig. 1, for a coverage of 0.85 monolayers. The dashed curve gives results of Princehouse [3]) for $x = 0.85$.

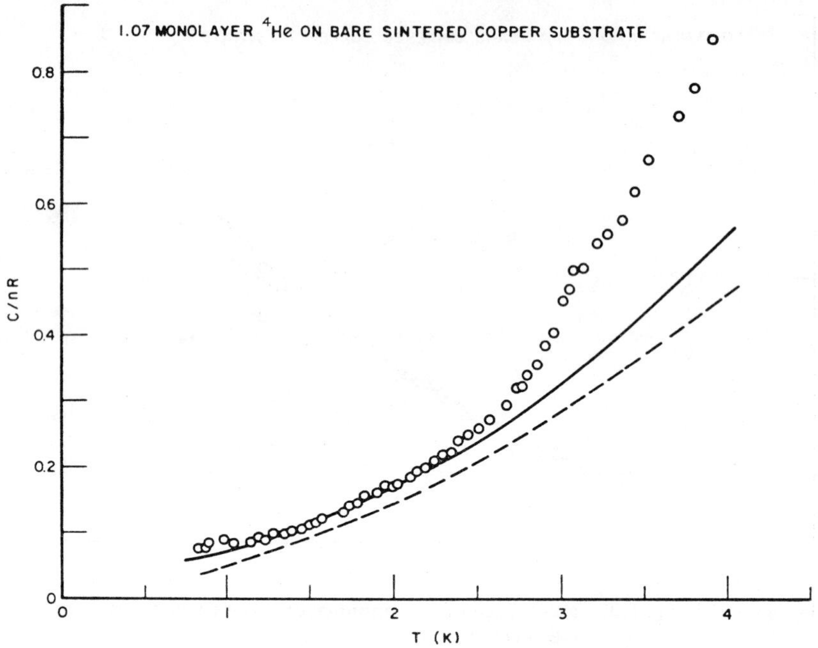

Fig. 5. The same as in fig. 1, for a coverage of 1.07 monolayers. The dashed curve gives results of Princehouse [3]) for $x = 1.05$.

effects, as is evident from figs. 4 and 5. Values of the constants occurring in eq. (1) have been obtained by computer fitting to the data and are given in table I.

The results of this work are compared in the figures with data of Princehouse[3]). The dashed curves in figures 1–5 represent his data for coverages $x \simeq 0.4$, 0.75, 0.85, 1.05, respectively. The following points may be noted. For the coverage of $x \simeq 0.37$, as shown in fig. 1, the two sets of data differ by about 20% on the average. For $x \simeq 0.61$ and 0.73, the data of Princehouse (dashed line) for a coverage $x \simeq 0.75$ seem to fit the curve representing our data obtained for $x \simeq 0.61$, better than that for $x \simeq 0.73$. It is seen in fig. 4 that for $x = 0.85$ the data of Princehouse match those obtained in this work very well. The data for $x = 1.05$

TABLE I

The constants of eq. (1) describing the data for ^{4}He on the bare sintered-copper substrate

Coverage x	a (dimensionless)	b $(K)^{-1}$	c $(K)^{-2}$	θ_D (K)
0.37	−0.0585	0.1189	0.0074	—
0.61	−0.0074	0.0578	0.0184	—
0.73	0.0427	0	0.0355	28.5
0.85	0.02	0	0.036	28.3
1.07	0.037	0	0.032	30.0

obtained by Princehouse, as shown in fig. 5, clearly deviate at the higher temperatures from our work.

In view of the probable errors involved in these measurements and of the difficulty of accurate assessment of the values of the fractional coverage, x, it is considered that our results and those of Princehouse are in general agreement. In view of the above considerations, it is also considered that the evaluations, given in table I of finite, small values of the constant a are fortuitous. This conclusion is supported by the fact that a, in table I, is both positive and negative depending on the value of x. In an overall interpretation of our data, therefore, it is assumed that $a = 0$.

With this assumption in mind, it is observed (see table I) that for the higher coverages, $x = 0.73$, 0.85, 1.07, the linear term in equation (1) is zero, yielding $C/nR = bT^2$ in the lower-temperature regions where desorption is negligible. Such a temperature variation, characteristic of a two-dimensional Debye solid, seems to be quite generally observed in adsorbed films near monolayer coverage, as evident for example in the work of Brewer *et al.*[13]) for ^{4}He adsorption on vycor glass, in the work of Stewart and Dash[2]) for ^{4}He and ^{3}He adsorption on argon-coated copper and in our own work[7,14]) for ^{4}He adsorption on argon-coated copper near monolayer coverage. In table I the characteristic 2-D Debye temperatures, θ_D, are listed in the last column, calculated from the known values of the constant c. It will be seen that there is little change in θ_D with change in x, and that the average value of θ_D of about 29 K is in line with those found for completed monolayers on other substrates[2,15]).

As in other observations[2]) of the specific heats of helium at low coverage on argon-coated copper, the results here show anomalous behavior for small x, which in this case for ^{4}He adsorbed on bare copper can be described by the introduction of a finite linear term in the specific heat. It is generally believed that this is due to inhomogeneities in the substrate, which have been shown to exist[5]) and which would have significant influence when x is small. A detailed and unambiguous understanding of the mechanism by which such inhomogeneities influence the specific heat is difficult to attain. However, the model of Roy and Halsey[16]) is of great interest. It postulates that adsorption occurs in patches at sites of high adsorption potential around which the potential shows a long-range variation. By characterizing this potential in terms of an appropriate density of states, the specific heat reveals a linear term:

$$C/nR = (\pi^2/3)\,(T/T^*x), \tag{2}$$

where T^* is a measure of the width of the energy distribution. For our data for $x = 0.37$ and 0.61, T^* has been calculated to be 75 K and 93 K, respectively, which, as would be expected[16]), lie somewhat below the adsorption energies at these coverages[5,17]).

In Roy and Halsey's model, the patches are assessed to be small, and as x

diminishes they become too small to reveal any appreciable Debye-mode contribution to the specific heat. This trend seems to be evident in our data by the marked diminution of the constant, c, as x is decreased below about 0.6.

It is worth noting that specific-heat measurements of some amorphous 3-D systems show a similar low-temperature anomaly, as evidenced for example in the recent work of Lasjaunius *et al.*[18]) on vitreous selenium and on other vitreous materials by other workers[19]). In many of these cases the low-temperature anomaly can be described as if an extra linear term in the specific heat were present. A possible explanation of these effects as due to tunneling states has been put forward by Phillips[19]). Considerations of this kind may be applicable for adsorbed submonolayers on inhomogeneous surfaces, where patches of adsorbed condensate of an amorphous character are very likely to occur.

Acknowledgments. We wish to thank Drs. F. Pollock and A. D. Novaco for valuable discussions, Drs. M. F. Panczyk and R. A. Scribner for help in some of the measurements and Messrs. J. Sangeorge, E. Karan and W. H. P. Van Iperen for their help in construction of the apparatus.

REFERENCES

1) McCormick, W. D., Goodstein, D. L. and Dash, J. G., Phys. Rev. **168** (1968) 249.
2) Stewart, G. A. and Dash, J. G., Phys. Rev. **A2** (1970) 918.
3) Princehouse, W. D., J. low Temp. Phys. **8** (1972) 287.
4) Goodstein, D. L., McCormick, W. D. and Dash, J. G., Cryogenics **6** (1966) 167.
5) Daunt, J. G. and Lerner, E., J. low Temp. Phys. **8** (1972) 79.
6) Wallace, J. L. and Goodstein, D. L., J. low Temp. Phys. **3** (1970) 283.
7) Mahadev, P., Panczyk, M. F., Scribner, R. A. and Daunt, J. G., Phys. Letters **41A** (1972) 221.
8) Heer, C. V. and Daunt, J. G., Phys. Rev. **76** (1949) 854.
9) Roberts, T. R. and Sydoriak, S. G., Phys. Rev. **102** (1956) 304.
10) Antcliffe, G. H., Einspruch, N. G., Pinattie, D. G. and Rorschach, Jr., H. A., Rev. sci. Instrum. **27** (1956) 240.
11) MD 60 "Druid" Copper from Alcan Metal Powders, Union, N.J.
12) Lerner, E. and Daunt, J. G., J. low Temp. Phys. **6** (1972) 241.
13) Brewer, D. F., Symonds, A. J. and Thomson, A. L., Phys. Rev. Letters **15** (1965) 182.
14) Daunt, J. G. and Mahadev, P., Physica, to be published.
15) Brewer, D. F., J. low Temp. Phys. **3** (1970) 3.
16) Roy, N. N. and Halsey, G. D., J. low Temp. Phys. **4** (1971) 231.
17) Pollock, F., Logan, H., Hobgood, J. and Daunt, J. G., Phys. Rev. Letters **28** (1972) 346.
18) Lasjaunias, J. C., Maynard, R. and Thoulouze, D., Solid State Commun. **10** (1972) 215.
19) See for some examples: Phillips, W. A., J. low Temp. Phys. **7** (1972) 351.

Physica **69** (1973) 111–118 © *North-Holland Publishing Co.*

THE STRUCTURE OF THE SPECTRUM OF Ta V

F. G. MEIJER and P. F. A. KLINKENBERG

Zeeman Laboratorium der Universiteit van Amsterdam, Amsterdam, Nederland

Received 12 February 1973

Synopsis

Thirteen lines of the spectrum of Ta, observed by means of a 6.650 m vacuum spectrograph with a hollow cathode and a sliding spark as light sources are identified as belonging to the spectrum of four times ionized Ta. These lines are classified in a level scheme consisting of 10 levels with the $5d^2D_{\frac{3}{2}}$ as ground level. The ionization potential was calculated to be 390400 (1000) cm^{-1} or 48.4 (0.1) V.

1. *Introduction.* The ground configuration of neutral tantalum is $5d^36s^2$ [1]), so the fifth spectrum is a one-electron spectrum. Isoelectronic extrapolation in the sequence Yb II [2])–Lu III [3])–Hf IV [4]) (Tm I could not be used because the levels of interest for this analysis are not known [5])) did expect that the lowest-lying configurations would appear in the following order: 5d, 6s, 6p, 6d, 7s. So the ground level of Ta V should be $5d^2D_{\frac{3}{2}}$. In the same sequence an extrapolation was made of the doublet splitting of the 6p configuration using the regular doublet law: $\Delta\sigma = K(Z - S)^4$. The screening parameter, S, was calculated for the known spectra and extrapolated to Ta V by means of the formula: $S = a + b\ (\zeta + 2)^{-1}$ [6]), where ζ is the core charge, in the case of Ta V, 5, and a and b are constants (see fig. 1).

In this way for the doublet splitting of $6p^2P$ a value of 12900 cm^{-1} was predicted and for the wavelengths of the 6p → 6s transitions 1720 Å and 1400 Å. Several years ago these lines were actually found at 1709.06 Å and 1392.50 Å on plates made available by Professor J. C. Boyce. These exposures were made with a 2 m grating vacuum spectrograph and a nitrogen spark. But confirmation of this interpretation had to wait for more precise measurements and an extension of the wavelength list to shorter wavelengths.

An analogous extrapolation was made for the 6p–5d transitions which resulted in a predicted doublet splitting of $5d^2D$ of 6800 cm^{-1}, while the wavelengths of these transitions should lie between 850 Å and 950 Å (see fig. 1).

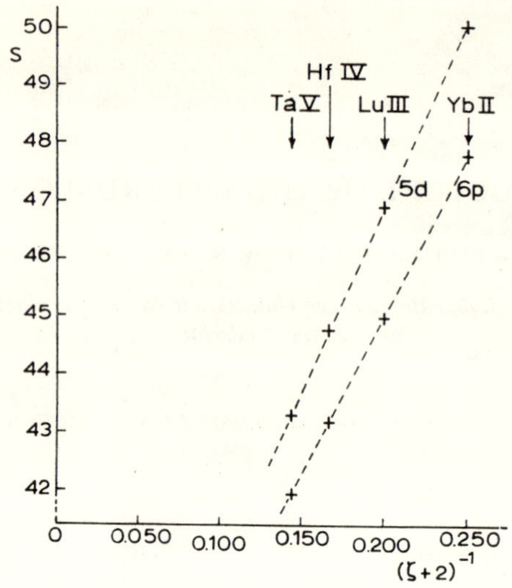

Fig. 1. The screening parameter S plotted against a function of the core charge ζ.

2. *Experimental procedure.* Exposures were made in the wavelength region 2350 Å–450 Å using the 6.650 m normal-incidence vacuum spectrograph of the Zeeman laboratory [7]), with special attention to the above-mentioned 6p–6s transitions.

The light sources were a pulsed hollow cathode discharge and a sliding spark [8]). The hollow cathode was a modification of a design by Glad [9]) (see fig. 2).

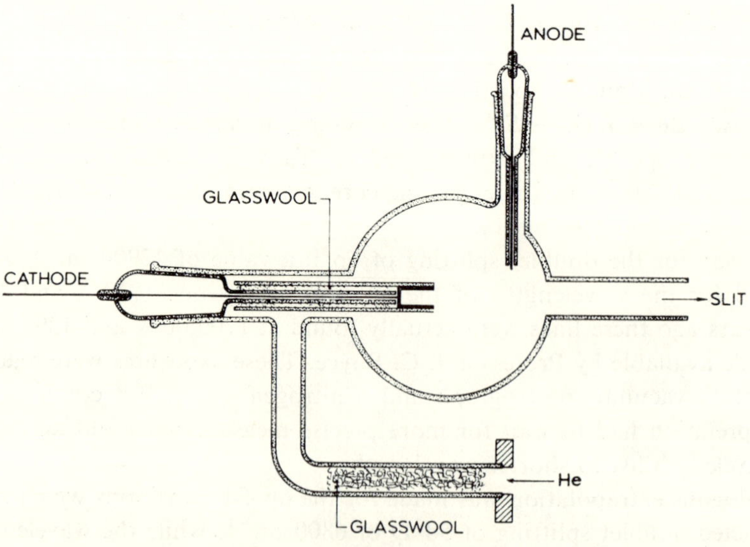

Fig. 2. The hollow cathode.

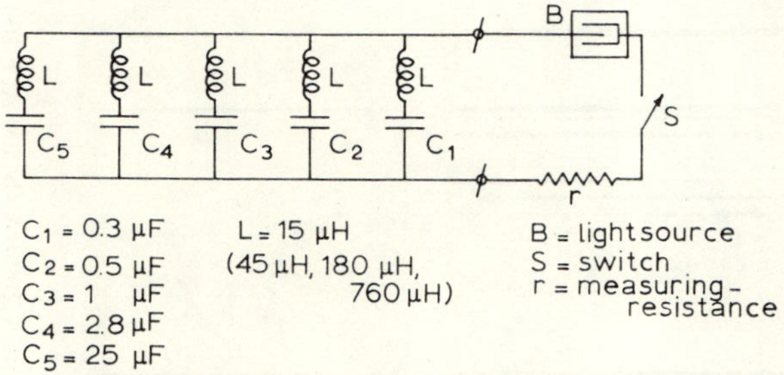

Fig. 3. The pulse-forming network.

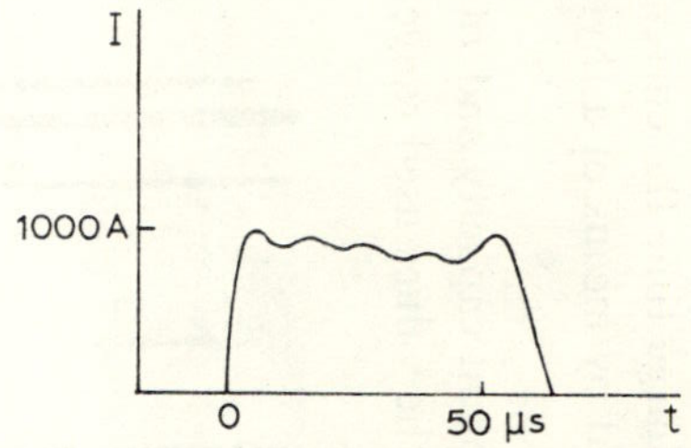

Fig. 4. Discharge current *vs.* time.

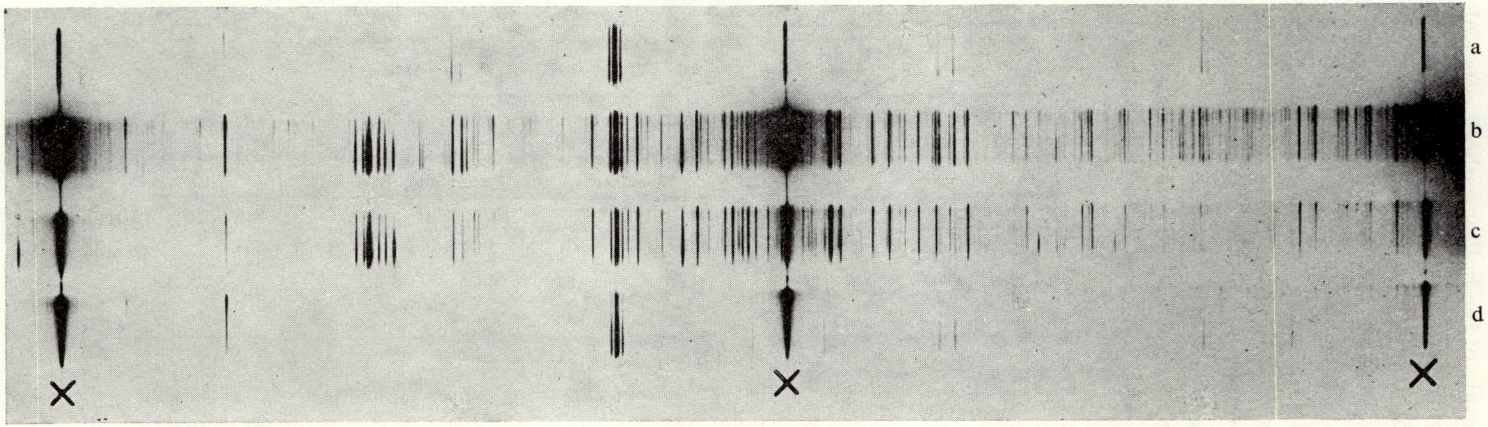

Fig. 5. The spectrum of Ta in the region 950–835 Å taken with a sliding spark; the resonance lines of Ta V are marked ×; a and d: discharge current: 500 A, b and c 1500 A.

The outside of the hollow cathode was isolated by means of a glass tube fitting around it; the remaining space between the cathode and the tube was filled with glass wool to prevent a discharge to the outside of the cathode. Helium was admitted in the bulb through a filter of glass wool, to prevent a discharge to the vacuum system, and pumped away through the slit, the pressure used was 1–2 torr.

Both light sources were fed through a pulse-forming network [10] (PFN) (see fig. 3) designed to assure that during most of the discharge time the current was nearly constant (see fig. 4). The discharge was triggered by means of a thyratron with a pulse rate up to 5 per second.

The PFN consists of an array of condensors of different capacity and of coils of equal self-inductance. By changing the set of coils (the values used range from

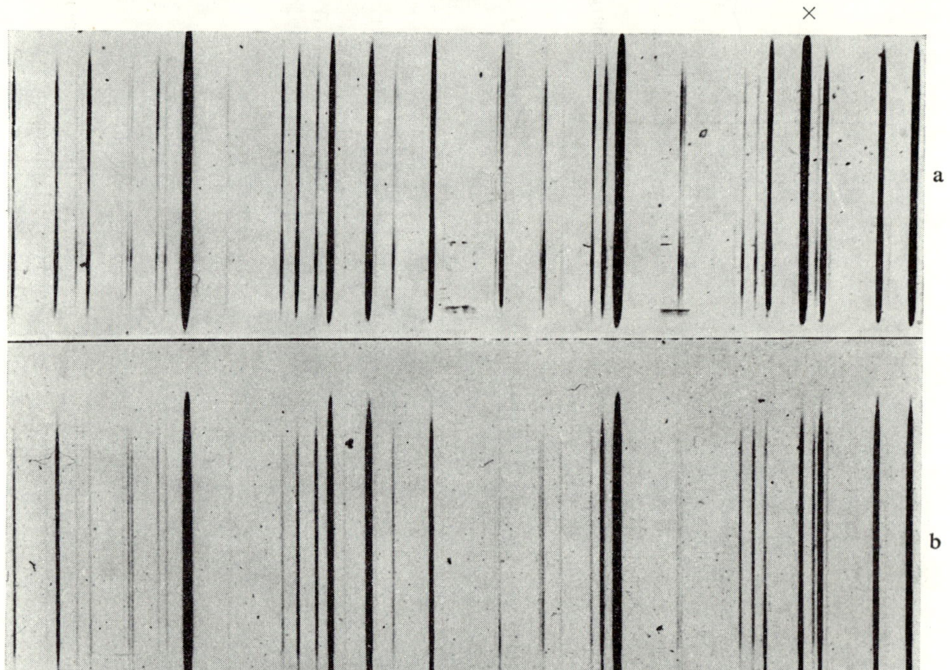

Fig. 6. Exposures made with a hollow cathode; discharge current: a 2000 A, b 800 A, c 200 A. The line λ 1393 of Ta V is marked ×.

15 μH to 760 μH) and by changing the applied voltage (between 500 V and 2000 V) the discharge current can be varied from 50 A to 2500 A; this can be used for discrimination between the various ionization stages.

Due to the near stigmatism of the spectrograph – though over a restricted wavelength region depending on the position of the source [11]) – it is possible to use the line-intensity distribution as a second means to allocate lines to a certain stage of ionization. The resonance lines of Ta V are shown in fig. 5; their behaviour under different conditions is outstanding.

In fig. 6 exposures of the hollow cathode in the wavelength region around 1500 Å are shown. Hollow-cathode exposures were not used below 1000 Å, because of the low number of lines recorded due to the absorption by the carrier gas.

3. *Wavelengths and energy levels*. The spectrograms obtained as described in the previous part were measured on the semi-automatic comparator COSPINSCA [12]). The wavelengths were calculated against impurity lines [13]), using a least-squares fit for a second-degree polynomial. As a result of the internal inconsistency of the set of reference lines the overall accuracy is only 0.01 Å although the positions of the lines were measured to the equivalent of 0.001 Å. Inspection of the plates and comparison with the lines on which the terms $6s^2S$, $6p^2P$ and $5d^2D$ could be based led to the allocation of more lines to the fifth spectrum. The complete list is collected in table I. The intensity numbers in this table are visual estimates from the photographic density on the plates. Due to varying grating reflectivity, photographic speed and absorption for different wavelengths they are not reliable for widely spaced lines.

TABLE I

Classified lines of Ta V

Int.	Wavelength	Observed wave number	Calculated wave number	Δ[a]	Classification
150	1708.997	58513.86	58513.10	0.76	$6p\ ^2P_{\frac{1}{2}} \rightarrow 6s\ ^2S_{\frac{1}{2}}$
100	1392.552	71810.60	71811.30	−0.70	$6p\ ^2P_{\frac{3}{2}} \rightarrow 6s\ ^2S_{\frac{1}{2}}$
40	1243.005	80450.2	80450.4	−0.2	$6d\ ^2D_{\frac{3}{2}} \rightarrow 6p\ ^2P_{\frac{3}{2}}$
60	1213.448	82409.8	82409.8	0	$6d\ ^2D_{\frac{5}{2}} \rightarrow 6p\ ^2P_{\frac{3}{2}}$
40	1140.514	87682.1	87682.9	−0.8	$7s\ ^2S_{\frac{1}{2}} \rightarrow 6p\ ^2P_{\frac{3}{2}}$
50	1066.680	93748.8	93748.6	0.2	$6d\ ^2D_{\frac{3}{2}} \rightarrow 6p\ ^2P_{\frac{1}{2}}$
10	990.276	100981.9	100981.1	0.8	$7s\ ^2S_{\frac{1}{2}} \rightarrow 6p\ ^2P_{\frac{1}{2}}$
80	947.279	105565.5	105565.1	0.4	$6p\ ^2P_{\frac{1}{2}} \rightarrow 5d\ ^2D_{\frac{3}{2}}$
70	890.829	112255.0	112255.0	0	$6p\ ^2P_{\frac{3}{2}} \rightarrow 5d\ ^2D_{\frac{5}{2}}$
30	841.305	118863.0	118863.3	−0.3	$6p\ ^2P_{\frac{3}{2}} \rightarrow 5d\ ^2D_{\frac{3}{2}}$
2	493.917	202463	202464	−1	$5f\ ^2F_{\frac{5}{2}} \rightarrow 5d\ ^2D_{\frac{5}{2}}$
5	493.077	202808	202808	0	$5f\ ^2F_{\frac{7}{2}} \rightarrow 5d\ ^2D_{\frac{5}{2}}$
4	478.300	209074	209073	+1	$5f\ ^2F_{\frac{5}{2}} \rightarrow 5d\ ^2D_{\frac{3}{2}}$

[a] Δ is the observed wave number minus the calculated wave number.

With this list it was possible to extend the analysis so that all lines could be classified. The resulting levels in cm^{-1} (= K) relative to the ground level are

TABLE II

Levels of Ta V

Designation		Level	Fine-structure interval
5d	$^2D_{\frac{3}{2}}$	0.0	6608.3
	$^2D_{\frac{5}{2}}$	6608.3	
6s	$^2S_{\frac{1}{2}}$	47052.0	
6p	$^2P_{\frac{1}{2}}$	105565.1	13298.2
	$^2P_{\frac{3}{2}}$	118863.3	
6d	$^2D_{\frac{3}{2}}$	199313.7	1959.4
	$^2D_{\frac{5}{2}}$	201273.1	
7s	$^2S_{\frac{1}{2}}$	206546.2	
5f	$^2F_{\frac{5}{2}}$	209073	343
	$^2F_{\frac{7}{2}}$	209416	

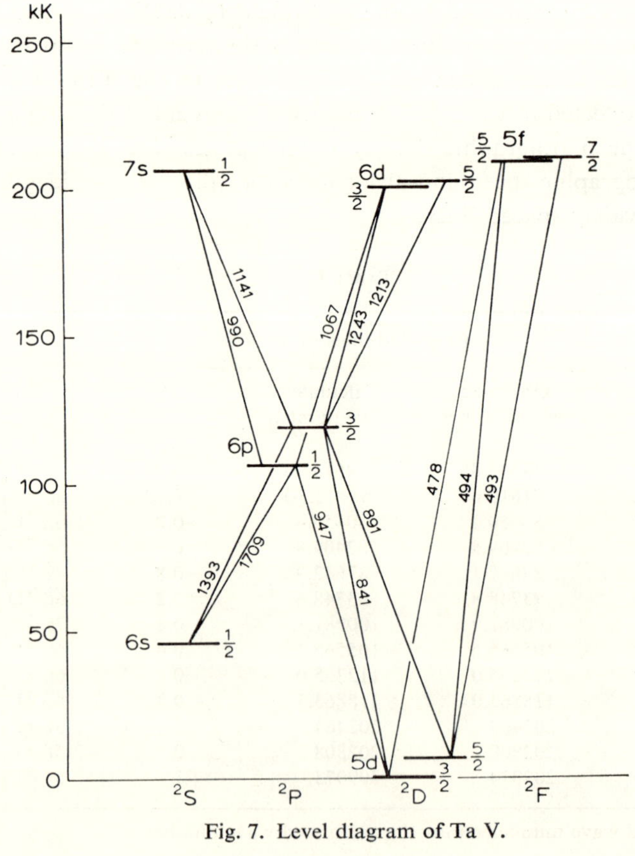

Fig. 7. Level diagram of Ta V.

TABLE III

Effective principal quantumnumbers and the ionization limit

	n^*	E'_l	E_l
5d	2.6593		
		391900 K	
6d	3.7859		
			390400 K
6s	2.8328		
		388925 K	
7s	3.8785		

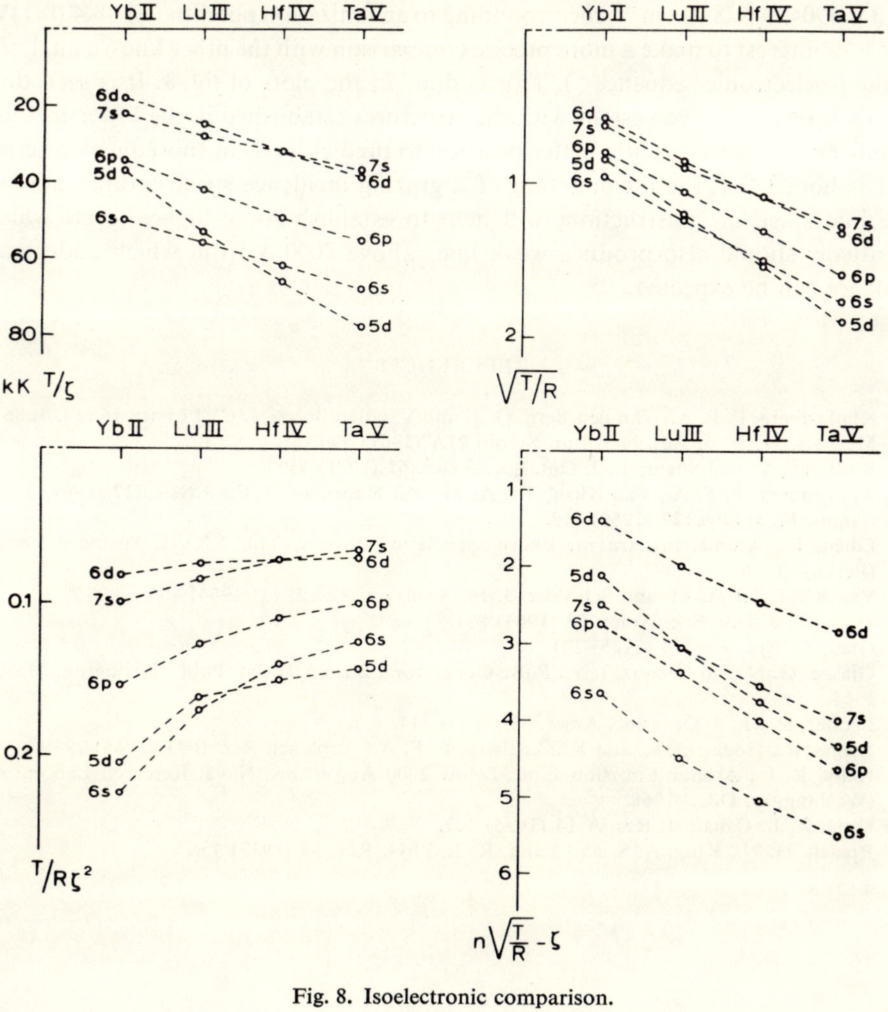

Fig. 8. Isoelectronic comparison.

given in table II, while fig. 7 shows a complete level and line diagram with term values in kK and wavelengths in Å.

4. *Ionization potential and isoelectronic comparison.* The ionization potential was calculated from the *n*s- and *n*d-series, with two members each, assuming certain values for the differences in effective principal quantum number. In the spectra of similar structure they have traditionally been taken as 1.05 for the 6s–7s and 1.15 for the 5d–6d jump, a procedure that seems to go back as far as 1936 [14, 15]). Recently the analysis of Lu III [3]) in which longer series are detected has given support to this rule. For Ta V it therefore seems appropriate to use the values found in Lu III, namely: 1.1266 and 1.0457 for the 6s and 7s respectively 5d and 6d terms. The results are collected in table III. The average for the series limit is 390400 (1000) cm^{-1} corresponding to an ionization potential of 48.4 (0.1)V.

It is of interest to make a more precise comparison with the other known analyses in the isoelectronic sequence [6]). This is done in the plots of fig. 8. It is seen that the Ta V results are consistent with the structures established in the lower-ionized members; this places us in a better position to predict levels in subsequent spectra.

It is hoped that the introduction of a grazing incidence spectrograph, now in the final stage of construction, will help to establish some higher levels which eventually should also produce weak lines above 2000 Å from which additional evidence can be expected.

REFERENCES

1) Klinkenberg, P. F. A., Van den Berg, G. J. and Van den Bosch, J. C., Physica **16** (1950) 861.
2) Meggers, W. F., J. Res. Nat. Bur. Stand. **71A** (1967) 396.
3) Kaufman, V. and Sugar, J., J. Opt. Soc. Amer. **61** (1971) 1693.
4) Klinkenberg, P. F. A., Van Kleef, Th. A. M. and Noorman, P. E., Physica **27** (1961) 1177.
5) Camus, P., J. Phys. **27** (1966) 717.
6) Edlén, B., Atomic Spectra in: Encyclopaedia of Physics, Vol. XXVII, Springer Verlag (Berlin), p. 80.
7) Van Kleef, Th. A. M. and Schröder, J. F., Appl. sci. Res. B **11** (1964) 465.
8) Sugar, J., J. Opt. Soc. Amer. **53** (1963) 831.
9) Glad, S., Ark. Fys. **10** (1955) 291.
10) Glasoe, G. N. and Lebaqz, J. V., Pulse Generators, Boston Techn. Publ. (Lexington, Mass.) 1964.
11) Beutler, H. G., J. Opt. Soc. Amer. **35** (1945) 311.
12) Poppe, R., Hoekstra, R. and Klinkenberg, P. F. A., Appl. sci. Res. B **11** (1964) 293.
13) Kelly, R. L., Atomic Emission Lines Below 2000 Ångströms, Naval Research Laboratory (Washington, D.C.) 1968.
14) Lang, R. J., Canad. J. Res. A **14** (1936) 127.
15) Russell, H. N., King, A. S. and Lang, R. J., Phys. Rev. **52** (1937) 456.

Physica **69** (1973) 119–128 © *North-Holland Publishing Co.*

LOW-TEMPERATURE SPECIFIC HEAT OF MAGNETICALLY ORDERING DILUTE Pt–Co AND Pt–Mn ALLOYS

G. J. NIEUWENHUYS, M. F. PIKART, J. J. ZWART, B. M. BOERSTOEL and G. J. VAN DEN BERG

Kamerlingh Onnes Laboratorium der Rijksuniversiteit, Leiden, Nederland

(Communication No. 403*a*)

Received 22 January 1973

Synopsis

Specific-heat measurements of a number of dilute Pt–Co and Pt–Mn alloys are presented. The results are compared with the results of the corresponding Pd-based alloys and are analysed in terms of model calculations. The model used is the Weiss molecular-field model with a distribution of *g* values artificially incorporated. From the fit of the model calculations to the data a magnetic moment of $4\mu_B$ per Co atom in Pt is found, which is close to the measured moment. For Mn in Pt–Mn a value of $2.6\mu_B$ is predicted. This (unrealistic) small value is attributed to the fact that Pt–Mn was recently found not to be ferromagnetic, though the specific heat *vs.* temperature curves can be described very well by the model.

1. *Introduction.* The magnetic behaviour of dilute alloys of Ni, Co, Fe and Mn in palladium has been investigated extensively during the past ten years (see refs. 1, 2, 13 and references therein). Less attention has been paid to the corresponding platinum-based alloys. The great interest, which palladium and its alloys have received, has mainly been due to the large enhancement of the electronic magnetic susceptibility of Pd. As a consequence of this, alloys of palladium with first-row transition elements exhibit ferromagnetic ordering at low temperatures down to very low concentrations and the magnetic moments, associated with the impurities, are very large as compared to what would be possible according to Hund's rule. The same, although to a lesser extent, is true for the corresponding platinum-based alloys, as was found by a number of workers[3−8]).

In order to compare the magnetic behaviour of dilute Pd–Co and Pd–Mn alloys with the platinum alloys in more detail, the specific heat of a number of Pt–Co and Pt–Mn dilute alloys was measured. The results of these measurements are presented in section 2 of this paper, followed in section 3 by calculations of the entropy and spin values from the specific-heat data; in section 4 an analysis of the specific-heat results based upon a modified Weiss molecular-field model is given. The moments obtained from this analysis are compared with those from magnetization measurements.

A few of the present specific-heat results have previously been published[9,10]).

2. *Measurements*. The Pt-based alloys measured were:

Pt–Co: 0.067, 0.5 and 0.8 at.%;
Pt–Mn: 0.36, 0.88 and 1.64 at.%.

The specimens were prepared by induction melting in an argon atmosphere and after melting kept at 1000 °C for at least 24 hours and subsequently quenched in water. The concentrations of the Pt–Co 0.5 at.% and of the Pt–Mn alloys were determined chemically; the analysis of the Pt–Co 0.8 at.% alloy was also carried out by neutron activation. The neutron-activation analysis of the Pt–Co 0.067 at.% alloy failed so that in this case only the nominal concentration is available.

The specific heat has been measured using the equipment described by Boerstoel *et al.*[11]). Some of the specimens have not been measured with the heater and the thermometer screwed into the specimen but fixed on to it using a nylon ring. The ring just fitted around the specimen and the addenda at room temperature so that a tight clamping was obtained at low temperatures due to the large thermal contraction of nylon. A small amount of silicone oil was used in order to further improve the heat transfer between the different components of the assembly.

In all cases the specific heat was measured in zero external field as well as in external magnetic fields up to 27 kOe.

Results for the excess specific heat, ΔC, *versus* temperature, T, for alloys containing 0.067, 0.5 and 0.8 at.%. Co are shown in fig. 1, fig. 2 and fig. 3, respectively. ΔC was obtained by subtracting the specific heat of Pt, as measured by Boerstoel *et al.*[12]), from the specific-heat data of the alloys. This procedure is correct only in those cases where the addition of the magnetic impurities has a negligible effect on the lattice specific heat of the host metal (see section 3). For clarity of the figures, in most cases the experimental points have been omitted from the graphs. It should be mentioned that the accuracy with which the value of C can be obtained is about 0.5 %[11]), the accuracy of ΔC depends on the ratio $\Delta C/C$ (which decreases with increasing temperature).

The dashed curves in the figures represent the results of model calculations, to be discussed in section 4.

The present specific-heat results are somewhat different from those obtained by Wheeler[8]), but this may be due to the limited temperature range in which Wheeler obtained his data.

In the figs. 4, 5 and 6 data are shown for the alloys containing 0.36, 0.88 and 1.64 at.% Mn, respectively. As can be seen from these graphs a common feature

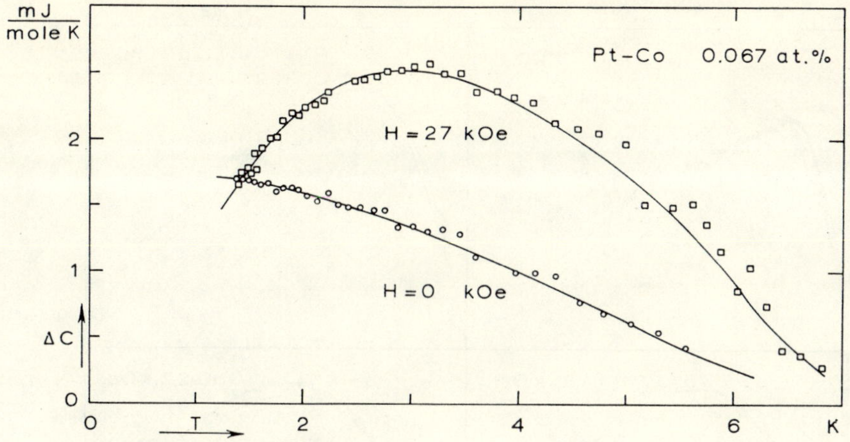

Fig. 1. ΔC *versus* T for Pt–Co 0.067 at.% in magnetic field $H = 0$ and $H = 27$ kOe.

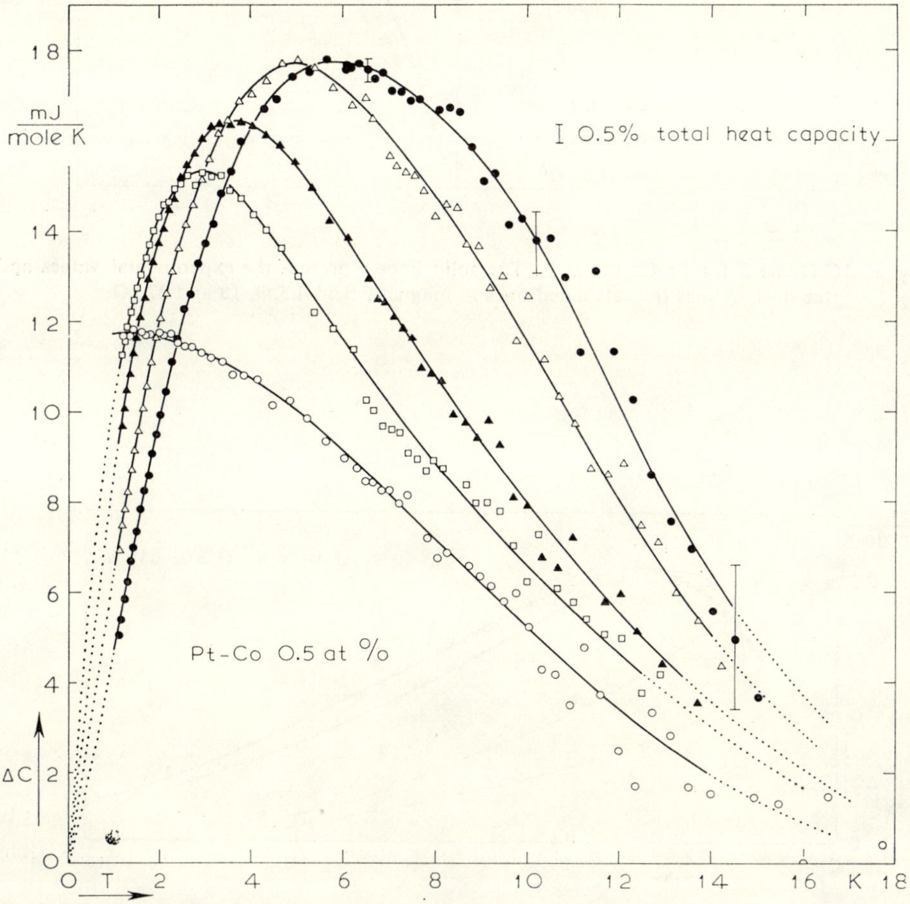

Fig. 2. ΔC *versus* T for Pt–Co 0.5 at.%. ○ : $H = 0$, □ : $H = 4.5$ kOe, ▲ : $H = 9$ kOe, △ : $H = 18$ kOe and ● : $H = 27$ kOe.

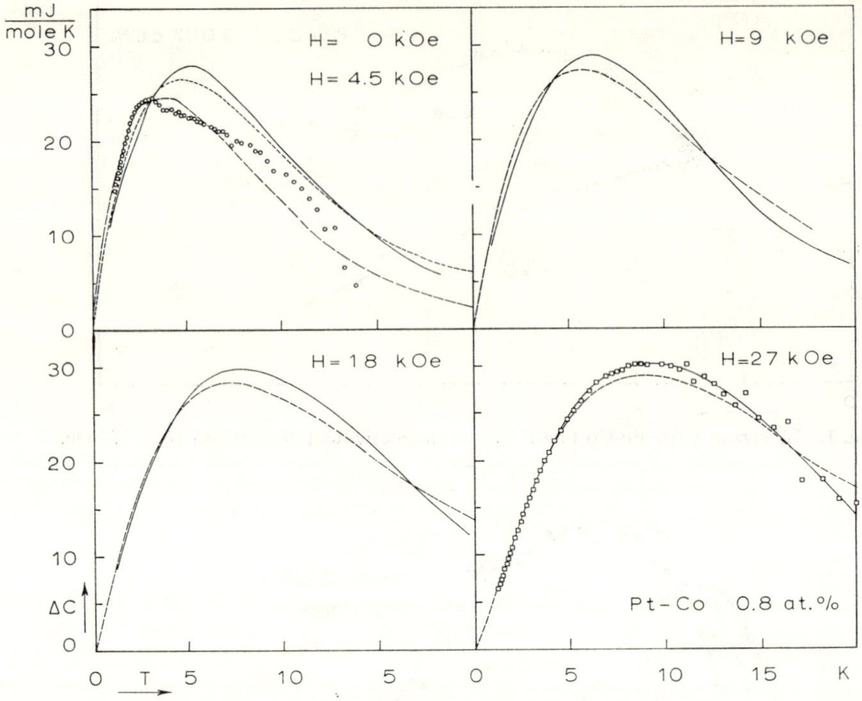

Fig. 3. ΔC *versus* T for Pt–Co 0.8 at.%. The solid lines represent the experimental values and the dashed lines the calculated ones in magnetic field 4.5, 9, 18 and 27 kOe.

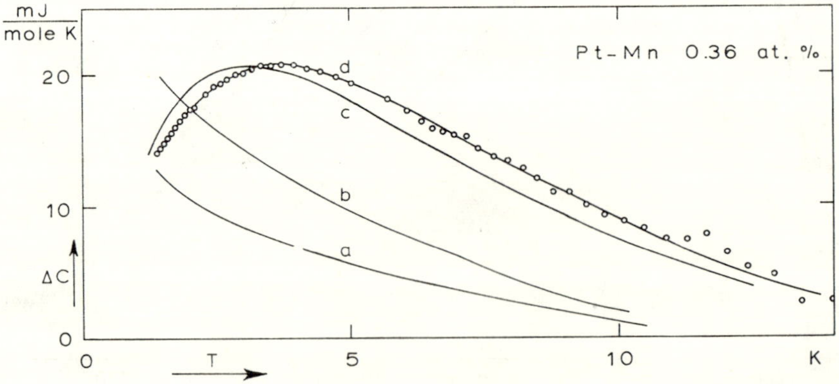

Fig. 4. ΔC *versus* T for Pt–Mn 0.36 at.%. a, b, c and d refer to $H = 0$, $H = 9$ kOe, $H = 22.2$ kOe and $H = 27$ kOe, respectively.

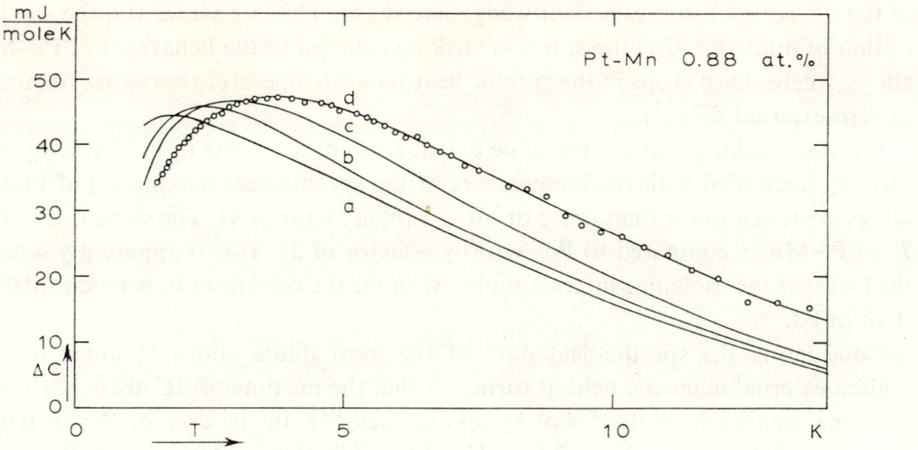

Fig. 5. *ΔC versus T* for Pt–Mn 0.88 at.%. a, b, c and d refer to $H = 0$, $H = 5.8$ kOe, $H = 11.6$ kOe and $H = 20.1$ kOe, respectively.

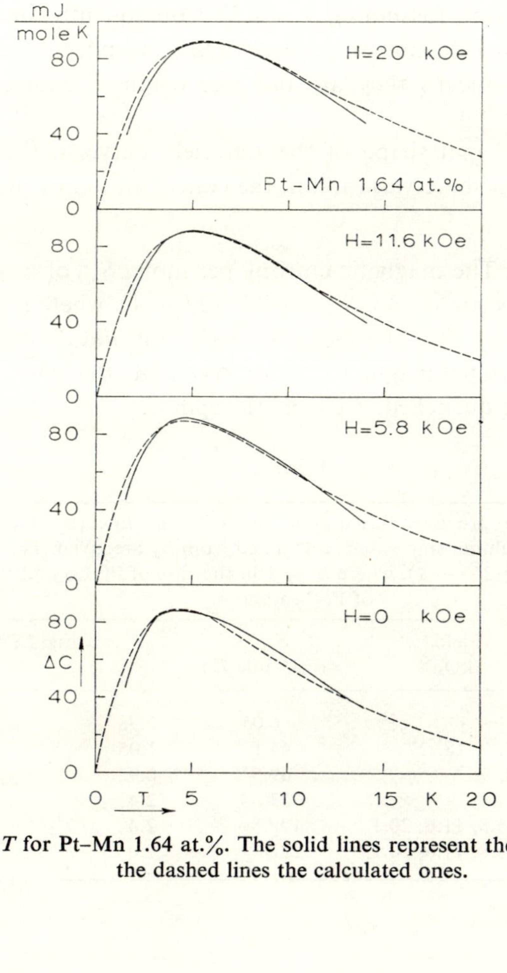

Fig. 6. *ΔC versus T* for Pt–Mn 1.64 at.%. The solid lines represent the experimental values and the dashed lines the calculated ones.

of the ΔC *versus* T curves is their wedge-like shape. This behaviour is quite similar to that of dilute Pd–Co alloys, but in striking contrast to the behaviour of Pd–Mn alloys, where sharp cusps in the specific heat *versus* temperature curve are obtained in zero external field[13]).

It is also striking that for the same cobalt concentration the transition temperature, T_c (identified with the temperature of the specific-heat maximum) of Pt–Co alloys are much lower than those of Pd–Co (by a factor of 4). The same is true for T_c of Pt–Mn as compared to Pd–Mn (by a factor of 2). This is apparently due to the fact that the exchange interaction between the d electrons in Pt is much smaller than in Pd.

Considering the specific-heat data of the most dilute alloys obtained at the highest external magnetic field, it turns out that the maxima of ΔC are much lower than the maximum of the Schottky specific heat[14]). In the case of Pt–Co 0.067 at.% the experimental value is 2.52 mJ/mol K, while the maximum of the Schottky specific heat is 3.55 mJ/mol K (assuming $S = 1$, see section 3). In the case of Pt–Mn 0.36 at.% the experimental value and the Schottky one are 20.8 mJ/mol K and 25.4 mJ/mol K, respectively (assuming $S = 2.5$). Consequently, one must conclude that the present systems do not obey the conditions under which the Schottky anomaly occurs; that means they are not free magnetic moments with equal magnitude (see ref. 2).

The somewhat abnormal shape of the zero-field curve in the case of Pt–Co 0.8 at.% may be due to some variation in the concentration of the specimen.

3. *Entropy and spin.* The magnetic entropy per mole, S_m, of a system consisting of cN magnetic carriers is given by $S_m = cR \ln (2J + 1)$, where c is the concentration of the solute atoms, R is the molar gas constant and J is the total angular momentum of an individual magnetic carrier. Assuming the orbital momentum of the solute atoms to be quenched, J equals the spin S.

TABLE I

In column 4 entropy values are given based upon measurements in external magnetic fields given in column 3. In the fifth column spin values calculated from S_m are given. The sixth column gives values for $\log(2S + 1)/\log(2S' + 1)$, where $S' = 1$ in the case of Pt–Co and $S' = 2.5$ in the case of Pt–Mn alloys.

Alloy	Conc. (at.%)	Field (kOe)	S_m (mJ/mole K)	S	$\log(2S + 1)/\log(2S' + 1)$ (%)
Pt–Co	0.067	27	6.05	0.98	98
	0.5	4.5, 9, 18, 27	44.1	1.05	105
	0.8	4.5, 9	69.5	0.92	92
Pt–Mn	0.36	27	53	2.4	99
	0.88	0, 5.8, 11.6, 20.1	129.5	2.4	99
	1.64	0, 5.8, 11.6, 20.1	222	2.0	91

The method used to obtain S_m from the experimental specific-heat data has been outlined in ref. 13. Entropy values obtained from measurements which allowed reasonably accurate estimates of the contributions outside the temperature range of the measurements are shown in table I. For the Pt–Co system a mean spin value $S = 1.0 \pm 0.05$ was calculated and for the two most dilute Pt–Mn alloys the value of S is 2.4. It is assumed that in the case of Pt–Mn 1.64 at.% the magnetic contribution to the entropy at relatively high temperatures can no longer be found by subtracting the specific heat of pure platinum from the total specific heat without introducing errors caused by a change in the lattice specific heat of platinum as a consequence of alloying. Therefore the value 2.0 of S, calculated from the measurements of the Pt–Mn 1.64 at.% is considered as less reliable. In the model calculations in section 4 a spin value of 2.5 for Pt–Mn has been assumed (since 2.5 is the half integral number which is closest to 2.4).

4. *Analysis of results*. Some numerical calculations have been performed of the specific heat of Pt–Mn 1.64 at.% and Pt–Co 0.8 at.%. The calculations are based upon the Weiss molecular-field (WMF) model, using a gaussian distribution of magnetic moments *via* a distribution of g values, giving the specific heat as a function of temperature at different applied magnetic fields. The relative width of the gaussian distribution of g values, F, and the ratio, p, of the external magnetic field and the molecular field at temperature $T = 0$ and H_{mol} (0) are adjustable parameters. A detailed description of this model is given in ref. 2. Here will be repeated only the argument for using a distribution in g values instead of a distribution in *e.g.* molecular-field constants. When no distribution in g values is incorporated the results of the WMF model for high external field (large p values) will approach the Schottky anomaly. This is, as already mentioned in section 2, not in agreement with the experiments where p values of the order of 3 and larger can easily be obtained for the most dilute alloys.

The fits to the specific-heat curves were made in the following way. The value of F is unambiguously determined by the value of the maximum of $\Delta C(T)$ obtained at zero external field. By adjusting the temperature of the maximum of the calculated curve to the one obtained from experiment a proper value of T_c was determined. From this point the values of T_c and F were kept constant and the ratio between p and H_{ex} was determined by adjusting the temperatures of the maxima of the calculated curves, so that they coincide with the temperatures obtained experimentally.

In fig. 3 the results of the calculations and the measurements for Pt–Co 0.8 at.% are shown. The values used for the parameters are: $S = 1$; $F = 0.7$; $T_c = 3.5$ K and for $H_{ex} = 4.5$ kOe : $p = 0.23$; for $H_{ex} = 9$ kOe : $p = 0.47$; for $H_{ex} = 18$ kOe : $p = 0.93$ and for $H_{ex} = 27$ kOe : $p = 1.4$. Using these parameters $H_{mol}(0)$ turns out to be 19.3 kOe and $g_0 = 4$, so that the magnetic moment of Co in Pt is $4\,\mu_B$. This value for the magnetic moment is close to 3.4 found by Bozorth *et al.*[15])

and Crangle and Scott[3]) from magnetization measurements.

In fig. 6 the results of the calculations and the experimental results for Pt–Mn 1.64 at.% are presented. The values used for the parameters are: $S = 2.5$; $F = 0.57$, $T_c = 5.5$ K and for $H_{ex} = 5.8$ kOe : $p = 0.05$; for $H_{ex} = 11.6$ kOe : $p = 0.115$ and for $H_{ex} = 20.1$ kOe : $p = 0.24$. As can be seen from the graphs the agreement between the measured and calculated results is unexpectedly good, considering the simplicity of the model. Part of the discrepancy for the curves obtained at zero external field must be due to the fact that the experimentally found spin value is 2.0 instead of the value 2.5 used in the model calculations. With respect to what is mentioned about this spin value in section 3 this fact should have its main influence on the high-temperature part of the curve. From the parameters used it follows that $g_0 = 0.85$ and $H_{mol}(0) = 83$ kOe so that for the magnetic moment of Mn in Pt a value of 2.6 μ_B is found. For comments on this surprisingly low moment see the next section.

5. *Discussion.* Unfortunately no microscopic theory exists which might account for the applicability of the WMF model to the excess specific heat of dilute Pt–Co and Pt–Mn alloys.

In ref. 2 a few probabilities have been suggested. It will be emphasized here that according to the specific heat of low-concentrated alloys obtained at high external fields a single impurity effect (like the Kondo effect or local spin fluctuations) is important. For it has been shown impossible[2]) to account for the wedge-shaped excess specific-heat curves with a model where only broadening effects in the interaction between the magnetic moments are taken into consideration (*e.g.* a distribution of molecular-field constants). Only when an effect connected with the magnetic moments themselves is incorporated in the model a description of the experimenttally obtained curves is possible. On the other hand one has to be careful with the results of the model calculations. For instance, the small moment of 2.6 μ_B for Mn in Pt is rather surprising. Until recently, no magnetization data were available on Pt–Mn alloys. Star[16]) measured the magnetization of the 1.64 at.% alloy and found that the ordering is not ferromagnetic but rather a mixture of ferro- and antiferromagnetism such as is observed in dilute Au–Fe and Cu–Mn alloys. This is consistent with the fact that Hansen and De Pater[17]) found a minimum in the electrical resistivity of a Pt–Mn 0.1 at.% alloy at about 0.36 K. The WMF model, assuming ferromagnetism, is therefore not applicable to the Pt–Mn system and the moment of Mn in Pt as predicted from the model calculations above should not be taken seriously. This can also be seen from a comparison between the experimentally obtained specific-heat curve for the Pt–Mn 0.36 at.% alloy obtained in an external field of 27 kOe. When the temperature of the maximum of this curve is compared with the calculations of Schottky a moment of 7 μ_B is found. (A distribution of g values has only a minor influence on the temperature of the maximum of the Schottky specific-heat curve.)

In view of the fact that specific-heat data on Pt–Mn are very well represented by the WMF-model calculations, even though the system is not ferromagnetic, one might raise some doubts as to the physical value of the model calculations for Pt–Co, Pd–Co and Pd–Fe[2]) and Pd–Mn[13]) alloys. The latter alloys are ferromagnetic, however, and the predicted moments are very close to the measured ones and do not depend on the concentration of the alloy analysed, so that in these cases the WMF-model calculations are believed to represent some essential physics.

A comparison between the deduced value for g_0 and the results of ferromagnetic resonance (Bagguley *et al.*[18])) and electron-spin resonance would not be useful because of the difference in experiments with respect to the influence of relaxation mechanisms of the localized moment.

Acknowledgements. The authors are very grateful to Dr. C. van Baarle for his stimulating interest during a main part of the measurements and to Dr. W. M. Star for sending his results of the magnetization measurements prior to publication and for the discussions on the analysis of the results; the authors also thank Mr. J. Turenhout and colleagues for their technical assistance, Dr. B. Knook and Mr. C. E. Snel for preparing the specimens and Mrs. M. A. Otten-Scholten (VS-L I) and Dr. H. A. Das (Reactor Centrum Nederland, Petten) for carrying out the analysis of the specimens.

This work is part of the research program of the "Stichting voor Fundamenteel Onderzoek der Materie (F.O.M.)" and has been made possible by financial support from the "Nederlandse Organisatie voor Zuiver Wetenschappelijk Onderzoek (Z.W.O.)" and from the "Nederlandse Centrale Organisatie voor Toegepast Natuurwetenschappelijk Onderzoek (Metaalinstituut T.N.O.)".

REFERENCES

1) Boerstoel, B. M., thesis Leiden, 1970.
2) Nieuwenhuys, G. J., Boerstoel, B. M., Zwart, J. J., Dokter, H. D. and Van den Berg, G. J., Physica **62** (1972) 278 (Commun. Kamerlingh Onnes Lab., Leiden No. 395 *c*).
3) Crangle, J. and Scott, W. R., J. appl. Phys. **36** (1965) 921.
4) Tsiovkin, Yu. N. and Volkenshteyn, N. V., Phys. Metals Metallog. (USSR) (English transl.) **19** (1965) 45.
5) Ericsson, T., Hirvonen, M. T., Katila, T. E. and Typpi, V. K., Solid State Commun. **8** (1970) 765.
6) Kobayashi, S. and Itoh, J., J. Phys. Soc. Japan **20** (1965) 1741.
7) Graham, L. D. and Schreiber, D. S., J. appl. Phys. **39** (1968) 963.
8) Wheeler, J. C. G., J. Phys. C. **2** (1969) 135.
9) Boerstoel, B. M. and Van Baarle, C., J. appl. Phys. **41** (1970) 1079.
10) Van Dam, J. E. and Van den Berg, G. J., Phys. Status solidi **A3** (1970) 11.
11) Boerstoel, B. M., Van Dissel, W. J. J. and Jacobs, M. B. M., Physica **38** (1968) 287 (Commun. Kamerlingh Onnes Lab., Leiden No. 363*a*).
12) Boerstoel, B. M., Zwart, J. J. and Hansen, J., Physica **54** (1971) 442 (Commun. Kamerlingh Onnes Lab., Leiden No. 385*c*).
13) Boerstoel, B. M., Zwart, J. J. and Hansen, J., Physica **57** (1972) 397 (Commun. Kamerlingh Onnes Lab., Leiden No. 388*b*).

14) Schottky, W., Phys. Z. **23** (1922) 448.
15) Bozorth, R. M., Davis, D. D. and Wernick, J. H., J. Phys. Soc. Japan **17**. Suppl. **B1** (1962) 112.
16) Star, W. M., private comm.
17) Hansen, J. and De Pater, C. J., Metalsgroup, Leiden (to be published).
18) Bagguley, D. M. S. and Robertson, J. A., Phys. Letters **27A** (1968) 516.

Physica **69** (1973) 129–135 © *North-Holland Publishing Co.*

A PULSED MAGNETIC FIELD OF HALF A MILLION OERSTEDS DURING 17.5 MILLISECONDS

H. A. JORDAAN, R. WOLF and D. DE KLERK

Kamerlingh Onnes Laboratorium der Rijksuniversiteit te Leiden, Nederland

(Communication No. 403*c*)

Received 5 June 1973

Synopsis

A pulsed magnetic field of 517 kOe with a duration of 17.5 milliseconds was obtained by discharging a condenser bank of 0.03 F, 3.5 kV through an air core coil with an inner diameter of 2 cm. The coil was wound from rectangular annealed copper wire and surrounded by a stainless-steel cylinder with a wall thickness of 2.5 cm. The accuracy of the field measurement was about one per cent.

1. *Introduction.* Until now the only method to produce magnetic fields well over 250 kOe is the pulse technique. A large amount of energy is stored and then suddenly discharged through a coil. Several methods have been used for the energy storage[1,2]). Kapitza, about half a century ago[3,4,5]), used a storage battery and, later, a motor generator which was suddenly short-circuited over the coil. At present the standard method is to make use of a large condenser battery. Only at the University of Amsterdam strong pulses are obtained directly from the city power plant[6]).

The shorter the pulse time and the smaller the field space the higher the field values that can be reached. The upper limit is set by destruction of the coil due to the Lorentz forces. Copper coils must be strongly reinforced and for very high fields copper beryllium alloys have been applied as winding materials[7,8]). Fields of the order of 750 kOe with a duration of 120 μs have been made in this way. Fields well over a megaoersted have only been produced with flux concentration techniques, the duration being a few microseconds. A detailed description with many references was given by Knoepfel[9]).

2. *The capacitor bank.* Our capacitor bank consists of 45 condensers, 660 μF each. It is divided into nine sections of five condensers, each section being operated by a separate switching device. A simplified circuit diagram is shown in fig. 1.

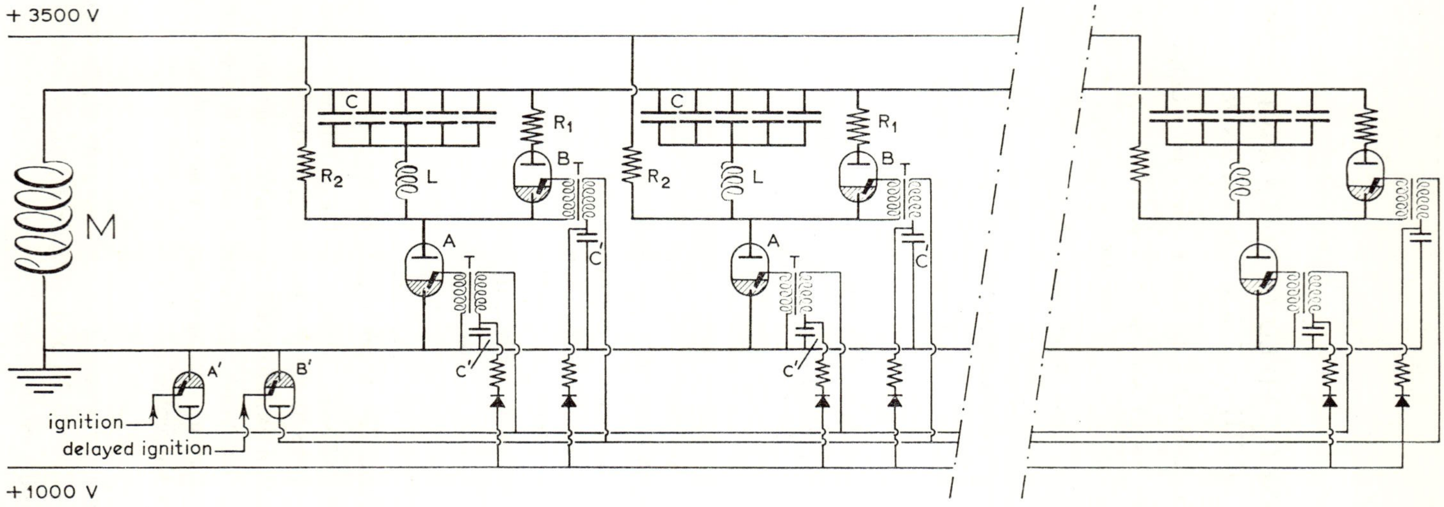

Fig. 1. 180 kJ condenser bank, consisting of nine sections, three of which are shown. M magnet coil; C main condensers; L chokes; A primary ignitrons, PL 5552A; B secondary ignitrons, PL 5552A; R_1 energy dissipating resistors, 1 Ω; R_2 charging resistors, 450 Ω; A′ auxiliary ignitron, PL 5551A; B′ auxiliary ignitron, PL 5551A; T pulse transformers; c′ primary ignition condensers, 1 μF; C′ secundary ignition condensers, 1 μF.

The maximum voltage is 3500 V, corresponding to an energy of 180 kJ. The condensers can be charged to full energy in about 10 s by means of a rectifier setup whose charging current (0–15 A) and upper voltage can be preset.

The discharge through the magnet coil (M in fig. 1) has approximately a half-sine shape, the discharge time being of the order of 20 ms. After charging the condensers the sections of the bank are discharged in parallel. The pulse is started by firing the ignitron A′ of fig. 1. This discharges the auxiliary 1000 V condensers c′ which, through the intermediate of the pulse transformers T, fire the nine primary ignitrons A. Just after the end of the pulse (when the voltage of the condensers is reversed) the auxiliary ignitron B′ is fired with the help of a delay circuit. This discharges the condensers C′ and fires the secondary ignitrons B which dissipate the condenser energy in the resistors R_1. This procedure prevents oscillations (and voltage doubling) between the sections of the condenser bank in case one of the A ignitrons might back-fire. Special circuits have been installed which indicate whether all the ignitrons have fired or not. More detailed descriptions of the installation and the operation have been given elsewhere[10, 11]).

Three magnet stations are available, two for experiments and one for testing new coils. Special arrangements have been made which make it impossible that two stations are connected simultaneously to the capacitor bank.

3. *The magnet coils.* Usually the inner diameter of our coils is about 2 cm, the outer diameter is of the order of 6 cm and the length is about 9 cm. The coils are operated at liquid-nitrogen temperature.

The cross section of a coil is shown in fig. 2. Our coils are wound from rectangular annealed copper wire, 3.4 × 1.6 mm and they are surrounded with a stainless-steel cylinder of 2.5 cm wall thickness. Older coils were reinforced with fibre glass and sometimes an extra steel cylinder between the layers. This system has been abandoned since the fibre glass was too brittle and the internal stainless-steel cylinder resulted into a considerable field loss and an increase in cooling time after the pulse.

After the winding our coils are vacuum-impregnated with araldite and before the hardening starts an air pressure of about 8 atm is applied in order to avoid small holes in the impregnation. It was found that araldite sticks better to the isolation of the copper than the isolation does to the wire. This has given rise to premature burn out of magnet coils and recently we have reimpregnated our coils from time to time with transformer oil. This has given considerable improvement.

New coils are trained with a series of pulses of increasing strength. During the higher pulses the coil and the stainless-steel cylinder are noticeably deformed, giving rise to a barrel shape as is clearly demonstrated by fig. 3. The right-hand coil has not yet been operated at high fields, the left-hand one has produced a series of fields well over 400 kOe. Sometimes the increase of the inner diameter was as much as 6 mm. The relative increase of the circumference of the inner turns

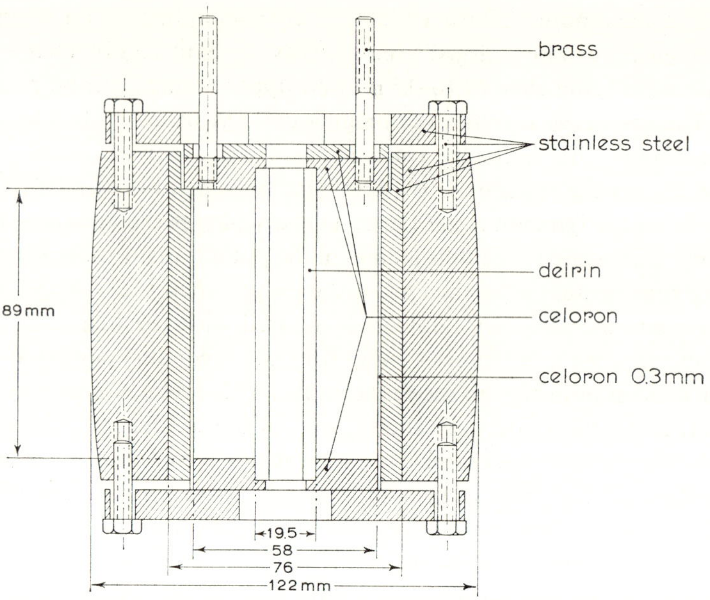

Fig. 2. Cross section of the 500 kOe magnet coil. The delrin core is removed after a number of pulses.

Fig. 3. Magnet coils; the right-hand coil has been operated in low fields only, the left-hand coil has been operated well above 400 kOe.

is appreciably larger than that of the outer ones. If a coil, after operation, is cut through radially it appears that the cross-section area of the central wires may have decreased by about 20 per cent.

A new coil is wound on a delrin cylinder (visible in fig. 2). After some pulses it is of no use any more and it is removed from the coil, giving rise to a useful increase of the experimental space.

Since the deformation of the stainless-steel mantle takes place at liquid-nitrogen temperature it results into appreciable work hardening. This has lead to the following fabrication procedure. A fourteen-layer coil (pulse time 25 ms) was constructed and pulsed up to about 430 kOe. After appreciable deformation of the stainless-steel cylinder the coil was removed. The inside of the cylinder was rebored on a lathe and an extra steel cylinder with a wall thickness of several millimeters was shrunk into the original one. Finally a new twelve layer coil (pulse time 17 ms) was mounted. This is illustrated in fig. 2. In this way our highest field values have been obtained.

After each pulse the resistance of the coil is measured, from which the course of the temperature during the cooling is derived. The impedance is found from the oscillating time of the coil connected to a condenser. This gives a qualitative indication of the deformation.

The field intensity is measured with the help of a pick-up coil mounted inside the magnet. It is connected to an integrating circuit and the peak value is registered on a digital voltmeter. The system is calibrated by means of the Faraday effect (magnetic rotation of the plane of polarization) in a flint-glass cylinder which, in turn, is calibrated in a 100 kOe superconducting coil[12]) by comparing it with proton resonance. The final accuracy is about one per cent.

Up to the highest fields the field intensity is almost linear with the magnet current (fig. 4a) and very little phase shift is observed between the field and the current. On the other hand, a pronounced saturation effect is observed if the field is plotted against the condenser voltage (fig. 4b). At the very highest fields the maximum field intensity does not increase any more with increasing voltage.

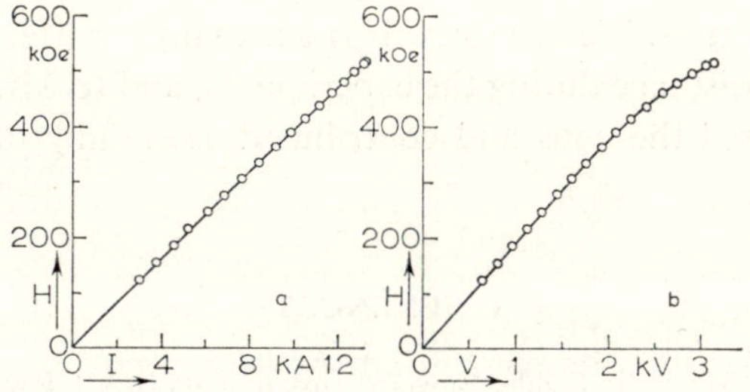

Fig. 4. a. Magnetic field *versus* the current. b. Magnetic field *versus* the condenser voltage.

Two explanations are possible: (a) the field per unit current decreases due to the coil deformation; (b) the increase in resistance during the pulse gives rise to such a decrease of the quality factor that all the extra energy goes into heating. The first possibility is ruled out because the field remains practically proportional to the current. The second possibility is corroborated by the fact that, for very large pulses, the course of the field with time shows a noticeable "tail", so that the curve deviates strongly from a half-sine.

This is illustrated in fig. 5 which represents a field pulse of over half a million oersteds (517 kOe), which was recently achieved. The dimensions of the magnet are those of fig. 2. The coil has 325 turns in 12 layers. The total pulse time was 17.5 ms, the maximum current 13.2 kA and the initial condenser voltage 3.12 kV.

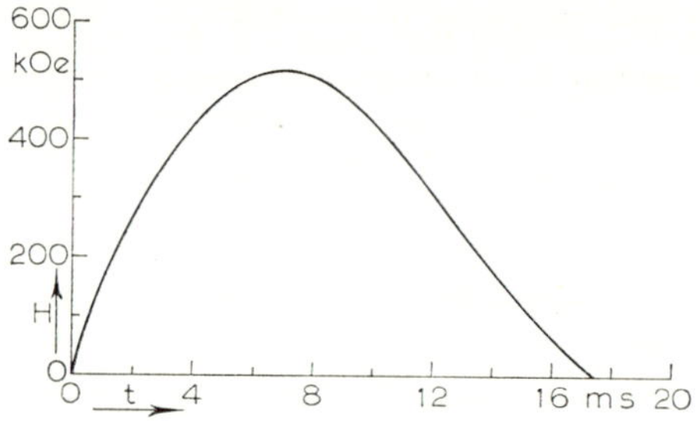

Fig. 5. 517 kOe field pulse.

For pulses up to 80 per cent of the maximum the field intensity was a reproducible function of the condenser voltage (within one per cent) and no alterations in the impedance were observed. At this level the coil seems to be stable and the life time is expected to be very long, certainly several hundred pulses.

The highest field values seem to be unique for this pulse duration and they are considerably higher than what is expected from theoretical considerations[13,14]). After such a pulse the coil was at room temperature but, mainly due to the good thermal contact between the liquid nitrogen and the inner turns, the cooling time was less than ten minutes, making a fast repetition rate of pulses possible.

Acknowledgements. We like to express our thanks to Messrs. R. Harten and J. J. M. Peters for assistance during the experiments, and to Mr. T. P. M. van den Burg, who constructed the coils and contributed essentially to the development of the magnets.

REFERENCES

1) De Klerk, D., High Magnetic Fields, Newport Instruments Ltd. (Newport Pagnell, 1965).
2) De Klerk, D., Bull. Belg. Phys. Soc., Ser. V, no. 2–3 (1966) 152.
3) Kapitza, P. L., Proc. Roy. Soc., London, **A105** (1924) 691.

4) Kapitza, P. L. and Skinner, W. H. B., Proc. Roy. Soc., London **A109** (1925) 224.
5) Kapitza, P. L., Proc. Roy. Soc., London **A115** (1927) 658.
6) Roeland, L. W., Muller, F. A. and Gersdorf, R., Proc. Conf. High Magnetic Fields, Nottingham, 1969, p. 153.
7) Foner, S. and Fisher, W. G., Rev. sci. Instrum. **38** (1967) 440.
8) Furth, H. P., Levine, M. A. and Waniek, R. W., Rev. sci. Instrum. **28**(1957) 949.
9) Knoepfel, H., Pulsed High Magnetic Fields, North-Holland Publ. Comp. (Amsterdam – London, 1970).
10) Van der Sluys, J. C. A., De Beun, H. R., Zweers, B. A. and De Klerk, D., Bull. Belg. Phys. Soc. Ser. V, no. 2–3 (1966) 165.
11) Van der Sluys, J. C. A., Thesis, Leiden, 1967.
12) Metselaar, J. W., Jordaan, H. A., Schutter, J. W. and De Klerk, D., Cryogenics **10** (1970) 220 (Commun. Kamerlingh Onnes Lab., Leiden No. 378*c*).
13) Melville, D. and Mattocks, P. G., J. Phys. D, Appl. Phys. **5** (1972) 1745.
14) Gersdorf, R., Muller, F. A. and Roeland, L. W., Rev. sci. Instrum. **38** (1965) 1100.

Physica **69** (1973) 136–140 © *North-Holland Publishing Co.*

OPTICAL OBSERVATIONS OF SECOND SOUND IN LIQUID HELIUM II

J. L. OLSEN

Laboratorium für Festkörperphysik, Eidgenössische Technische Hochschule, Zurich, Switzerland *

Received 9 April 1973

Synopsis

A Schlieren method has been used to observe the deformation of the free surface of liquid helium II caused by standing waves of second sound within the liquid. Results for a cylindrical cavity excited thermally on its axis are shown.

1. *Introduction*. Although the existence and properties of second-sound waves in superfluid helium have been well established and explored, it is still of interest to make such waves visible. This would be a first step towards the realization of a new kind of holography using second sound[1]).

Optical observations have been made by Jacucci *et al.*[2, 3]) showing that a laser beam can be diffracted by a continuous beam of second sound, and Goulayaev[4, 5]) has shown that a second-sound pulse can be made visible by a Schlieren method.

For holography patterns of waves are required, but so far no such observations have been reported. It therefore seemed useful to study the possibility of seeing or photographing wave patterns.

In this note we describe the use of a Schlieren technique to observe the very slight waves created on a free helium II surface by the propagation of second sound within the liquid[6]). The results shown here were obtained from standing-wave patterns in a cylindrical second-sound resonator.

2. *Experimental method*. Landau[7]) has pointed out that within the framework of the two-fluid model for helium II there exists an equivalent of the Bernoulli equation:

$$p + (\rho_n + \rho_s)gz + \tfrac{1}{2}(\rho_n v_n^2 + \rho_s v_s^2) = \text{const},$$

where p is the pressure, z the height, and ρ_n, ρ_s, v_n and v_s are respectively the

* The writing of this paper was completed during a visit to the Technion, Haifa, Israel.

densities and velocities of the normal and superfluid components of the liquid. Pellam[8]) has made use of a pitot tube to show the pressure differences in a resonant cavity predicted by this equation[9]).

At the free surface of a liquid p is approximately constant so that we may expect slight variations in surface height, z, associated with the propagation of second sound parallel to the surface. Obviously

$$z = z_0 - (\rho_n v_n^2 + \rho_s v_s^2)(2\rho g)^{-1}.$$

We may use the relation[10, 11])

$$(\rho_n v_n^2 + \rho_s v_s^2) = W^2(c_2^2 \rho C T)^{-1}$$

to relate the kinetic energy of the liquid to the heat flux, W, per unit area. Here c_2 is the velocity of second sound, ρ the total density, C the specific heat, and T the temperature of the helium. Then

$$z = z_0 - W^2(2\rho^2 c_2^2 CgT)^{-1}.$$

A typical case might be a heat current of 10^{-1} W cm^{-2} at 1.5 K, and we should then expect a wave height of 4×10^{-4} cm.

The arrangement used in our experiments is shown schematically in fig. 1. This consists of a metal cylinder, M, with a vertical axis closed at top and bottom by

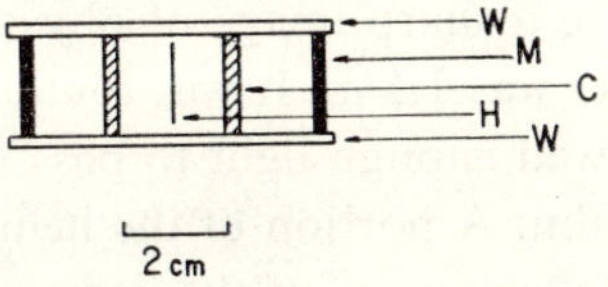

Fig. 1. Vertical section of helium chamber and resonant cavity.

glass windows, W. The metal sides were cooled by an external helium bath, and the container could be filled to any desired level with liquid helium. Within this container a vertical cylindrical cavity, C, made of plexiglass and fitting tightly between upper and lower windows was placed. Access between inner cavity and the main container was provided by two small holes in the wall of the cavity.

Thermal waves were generated by alternating-current heating of a vertical wire, H, on the axis of the cavity. Excess normal fluid could leave through the holes in the wall and be replaced by superfluid.

The free surface of the liquid was observed using the Schlieren system indicated in fig. 2. Light from the source, L, was focussed on an aperture, A, and traversed the helium chamber to be reflected at the spherical mirror, S. With a horizontal helium surface the image of A was at A′ where a small obstacle, O, prevented the light from entering the camera, C. A typical light beam is shown as a full line in fig. 2. Light crossing a sloping portion of the helium surface (see dashed line) is returned on a path not intersecting the obstacle, and could thus enter the camera,

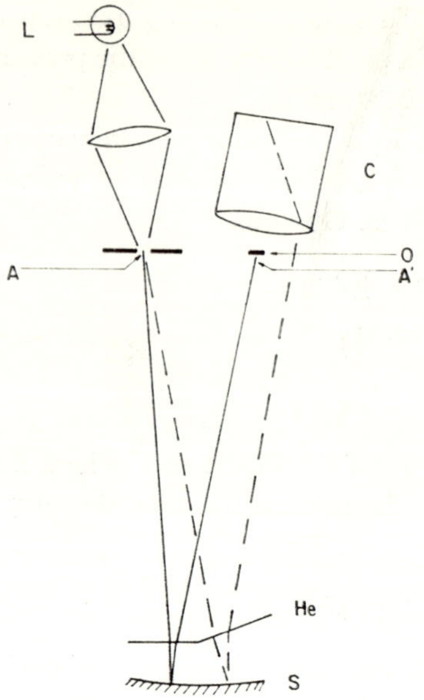

Fig. 2. Schlieren arrangement. Light ray falling on horizontal helium surface is drawn full. Ray falling on sloping surface is shown dashed.

C, which was focussed to give a sharp image of objects in the helium chamber. The light path, l, from S to O was 1.5 m. It was found that a deflection, d, of the image by about 0.5 mm allowed enough light to pass the obstacle to give a good photographic image on the film. A portion of the helium surface with a slope, α, from the horizontal gave a deflection, d, of the beam:

$$d = 2l\alpha(n - 1),$$

where n is the index of refraction of the helium. Thus areas with a slope of $\alpha \simeq 5 \times 10^{-3}$ showed up brightly in the camera, and differences in slope of 10^{-3} could just be observed.

3. *Results*. On heating with alternating current of frequency, f, it was found that at certain frequencies a standing-wave pattern could be observed. A number of typical patterns are shown in fig. 3.

A slight detuning made the wave systems disappear indicating an effective Q for the cavity of approximately $Q \simeq 30$. With the present arrangement a total heat input of ca. 1 watt was required to make the waves easily visible while an increase of some 20 % beyond this value led to boiling in the cavity.

Standing wave patterns could be seen at a range of frequencies from ca. 900 Hz to 7000 Hz. The exposure times used lay between 1/30 and 1/125 s so that the observations in fig. 3 do indeed correspond to standing-wave effects. Figs. 3a and

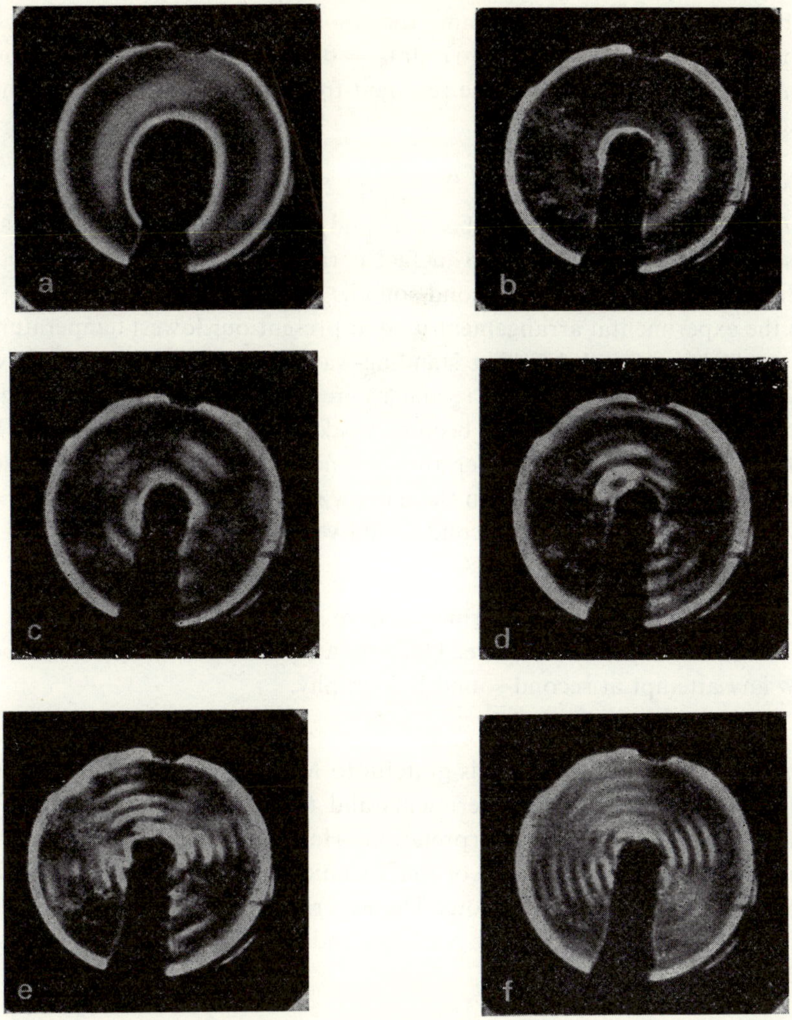

Fig. 3. Photographs of standing-wave patterns at different frequencies, f, of the heater current. a) $f = 1180$ Hz, b) $f = 1660$ Hz; c) $f = 2150$ Hz, d) $f = 3910$ Hz; e) $f = 5200$ Hz, f) $f = 5720$ Hz. The diameter of the cavity is 2 cm.

3b arise from purely radical modes while the patterns 3c, 3d, 3e and 3f are somewhat more complicated.

It should be noted that the dark portions of the figures come from areas where the surface is horizontal. It is easily shown that in our standing-wave system this is the case where

$$dT/dr = 0 \quad \text{or} \quad d^2T/dr^2 = 0.$$

Clearly then the distance between the dark rings is about a quarter of a wavelength.

The boundary conditions determine the resonant frequencies. At the cylinder wall where $r = R$ we must have $(\mathrm{d}T/\mathrm{d}r)_R = 0$ since there is no heat transport through the plexiglass cylinder. The resonant frequencies are then determined by the condition

$$\mathrm{d}J_n(z)/\mathrm{d}z = 0, \quad \text{with } z = 4\pi f R/c_2$$

where J_n are Bessel functions of the first kind of order n. It is found that the resonance frequencies observed do in fact correspond to the observed patterns being due to standing waves of second sound.

With the experimental arrangement used at present our lowest temperature that can be reached is about 1.4 K. The standing-wave patterns are most easily visible at the lowest temperatures where v_s and v_n are largest for a given heat current. At higher temperatures the waves become weaker and disappear at about 1.7 K. Careful determinations of the temperature dependence of the resonance frequencies as a function of temperature within the narrow range of observation are in agreement with this slight change of second-sound velocity in this interval.

4. *Discussion.* The present experiments have shown that it is possible to make second-sound wave patterns visible. Unfortunately the sensitivity is still too low to allow any attempt at second-sound holography.

Acknowledgements. The author is grateful to Mr. P. Caminada for his untiring and effective help with these experiments and to Professor I. Rudnick for an interesting discussion of their interpretation. He is also grateful to Professor Y. Eckstein and the Physics Institute of the Technion in Haifa for their kind hospitality during the writing of this note. The experimental equipment was provided by a grant from the Schweizerische Nationalfonds zur Förderung der wissenschaftlichen Forschung.

REFERENCES

1) Lucosz, W., J. low Temp. Phys. **1** (1969) 407.
2) Jacucci, G. and Signorelli, G., Phys. Letters **26A** (1967) 5.
3) Consolo, S., Grillo, G. and Jacucci, J., Proc. 12th Int. Conf. Low Tempt. Physics, Kyoto 1970, ed. K. Kanda, Academic Press Japan (1971) p. 49.
4) Goulayaev, A. I., JETP Letters **5** (1967) 325.
5) Goulayaev, A. I., Zh. eksper. teor. Fiz (USSR) **57** (1969) 59.
6) Olsen, J. L., Helv. Phys. Acta **46** (1973) 35.
7) Landau, L. D., J. Phys. Moscow **5** (1941) 71.
8) Pellam, J. R., Phys. Rev. **78** (1950) 818.
9) Rudnick, I., Private cummunication, has suggested that further terms should be included but we may use this expression for an order of magnitude estimate of the effect.
10) Wilks, J., Liquid and solid Helium, Oxford University Press (Oxford, 1964) p. 66.
11) London, F., Superfluids, Vol. II, Wiley (New York, 1954) p. 79.

Physica **69** (1973) 141–147 © *North-Holland Publishing Co.*

MEASUREMENTS OF THE SURFACE TENSION IN HELIUM BY MEANS OF SURFACE WAVES

S. T. BOLDAREV and V. P. PESHKOV

Institute for Physical Problems, Academy of Sciences of the USSR, Moscow, USSR

Received 25 April 1973

Synopsis

A new method of exiting capillary-gravitational waves is suggested. This method causes a minimum overheating of the liquid. The surface-tension coefficients of ^{4}He and ^{3}He on the liquid–vapour interface are determined over a wide temperature range by measurements of the surface wavelengths. The results are in good agreement with data of other authors. The surface-tension coefficient of the interface between the two liquid phases of a ^{3}He–^{4}He mixture was also measured; it appeared to increase monotonically from 0.007 to 0.014 erg/cm^2 as the temperature decreases from 0.68 to 0.42 K.

The investigation of properties of a two-dimensional Fermi system formed by ^{3}He atoms on the dilute solutions of ^{3}He in ^{4}He surface[1,2]) requires a rather precise determination of the surface-tension coefficient at low temperatures. For this purpose one usually measures the capillary ascent of the liquid in a capillary tube or in the narrow gap between the plates of a condenser, the capacitance of which depends on the height of the liquid rise. In both cases it is necessary to ensure the establishment of a strictly constant temperature along a very thin (≈ 0.1 mm) layer of liquid, bounded by solid walls. The presence of even insignificant heat flows can evoke in that layer appreciable temperature and concentration gradients. Highly uncomfortable is also a long time delay of heat equilibrium in the bulk of the liquid and between the liquid and the walls. More reliable seems the capillary-waves method, which allows one to perform measurements on an undisturbed surface of a rather great volume of liquid. However, by exciting surface waves some part of the energy of the exciter is usually dissipated (turns into sound, dissipates into viscous friction, *etc.*); these losses may disturb the equilibrium in the liquid because of a low heat conductivity in solutions and the existence of thermoosmosis. For this reason the method of generation is particularly important. Atkins *et al.*[3,4]) used for surface-wave excitation a pulse infrared radiation focused as a thin strip on the liquid surface. A part of the liquid was considered to be evaporated by the radiation effect giving in such a way periodic distortions of the surface. It is obvious, however, that in this case the liquid helium was overheated and rather intensive second sound must be radiated. In solutions such a radiation source is unsuitable. King and Wyatt[5]) have excited surface waves by means of mechanical vibrations of a cylinder with the lower end submerged at considerable depth in the liquid. The standing-waves pattern was observed through the transparent wall of the cylinder and the corresponding frequency was measured. This method demands the presence of a rather powerful swing system for the cylinder and is limited in frequency; besides, losses to first-sound radiation and to viscous friction are inevitable.

We succeeded in making a source of surface waves almost free from background radiation. It allowed us to apply it to a wide range of temperatures and concentrations both on the vapour–liquid interface and on the stratification boundary of two liquid phases of a ^{3}He–^{4}He mixture. The operation was based on the effect of subjecting the dielectric (liquid helium) to an electric field. The exciter (1, fig. 1)

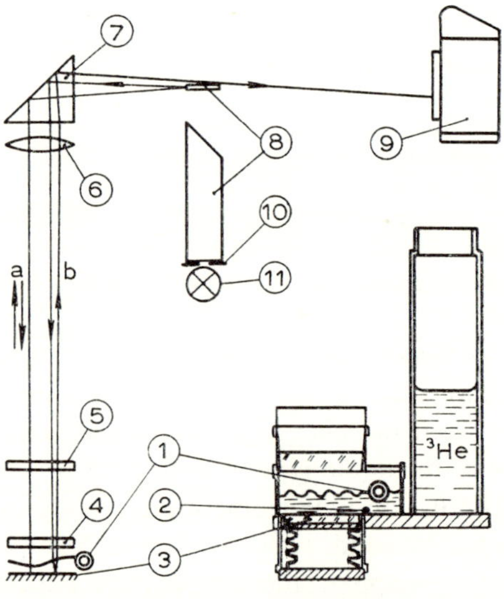

Fig. 1. Optical scheme of the device and layout of the lower part of the device: 1) exciter of surface waves; 2) thermometer; 3) mirror; 4) optical window in cover of cell; 5) light filter; 6) lens ($f = 40$ cm); 7, 8) total internal reflection prisms; 9) camera; 10) diaphragm; 11) light source.

was a piece of glass tube (Ø 5 mm, length 11 mm) with two copper wires of 20 μm in diameter wound around it, each forming a coil in the same layer. The tube was partially immersed into the liquid (the axis was parallel to the surface). The putting on of the voltage between the neighbouring coils gave rise to strong electric fields located in a thin layer with a thickness of the order of the coil step. At the places where the liquid surface touched the coil the application of the electric field caused an additional ascent of some mass of the liquid. The application of the alternating voltage between the wires evoked periodic ascents and descents of the liquid in a layer adjacent to the side with doubled frequency. The small thickness of the region in which the generation of surface vibrations took place ensured getting sufficiently short surface waves, the frequency of which could easily be regulated by means of a change of the generator frequency.

The wave pattern in the cell was observed through the transparent upper cover using a dark-field method. Fig. 1 shows the optical scheme of the device; in the right lower corner the arrangement of the measuring cell is shown. The cooling of the cell was carried out through its copper bottom, common with the bottom of the ^{3}He evaporation bath. The temperature was measured with a thermometer made out of 30 μm phosphor bronze wire 2, calibrated with the ^{3}He vapour pressure. Mirror 3 was attached to a bellow, soldered to the bottom of the cell; it allowed one to adjust the inclination of the mirror. The plate–parallel window 4 was glued vacuum tight into the cover of the cell. The light filter 5 was in thermal contact with the helium bath and was used for absorption of infrared radiation going from the upper part of the device through the optical tube. Lens 6 and the total internal-reflection prism 7 were arranged on the cap. Prism 8 of 1 mm in thickness was in the focal plane of lens 6; it served as a diaphragm for incoming light and simultaneously as a screen for the nondeflected part of the reflected light (ray a). Light, deflected on the non-horizontal helium surface (ray b) passed above or under prism 8 and got into camera 9. At the position of exact tuning, of the dark field the horizontal regions of the liquid's surface looked as dark strips and the nonhorizontal as bright ones; the distance between two neighbouring dark strips was in this case equal to half the wavelength. However, when operating with travelling waves it appeared convenient to double the period of the picture by means of shutting the light from above (or below) prism 8; in practice this was reached by moving the prism 8

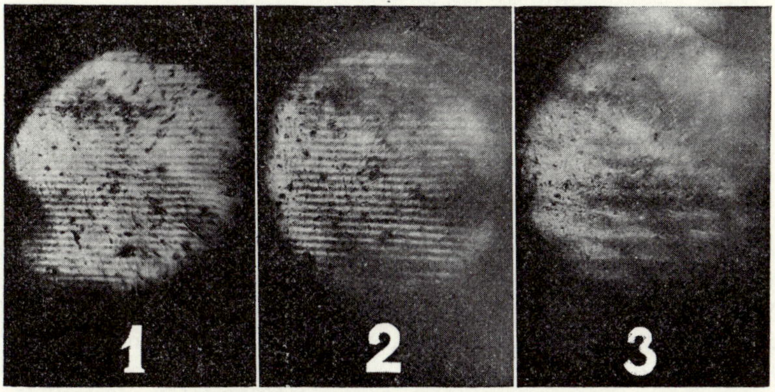

Fig. 2. Photographs of travelling wave in the cell: 1) ^{4}He, 500 Hz, 1.9 K; 2) ^{3}He, 400 Hz, 0.60 K; 3) stratification boundary, 22.2 Hz, 0.48 K.

slightly up (or down) the optical axis. The observation could be visual (standing waves at continuous lighting or travelling waves at stroboscopic) or photographic using a flash lamp. Photographs of the wave picture in the cell are presented in fig. 2. The period of the picture is here equal to the wavelength.

The surface-tension coefficient α has been derived from the classical formula

$$\omega^2 = \frac{\alpha}{\rho_1 + \rho_2} k^3 + g \frac{\rho_1 - \rho_2}{\rho_1 + \rho_2} k, \tag{1}$$

where $\omega = 2\pi\nu$, ν and k are frequency and reciprocal wavelength, ρ_1 and ρ_2 are the densities of the lower and upper phases, g is the gravity acceleration. As it was shown by Khalatnikov[6]) this formula holds its validity in two-fluid hydrodynamics too; it has been confirmed experimentally for ^4He[4, 5]) at frequencies up to 65 Hz. We succeeded in investigations over a much wider frequency range. There were no deviations from formula (1). Fig. 3 shows the dependence of ω on k at temperatures close to 1.3 K. Closed circles indicate the results which were obtained in one of the earlier experiments by a resonant method. There frequencies were measured of standing surface waves between the source and plane reflector.

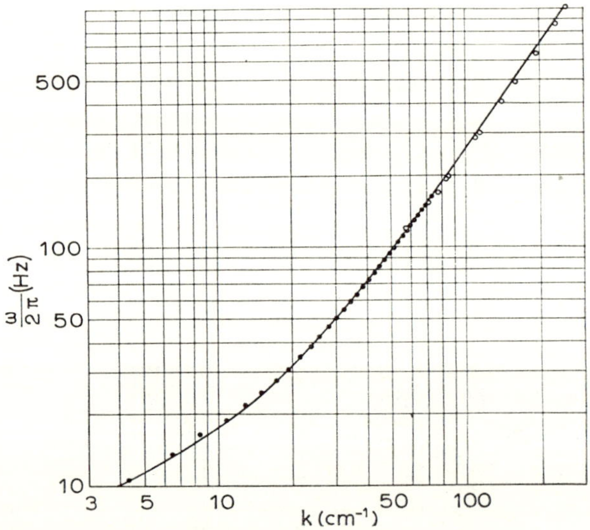

Fig. 3. Dispersion of surface waves on liquid ^4He ($T = 1.3$ K): close circles, standing waves; open circles, progressive waves; solid line, eq. (1).

33 successive resonances were found from 10.2 to 162 Hz; at higher frequencies we failed to get a resonant picture, apparently because of strong absorption at the reflector. The number of resonance necessary for calculations of k was easily obtained from the first set of points (lowest frequencies). The effective resonator length appeared to be slightly longer than the distance between exciter and re-

flector; it was taken in such a way to put the last point (162 Hz) on the theoretical curve. The theoretical dependence (1) with $\alpha = 0.361$ erg/cm^2 (Zinov'eva and Boldarev[2]) is shown in fig. 3 as a solid line. Open circles correspond to the data obtained by photographing of the travelling waves with flash-lamp lighting.

The method described was used for the investigation of the temperature dependence of the surface-tension coefficients of the pure helium isotopes. Measurements were performed at frequencies of 500 and 600 Hz for ^{4}He and 300, 400 and 500 Hz for ^{3}He by photographing the travelling waves. No special precautions for decreasing the reflection of the waves at the sides of the cell were undertaken. This did not allow us to get reliable results in ^{4}He at temperatures below 0.8–0.9 K where a strong interference of reflected waves prevented us from performing measurements. The results obtained are presented in fig. 4 as closed circles. The accuracy of the α data is about 3%. For comparison, the data of other authors are shown as solid lines. These were obtained by a capillary-rise method (curves 1, 3, 4) and by an estrangement method (curve 2).

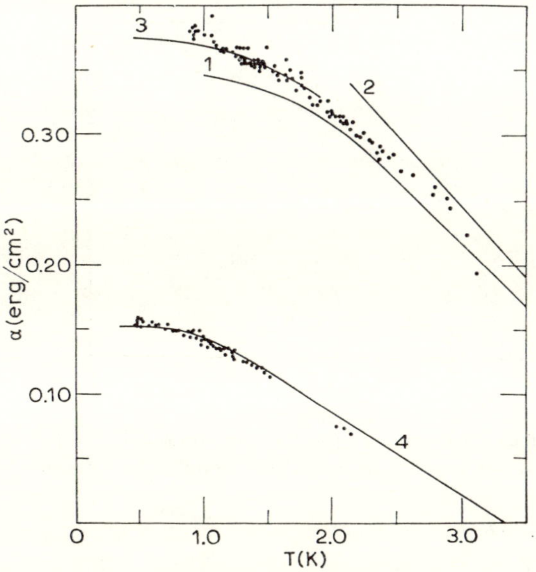

Fig. 4. Surface tension of pure liquid helium isotopes: points, data of present work; curves, after the data of: 1) Allen and Misener [7]; 2) Devaraj and Hollis Hallett [8]; 3) Zinov'eva and Boldarev [2]; 4) Zinov'eva [9].

The question of the value of the surface tension at the separation boundary of the two liquid phases of ^{3}He–^{4}He mixtures was up to the present time not elucidated. In the work of Dickson, Caroline and Mendoza[10]) the temperature dependence of curve $\alpha(T)$ was investigated in the range of 0.33–0.68 K. Guo, Edwards, Sarwinski and Tough[8]) presented values only at three temperatures (0.079, 0.219 and 0.515 K) and their value ($\alpha = 0.011 \pm 0.003$ erg/cm^2) at 0.515 K was 8 times lower than that given in ref. 10. In both cases the method of capillary ascent between capacitor plates was used. We carried out corresponding measurements by means of the surface-waves method in the temperature range between 0.42 and 0.68 K. Special difficulties arose in these measurements because of the proximity of the dielectric constants and the refraction of both phases which reduced the excitation efficiency and the contrast of the picture. (A good idea about that is given by the third photograph in fig. 2.) For this reason we succeeded in getting results only in a very narrow frequency range (from 16.7 up to 40 Hz) and at temperatures below 0.685 K. The accuracy of the data depended mainly on the accuracy in wavelength definition which did not exceed 5–6 % in this case; as a result the error in the determination of α could amount up to 20 %. First of all we have checked the validity of the common dispersion law (1) for waves on the boundary between the two liquid-helium mixture phases. In fig. 5 the experimental dependence is presented between frequency and reciprocal wavelength in $\omega^2/k^3(k^{-2})$ coordinates (open circles). In these coordinates eq. (1) gives a straight

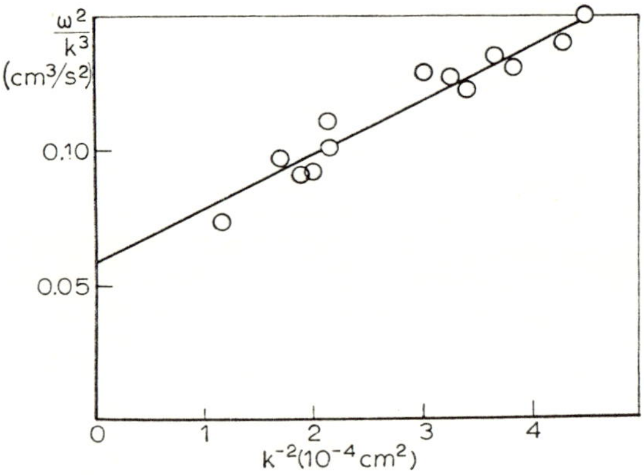

Fig. 5. Dispersion of surface waves on the ^3He–^4He mixture separation boundary, $T = 0.46 \pm 0.01$ K. Open circles, experimental; straight line, eq. (1).

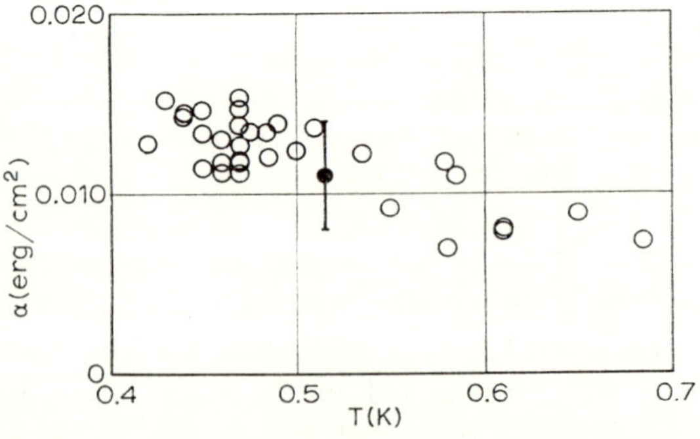

Fig. 6. Surface tension on mixture separation boundary (closed circle, after Guo *et al.* [11]).

line (solid line); its slope depends only on phase densities and the segment cut off on the ordinate axis is equal to $\alpha/(\rho_1+\rho_2)$. The points presented on the diagram are taken from different experiments and correspond to temperatures 0.45, 0.46 and 0.47 K; the straight line is given by eq. (1) with $\alpha = 0.013$ erg/cm^2 and phase densities corresponding to the appropriate temperature are substituted. Fig. 6 shows the temperature dependence of the surface-tension coefficient between the liquid phases of the mixture. Most of the points are taken at frequencies 22 and 30 Hz. Within the temperature interval considered the surface tension changes twice. Despite a rather large scattering a monotonic rise of α at decreasing temperature is distinctly visible. The comparison with the previous data confirms the correctness of the value $\alpha = 0.011 \pm 0.003$ erg/cm^2 at 0.515 K by Guo *et al.*[11]) (closed circle in fig. 6). The data of Dickson *et al.*[10]) who observed in the same temperature region an increase of the surface-tension coefficient of almost a factor 10 are apparently incorrect.

In conclusion we would like to note that the suggested method of surface-waves excitation is most convenient and may be used succesfully in any dielectric liquid. The precision of the surface-tension measurements can be increased; we intend to achieve it in the future by means of some modification in the design of the optical system.

REFERENCES

1) Andreev, A. F., Zh. eksper. teor. Fiz. **50** (1966) 1415; Soviet Physics – JETP **23** (1966) 939.
2) Zinov'eva, K. N. and Boldarev, S. T., Zh. eksper. teor. Fiz. **56** (1969) 1089; Soviet Physics – JETP **29** (1969) 585.
3) Everitt, C. W. F., Atkins, K. R. and Denenstein, D., Phys. Rev. **136** (1964) 1494.
4) Pikar, K. A. and Atkins, K. R., Phys. Rev. **178** (1969) 399.
5) King, P. I. and Wyatt, A. F. G., Proc. Roy. Soc. **A322** (1971) 355.
6) Khalatnikov, I. M., An Introduction to the Theory of Superfluidity, W. A. Benjamin, Inc. (New York, 1965), p. 138.
7) Allen, J. F. and Misener, A. D., Proc. Cambridge Phil. Soc. **34** (1938) 209.
8) Devaraj, N. and Hollis Hallett, A. C., Canad. J. Phys. **45** (1967) 2113.
9) Zinov'eva, K. N., Zh. eksper. teor. Fiz. **29** (1955) 899.
10) Dickson, D. P. E., Caroline, D. and Mendoza, E., Phys. Letters **32A** (1970) 419.
11) Guo, H. M., Edwards, D. O., Sarwinski, R. E. and Tough, J. T., Phys. Rev. Letters **27** (1971) 1259.

Physica **69** (1973) 148–158 © *North-Holland Publishing Co.*

ELECTRICAL RESISTIVITIES OF LIQUID ALKALI METALS AND ALLOYS

W. VAN DER LUGT and A. J. DEKKER

Laboratorium voor vaste stof fysica van de Rijksuniversiteit te Groningen, Nederland

Received 8 May 1973

Synopsis

A report is given of the results of a comparative study of the measured electrical resistivity of liquid alkali metals and alloys, and the theoretical predictions for this quantity obtained within the diffraction model. Calculated structure factors for liquid Na and K are checked against experimental data available in the literature. The results are used in the discussion of alloys. Form factors were calculated on the basis of Shaw model potentials with corrections for electron–electron interaction according to Toigo and Woodruff. The melting transition is also discussed briefly.

1. *Introduction.* Considerable progress has been made during the last decade towards a rather detailed analysis of the physical properties of "simple" (non-transition) metals and alloys. This is particularly true for highly disordered systems such as concentrated solid alloys, and liquid metals and alloys, where lack of translation symmetry does not allow the conventional treatment in terms of Bloch functions, Brillouin zones, *etc.* It is satisfying that all these systems can be discussed from a single viewpoint which contains the conventional approach for periodic structures as a special case. This viewpoint is embodied in the so-called "diffraction model" developed by Ziman[1]) and others[2,3]).

In this contribution we wish to report on a comparative study carried out in our laboratory of the measured electrical resistivity of liquid alkali metals and alloys, and the theoretical predictions for this quantity obtained within the Ziman formalism. For this purpose we first mention some of the essential ingredients that go into the physics of the diffraction model in section 2. After brief reference to the experimental work in section 3, we proceed in section 4 with a comparison between theory and experiment for the pure liquid metals sodium and potassium. In section 5 the results for the alloy systems Na–K and Na–Rb are reviewed. The melting transition is briefly discussed in section 6.

2. *The diffraction model.* A "simple" metal or alloy is considered to consist of some arrangement of small non-overlapping ion cores embedded in an electron gas. At this stage the arrangement need not be specified; it may be a liquid as well as a solid. The electrons will of course respond to the presence of the charged ions by a slight redistribution of their density, thereby changing the bare ion-core potentials to screened potentials. In a linearized Hartree approach, neglecting exchange and correlation effects, the screening can be described by attributing to the electron gas a wave-vector-dependent Lindhard dielectric constant

$$\varepsilon(q) = 1 + \frac{4\pi e^2}{q^2} D(E_F) \left[\frac{1}{2} + \frac{4k_F^2 - q^2}{8qk_F} \ln \left| \frac{2k_F + q}{2k_F - q} \right| \right], \tag{1}$$

where $D(E_F) = 3n/2E_F$ represents the density of states at the Fermi energy E_F, n the number density and k_F the radius of the Fermi sphere. The convenience of introducing a dielectric response function $\varepsilon(q)$ lies in the fact that the Fourier component $v(q)$ of a screened potential is immediately obtained from the corresponding component $v_b(q)$ of the bare potential by writing $v(q) = v_b(q)/\varepsilon(q)$; transforming back to real space one can find $v(r)$. Components of small q are screened very effectively, while those of large q are screened weakly.

2.1. Pseudo-potentials. In the diffraction model the screened ion cores are assumed to act as *weak* scatterers for the conduction electrons. The justification for this assumption lies in the development of pseudo-potential theory, in which the actual strong ion-core potential is replaced by a weak (nonlocal) pseudo-potential which produces the same scattering amplitude for the conduction electrons. Within the OPW formalism, for example, the orthogonalization of the conduction-electron wave functions with the core states produces an effective repulsive potential which tends to cancel the true attractive ion-core potential and thus leads to a weak pseudo-potential[2, 3, 4]). This allows the use of perturbation theory and essentially justifies a nearly free electron treatment.

2.2 Resistivity. Within this scheme we now outline briefly some aspects of the electrical resistivity. Consider a specimen of volume Ω containing N similar ion cores of charge Ze in a free-electron gas of density $n = NZ/\Omega = Z/\Omega_0$, where Ω_0 is the atomic volume. According to Boltzmann transport theory (which is satisfactory as long as the mean free path of the electrons is large compared to their wavelength), the resistivity is

$$\rho = m/ne^2\tau_F, \tag{2}$$

where τ_F is the relaxation time of electrons with the Fermi energy. In the customary "older" approach developed for crystalline metals, τ_F was related to Fermi-surface scattering resulting from deviations of the potential from perfect periodicity (phonons, impurities, *etc.*). Such an approach is of course inapplicable to disordered systems because they lack translation symmetry. In the diffraction model, therefore, one considers the scattering by the whole system of screened ion cores, *i.e.* the scattering pseudo-potential seen by the conduction electrons is written as

$$W(\boldsymbol{r}) = \sum_j w(\boldsymbol{r} - \boldsymbol{R}_j), \tag{3}$$

where $w(\boldsymbol{r}-\boldsymbol{R}_j)$ represents the screened pseudo-potential energy of an electron at $\boldsymbol{r}$ due to the ion at $\boldsymbol{R}_j(1 \leqq j \leqq N)$. Denoting the electron states by $|\boldsymbol{k}\rangle = (1/\Omega)^{\frac{1}{2}} \exp(\mathrm{i}\boldsymbol{k} \cdot \boldsymbol{r})$ the relaxation time is obtained in the usual way from the expression[4])

$$\frac{1}{\tau_{\mathrm{F}}} = \frac{\Omega m k_{\mathrm{F}}}{2\pi\hbar^3} \int |\langle \boldsymbol{k} + \boldsymbol{q}|W|\boldsymbol{k}\rangle|^2 (1 - \cos\theta) \sin\theta \, \mathrm{d}\theta, \tag{4}$$

where both $|\boldsymbol{k}\rangle$ and $|\boldsymbol{k} + \boldsymbol{q}\rangle$ are states with the Fermi energy $E_{\mathrm{F}} = \hbar^2 k_{\mathrm{F}}^2/2m$; $\boldsymbol{q}$ is the scattering vector and θ the scattering angle so that $\sin\frac{1}{2}\theta = q/2k_{\mathrm{F}}$ (see fig. 1).

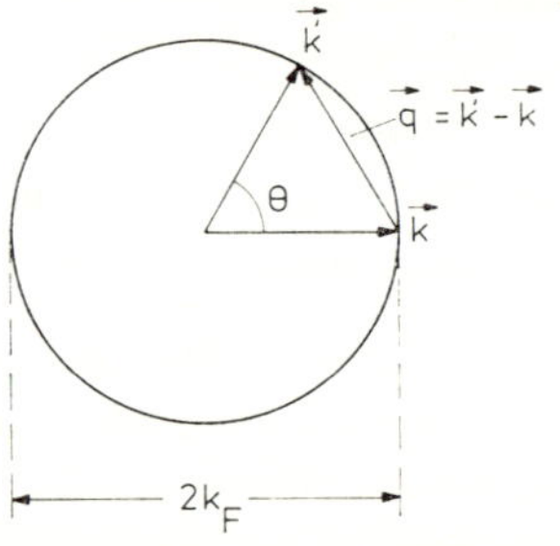

Fig. 1. Geometry of scattering from a state $\boldsymbol{k}$ to another state $\boldsymbol{k}' = \boldsymbol{k} + \boldsymbol{q}$ on the surface of a Fermi sphere of radius k_{F}.

The essential point of the treatment is that the matrix element can be factorized into a form factor $\langle \boldsymbol{k} + \boldsymbol{q}|w|\boldsymbol{k}\rangle$ which depends only on the scattering properties of a single ion core, and a structure factor $S(\boldsymbol{q})$ which depends only on the spatial arrangement of the ion cores. In fact,

$$\begin{aligned}\langle \boldsymbol{k} + \boldsymbol{q}|W|\boldsymbol{k}\rangle &= (1/\Omega) \int \exp[-\mathrm{i}(\boldsymbol{k} + \boldsymbol{q}) \cdot \boldsymbol{r}] \sum_j w(\boldsymbol{r} - \boldsymbol{R}_j) \exp(\mathrm{i}\boldsymbol{k} \cdot \boldsymbol{r}) \mathrm{d}^3 r \\ &= S(\boldsymbol{q}) \langle \boldsymbol{k} + \boldsymbol{q}|w|\boldsymbol{k}\rangle\end{aligned} \tag{5}$$

with

$$S(\boldsymbol{q}) = (1/N) \sum_j \exp(-\mathrm{i}\boldsymbol{q} \cdot \boldsymbol{R}_j)$$

and

$$\langle \boldsymbol{k} + \boldsymbol{q}|w|\boldsymbol{k}\rangle = (1/\Omega_0) \int \exp[-\mathrm{i}(\boldsymbol{k} + \boldsymbol{q}) \cdot \boldsymbol{r}] w(\boldsymbol{r}) \exp(\mathrm{i}\boldsymbol{k} \cdot \boldsymbol{r}) \mathrm{d}^3 r. \tag{6}$$

Substitution into (4) and (2) then leads to the Ziman formula

$$\rho = \frac{3\pi m \Omega_0}{8\hbar e^2 E_{\mathrm{F}}} \int_0^2 a(q) |\langle \boldsymbol{k} + \boldsymbol{q}|w|\boldsymbol{k}\rangle|^2 x^3 \, \mathrm{d}x \tag{7}$$

with $x = q/2k_F$ and the interference function $a(q) = N\overline{|S(\boldsymbol{q})|^2}$, where the bar indicates an ensemble average. One recognizes that $a(q)$ is directly proportional to the intensity of X-ray or neutron diffraction by the system of ion cores, and that as such it represents a quantity that can be obtained from an independent experiment. In a liquid metal $a(q)$ is essentially the Fourier transform of the pair correlation function $P(R)$,

$$a(q) = 1 + \frac{N}{\Omega}\int_0^\infty 4\pi R^2\{P(R) - 1\}\frac{\sin qR}{qR}\,\mathrm{d}R, \tag{8}$$

$(N/\Omega)P(R)$ represents the probability to find another ion per unit volume at a distance R from a given ion.

2.3. General features of the form factor and the interference function. It is worthwhile to mention the general features of the factors that make up the integrand in (7). If we consider the pseudo-potential of a single ion core as an ordinary potential, the matrix element $\langle \boldsymbol{k}+\boldsymbol{q}|w|\boldsymbol{k}\rangle$ simply becomes the Fourier transform $w(q)$ of $w(r)$. Suppose for a moment that the cancellation of the true ion-core potential as a result of the orthogonalization of the conduction-electron states on the core states were complete; the potential energy of an electron in the field of the bare pseudo-ion would then be

$$w_b(r) = \begin{cases} -Ze^2/r & \text{for } r > r_c \\ 0 & \text{for } r < r_c, \end{cases} \tag{9}$$

where r_c is the core radius. For small q we then obtain from (6) and (1) for the screened potential

$$w(q) = \frac{w_b(q)}{\varepsilon(q)} = -\frac{4\pi Ze^2N}{(q^2+k_s^2)\Omega}\cos qr_c \quad \text{or} \quad w(0) = -\tfrac{2}{3}E_F;\ k_s^2 \equiv 4\pi e^2 D(E_F) \tag{10}$$

independent of the specific properties of the ion core. As q increases, the magnitude of $w(q)$ decreases and the function passes through zero at a q-value determined by the core radius, as indicated in fig. 2. In the same figure the general

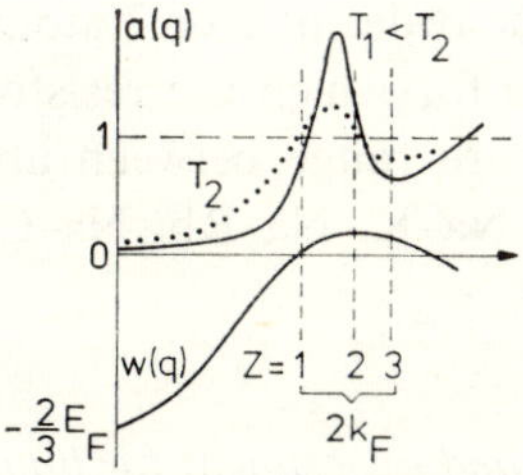

Fig. 2. Schematic representation of a form factor $w(q)$ and an interference function $a(q)$ for a liquid metal. The vertical dashed lines correspond to $q = 2k_F$ for various valencies. Comparison of the structure factors at two temperatures in combination with equation (7) indicates that for divalent metals $\mathrm{d}\rho/\mathrm{d}T$ may be negative.

shape of $a(q)$ has been sketched for a liquid metal. For small q-values, $a(q)$ will be very small; in fact, according to the classical theory of Ornstein and Zernike,

$$a(0) = (N/\Omega)k_B T\chi_T, \tag{11}$$

where χ_T is the isothermal compressibility. For a metal just above its melting point a typical value would be $a(0) \approx 10^{-2}$.

In combination with the presence of the factor $(q/k_F)^3$ in the integrand of (7) it is evident that the resistivity is determined largely by the values of the various quantities in the q region between, say, k_F and $2k_F$. Also note that any temperature dependence of ρ arises from the temperature dependence of the interference function $a(q)$.

The limitations of the Ziman formalism have been discussed a.o. by Faber[2, 3]; since it describes the resistivity to first order in the scattering probability one may expect an accuracy of, say, ten percent in its predictions for metals with nearly free electrons.

3. *Experiments.* Although the alkali metals are very attractive from a theoretical point of view, their high reactivity of course requires special experimental techniques and a good deal of know-how. For the handling of these materials and the preparation of alloys, for example, a high-purity argon glove box is indispensible. Furthermore, in view of the high price of the pure metals, it is desirable to use small samples. The resistivities were measured by passing a d.c. current through a sample of well-known dimensions and determining the potential difference between two points along the sample. For this purpose the liquid metal or alloy was enclosed in a cylindrical tube of stainless steel, which of course forms an electrical shunt. In view of the reactivity and bad wetting properties of these metals with respect to stainless steel, a number of checking procedures was followed to guarentee maximum reliability of the measurements. For details on this subject we refer to Hennephof, van der Lugt and Wright[5]. The inaccuracy of relative resistivity measurements did not exceed 0.2 %; the absolute error in ρ amounted to about 0.7 %. The inaccuracy in $d\rho/dT$ was estimated to be a few percent. The uncertainty in the alloy compositions is of the order of 1 or 2 atomic percent.

The liquid alkali-alloy systems for which the resistivity has been measured in our laboratory over a temperature range between about 50 and 125 °C for a variety of compositions include Na–K, Na–Rb, Na–Cs, K–Cs[5, 6] and since recently, Rb–Cs.

4. *Comparison between theory and experiment for liquid Na and K.* 4.1. Theoretical form factors. For the pure liquid metals Na and K we are in the fortunate situation that Greenfield, Wellendorf and Wiser[7] (GWW) have recently measured the interference function $a(q)$ with high accuracy (better than 2.5 %) at

100 and 200 °C, and at 65 and 135 °C, respectively. These measurements employed X-ray diffraction in a transmission geometry and are considered to constitute a considerable improvement over earlier neutron diffraction results as well as over theoretical predictions. Employing these $a(q)$-values in the Ziman formula (7) in combination with calculated form factors $w(q)$, these metals thus provide an excellent test case for comparison between theory and experiment. A detailed analysis of this kind has been performed recently in our laboratory by Devlin and Van der Lugt[8]). To illustrate the degree of agreement that can be obtained at present between experimental and theoretical resistivities within the Ziman formalism we reproduce some of the results in table I.

TABLE I

Resistivities (in $\mu\Omega$ cm) for liquid Na and K calculated from the experimental GWW structure factors and theoretical form factors; the form factors were obtained by applying Lindhard and Toigo–Woodruff screening. The k_F-values are in atomic units.

Screening function	ρ_{Na} 100 °C $k_F = 0.4742$	ρ_{Na} 200 °C $k_F = 0.4699$	$\left(\frac{\partial \rho}{\partial T}\right)_{Na}$	ρ_K 65 °C $k_F = 0.3824$	ρ_K 135 °C $k_F = 0.3799$	$\left(\frac{\partial \rho}{\partial T}\right)_K$
Lindhard	5.62	7.36	0.0174	10.11	12.89	0.0397
Toigo–Woodruff	8.60	11.21	0.0261	12.84	16.63	0.0541
Experiment	9.6	13.4	0.038	13.1	16.8	0.053

To calculate the form factors $w(q)$ for Fermi-surface scattering they employed the Shaw[9]) model pseudo-potential; this potential is constructed to provide the correct experimental spectroscopic term energies of the free ion. In combination with screening effects described by the dielectric function (1) this leads to the calculated resistivities labelled "Lindhard" in table I. It turns out that the agreement between calculated and experimental resistivities can be improved considerably by taking into account exchange and correlation effects in the screening function. Of the various ways of including many-electron effects available in the literature, one recently proposed by Toigo and Woodruff[10]) (TW) appears particularly promising. The resistivities calculated on this basis are also presented in table I; the agreement with experiment is seen to be quite good. For $(d\rho/dT)$ the discrepancy between theory and experiment is larger than for ρ; nevertheless, even these results can be considered as being satisfactory because the temperature dependence of ρ is determined by the rather small changes with temperature of the interference function.

4.2 Theoretical structure factors. The experimental value for $a(q)$ obtained for Na and K by GWW[7]) of course also provides the possibility of examining the applicability of theoretical structure factors for mono-atomic liquids. Of the various integral equations available for $a(q)$ in the literature, that of Percus–

Yevick[11]) has received particular popularity, because it has yielded a closed-form expression for $a(q)$, be it that this expression has been derived for the rather unphysical case of a hard-sphere interatomic potential. In the hard-sphere solution obtained by Wertheim[12]) and Thiele[13]), the interference function $a(q)$ is represented by a rather complicated algebraic expression in terms of the packing fraction η and the hard-sphere diameter σ. For $q = 0$ the expression reduces to

$$a(0) = (1-\eta)^4/(1 + 2\eta)^2, \tag{12}$$

η and σ are related to each other through the number density (N/Ω) of the spheres,

$$\eta = \frac{1}{6}\frac{N}{\Omega}\pi\sigma^3. \tag{13}$$

In the expression for a(q) the temperature does not enter, except through the insignificant temperature dependence of N/Ω. Ashcroft and Lekner[14]) therefore proposed to introduce a temperature dependence in η by combining (12) with the Ornstein–Zernike relation (11),

$$\frac{N}{\Omega} k_B T\chi_T = a(0) = \frac{(1 - \eta)^4}{(1 + 2\eta)^2}. \tag{14}$$

$\eta(T)$ can then be obtained from compressibility measurements; if these are lacking Ashcroft and Lekner proposed to choose $\eta(T)$ to give the correct height for the first peak in $a(q)$ at each temperature. Then $\sigma(T)$ was computed from (13).

A detailed comparison between the theoretical hard-sphere structure factors and the experimental ones for liquid Na and K has been made recently by Greenfield, Wiser, Leenstra and Van der Lugt[15]) (GWLL). For this purpose they modified the hard-sphere model by considering η and σ as independent parameters, thereby violating (13). In this way they hoped to get enough flexibility to obtain a good theoretical fit for $a_{\text{expt}}(q)$. It turned out, however, that no σ–η pairs could be found to provide a good quantitative fit to the experimental data over the entire range of q-values. It is possible, however, to deduce from their analysis optimized pairs of σ–η values which reproduce the experimental $a(q)$-values to within 20 % over the limited range $0 < q < 2k_F$. These values are given in table II, together

TABLE II

Optimized η–σ pairs for liquid Na and K obtained by fitting the modified hard-sphere solutions to the experimental GWW structure factors. The resistivities were calculated from the hard-sphere structure factors in combination with the form factors calculated with Toigo–Woodruff screening

	T (°C)	η	σ (Å)	ρ_{calc} ($\mu\Omega$ cm)	ρ_{expt} ($\mu\Omega$ cm)
Na	100	0.455	3.25	9.28	9.6
Na	200	0.426	3.15	11.76	13.4
K	65	0.445	4.05	14.87	13.1
K	135	0.423	4.05	19.19	16.8

with the resistivities calculated from (7) on the basis of these structure factors in combination with the form factors calculated as in part 1 of this section, by Devlin, Leenstra and Van der Lugt[16]).

5. *Comparison between theory and experiment for liquid binary alkali alloys.* An extension of the Ziman formula (7) to binary alloys has been given by Ashcroft and Langreth[17]). For an alloy of metals 1 and 2 with atomic concentration $(1-c)$ and c, respectively, they find for the electrical resistivity as a function of composition

$$\rho(c) = \frac{3\pi m\Omega_0}{8\hbar e^2 E_F}\int_0^2 [(1-c)|w_1(q)|^2 a_{11}(q) + c|w_2(q)|^2 a_{22}(q) + 2\{c(1-c)\}^{\frac{1}{2}} w_1(q) w_2(q) a_{12}(q)] x^3\, dx, \tag{15}$$

where, as before, $x = q/k_F$; a_{11}, a_{22} and a_{12} refer to the partial structure factors. If one wishes to calculate the resistivity of an alloy for a given composition in order to compare the result with the experimental value, one immediately runs into a number of problems. For example, since no experimental data are available for the densities of the alloys, of interest, one has to make a reasonable choice for

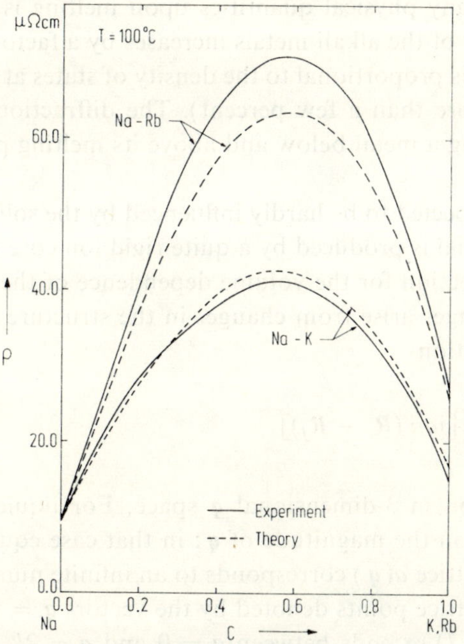

Fig. 3. The fully drawn curves represent the experimental resistivities of liquid Na–K and Na–Rb alloys at 100 °C obtained by Hennephof, Van der Lugt and Wright [5]). The dashed curves were calculated by Devlin, Leenstra and Van der Lugt [16]).

the concentration dependence of Ω_0 and k_F (which also enters into the form factors). However, by assuming a linear relation for $\Omega_0(c)$ one would not expect to introduce any serious errors. Much more serious problems arise in connection with the structure factors, since no experimental data are available for the alloys. The best one can do in this respect at present is to rely on the Lebowitz[18]) hard-sphere solutions of the Percus–Yevick equation for a binary system, although it must be admitted that this model remains somewhat unsatisfactory from the physics point of view. Nevertheless, Devlin, Leenstra and van der Lugt[16]) have recently carried out such calculations for the Na–K, Na–Rb and K–Rb systems. For this purpose they extended the modification of the model as mentioned in section 4.2 into the binary systems and made maximal use of the experimental GWW structure factors for Na and K. Without presenting here the detailed arguments for some "intelligent guesses" that had to be made, we simply illustrate the degree of agreement between the calculations and experiment by referring to the dashed and fully drawn curves in fig. 3. Although the agreement is not bad, it is evident from this discussion that the statistical theory of structure factors in liquid metals and alloys remains a subject for further study.

6. *The melting transition of simple metals.* The band structure existing in a solid metal is expected to break down almost completely upon melting. On the other hand, the change in many physical quantities upon melting is remarkably small (the electrical resistivity of the alkali metals increases by a factor of, say, 1.5 while the Knight shift, which is proportional to the density of states at the Fermi surface, even changes by no more than a few percent). The diffraction model offers the possibility of considering a metal below and above its melting point from a single point of view.

The form factor is expected to be hardly influenced by the solid-liquid transition because the bare potential is produced by a quite rigid ion core and all that would seem required is a correction for the volume dependence of the screening. Consequently, the major changes arise from changes in the structure factor.

The interference function

$$a(\boldsymbol{q}) = \frac{1}{N} \sum_i \sum_j \exp\left[i\boldsymbol{q} \cdot (\boldsymbol{R}_i - \boldsymbol{R}_j)\right] \tag{16}$$

is a function of position in 3-dimensional $\boldsymbol{q}$ space. For liquids the interference function only depends on the magnitude of $\boldsymbol{q}$; in that case equation (16) reduces to (8). For a periodic lattice $a(\boldsymbol{q})$ corresponds to an infinite number of δ-functions situated at reciprocal lattice points denoted by the vectors $\boldsymbol{q} = \boldsymbol{G}$. The integration in the Ziman formula (7) extends between $q = 0$ and $q = 2k_F$. For monovalent metals the reciprocal-lattice points (apart from the origin itself) lie outside a sphere of radius $2k_F$, so that the resistivity (7) vanishes, as expected for an ideal lattice. As clearly pointed out by Harrison[19]), a phonon of wave vector $\boldsymbol{Q}$ creates extra peaks in $\boldsymbol{q}$ space at positions $\boldsymbol{q} = \boldsymbol{G} \pm \boldsymbol{Q}$; these may contribute to the resistivity. A calculation of the resistivity of a solid metal thus requires exact knowledge of the phonon spectrum. Calculations of the resistivity as a function of temperature have been performed along these lines for sodium by Greene and Kohn[20]), and Kaveh and Wiser[21]).

Just below the melting point another approach may be useful. As the excursions of different atoms from their equilibrium positions become less and less correlated at higher temperatures, one may adopt an approach common in the description of thermal diffuse scattering of X rays and start from a system of independently vibrating atoms as a first approximation (Einstein model). Correlations between the deflections u_m and u_n of atoms m and n, measured along the direction of $\boldsymbol{q}$, can then be introduced by means of a correlation coefficient α_{mn} defined through $\overline{u_m u_n} = \overline{u^2}\alpha_{mn}$[22]). Then $a(\boldsymbol{q})$ becomes

$$a(\boldsymbol{q}) \approx (1 - e^{-2M}) \sum_m \sum_n \alpha_{mn} \exp\left[i\boldsymbol{q} \cdot (\boldsymbol{R}_m - \boldsymbol{R}_n)\right], \tag{17}$$

where $2M = q^2\overline{u^2}$. In the case of completely disordered thermal motion $\alpha_{mn} = \delta_{mn}$ so that

$$a(\boldsymbol{q}) \approx 1 - \exp\left(-q^2\,\overline{u^2}\right).$$

If one substitutes for $\overline{u^2}$ values based on the Lindemann melting rule[23, 24]) and calculates the electrical resistivity one finds already agreement with experiment within, say, 50 %. This is a remarkably good result in view of the approximations involved and considering the high sensivity of the resistivity integral (7) to the input parameters.

For polyvalent metals the situation becomes more complicated. The sphere with radius $2k_F$ in $\boldsymbol{q}$ space now contains some of the reciprocal lattice points, corresponding to the intersections of the Fermi surface with Brillouin-zone boundaries. Although the width of the peaks of $a(\boldsymbol{q})$ at the reciprocal-lattice sites decreases as the lattice approaches perfect periodicity, their height increases correspondingly, so that the contribution to the resistivity integral (7) may still be significant. Physically this means that a very small number of electrons are scattered extremely strongly, whereas the remaining ones are not scattered at all, so that we still can understand that the resistivity vanishes. In the presence of thermal motion it is not always easy to distinguish critically between the diffuse scattering part of $a(\boldsymbol{q})$ contributing to the resistivity, and the remaining Bragg peaks that correspond to electrons that do not contribute to the conductivity. Anyhow, a rash application of equation (7) may lead to ambiguous results in these cases. We believe that this problem deserves thorough theoretical consideration.

REFERENCES

1) Ziman, J. M., Phil. Mag. **6** (1961) 1013.
2) Faber, T. E., An Introduction to the Theory of Liquid Metals, Cambridge University Press, (Cambridge, 1972).
3) Faber, T. E., in Physics of Metals, **1** Electrons, Ziman, J. M., ed., Cambridge University Press, (Cambridge, 1969).
4) See for example Harrison, W. A., Pseudo-Potentials in the Theory of Metals, W. A. Benjamin, Inc. (New York, 1966).
5) Hennephof, J., Van der Lugt, W. and Wright, G. W., Physica **52** (1971) 279.
6) Hennephof, J., Van der Lugt, W., Wright, G. W. and Mariën, T., Physica **61** (1972) 146.
7) Greenfield, A. J. and Wiser, N., Phys. Letters **34A** (1971) 123; Greenfield, A. J., Wellendorf, J. and Wiser, N., Phys. Rev. A **4** (1971) 1607.
8) Devlin, J. F. and Van der Lugt, W., Phys. Rev. B **6** (1972) 4462.
9) Shaw jr., R. W., Phys. Rev. **174** (1968) 769.
10) Toigo, F. and Woodruff, T. O., Phys. Rev. B **2** (1970) 3958.
11) Percus, J. K. and Yevick, G. J., Phys. Rev. **110** (1958) 1; Percus, J. K., Phys. Rev. Letters **8** (1962) 462.
12) Wertheim, M. S., Phys. Rev. Letters **10** (1963) 321.
13) Thiele, E., J. chem. Phys. **39** (1963) 474.
14) Ashcroft, N. W. and Lekner, J., Phys. Rev. **145** (1966) 83.
15) Greenfield, A. J., Wiser, N., Leenstra, M. R. and Van der Lugt, W., Physica **59** (1972) 571.
16) Devlin, J. F., Leenstra, M. R. and Van der Lugt, W., Physica (in press); see also, Van der Lugt, W., Devlin, J. F., Hennephof, J. and Leenstra, M. R., in "The Properties of Liquid Metals", Sakae Takenchi, ed., Taylor and Francis Ltd. (London, 1973).
17) Ashcroft, N. W. and Langreth, D.C., Phys. Rev. **159** (1967) 500.
18) Lebowitz, J. L., Phys. Rev. **133** (1964) A 895.
19) Harrison, W. A., Solid State Theory, McGraw-Hill (New York, 1970), p. 394.
20) Greene, M. P. and Kohn, W., Phys. Rev. **137** (1965) 513.
21) Kaveh, M. and Wiser, N., Phys. Rev. B **6** (1972) 3648.
22) Azároff, L. V., Elements of X-ray crystallography, McGraw-Hill (New York, 1968) p. 240.
23) Lindemann, F. A., Z. Phys. **11** (1910) 609.
24) Gilvarry, J. J., Phys. Rev. **102** (1956) 308.

Physica **69** (1973) 159–170 © *North-Holland Publishing Co.*

ON THE A.C. SUSCEPTIBILITY OF METALS IN THE NORMAL OR SUPERCONDUCTING STATE

L. J. M. VAN DE KLUNDERT, E. A. GIJSBERTSE and L. C. VAN DER MAREL

Afdeling der Technische Natuurkunde van de Technische Hogeschool Twente, Enschede, Nederland

Received 3 Mei 1973

Synopsis

Models describing the a.c. behaviour due to surface superconductivity can be extended to include frequency effects. It is necessary to take normal currents into account and to assume that superconducting currents can only change under the influence of electrical fields. The model has been verified by means of susceptibility measurements and direct observation of the local *b–h* loops.

1. *Introduction.* Many processes involving the magnetic behaviour of non-conducting materials can be described in terms of one or more relaxation times. A similar description method is used for the behaviour of (non-magnetic) conductors subject to time-dependent fields. Several techniques have been developed to investigate the values of these time constants. Step-field methods have been used, for example, for paramagnetic salts when the relaxation time is larger than one second[1]). In conductivity measurements the step-field response method is applied for τ-values down to a few microseconds[2, 3, 4]).

Another method, introduced in the thirties in the field of paramagnetism of non-conducting magnetic materials is the induction method[5]). Materials are here investigated in magnetic fields: $H = H_0 + h_0 e^{-i\omega t}$, $h_0 \,//\, H_0$ and $|h_0| \ll |H_0|$. These induction measurements, overshadowed now by resonance experiments, largely contributed to the insight in paramagnetic relaxation processes. They gave the impetus to the famous papers of Van Vleck[6]) in 1941 where quantitative calculations about temperature and magnetic-field behaviour of relaxation times were presented and where for the first time the existence of a phonon bottleneck was argued. Results of measurements on magnetic salts of different concentration of the magnetic ions for the second time convinced Gorter *et al.*[7]) of the existence of this phonon bottleneck and in the same school of Gorter it was demonstrated that also the heat conductivity of the crystal as well as the Kapitza resistance between sample and liquid helium may influence the relaxation processes[8]).

Originally these induction methods were developed with experiments on metals. Already in 1902 Zenneck[9]) applied such a method on non-magnetic metals and in 1919 Wwedensky[10]) investigated magnetic metals with the same method. Later on Kouwenhoven and Daiger[11]) succeeded in extending largely the frequency range of the self-inductance bridge and in 1955 for the first time a Hartshorn-bridge device was used in the Leiden laboratory[12]). With an analogous method we performed in our laboratory a number of experiments on some metals. The response of the coil system which surrounds the cylindrical samples contains the information on the conductive and magnetic properties of the metal to be investigated. When the sample is a non-magnetic normal conducting solid cylinder the response is linear with respect to the amplitude of the modulating field and depends only on the frequency and the conducting properties. In the case of samples in the superconducting state the response will be in general nonlinear and depends strongly on frequency, amplitude and pinning mechanisms.

The basic features of the theory of the a.c. behaviour were outlined in the early sixties by introducing the concept of the critical state[13, 14]). After that many refinements concerning the field dependence of the critical current and the relation to the pinning mechanisms were published[15, 16]). Since in the critical-state model surface currents and flux gradients play an important rôle, thin-walled cylinders have great advantage in showing the effects of the associated currents in an enhanced way.

In this paper we shall confine ourselves to the influence of geometrical factors on the a.c. behaviour of metals both in the normal and superconducting states. In section 2 the general solution method of normal conducting hollow and solid cylinders is outlined and the obtained results are presented. An extension to superconducting materials in the vicinity of T_c is given. In section 3 the well-known Fink–Rollins–Silcox[17, 18]) model is extended to include frequency-dependent effects. Comparison with our experimental results is made in section 4 and leads to further extensions of the prior model which are presented in section 5.

2. *Influence of the geometry on the a.c. susceptibility.* The susceptibility χ of a normal conducting cylinder is defined as

$$\chi = -1 + \mu = -1 + 2\int_0^a B(r) r \, \mathrm{d}r / a^2 B(a), \tag{2.1}$$

where $B(r)$ is the complex amplitude of the induction inside the cylinder at a distance r from the axis and $B(a)$ the amplitude of the applied field at the sample surface ($r = a$). Values of χ can be calculated starting from Maxwell's equations:

$$\nabla \times \boldsymbol{E} = \mathrm{i}\omega \boldsymbol{B}, \tag{2.2}$$

$$\nabla \times \boldsymbol{H} = \boldsymbol{j}. \tag{2.3}$$

Introducing appropriate constitutive equations governing the magnetic and conductive properties, *e.g.*,

$$\boldsymbol{B} = \mu_0 \boldsymbol{H}, \quad \boldsymbol{j} = \sigma \boldsymbol{E} \tag{2.4}$$

(factors $e^{-i\omega t}$ are omitted for shortness; terms involving $\dot{\boldsymbol{D}}$ can be shown to be negligible at the low frequencies here of interest). Introduction of cylindrical coordinates with z parallel to the cylinder axis and the applied field $\boldsymbol{H} = (0, 0, H_z)$ yields the following form of Maxwell's equations:

$$E_\theta/r + \partial E_\theta/\partial r = i\omega B_z, \quad -\partial H_z/\partial r = j_\theta. \tag{2.5}$$

Inserting the constitutive equations we obtain the following differential equations for H_z and E_θ:

$$\begin{aligned}(kr)^2\partial^2 E_\theta/\partial(kr)^2 + kr\,\partial E_\theta/\partial(kr) + \{(kr)^2 - 1\}E_\theta = 0,\\ (kr)^2\partial^2 B_z/\partial(kr)^2 + kr\,\partial B_z/\partial(kr) + (kr)^2 B_z = 0,\end{aligned} \tag{2.6}$$

with $k^2 = i\omega\mu_0\sigma$. The general solution of (2.6) is

$$\begin{aligned}B_z(r) = \alpha_1 J_0(kr) + \alpha_2 Y_0(kr),\\ E_\theta(r) = \beta_1 J_1(kr) + \beta_2 Y_1(kr),\end{aligned} \tag{2.7}$$

J_n and Y_n being the Bessel and Neumann function of order n, respectively. The boundary conditions on the solution for B_z can be inserted by noticing that B_z should be bounded everywhere in the sample and continuous across the sample surface $r = a$. So we obtain

$$\begin{aligned}\alpha_1 = B_z(a)/J_0(ka), \quad \alpha_2 = 0,\\ \beta_1 = i\omega B_z(a)/kJ_0(ka), \quad \beta_2 = 0.\end{aligned}$$

Applying the definition of susceptibility (2.1) leads to

$$\chi = J_2(ka)/J_0(ka) = -1 + 2J_1(ka)/kaJ_0\,(ka). \tag{2.8}$$

Formally, the complex skin depth $\delta = i/k$ can be assumed to depend on such parameters as frequency, external fields, conductive properties, *i.e.*, $\delta = \delta(\omega, H_0, \sigma, \ldots)$. So if we put $ka = z = r\,e^{i\phi}$, r and ϕ both may depend on these parameters:

$$r = r(\omega, H_0, \sigma, \ldots), \tag{2.9a}$$

$$\phi = \phi(\omega, H_0, \sigma, \ldots). \tag{2.9b}$$

Although it may not be possible to calculate the functions (2.9a and b) explicitly, it will be useful to express experimental results in terms of r and ϕ rather than χ' and χ''. This is always possible since (2.8) defines a one to one correspondence from the χ'–χ'' plane to the r–ϕ plane ($0 \leqq \phi \leqq 2\pi$, $0 \leqq r < \infty$). In fig. 1 this is illustrated by drawing lines of constant r and ϕ in the χ'–χ'' plane. The lines

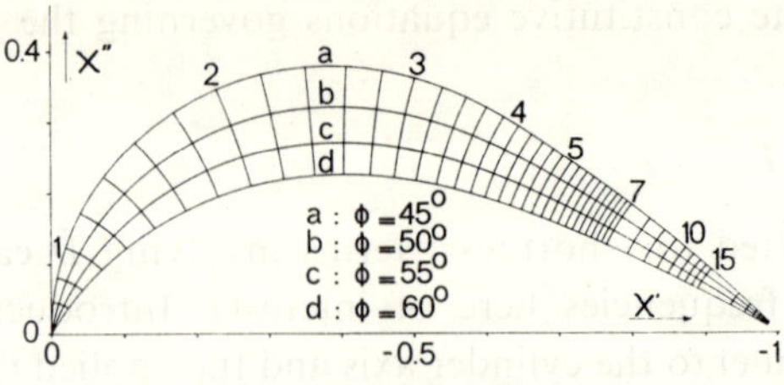

Fig. 1. Lines of constant r and ϕ in the χ'–χ'' plane for a solid cylinder (2.8). Values of r are indicated.

$\phi = \pi/4$ and $\phi = \pi/3$ denote the classical skin effect and the anomalous limit, respectively. It may be mentioned here that for a slab of thickness $2d$ an analogous procedure leads to the result:

$$\chi = -1 + \text{tg}(kd)/kd. \tag{2.10}$$

In practice the shape of the χ'–χ'' curves is not much influenced by the geometry of the sample as can be seen from fig. 2.

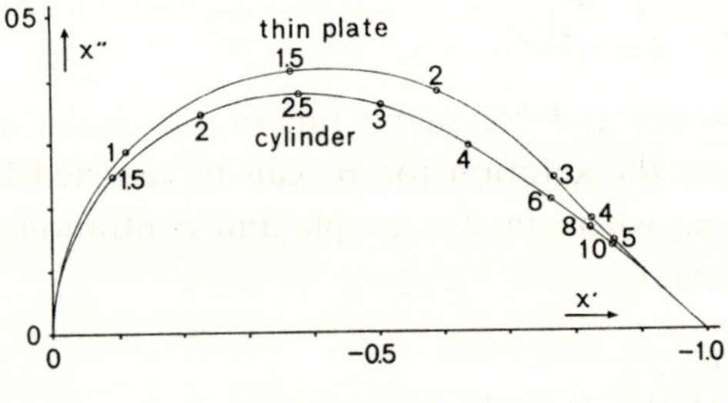

Fig. 2. Comparison of the χ'–χ'' curves for a solid cylinder (2.8) and a thin plate (2.10). Dimensionless values of r are indicated on the curves; $r = ka\ \mathrm{e}^{-\pi i/4}$ for a cylinder and $kd\ \mathrm{e}^{-\pi i/4}$ for a thin plate.

As an extension of the former calculation we shall treat the case of the hollow cylinder with inner radius b and outer radius a. Using appropriate boundary conditions we arrive at the result

$$\chi = -1 + \frac{2}{ka}\frac{J_1(ka) - \alpha Y_1(ka)}{J_0(ka) - \alpha Y_1(ka)}, \tag{2.11}$$

with

$$\alpha = \frac{kbJ_0(kb) - 2J_1(kb)}{kbY_0(kb) - 2Y_1(kb)}.$$

In fig. 3a the χ dependence on the ratio b/a is shown for some fixed normalized frequencies. The frequency behaviour is shown in fig. 3b for some fixed values of b/a. It is noted that in the limit $b \to a$ the χ'–χ'' curve tends to a half circle which can be interpreted as the diamagnetic analogue of the Casimir–Du Pré[19]) curves

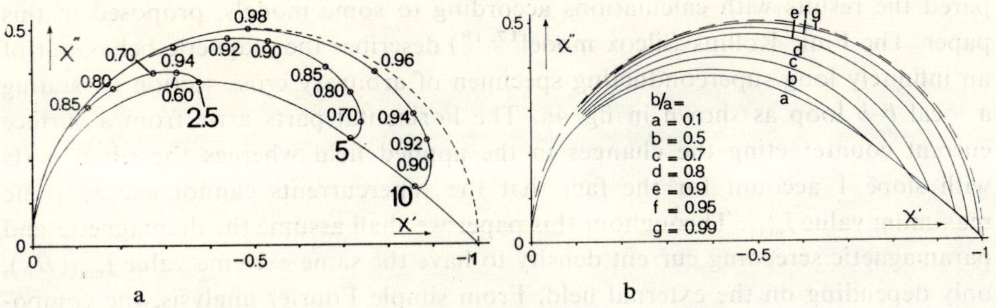

Fig. 3a. χ values for hollow cylinders (2.11) for some r values; $r = ka\, e^{-\pi i/4} = 2.5$, 5 and 10. The figures along the lines indicate b/a values.

Fig. 3b. χ values for hollow cylinders (2.11) for some b/a values. The parameter along each curve is r ($0 < r < \infty$).

for non-conducting paramagnetic materials. Formula (2.11) is also valid for the case of concentric solid cylinders with different conductivities σ_2 and σ_1 in the regions $0 \leqq r \leqq b$ and $b \leqq r \leqq a$, respectively. The value of α is then given by

$$\alpha = \frac{k_2 J_1(k_1 b) J_0(k_2 b) - k_1 J_0(k_1 b) J_1(k_2 b)}{k_2 Y_1(k_1 b) J_0(k_2 b) - k_1 Y_0(k_1 b) J_1(k_2 b)}, \tag{2.12}$$

with $k_1{}^2 = i\omega\mu_0\sigma_1$ and $k_2{}^2 = i\omega\mu_0\sigma_2$. Without derivation[20]) we may mention the more general formulae of χ for an arbitrary $\boldsymbol{j}(\boldsymbol{E})$ relation:

$$\chi = \mu_0 \int_0^a r^2 j(r)\,\mathrm{d}r / a^2 B_z(a), \tag{2.13}$$

$$\chi = \{E(a) - aE'(a)\}/\{E(a) + aE'(a)\}, \tag{2.14}$$

with $E'(a) = \{\mathrm{d}E_\theta(r)/\mathrm{d}r\}_{r=a}$.
Especially the latter is useful in anomalous skin-effect calculations where the relation $\boldsymbol{j}(\boldsymbol{E})$ is rather complicated[21]).

A further extension of this formulation may be obtained for the low-frequency behaviour of superconductors in the Meissner state (see *e.g.* Kubo[22])). Calculation of χ now results in the same relation (2.8) but with $k^2 = k_s^2 = i\omega\mu_0\sigma$ $(1 - x - x/i\omega\tau_F)$, $x = n_s/n$ being the fraction of superconducting electrons; τ_F is the electron relaxation time at the Fermi surface. At temperatures well below T_c, k_s^2 becomes independent of ω at sufficient low frequencies: $k_s^2 = -\mu_0 n_s e^2/m$. The real part of the corresponding skin depth equals the London penetration depth λ_L.

For a more extensive discussion we refer to the thesis of one of us (V.d. K.)[20]).

3. *Frequency effects in hollow superconducting cylinders.* In the literature two mechanisms are proposed to describe the static magnetization curves of superconductors: surface currents and bulk currents. To distinguish between their contributions we performed measurements on thin-walled hollow cylinders and com-

pared the results with calculations according to some models, proposed in this paper. The Fink–Rollins–Silcox model[17, 18]) describes the magnetic behaviour of an infinitely long superconducting specimen of arbitrary cross section by stating a local *b*–*h* loop as shown in fig. 4a. The horizontal parts arise from a surface current counteracting the changes in the applied field whereas the tilted parts with slope 1 account for the fact that the supercurrents cannot exceed some maximum value j_{max}. Throughout this paper we shall assume the diamagnetic and paramagnetic screening current density to have the same extreme value $j_{max}(H_0)$, only depending on the external field. From simple Fourier analysis, the components of χ can be written (for θ_2 see fig. 4a):

$$1 + \chi' = \mu' = \pi^{-1} (\pi - \theta_2 + \sin \theta_2 \cos \theta_2), \tag{3.1}$$

$$\chi'' = \mu'' = \pi^{-1} \sin^2 \theta_2 . \tag{3.2}$$

The main discrepancies between the above outlined one-parameter model and the experimental results on χ or the observed shape of the *b*–*h* loop can be summarized as follows.

a) There is a large influence of the frequency.

b) Observed *b*–*h* loops never show a horizontal part, indicating that an electrical field is necessary to change the value of the supercurrent.

c) Measured values of $(\partial\chi''/\partial\chi')_{\chi' = -1}$ have a finite value in contradiction to the infinite value of the above model.

The simplest way to include frequency effects is to take into account normal currents. For a thin-walled cylinder, wall thickness d, radius r, $d \ll r$, Maxwell's equations are approximated by:

$$E = -\tfrac{1}{2} r \mu_0 \, \mathrm{d}h_i/\mathrm{d}t, \tag{3.3}$$

$$h_i - h = j_{tot}\, d, \tag{3.4}$$

h_i and h being the fields inside and outside the cylinder, respectively. Further we assume

$$j_{tot} = j_n + j_s, \quad j_n = \sigma E, \tag{3.5}$$

j_n and j_s being the normal and superconducting current densities, respectively. Combining (3.3)–(3.5) we obtain a differential equation for the field h_i:

$$\tau \, \mathrm{d}h_i/\mathrm{d}t + h_i = h_0 \cos \omega t + j_s d, \tag{3.6}$$

$\tau = \tfrac{1}{2} r d \mu_0 \sigma$ is a time constant depending on geometrical factors as well as material constants.

In (3.6) j_s will vary between the extreme values $\pm j_{max}$. Let for

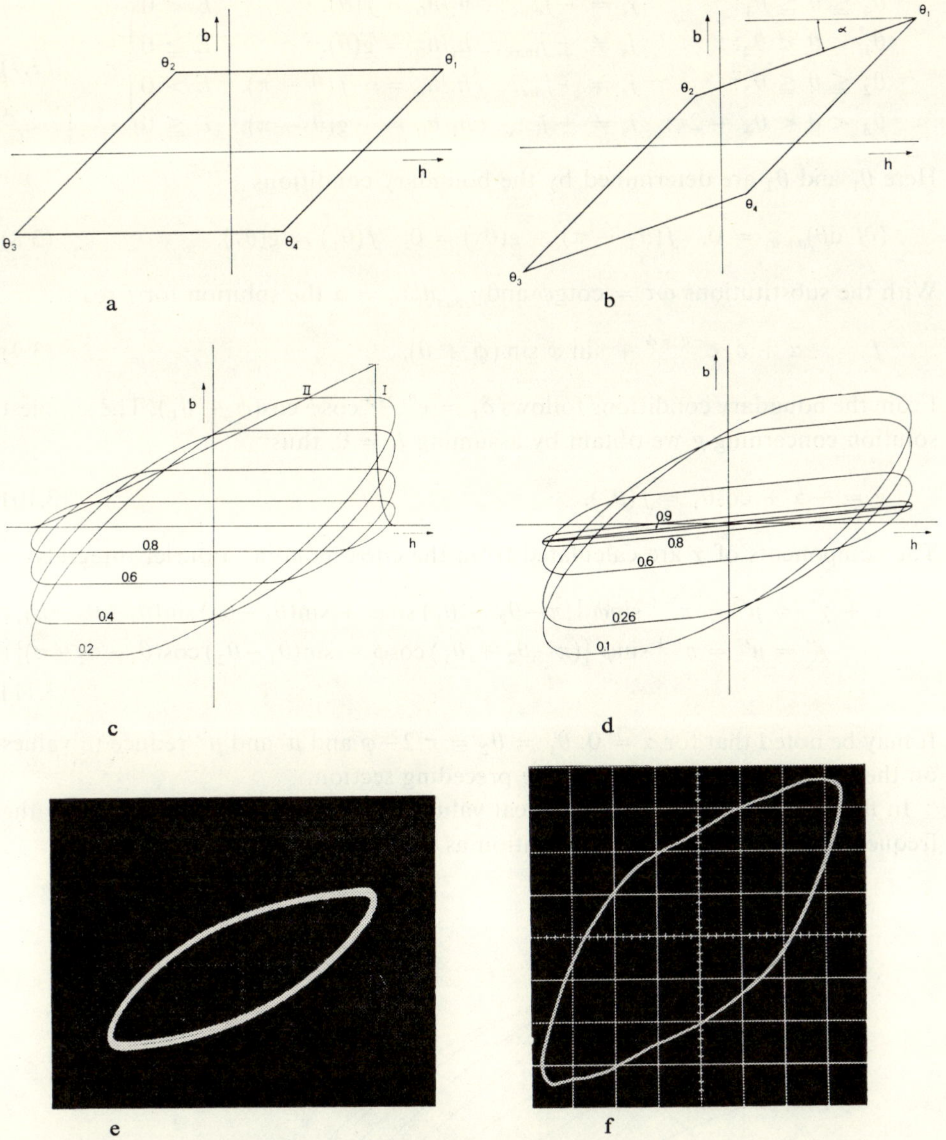

Fig. 4a. b–h loop according to Rollins and Silcox [18]).

Fig. 4b. Assumed zero-frequency limit b–h loop (see section 5).

Fig. 4c. Calculated b–h loops according to (3.9) and (3.10); $\omega\tau = 0.51$. The lines I and II indicate the values of θ_1 and θ_2 depending on α. The values of α are indicated in the figure.

Fig. 4d. Calculated b–h loop according to (3.9) and (5.4); $\tau/\tau_1 = 10$, $\omega\tau = 0.73$. The values of α are indicated in the figure.

Fig. 4e. Observed b–h loop after heat treatment; $T = 4.2$ K, $f = 128$ Hz, $h_0 = 11$ Oe, $H_0 = 1500$ Oe ($\approx H_{c_1}$).

Fig. 4f. Observed b–h loop before heat treatment; $T = 4.2$ K, $f = 5$ Hz, $h_0 = 31$ Oe, $H_0 = 4960$ Oe ($> H_{c_2}$).

$$\left.\begin{array}{llll} \theta_4 \leqq \theta \leqq \theta_1: & j_s = -j_{max}, & h_i/h_0 = f(\theta), & E < 0 \\ \theta_1 < \theta < \theta_2: & j_s \neq \pm j_{max}, & h_i/h_0 = g(\theta), & E \geqq 0 \\ \theta_2 \leqq \theta \leqq \theta_3: & j_s = +j_{max}, & h_i/h_0 = -f(\theta - \pi), & E > 0 \\ \theta_3 < \theta < \theta_4 + 2\pi: & j_s \neq \pm j_{max}, & h_i/h_0 = -g(\theta - \pi), & E \leqq 0 \end{array}\right\} \quad (3.7)$$

Here θ_1 and θ_2 are determined by the boundary conditions

$$(\partial f/\mathrm{d}\theta)_{\theta=\theta_1} = 0, \quad f(\theta_2 - \pi) + g(\theta_2) = 0, \quad f(\theta_1) = g(\theta_1). \quad (3.8)$$

With the substitutions $\omega\tau = \mathrm{cotg}\phi$ and $j_{max}d/h_0 = \alpha$ the solution for f reads:

$$f = -\alpha + \delta_1 \mathrm{e}^{-\theta\,\mathrm{tg}\,\phi} + \sin\phi\,\sin(\phi + \theta). \quad (3.9)$$

From the boundary conditions follows $\delta_1 = \mathrm{e}^{\theta_1\,\mathrm{tg}\phi}\cos\phi\,\cos(\phi + \theta_1)$. The simplest solution concerning g we obtain by assuming $E = 0$, thus

$$g = -\alpha + \cos\theta_1 = f(\theta_1). \quad (3.10)$$

The components of χ are calculated from the corresponding Fourier integrals:

$$\left.\begin{array}{l} 1 + \chi' = \mu' = \pi^{-1}\sin\phi\,\{(\pi-\theta_2+\theta_1)\sin\phi + \sin(\theta_1-\theta_2)\sin(\theta_1+\theta_2-\pi)\} \\ \chi'' = \mu'' = \pi^{-1}\sin\phi\,\{(\pi-\theta_2+\theta_1)\cos\phi - \sin(\theta_1-\theta_2)\cos(\theta_1+\theta_2-\pi)\} \end{array}\right\} \quad (3.11)$$

It may be noted that for $\alpha = 0$: $\theta_1 = \theta_2 = \pi/2-\phi$ and μ' and μ'' reduce to values on the half-circle as discussed in the preceding section.

In fig. 4c some *b–h* loops for typical values of $\omega\tau$ and α are given. In fig. 5 the frequency dependence of the dissipation as function of α is presented.

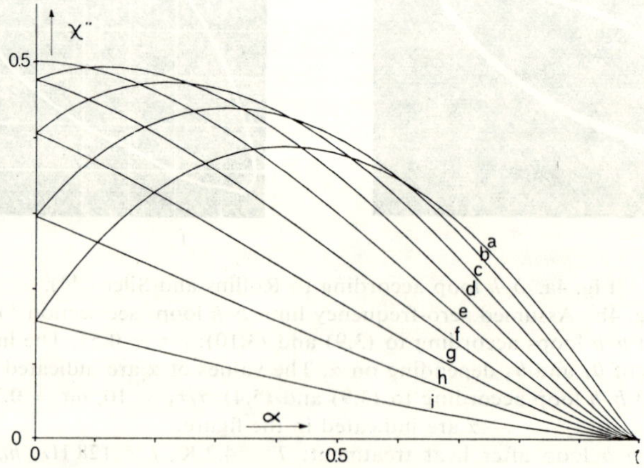

Fig. 5. χ'' as a function of α at different frequencies; $\omega\tau = \mathrm{cotg}\,\phi$ with $\phi = k\,\pi/20$, $k = 9, 8,..,1$ for the curves *a–i*, respectively.

4. *Experiments.* The experiments were performed on a hollow niobium cylinder of 25 mm length, 3 mm outer radius and 0.3 mm wall thickness. Data were obtained before and after the sample had passed an inductive heat treatment at 2200 °C for 2 hours in a vacuum better than 10^{-5} torr.

The consequences of the model in the preceding section were verified by means of two types of experiments. First the a.c. susceptibility was measured with a Hartshorn bridge[20]). Secondly the off-balance voltage of the bridge was integrated to show the local b–h loops on an oscilloscope and recorded on 16 mm film. The three parameters that have been varied are the frequency and amplitude of the modulating field and the static field. Above H_{c2} no hysteretic behaviour was observed. The frequency dependence of χ of the sample before the heat treatment is presented in fig. 6. The calculated frequency dependence of the χ'–χ'' curves fits

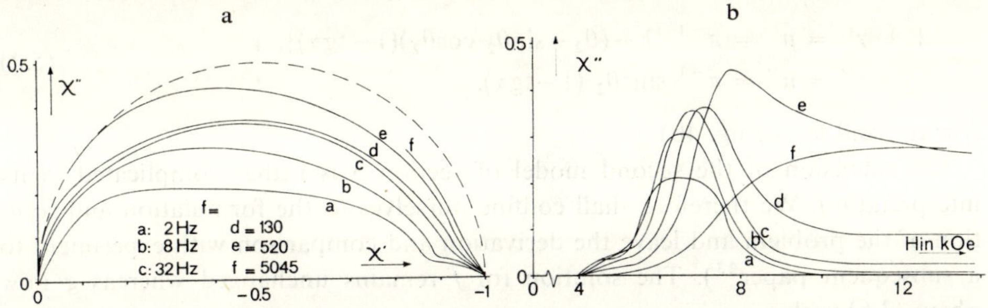

Fig. 6a. χ'–χ'' curves at different frequencies; $T = 4.2$ K, $h_0 = 6$ Oe. The parameter along each curve is the static field.
Fig. 6b. Corresponding χ'' *vs.* H_0 curves.

rather well the observed shape at high values of the static field and not too small values of the amplitude. However, the fact that an amplitude dependence of the χ'–χ'' curve experimentally is also found cannot be explained with the help of the two-parameter model of section 3. The influence of the amplitude can also be seen by plotting χ'' as a function of log h_0 at fixed values of H_0 and comparing it with the function predicted in section 3. In fig. 7 it is shown that although a single function can describe the χ''–h_0 dependence (even to values of H_0 below H_{c2} after the sample has been heat-treated) this function largely deviates from the predicted shape. The main reason for this discrepancy can be found from the shape

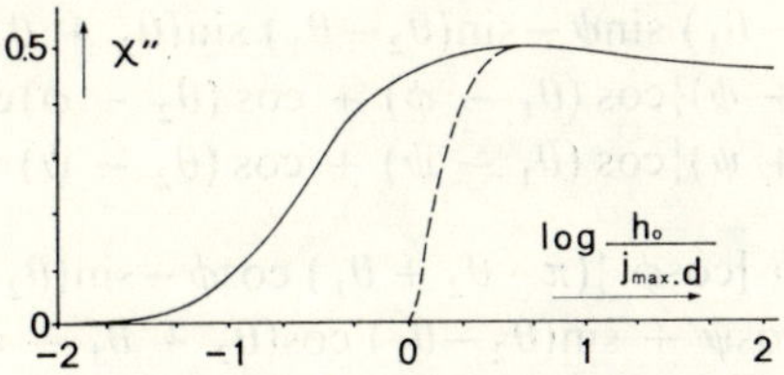

Fig. 7. χ'' *vs.* log $h_0/j_{max}d$ at 130 Hz ($\omega\tau \approx 1$) after heat treatment. Solid line: experimental values. Dashed line: according to (3.11) with $\omega\tau \approx 1$.

of the b–h loops. Some are presented in fig. 4e and f. It is seen there that no horizontal parts occur, in contradiction to our assumptions.

5. *Extensions of the models of section* 3. To overcome the difficulties mentioned before we must supplement the assumptions of section 3. The absence of horizontal parts indicates that the changes in the superconducting current are caused by an electrical field and can be described by a London-like equation:

$$\mathrm{d}j_s/\mathrm{d}t = \sigma E/\tau_1 . \tag{5.1}$$

For the zero-frequency limit b–h loop (see fig. 4b) this means a parallelogram with non-horizontal parts providing an electrical field in accordance with Maxwell's equation (3.3). For this type of b–h loop χ' and χ'' can be written:

$$\left.\begin{aligned} 1 + \chi' &= \mu' = \pi^{-1} \{\pi - (\theta_2 - \sin\theta_2 \cos\theta_2)(1 - \mathrm{tg}\alpha)\}, \\ \chi'' &= \mu'' = \pi^{-1} \sin^2\theta_2 \, (1 - \mathrm{tg}\alpha), \end{aligned}\right\} \tag{5.2}$$

(for $\mathrm{tg}\alpha$ and θ_2 see fig. 4b).

The extension of the second model of section 3 is rather complicated in its interpretation. We therefore shall confine ourselves to the formulation and solution of the problem and leave the derivation and comparison with experiment to a subsequent paper[23]). The solution for f remains unchanged whereas g now obeys (3.6) with

$$j_s = (\sigma/\tau_1) \int_{t_1}^{t} E \, \mathrm{d}t - j_{\max} = -(\tau/\tau_1) h_i(t) - j_{\max} + (\tau/\tau_1) h_i(t_1). \tag{5.3}$$

For g then follows:

$$\begin{aligned} g(\theta) = {} & -\alpha + \cos\theta_1 (1 - \mathrm{tg}\,\phi/\mathrm{tg}\,\psi) \\ & + \mathrm{tg}\,\phi/\mathrm{tg}\,\psi \{\delta_2 \mathrm{e}^{-\theta\,\mathrm{tg}\,\psi} + \sin\psi \sin(\psi + \theta)\}. \end{aligned} \tag{5.4}$$

with $\delta_2 = \mathrm{e}^{\theta_1 \mathrm{tg}\psi} \cos\psi \cos(\psi + \theta_1)$ (from $(\mathrm{d}g/\mathrm{d}\theta)_{\theta=\theta_1} = 0$); $\mathrm{tg}\psi = (1 + \tau/\tau_1)\,\mathrm{tg}\phi$. The boundary condition (3.8) now allows for several solutions of θ_1, θ_2-combinations of which the following two cases may be mentioned:

A. $\theta_2 - \theta_1 < \pi$, *i.e.*, $\pi/2 - \psi < \theta_1 \leqq \pi/2 - \phi$,

$$\begin{aligned} 1 + \chi' = \mu' = \pi^{-1} \mathrm{tg}\phi \, [& \cos\phi \, \{(\pi - \theta_2 + \theta_1) \sin\phi + \sin(\theta_2 - \theta_1) \sin(\theta_2 + \theta_1 \\ & + \phi)\} + \cos\psi \, \{(\theta_2 - \theta_1) \sin\psi - \sin(\theta_2 - \theta_1) \sin(\theta_2 + \theta_1 + \psi)\} \\ & - 2 \cos^2\phi \cos(\theta_1 + \phi) \{\cos(\theta_1 - \phi) + \cos(\theta_2 - \phi) \mathrm{e}^{(\pi - \theta_2 + \theta_1)\,\mathrm{tg}\,\phi}\} \\ & + 2 \cos^2\psi \cos(\theta_1 + \psi) \{\cos(\theta_1 - \psi) + \cos(\theta_2 - \psi) \mathrm{e}^{(\theta_1 - \theta_2)\,\mathrm{tg}\,\psi}\}], \end{aligned}$$

$$\begin{aligned} \chi'' = \mu'' = \pi^{-1} \mathrm{tg}\phi \, [& \cos\phi \, \{(\pi - \theta_2 + \theta_1) \cos\phi - \sin(\theta_2 - \theta_1) \cos(\theta_2 + \theta_1 + \phi)\} \\ & + \cos\psi \, \{(\theta_2 - \theta_1) \cos\psi + \sin(\theta_2 - \theta_1) \cos(\theta_2 + \theta_1 + \psi)\} \\ & - 2 \cos^2\phi \cos(\theta_1 + \phi) \{\sin(\theta_1 - \phi) + \sin(\theta_2 - \phi) \mathrm{e}^{(\pi - \theta_2 + \theta_1)\,\mathrm{tg}\,\phi}\} \\ & + 2 \cos^2\psi \cos(\theta_1 + \psi) \{\sin(\theta_1 - \psi) - \sin(\theta_2 - \psi) \mathrm{e}^{(\theta_1 - \theta_2)\,\mathrm{tg}\,\psi}\}]. \end{aligned} \tag{5.5}$$

B. $\theta_2 - \theta_1 = \pi$, *i.e.*, $\theta_1 = \pi/2 - \psi$,

$$1 + \chi' = \mu' = \sin\psi \cos\psi \,\mathrm{tg}\phi,$$
$$\chi'' = \mu'' = \cos^2\psi \,\mathrm{tg}\phi. \qquad (5.6)$$

Some typical shapes of the *b–h* loops and χ'–χ'' curves are presented in figs. 4d and 8, respectively.

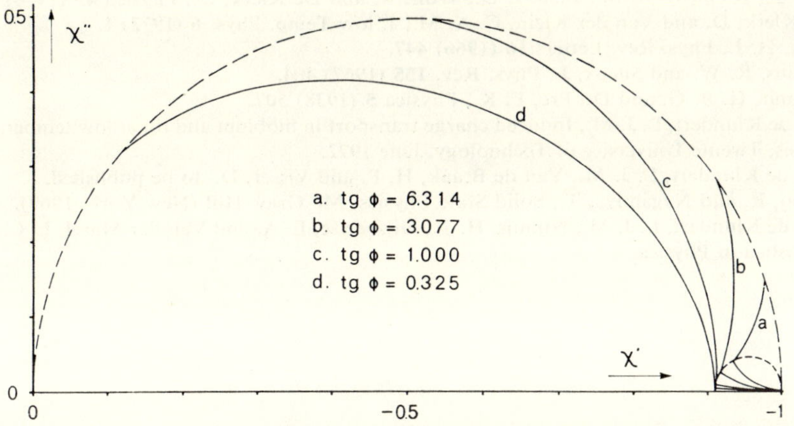

Fig. 8. χ' *vs.* χ'' curves according to (5.5) (between the dashed half-circles) and (5.6) (inside the smaller half circle); $\tau/\tau_1 = 10$.

The main advantage of this 3-parameter model is the fact that the χ'–χ'' curves consist of two parts in agreement with the experimental results. Apart from the frequency only the external field dependence of the parameters σ and τ/τ_1 plays a rôle. Also the slope $d\chi''/d\chi'$ at $\chi = -1$ has a finite value in agreement with the experiments.

Acknowledgements. The authors are indebted to Professor H. G. de Winter for his interest in this work and for valuable discussions. They wish to thank Mr. H. A. Steffens, Mr. J. A. Ulfman and Mr. M. Caspari for their technical support. The cooperation of the university computer centre "Rekencentrum" during the calculations and in preparation of some figures is gratefully acknowledged.

REFERENCES

1) Van den Broek, J., Van der Marel, L. C. and Gorter, C. J., Physica **25** (1959) 371.
2) Bean, C. P., De Blois, R. W. and Nesbitt, L. B., J. appl. Phys. **30** (1959) 1976.
3) Cotti, P., Phys. Letters **4** (1963) 114; Phys. Kondens. Materie **3** (1964) 40.
4) Clark, A. F., Deason, V. A. and Powell, R. L., Cryogenics **12** (1972) 35.
5) De Haas, W. J. and Du Pré, F. K., Physica **5** (1938) 501.
6) Van Vleck, J. H., Phys. Rev. **59** (1941) 724 and 730.
7) Gorter, C. J., Van der Marel, L. C. and Bölger, B., Physica **21** (1955) 103.

8) Van den Broek, J., Van der Marel, L. C. and Gorter, C. J., Physica **27** (1961) 661.
Van den Broek, J. and Van der Marel, L. C., Physica **29** (1963) 948.
9) Zenneck, J., Ann. Phys. **9** (1902) 497.
10) Wwedensky, B., Ann. Phys. **64** (1921) 609.
11) Kouwenhoven, W. B. and Daiger, G. P., Rev. sci. Instr. **5** (1934) 94.
12) Van den Berg, G. J. and Van der Marel, L. C., Suppl. Bull. I.I.F. Annexe 1955-2, 161.
13) Bean, C. P., Phys. Rev. Letters **8** (1962) 250.
14) London, H., Phys. Letters **6** (1963) 162.
15) Van der Klein, C. A. M., Elen, J. D., Wolf, R. and De Klerk, D., Physica **49** (1970) 98.
16) De Klerk, D. and Van der Klein, C. A. M., J. low Temp. Phys. **6** (1972) 1.
17) Fink, H. J., Phys. Rev. Letters **16** (1966) 447.
18) Rollins, R. W. and Silcox, J., Phys. Rev. **155** (1967) 404.
19) Casimir, H. B. G. and Du Pré, F. K., Physica **5** (1938) 507.
20) Van de Klundert, L. J. M., Induced charge transport in niobium and tin at low temperatures, Thesis, Twente University of Technology, june 1972.
21) Van de Klundert, L. J. M., Van de Braak, H. P. and Visser, D., to be published.
22) Kubo, R. and Nagamiya, T., Solid State Physics, Mc Graw-Hill (New York, 1969).
23) Van de Klundert, L. J. M., Nijnuis, H. T., Gijsbertse, E. A. and Van der Marel, L. C., to be published in Physica.

Physica **69** (1973) 171–176 © *North-Holland Publishing Co.*

THE THERMOELECTRIC POWER OF A METAL IN THE LIMIT OF HIGH PURITY AND LOW TEMPERATURE *

P. G. KLEMENS

Department of Physics and Institute of Materials Science, University of Connecticut, Storrs, Connecticut, USA

Received 13 April 1973

Synopsis

The electronic component of the thermoelectric power of metals is discussed in the case when a unique relaxation time cannot be defined. It is argued that the relaxation time to be used in the standard expression should be the relaxation time appropriate to isothermal electrical conduction. An old argument due to Bethe is modified to show that the logarithmic derivative of the relaxation time vanishes to first order in the limit when the temperature is low but the electrical resistivity arises from electron–phonon interactions. The thermoelectric power in that case varies as the first power of temperature.

1. *Introduction.* The thermoelectric power of metals at low temperatures is not well understood because it is composed of an electronic and a phonon-drag component, because it can be affected by impurities which have an anomalously large influence on the thermoelectric properties, and because the electron scattering cannot be described by a unique relaxation time. The present paper will not solve all these problems, and will thus not lead to an understanding of low-temperature thermoelectric properties. Its purpose is merely to clarify the last-named difficulty, namely how to treat the electronic component when the electron relaxation time cannot be uniquely defined. The paper thus represents only a small step towards the understanding of thermoelectricity. More specifically it will be pointed out that the relaxation time appropriate for thermoelectricity is the same relaxation time as for electrical conduction, while thermal conduction is to be described by a different relaxation time. At very low temperatures in the ideal resistivity region, where this distinction becomes important, the electrical-conductivity relaxation time is essentially independent of electron energy.

2. *Formal theory of thermoelectricity.* The thermoelectric properties are best calculated in terms of the Peltier coefficient, for this is defined in terms of an iso-

* Supported by the U.S. Army Research Office, Durham, North Carolina.

thermal situation, and the Boltzmann equation is then relatively simple. The current density j due to an electric field F can be expressed as[1])

$$j = \sigma F = -F \int \sigma(E) \frac{\mathrm{d}f^0}{\mathrm{d}E} \,\mathrm{d}E, \tag{1}$$

where σ is the electrical conductivity, E is the energy of an electron state, $f^0(E)$ is the Fermi–Dirac distribution function, and $\sigma(E)$ is the partial electrical conductivity. In a simple model $\sigma(E)$ is the product of the density of states and the average mobility of all electrons of energy E. For our purposes it is sufficient to note that

$$j(E)\,\mathrm{d}E = F\left(-\frac{\mathrm{d}f^0}{\mathrm{d}E}\right)\sigma(E)\,\mathrm{d}E \tag{2}$$

is the contribution to the current density from electrons in the energy interval E, $\mathrm{d}E$.

Heat being energy measured from the Fermi energy ζ, the heat current density is given by

$$Q = \frac{1}{e}\int j(E)(E-\zeta)\,\mathrm{d}E = \frac{F}{e}\int (E-\zeta)\sigma(E)\left(-\frac{\mathrm{d}f^0}{\mathrm{d}E}\right)\mathrm{d}E. \tag{3}$$

The Peltier coefficient, defined as $\Pi = Q/j$ in the absence of a temperature gradient, can now be readily derived. It is convenient to express energies in reduced energies relative to the Fermi energy, *i.e.*,

$$\varepsilon = (E-\zeta)/KT. \tag{4}$$

Then one can define a set of moments of the function $(-\mathrm{d}f^0/\mathrm{d}\varepsilon)\sigma(\varepsilon)$, *i.e.*

$$\begin{aligned} K_0 &= \textstyle\int \sigma(\varepsilon)(-\mathrm{d}f^0/\mathrm{d}\varepsilon)\,\mathrm{d}\varepsilon,\\ K_1 &= \textstyle\int \sigma(\varepsilon)\varepsilon(-\mathrm{d}f^0/\mathrm{d}\varepsilon)\,\mathrm{d}\varepsilon,\\ K_2 &= \textstyle\int \sigma(\varepsilon)\varepsilon^2(-\mathrm{d}f^0/\mathrm{d}\varepsilon)\,\mathrm{d}\varepsilon \end{aligned} \tag{5}$$

and one finds that

$$\Pi = (KT/e)(K_1/K_0). \tag{6}$$

In the case of high degeneracy, when one can expand $\sigma(E)$ or $\sigma(\varepsilon)$ as a Taylor series about the Fermi energy, one obtains the familiar form

$$\Pi = \frac{\pi^2}{3}\frac{(KT)^2}{e}\frac{1}{\sigma}\left[\frac{\mathrm{d}\sigma(E)}{\mathrm{d}E}\right]_\zeta, \tag{7}$$

where the derivative is taken with ζ kept constant and at the electron energy $E = \zeta$. Note that $[\mathrm{d}\sigma(E)/\mathrm{d}E]_\zeta$ must not be interpreted, as is sometimes done, as the derivative of the total conductivity σ with respect to the value of the Fermi energy. This distinction is not important when the scattering processes are elastic, but will be vital in the case of low-temperature ideal resistivity, discussed below.

The thermoelectric power is derivable from the Peltier coefficient by means of

$$S = \Pi/T = \frac{\pi^2}{3}\left(\frac{K}{e}\right)\frac{KT}{\sigma}\left[\frac{d\sigma(E)}{dE}\right]_{\zeta}. \tag{8}$$

Note that the quantity (K/e) is negative, because the electronic charge is negative.

3. *Relaxation time approximation.* The quantity $\sigma(E)$ can be expressed in terms of the relaxation time $\tau(\boldsymbol{k})$ of each electron state, where the electron state is specified by a wave vector $\boldsymbol{k}$ as well as by a spin component. One can readily show that

$$\sigma(E) = \frac{2e^2}{3(2\pi)^3}\oint \frac{v^2\tau(\boldsymbol{k})}{(dE/dk)_n}\, dS, \tag{9}$$

where the integration extends over an energy contour (E constant) in $\boldsymbol{k}$-space, dS is a surface element of that contour, $(dE/dk)_n$ is the normal derivative and v the electron velocity. The relaxation time $\tau(\boldsymbol{k})$ needs to be known at each point $\boldsymbol{k}$ on the contour. Formally the relaxation time is defined for each electron state $\boldsymbol{k}$ by the relation

$$\left.\frac{df}{dt}\right] = -g(\boldsymbol{k})/\tau(\boldsymbol{k}), \tag{10}$$

where the left-hand side denotes the rate of return to equilibrium of an electron distribution function $f(\boldsymbol{k})$ which departs from its equilibrium value by an amount $g(\boldsymbol{k})$. We are only interested in the problem when $df/dt]$ is a linear function of the deviations $g(\boldsymbol{k}')$ of all the other electron states $\boldsymbol{k}'$, since the g's are assumed to be small. However, $df/dt]$ depends in general on the functional form of $g(\boldsymbol{k}')$, so that $\tau(\boldsymbol{k})$ is a functional of $g(\boldsymbol{k}')/g(\boldsymbol{k})$. In the special case when $\tau(\boldsymbol{k})$ is independent of the functional form of $g(\boldsymbol{k}')$, the relaxation time is unique. However, one can always define a relaxation time $\tau(\boldsymbol{k})$ for a particular physical situation in terms of the functional form of $g(\boldsymbol{k}')/g(\boldsymbol{k})$ appropriate to the steady-state distribution of that physical situation.

For a spherical Fermi surface and an isotropic relaxation mechanism, $\tau(\boldsymbol{k})$ will be independent of the direction of the electric field or temperature gradient, but will be a function of electron energy. In this case we shall be concerned with the energy dependence of $g(\boldsymbol{k}')$. In that case one can write (9) in the form

$$\sigma(E) \propto v(E)k^2(E)\tau(E), \tag{11}$$

where $k(E)$ is the radius of the energy contour E in $\boldsymbol{k}$-space; one can regard the logarithmic derivative of $\sigma(E)$ in (8) to be additively composed of the logarithmic derivative of each term in (11).

4. *Solution of the Boltzmann equation at low temperatures.* We are now interested in the case when the temperature is low compared to the Debye temperature, but sufficiently high so that the electron–phonon interaction predominates in the electrical-resistance mechanism. This implies, of course, a very pure metal specimen.

The thermoelectric power in this case was treated by Bethe[2]). If one corrects an elementary mistake in his argument he would have concluded that the effective relaxation time is an even function of ε, or more precisely, that $\tau v/k$ is an even function of ε, so that the logarithmic derivative of $\sigma(E)$ is given by the logarithmic derivative of $k^3(E)$.

First we note that the Boltzmann equation to be solved is that appropriate for isothermal electrical conductivity. There was nothing in the derivation of equation (7) which required $\sigma(E)$ to be expressible in terms of a unique relaxation time; the quantity $\sigma(E)$ is defined by (2) in the case when the conditions are isothermal.

Let us now consider the Boltzmann equation for isothermal electrical conduction. Using the notation of Bethe[2]) we may write it in the form

$$S \cdot c(E) = A(E), \tag{12}$$

where

$$A(E) = \frac{9\pi M u}{\hbar C^2 a^3}\, eF \,\frac{1}{k}\left(\frac{\mathrm{d}E}{\mathrm{d}k}\right)^2. \tag{13}$$

Here M is the ionic mass, u the sound velocity, a^3 the atomic volume and C the electron–phonon interaction parameter. The quantity $A(E)$ depends on electron energy through the factors C^2, k and $\mathrm{d}E/\mathrm{d}k$.

The quantity $c(E)$ is a measure of the deviation of the electron distribution $f(\boldsymbol{k})$ from its equilibrium value $f^0(E)$, and can be formally related to the effective relaxation time τ (now only a function of E), through

$$g(\boldsymbol{k}) = (e\boldsymbol{F}\cdot\boldsymbol{v})\frac{\mathrm{d}f^0}{\mathrm{d}E} = -\frac{1}{F}(\boldsymbol{k}\cdot\boldsymbol{F})\frac{\mathrm{d}f^0}{\mathrm{d}E}\,c(E) \tag{14}$$

so that $c(E) = eF(\tau v/k)$. The operator S is the integral operator for the rate of change of the electron distribution due to phonon interactions, and has the explicit form

$$\begin{aligned} S \cdot c(E) = \int N(q)q^2\,\mathrm{d}q \Big\{ &[(1 + \omega/vk - q^2/2k^2)c(E + \hbar\omega) - c(E)] \\ &\times \frac{f_0(E + \hbar\omega)}{f_0(E)}\,\mathrm{e}^{\hbar\omega/KT} \\ &+ [(1 - \omega/vk - q^2/2k^2)c(E - \hbar\omega) - c(E)]\,\frac{f_0(E - \hbar\omega)}{f_0(E)} \Big\}. \end{aligned} \tag{15}$$

The method of solution due to Bloch[3]) and discussed by Bethe[2]) differs from the variational method used today, but can be shown to be equivalent in the case of (12) when the variational trial function for $c(E)$ is chosen to be a constant. One divides S into two parts

$$\mathsf{S} = \mathsf{S}_0 + \mathsf{S}_1, \tag{16}$$

where S_0 consists of the first and last term in each square bracket, and S_1 consists of the other two terms. One notes that S_0 has the property

$$\mathsf{S}_0 \cdot \text{constant} \equiv 0. \tag{17}$$

Also, S_0 can be seen to be even in ε, but S_1 has a small odd component due to the factors $1/k$ and $1/k^2$. Thus we may write

$$\mathsf{S}_1(E) \equiv Q(E)\mathsf{S}_1(\zeta) = [Q(\zeta) + KT\varepsilon Q'(\zeta)]\mathsf{S}_1(\zeta). \tag{18}$$

Consider the two basic equations

$$\mathsf{S}(\zeta) \cdot c_0 = 1 \tag{19}$$

and

$$\mathsf{S}(\zeta) \cdot c_1 = \varepsilon. \tag{20}$$

The first is essentially the integral equation (12) for electrical conduction; the second is essentially the integral equation for thermal conduction[2, 4]). Equation (12) can now be written as

$$[\mathsf{S}_0 + (1 + KT\varepsilon Q'/Q)\mathsf{S}_1]c = A(\zeta) + KT\varepsilon A'(\zeta) \tag{21}$$

and has a formal solution

$$c = A(\zeta)c_0 + KT(A' - AQ'/Q)c_1, \tag{22}$$

where c_0 is an even function of ε and c_1 is an odd function. We can also show that c_1 is much less than c_0, since

$$c_1/c_0 = L/L_0, \tag{23}$$

where L is the Lorenz number for pure metals at the temperature in question, and L_0 is the Sommerfeld value of the Lorenz number. Since $L/L_0 \simeq 8(T/\theta)^2$ – see ref. 4 – it follows that c is mainly even, and that the odd component, instead of being of order (KT/ζ), is of order $KT^3/\zeta\theta^2$, where θ is the Debye temperature. Thus at low temperatures the logarithmic derivative of $\tau v/k$ vanishes to first order, and the thermoelectric power is given by

$$S = \frac{\pi^2}{3}\left(\frac{K}{e}\right) KT \left[\frac{\mathrm{d} \log k^3(E)}{\mathrm{d}E}\right]_\zeta . \tag{24}$$

The factor $\mathrm{d} \log k^3(E)/\mathrm{d}E = 3/2\,\zeta$ for a spherical Fermi surface.

Bethe, overlooking the factor $k^3(E)$ in the relation $\sigma \propto k^3 c(E)$, concluded that the thermopower at low temperatures varies not as T but as T^3. His correct conclusion should have been that the term in T should be

$$S = \frac{\pi^2}{2}\left(\frac{K}{e}\right)\frac{KT}{\zeta} \tag{25}$$

and the logarithmic derivation of $\tau v/k$ should only contribute a smaller term proportional to T^3.

This result has a simple physical interpretation. The electron–phonon interaction changes both the direction and energy of an electron. The operator S_0 describes essentially the change in electron energy associated with each interaction, the operator S_1 the change in direction. For electrical resistivity the change in energy is unimportant; the electron has to randomise its direction for an interaction to be effective. At low temperatures this is a many-step random walk on the Fermi surface, referred to as horizontal motion[4]). For thermal resistance the change in energy is also effective. This motion, termed vertical motion[4]), dominates the phonon-induced thermal resistance at low temperatures. Because vertical motion is a single-step process, while horizontal motion is a many-step process, $c_1/c_0 = L/L_0$ is of order $(T/\theta)^2$.

For thermoelectricity, we are interested in the energy dependence of the relaxation time τ under the condition of isothermal electrical conduction. Since each electron moving horizontally over the Fermi surface in a many-step random walk changes its energy at every step, it soon loses memory of its initial energy. The relaxation time τ, being a measure of the time it takes to randomise direction by this random walk, is thus independent of the initial energy of the electron. The full argument leads to a slightly different conclusion: it is not τ but $c \propto \tau v/k$, which is independent of ε.

REFERENCES

1) See, for example, Klemens, P. G., in Thermal Conductivity, ed. R. P. Tye, vol. 1, p. 1 (Academic Press, London, 1969).
2) Bethe, H., in Sommerfeld, A. and Bethe, H., Elektronentheorie der Metalle, Handb. d. Physik vol. 24/2, Springer, Berlin 1933; reprinted under the above title, 1967.
3) Bloch, F., Z. Phys. **52** (1928) 555; *ibid.* **57** (1929) 545.
4) Klemens, P. G., in Hand. d. Physik vol. 14, Springer, Berlin, 1956.

Physica **69** (1973) 177–192 © *North-Holland Publishing Co.*

$\chi = C/(T+\Delta)$, THE MOST OVERWORKED FORMULA IN THE HISTORY OF PARAMAGNETISM

J. H. VAN VLECK

Lyman Laboratory of Physics, Harvard University, Cambridge, Massachusetts, USA

Received 4 June 1973

Synopsis

A review is presented of the values to be expected theoretically for the coefficient of $1/T^2$ in the expansion of the paramagnetic susceptibility in powers of $1/T$ under various conditions. In particular this coefficient vanishes for a magnetically dilute powder when only a single J manifold is inhabited. Apart from the molecular-field approximation for magnetically concentrated materials, the relation $\chi = C/(T + \Delta)$ appears to have no theoretical justification, but often works surprisingly well empirically.

Foreword. None of the material in the present article is particularly new. One of the points which is emphasized is the absence of the $1/T^2$ term in the expansion in $1/T$ of the susceptibility of magnetically dilute powders. This result was derived in the early papers of Penney and Schlapp[1]). However, it was presented in a rather incidental way. It was somewhat more explicitly stressed in my monograph in the Annales de l'Institut Henri Poincaré[2]). However, this reference is not too readily available; so the theorem does not appear to be too generally known. At any rate, at least one paper[3]) has been published by a competent theoretical physicist in which a non-vanishing coefficient of $1/T^2$ was calculated (due to a computational error discovered later) and an attempt made to obtain information about the crystalline field therefrom. Also in general the formula $\chi = C/(T + \Delta)$ has been used far too generally. So the present paper is perhaps not superfluous. Also it is to a limited extent a review of the history of paramagnetism, a subject appropriate for an issue of Physica honoring Gorter. Although one thinks first of all of his spectacular pioneer work in paramagnetic relaxation and his research in superconductivity, one must not forget that Gorter's doctoral thesis[4]) was on paramagnetic susceptibilities, and that over the years he has headed an extensive program on measurements of paramagnetism.

It is indeed a pleasure to contribute an article on the present occasion, as my acquaintance with Gorter has been rewarding to me scientifically and enjoyable personally. I like to think of him as a fellow Dutchman, but my doing so is rather presumptuous inasmuch as Tielman Van Vleeck came to Nieuw Amsterdam in 1658. However, I have visited Leiden many times and so has Gorter the U.S.A. I had the honor of being Lorentz Professor at Leiden in 1960, and we had that of having Gorter as visiting professor at Harvard in the summer of 1947.

1. *Introduction – The period 1907–1931 and the Weiss molecular field.* In 1970 Weiss[5]) proposed his celebrated theory of the molecular field. His basic idea was that the effective field H_{eff} acting on an elementary magnet is given by

$$H_{\text{eff}} = H + qM, \tag{1}$$

where M is the intensity of magnetization and q is a constant. The present article will be concerned only with paramagnetism, with neglect of saturation effects in strong fields. So we shall not discuss the successes of the Weiss theory below the Curie point. Instead we will confine our attention to paramagnets (or the paramagnetic region above the Curie or Néel points of ferromagnets or antiferromagnets) where the magnetic moment is a linear function of the applied field. In 1905 Langevin showed that the moment per unit volume of a free elementary magnet in classical statistical mechanics obeys Curie's law.

$$M = \frac{C}{T} H. \tag{2}$$

He also showed that the Curie constant C has the value $N\mu^2/3k$ where N is the number of atoms (or molecules) per unit volume and μ is the dipole moment of a single atom or molecule. Replacement in (2) of H by H_{eff} as given by (1) yields immediately for the susceptibility $\chi = M/H$ the formula

$$\chi = \frac{C}{T - \theta}, \tag{3}$$

where $\theta = Cq$.

Soon after 1907, it was found that (3) represents exceedingly well the behavior of ferromagnetics unless one is close to the Curie point. To be sure, there are breaks in the linearity of $1/\chi$ plotted against T, but this behavior was attributed to polymorphic transitions which give discontinuities in the values of θ and perhaps C.

The origin of the molecular field remained a mystery until 1928, when Heisenberg[6]) showed it was due to a quantum-mechanical exchange effect. He demonstrated that with a certain simplifying assumption (supposition that exchange is isotropic and that all states of the same total spin for the whole crystal have the same energy) one obtains exactly the result (3), with θ proportional to the exchange integral. The exchange integral can have either sign, and if it is negative so also are q and θ. Then if one sets $\Delta = -\theta$ and takes $\Delta \gg T$ one has a weak paramagnetic susceptibility almost independent of temperature, as the writer pointed out when he wrote his book in 1932[7]). This explained the behavior of what today are called antiferromagnetic materials well above the Néel point. He did not recognize the fact that there was a critical temperature below which antiferromagnetic ordering sets in, in which the moment is still a linear function of *H*, but the expression for the susceptibility is given by a different expression than (3). Instead Néel[8]) was the first to predict this behavior, soon confirmed experimentally. Today it is realized that antiferromagnetic materials are quite common, but often the Néel temperatures are low, and so the critical behavior characteristic of the Néel point was first revealed for many substances by experiments made at Leiden. (The first definitely established antiferromagnets, however, were reported by Bizette, Squire and Tsai[9]) in France in 1938–9; the materials were MnO and MnSe which have a Néel temperature so high that low temperatures are not necessary to observe the critical transition.)

Even for ideal ferromagnetic or antiferromagnet materials devoid of appreciable crystalline field (atomic S states) eq. (3) is but an approximation. Actually the susceptibility is instead expressible only in a poorly convergent power series

$$\chi = \frac{C}{T} + \frac{a}{T^2} + \frac{b}{T^3} + \ldots. \tag{4}$$

The labour of calculating the various coefficients increases enormously the further out one goes. Up to ten or eleven have been calculated in some instances. However, if one writes the susceptibility in the form

$$\chi = \frac{C}{T - \theta(T)}, \tag{5}$$

with θ considered a function of temperature rather than a constant, then $\theta(T)$ is but a slowly varying function of temperature and clearly $\theta(T_C) = T_C$. The ratio $\theta(\infty)/\theta(T_C)$ is the same as the ratio of the so-called paramagnetic and ferromagnetic Curie temperatures (determined respectively by the asymptotic behavior of χ for large T and the temperature at which χ becomes infinite). The value of $\theta(\infty)$ is just $-a/C$, which is easily calculated, while $\theta(T_C)$ can be estimated by various extrapolative schemes (Padé approximation, *etc.*). The value of $\theta(\infty)/\theta(T_C)$ depends not only on the atomic spin but also the lattice geometry. This ratio ranges from about 1.2 to 1.6 for the Heisenberg model. For detailed references on the most accurate values for various cases the reader is referred to a book by Stanley[10]).

2. *Magnetically dilute materials and the crystalline field.* So far we have discussed magnetically concentrated materials, the type of substances Weiss originally had in mind. In section 1 we tacitly assumed that the crystalline-field effects are of

subordinate importance. We now turn to the case of magnetically dilute materials, where exchange can be neglected except at very low temperatures, and where the deviations from Curie's law are caused primarily by the crystalline field (except for the well-known cases of the Eu^{3+} and Sm^{3+} ions). Here, at least from a theoretical standpoint, the formula $\chi = C/(T + \Delta)$ has even less foundation than for concentrated materials.

When a material which would obey Curie's law were its ions free, is subject to a crystalline field, the susceptibility can be developed as a power series of the form (4), provided the splittings of energy levels caused by the field are small compared to kT. This is obvious from the fact that the Boltzmann factors $e^{-E/kT}$ involved in the partition function can be expanded as Taylor's series in $1/kT$. However, what is not so obvious, is that for the powder susceptibility, *i.e.* the average of the principal susceptibilities, the term a in eq. (4) is completely absent, although it can exist for an individual principal susceptibility. Thus for a powder the conventional Weiss formula is not even asymptotically correct, as

$$\frac{C}{T + \Delta} = \frac{C}{T} - \frac{C\Delta}{T^2} + \frac{C\Delta^2}{T^3} + \dots \tag{6}$$

and actually one has instead

$$\chi = \frac{C}{T} + \frac{b}{T^3} + \frac{c}{T^4} + \dots . \tag{7}$$

The theoretical non-existence of the $1/T^2$ term for the powder was not known until over five years after the advent of quantum mechanics. However, only a rather rudimentary quantum-mechanical calculation is required, as we will show in section 3, where the proof is presented in a slightly different form from the original demonstration by Penney and Schlapp. Since their paper did not appear until the latter part of 1932, it was natural in view of the success of the Weiss molecular-field theory for magnetically concentrated materials, that through early 1932 writers debonairely used (3) for magnetically dilute materials. Gorter's doctor's thesis and my own book on Electric and Magnetic Susceptibilities in particular appeared just a little before the theorem relating to the $1/T^2$ term became known. Gorter derived "experimental" values of θ or Δ for a number of magnetically dilute materials and in the table of p. 304 of my book I quote values of Δ for a number of such substances, measured chiefly at Leiden.

Even after 1932, the non-occurrence of the $1/T^2$ term for the powder does not appear to have been generally recognized in the literature. For instance the chapter documenting paramagnetic susceptibilities for the rare-earth compounds in the Landoldt Bornstein tables[11]) published in 1962 tabulates values of Δ for the powder susceptibilities of many magnetically dilute materials, and the introduction says "since the crystal-field splitting is relatively small for compounds of the rare earths, at sufficiently high temperature ($\approx$ room temperatures) all crystal-field components of the ground state are strongly occupied. In this case the susceptibility follows a Curie–Weiss law in close approximation

$$\chi + K = \frac{C}{T + \theta_p}.\text{''} \tag{8}$$

Actually, especially in the salts of the heavy rare earths, the over-all splitting caused by the crystalline field is often comparable or greater than kT at room temperatures, so that some components are only weakly inhabited. In other words, the measurements represented by (8) do not extend to high enough temperatures for good convergence of the series (7) and so are not informative on the term in $1/T^2$. As we discuss more fully later, it is more or less an accident that a formula of the type (8) works as well as it does over a limited temperature range.

It is refreshing by contrast to find that Van den Handel in his thesis[12]) written under de Haas at Leiden in 1940 appreciated the fact that theory requires the absence of the term in $1/T^2$ and gave appropriate reference to Penney and Schlapp. Nor did this thesis try to extract values of Δ.

3. *Proof of absence of $1/T^2$ term for a magnetically dilute powder.* We now proceed to prove the absence of the $1/T^2$ term in (4) or (7) under the specified conditions. We note first of all that the moment in the direction of the applied field H is given by the well-known formula

$$M_H = -\partial F/\partial H, \tag{9}$$

where F is the free energy

$$F = -NkT \log Z \tag{10}$$

and Z is the partition function

$$Z = \sum_j \exp(-E_j/kT) = \operatorname{Tr} \exp(-\mathscr{H}/kT). \tag{11}$$

Here $\mathscr{H}$ denotes the hamiltonian function, whose eigenvalues are the E_j. If the principal directions of the magnetic susceptibility be denoted by $i = 1, 2, 3$ and the corresponding susceptibilities by χ_1, χ_2, χ_3, then

$$\chi_i = -\frac{1}{H}\frac{\partial F}{\partial H} \tag{12}$$

with the understanding that the magnetic field H is applied in the direction corresponding to χ_i, and that only terms in F through the second order in H are to be retained (*i.e.* saturation effects neglected). The trick is now to note that, thanks to the invariance of the trace, it is not necessary to calculate the individual eigenvalues of $\mathscr{H}$ and one can instead develop Z or F as a power series in $1/kT$ and look at the values of the traces. Let us suppose that we are dealing with a J manifold, composed of $2J + 1$ substates. Then we can write

$$\mathscr{H} = g_J \beta(\boldsymbol{J} \cdot \boldsymbol{H}) + V, \tag{13}$$

where J is the angular momentum vector (measured in multiples of $h/2\pi$), β is the Bohr magneton $he/4\pi mc$ and V is the crystalline potential. We now expand Z as a power series in $1/kT$ and terminate the development with terms in $1/k^3T^3$. We thus have, supposing H directed along the z axis

$$Z = (2J + 1)\left[1 - \frac{\langle V\rangle}{kT} + \frac{\langle V^2\rangle}{2k^2T^2} - \frac{1}{6}\frac{\langle V^3\rangle}{k^3T^3} + \frac{g_J^2\beta^2H^2}{2k^2T^2}\langle J_z^2\rangle - \frac{g_J^2\beta^2H^2}{6k^3T^3}\langle J_z^2V + J_zVJ_z + VJ_z^2\rangle + \dots\right]. \tag{14}$$

Here $\langle\ \rangle$ denotes the expectation value for the J manifold computed without the Boltzmann factor, *i.e.*, for $T = \infty$. Expectation values of this type containing odd powers of H necessarily vanish since left- and right-handed senses of rotation are equally probable. Hence (14) contains no odd power of H.

The traces involved in our problem involve summation over only a finite number of states, and so

$$\langle abc\rangle = \langle bca\rangle = \langle cab\rangle, \quad etc. \tag{15}$$

Furthermore there is the familiar relation

$$\langle J_z^2\rangle = \tfrac{1}{3}J(J + 1). \tag{16}$$

If we utilize (15) and (16) we find from (10) and (12) that

$$\chi_z = \frac{N\beta^2g_J^2J(J + 1)}{3kT}\left\{1 + \frac{1}{kT}\left[\langle V\rangle - \frac{3\langle VJ_z^2\rangle}{J(J + 1)}\right] + \mathscr{O}\left(\frac{V^2}{k^2T^2}\right)\right\}. \tag{17}$$

Since $J_x^2 + J_y^2 + J_z^2 = J(J + 1)$, we see immediately that the $1/T^2$ drops out from the powder susceptiblity $\chi = (\chi_1 + \chi_2 + \chi_3)/3$, in agreement with (7), which is thus established.

Some further comments relative to the preceding analysis are in order. In the first place it shows that the Langevin formula $\chi = N\mu^2/3kT$ (appropriately specialized to a J manifold, where $\mu^2 = g_J^2\beta^2J(J + 1)$) is valid as long as the crystalline potential is small compared to kT, and cooperative effects are neglected. For under these conditions one can neglect all terms involving V in (15). This proof is more elegant, but also more subtle, than the one given in my book or original 1927 paper[13]), where the first- and second-order Zeeman energies are computed explicitly, and appropriate pairing of terms is made to make the Langevin formula come out. It disposes of any objections which can be raised by the fact that the formulas for the energies of the individual energy states may involve complicated radicals or not be expressible except as roots of high-order algebraic equations, when the Zeeman energy is comparable with the crystalline potential. It is only necessary that the crystalline potential be small compared to kT. This feature seems to be misunderstood sometimes even today, although the writer emphasized it in 1927, though in a more general context, as at that time the role of the crystalline potential was unknown. The point is that the traces involved in the expansion of the crystalline potential can be expressed as power series in the various parameters without resorting to solution of the secular equation to find the individual energy levels. The latter are needed for experiments on magnetic resonance, but not for magnetic susceptibilities as long as the splittings are small compared with kT.

Another comment is that the absence of the $1/T^2$ term in the series expansion of the powder susceptibility is practically obvious from symmetry and dimensional considerations. The way the dimensions are involved shows that the crystalline potential enters linearly in the $1/T^2$ term. Hence if we have a rhombic or second-order crystalline potential, *i.e.*

$$V = Ax^2 + By^2 + Cz^2, \tag{18}$$

the coefficient of the $1/T^2$ term for the powder must be proportional to $A + B + C$, as for the powder the x, y, z directions must enter symmetrically. Without loss of generality one can suppose that $A + B + C = 0$. This condition is met if (18) is a second-order harmonic. (If not it can be made one by subtracting $\frac{1}{3}(A + B + C)r^2$, which is a centro-symmetric term, a trivial additive constant as far as the alignment of the magnetic moment is concerned.) This is essentially the argument originally used by Schlapp and Penney. The case that V contains higher-order harmonics may appear not to be covered but can be taken care of by the following reasoning based essentially on rotation group theory. The partition function, by its very nature, cannot depend on how one chooses axes. The term in $1/T^2$ in χ involves the product of two powers of the Zeeman energy and one of the crystalline potential. Since the Zeeman term transforms like a vector, the product of two Zeeman terms cannot involve a higher harmonic of the rotation group than the second. The direct product of a second-order and a still higher-order harmonic cannot possibly yield an invariant other than zero.

As a final comment we should mention that it is not necessary that the J manifold we have employed be one associated with free rotation, such as is spanned by the inner quantum number (or in appropriate cases L or S instead of J). It is only necessary that the square $\mu_x^2 + \mu_y^2 + \mu_z^2$ of the moment has a constant value inside the manifold and that one neglects all matrix elements of the hamiltonian that take one out of this manifold. If this neglect is not allowable, it is no longer justifiable to expand in terms of $1/kT$. If the separation between manifolds is large compared to kT, and there is perfect cubic symmetry, the main effect of the inter-manifold terms is to generate a contribution to the susceptibility which is independent of temperature. The validity of the statements which we have made can be seen from the general group-theory arguments which we have presented above, or by obvious adaptations of the more explicit proof we have given at the beginning of the present section (*e.g.* $J(J+1)g^2\beta^2$ replaced by μ^2, *etc.*).

Examples of these cubic manifolds not identifiable with a specific angular-momentum quantum number are the Γ_2, Γ_4, Γ_5 manifolds in which an orbital $L = 3$ manifold is decomposed by a cubic field, or the Γ_3, Γ_5 resulting from the decomposition of $L = 2$. (We use the Bethe notation; his states Γ_1, Γ_2, Γ_3, Γ_4, Γ_5, are labelled A_1, A_2, E, T_1, T_2 by Mulliken.) In the early days of quantum mechanics, the magnetic susceptibilities of salts of the iron group were treated by taking the "spin-only" formula $\chi = 4N\beta^2S(S+1)/3kT$ as the starting point or zeroth-order approximation in the analysis. Unless a Γ_1, Γ_2 or Γ_3 orbital state is lowest (true for Fe^{3+}, Mn^{2+}, Ni^{2+}, Cu^{2+} but not for Fe^{2+} or Co^{2+}), the spin-only approximation is warranted as a point of departure only if the non-cubic portion of the crystalline field is large compared to the spin–orbit interaction. Actually, it has become increasingly realized over the years, and as is stressed particularly in Griffith's[14]) book, that it is usually a better approximation to assume that the cubic portion of the crystalline field is large compared to the spin–orbit interaction, but that the latter is more important than the deviations of the crystalline field from cubic symmetry. One therefore starts with orbital states in a field of cubic symmetry, without spin–orbit interaction. If the deepest orbital state is Γ_4 or Γ_5, its orbital moment is not completely quenched, and is represented by 3×3 matrices which differ by a factor γ from those of a state $L = 1$. The interaction of the spin with this orbital moment interior to Γ_4 or Γ_5 generates a series of energy levels which we shall call a pseudo spin–orbit multiplet, in many ways like a multiplet generated by L, S coupling for a free atom with $L = 1$. (We use the term pseudo because of the anomalous γ factor.) Different multiplet components correspond to different representations of the cubic group inclusive of spin. How one calculates γ and the g-factors for the different components of the pseudo-multiplet is explained elsewhere in the literature[15]), and so we need not enter into this question here. The point we want to make is that if the intervals in the pseudo spin–orbit multiplet are so great that one need consider only the lowest component of the pseudo-multiplet and retain only the part of the Zeeman and non-cubic hamiltonians internal to it, there will be no $1/T^2$ term in the expansion of the powder susceptibility in $1/T$. This is true because one is still working in a manifold of cubic symmetry, where $\mu_x^2 + \mu_y^2 + \mu_z^2$ has the same value for all the different substates.

The concept of pseudo-multiplets is useful only if the cubic manifold is Γ_4 or Γ_5. If instead it is Γ_1, Γ_2, or Γ_3 the spin–only formula holds perfectly except insofar as other levels are mixed in either because of the crystalline field or spin–orbit interaction. If the mixing field has only rhombic symmetry, even the Curie constant can be different for different directions.

4. *Cases where the $1/T^2$ term should be present for the powder.* So far we have concentrated on the circumstances where the $1/T^2$ term should not occur. We now shall mention some of the situations where it should be present even for the powder.

4.1. Exchange coupling. The standard example is that of the isotropically coupled magnets of the Heisenberg model. (Anisotropic exchange is readily shown to make no contribution to the order under consideration.) For the Heisenberg model the hamiltonian function is

$$\mathscr{H} = g\beta H \sum_i S_{z_i} - 2\sum_{j>i} J_{ij} \boldsymbol{S}_i \cdot \boldsymbol{S}_j,$$

where J_{ij} is the exchange integral coupling atoms i, j of spin S_i, S_j, respectively. If one expands the partition function through $1/T^3$, [which corresponds to $1/T^2$ in the susceptibility because of the factor T in eq. (10)], there are non-vanishing terms of type $\langle S_{iz}(J_{ij} S_{iz} S_{jz}) S_{zj}\rangle$. Since $\langle S_{iz}^2\rangle = S(S+1)/3$ *etc.*, the corresponding value of θ in the expansion

$$\chi = \frac{Ng^2\beta^2 S(S+1)}{3kT}\left[1 + \frac{\theta}{T} + \ldots\right]$$

is easily found to be

$$\theta = \tfrac{2}{3}S(S+1)\sum_j J_{ij}/k. \tag{19}$$

This is a well-known result, derivable in a number of other ways. If one forgets about further terms in the development and if one replaces $1 + (\theta/T)$ by $1/[1 - (\theta/T)]$ then the susceptibility becomes infinite at $T = \theta$, which is consequently interpreted as the Curie point. The Curie temperature T_C is then the same as the expression (19). This rather arbitrary procedure yields the same formula for T_C as the so-called random-phase approximation or the Weiss molecular-field model.

The $1/T^2$ term is also present if one uses the Ising rather than Heisenberg model. The Ising case is realized physically if $S = \frac{1}{2}$ and if the crystalline field is so strong that the elementary magnets have non-vanishing components only along a particular direction.

4.2. Multiplet spacings small compared to kT. Another case where the $1/T^2$ term is present, even without a crystalline field, is a magnetically dilute system composed of atoms whose spin–orbit multiplet is small compared to kT. The hamiltonian function is

$$\mathscr{H} = \sum_i [H\beta(L_{z_i} + 2S_{z_i}) + \lambda \boldsymbol{L}_i \cdot \boldsymbol{S}_i].$$

For our purposes the multiplet structure first manifests itself in the terms of type $S_{z_i}(\lambda S_{z_i} L_{z_i}) L_{z_i}$ in the expansion of the partition function to the order $1/k^3T^3$, and one finds

$$\chi = \frac{N\beta^2}{3kT}\left\{[L(L + 1) + 4S(S + 1)] - \frac{4\lambda L(L + 1)S(S + 1)}{3kT}\right\}. \qquad (20)$$

The case of a "pseudo-multiplet" found in a very powerful purely cubic field as described in the preceding section is included as a variant of (20), by replacing $L(L + 1)$ by $2\gamma^2$. This is true because, except for a factor γ as previously explained, a pseudo-multiplet is equivalent to an ordinary multiplet with $L = 1$.

4.3. Inhabited manifold not of cubic symmetry. The most common cause of the occurrence of a $1/T^2$ term for a magnetically dilute powder probably is a situation in which the manifold or collection of states that have appreciable Boltzmann factors does not have cubic symmetry. Then $\mu_x^2 + \mu_y^2 + \mu_z^2$ no longer has the same constant value for all the substates of the manifold, and the tenets basic to the analysis in section 3 cease to apply. The redistribution among the various substates gives rise to a term in $1/T^2$. In this connection one must not overlook the fact that in the Boltzmann expression $Ce^{-E/kT}$, the factor C is a function of temperature.

A good example of the situation we are now discussing is furnished by cerium ethyl sulphate at temperatures of liquid air and below. The crystalline field is approximately axial, of such a nature that the states $M_J = \pm 1/2, 5/2$ are separated by only a few cm^{-1}, and are[16]) about 95 cm^{-1} below $M_J = \pm 3/2$, whose Boltzmann factor is consequently small for the temperature range. The redistribution between $|M_J| = 1/2, 5/2$ as T is varied give a $1/T^2$ term, not just because of the matrix elements of magnetic moment interior to the $\pm 1/2, \pm 5/2$ manifold, but also because the effect of the elements joining $\pm 1/2, \pm 5/2$ to $\pm 3/2$. The contribution of these non-diagonal elements to χ ceases to be a constant independent of temperature, as it would if $\pm 1/2, \pm 5/2$ had identical Boltzmann factors when $H = 0$.

5. *Experimental evidence on the $1/T^2$ term.* There is but a limited amount of experimental data relating to the theoretical prediction that the $1/T^2$ term should be present for individual directions but average to zero for a magnetically dilute powder. The proper experimental measurements are difficult and require a judicious choice of materials. Unless the crystalline field splittings are small, measurements must be made at very high temperatures in order for series such as (7) to converge well and then the susceptibility is small and hard to measure accurately. On the other hand if the splittings are low and the measurements can be made at low temperatures, the complications of cooperative phenomena set in, unless the dilu-

tion is very great. Thus for purposes of examining the $1/T^2$ term as such, rather than the predictions of crystalline-field theory generally, the suitable materials are confined to ions in S states (Mn^{++}, Fe^{+++}, Gd^{+++}).

The leading or $1/T$ term in (17) is independent of the choice of axes. On the other hand because of the crystalline potential this is not true of the next term, *i.e.* the term in $1/T^2$. Hence if the principal susceptibilities are denoted by χ_1, χ_2, χ_3, the anisotropies $\chi_1 - \chi_2, \chi_1 - \chi_3$, should vary as $1/T^2$ provided T is sufficiently high. As far as we know the only attempt to test this prediction as such is found in some measurements reported by Krishnan, Mookherji and Bose[17]) in 1939 who measured the anisotropies of a dilute salt containing Mn^{++} at three different temperatures as shown in table I. (The experimental values are after a small correction for the diamagnetic term for the salt, which we do not discuss.)

Table I

Ratio of $1/T^2$ and paramagnetic anisotropy of $Mn(NH_4)_2(SO_4)_2 \cdot 6H_2O$ at temperatures respectively 303, 194.5, and 90 K

$1/T^2$	$\chi_1-\chi_2$	$\chi_1-\chi_3$
1 : 2.4 : 11.3	1 : 2.6 : 11.9	1 : 2.3 : 9.0

The agreement is as good as can be expected in view of the uncertainty in the diamagnetic corrections, possible effect of impurities and also the extreme difficulties in measuring the very small anisotropies, especially at the higher temperatures. On the other hand, Krishnan *et al.* did make their measurements at sufficiently high temperatures that neglect of the terms beginning with $1/T^3$ in (7) is not an important effect. In this respect their measurements differ from the usual ones made at lower temperatures or on paramagnetic salts having larger splittings due to the crystalline field.

The Mn^{++} ion is in a ^6S state, and so would conform perfectly to Curie's law, were it not for the mixing by spin–orbit interaction with other states having $J = 5/2$. Table I furnishes evidence that this mixing is more important than that caused by the crystalline field, in which case the behavior would be different. On the other hand, the measurements of Krishnan *et al.*[17]) on dilute salts containing a Ni^{++} ion require and confirm a more complicated theory first developed by Schlapp and Penney[1]), involving admixture of Γ_4, Γ_5 into Γ_2, with all three Γ levels belonging to the state ^3F of Ni^{++}, the type of situation mentioned in the final portion of section 3. This kind of admixture does not occur in Mn^{++} as Γ_1 is the sole cubic orbital manifold contained in ^6S.

The period following World War II brought important developments in magnetic research, both a wider variety of tools and of research centers. Paramagnetic resonance, in conjunction with improved conventional solid-state spectroscopy furnished a much more direct method of determining the energy levels associated with the crystalline field than is possible from measurements of the paramagnetic susceptibility alone. Also material containing rare earths became more generally available, including single crystals. The most extensive early determination of crystalline field parameters were those of Bleaney's group at Oxford. One should not form the impression that the new tools have outmoded measurements of magnetic susceptibilities and so made them superfluous. Instead the spectroscopic analysis involves so many parameters and alternatives in assignments (including spurious vibrational levels) that it is advisable to see if the spectroscopically determined parameters are consistent with the susceptibility data, and it is reassuring if this is the case. Unfortunately there are comparatively few materials on which proper spectroscopic or resonance data and measurements of principal susceptibilities are simultaneously available. The rare-earth materials for which the magnetic and spectroscopic analysis is simplest are probably the rare-earth ethyl sulphates $R(C_2H_5SO_4)_3 \cdot 9H_2O$ which have the advantage that there is only one atom in the unit cell, as well as a high degree of magnetic dilution because of the nine water molecules. Crystalline-field parameters have been obtained spectroscopically for practically all of the rare-earth sulphates, and the results of different laboratories usually agree with each other pretty well. The most comprehensive studies of whether the spectroscopically determined parameters are consistent with the behavior of the paramagnetic susceptibility are those which were made by Hellwege, Schembs and Schneider[18]) for PrES and by Cooke, Lazenby and Leask for NdES and ErES[19]). The principal susceptibilities were measured over a wide temperature range, and practically perfect accord was found with the values calculated from the spectroscopically determined parameters. The results for ErES are shown in fig. 1. Because of the hexagonal symmetry two of the principal susceptibilities are equal. It is clear that the temperature is not high enough relative to the large crystalline-field splitting so that there is much on the way of conver-

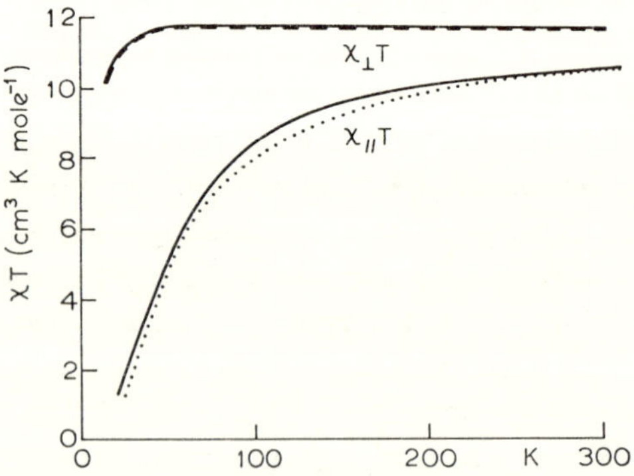

Fig. 1. Magnetic susceptibility of erbium ethyl sulphate parallel and perpendicular to the axis of symmetry as a function of temperature. Broken curves are experimental [19]), solid ones are calculated with crystal-field parameters derived by Erath. The powder susceptibility is $(\chi_{\parallel}+2\chi_{\perp})/3$.

gence for the series (4) or (7). If there were, $(\chi_{\parallel} + 2\chi_{\perp}) \cdot T$ would deviate less from the constant asymptotic value than does either $\chi_{\parallel} T$ or $\chi_{\perp} T$, but even at the extreme high-temperature end of the figure $\chi_{\perp} T$ shows the least deviation.

Because of investigations spurred by its leading role in paramagnetic relaxation and also because of the interest in the cooperative phenomena manifested at low temperatures, proportionally less of the Leiden magnetic research program has been focused on magnetically dilute materials than earlier in the century. On the other hand, a number of laboratories elsewhere in the world have had extensive research programs connected with the measurement of paramagnetic susceptibilities, notably Japan and India. The Indian laboratories in particular have concentrated on the measurement of magnetic anisotropy. This seems a judicious joice of effort, both because it is carrying on a tradition of research in a field pioneered by Sir Krishnan, and because many Indian laboratories have lacked the facilities for very low temperatures needed for the study of cooperative phenomena in paramagnetic materials, or the elaborate electronic gear needed in connection with paramagnetic resonance. Examination of the most recent edition of the Landoldt–Bornstein tables[11]) shows that more magnetic anisotropies for paramagnetic salts of nickel have been measured in India than in all other countries of the world combined.

6. *Why the seeming successes of the formula* $\chi = C/(T + \Delta)$? One matter that needs further clarification, and is almost a mystery, but more likely an accident, is why the formula $\chi = C/(T + \Delta)$ is often a good description of the experimental data for magnetically dilute powders over a fairly extensive range of temperatures. In other words χT is a linear function of T over this range. This state of affairs, however, cannot possibly extend all the way from $T = 0$ to $T = \infty$.

Let us see if we can explain the situation. A typical quantum-mechanical expression for a part of the susceptibility arising from off-diagonal elements connecting states with an energy difference 2Δ is

$$\chi = \frac{C}{\Delta} \tanh \frac{\Delta}{kT}, \tag{21}$$

where C is an appropriate constant. We have made the normalization such that (21) agrees with $C/(T + \Delta)$ for $T = 0$ and also asymptotically for $T = \infty$ (but without the term in T^{-2}). We can define a function $\delta(T)$ by artificially setting

$$\chi = \frac{C}{T + \delta(T)} \tag{22}$$

with χ as given by (21). This procedure yields

$$k\delta(T) = \Delta \cdot \left(\coth x - \frac{1}{x}\right) = \Delta \cdot L(x) \quad \text{with} \quad x = \frac{\Delta}{kT}, \tag{23}$$

where $L(x)$ is the familiar Langevin function. This expression creeps down very slowly to its asymptotic value for $T = \infty$ as shown in table II.

TABLE II

Dependence on T of the function (23)

$T/\Delta = 0$	0.1	0.2	0.5	1	2	5	10	∞
$\delta(T) = 1.0$	0.90	0.80	0.54	0.31	0.16	0.07	0.03	0.00

As the susceptibility is quite hard to measure at high temperatures it is quite possible for experimentalists to fit their data fairly well over a limited range of temperatures with Δ treated as constant. Even so this does not explain why this procedure works as well as it sometimes does. In writing (21) or (23) we have assumed that the upper and lower states have equal statistical weights. If instead they are unequal or if the susceptibility contains contributions from diagonal elements of the moment matrix, the susceptibility contains a true term in $1/T^2$ as discussed in section 4 and by proper choice of constants one could certainly make $\delta(T)$ more nearly constant than in the preceding table. However, any attempt to do this on a general basis is sheer numerology as far as we can see. It is more appropriate to take the supposedly known crystalline potential for a specific salt and see how nearly the accurate expression for the susceptibility, which is necessarily of the form

$$\chi = \sum_i (a_i + b_i T^{-1}) e^{-E_i/kT} / \sum_i e^{-E_i/kT} \tag{24}$$

happens to agree with $C/(T + \Delta)$ under proper choice of a constant Δ. Oftentimes when the measurements of the susceptibility extend over a greater temperature interval, the deficiency of this approximation becomes more apparent. For example in the measurements of Cooke *et al.* on ErES shown in fig. 1, certainly χT is not a linear function of T.

7. *Classical theory – A conversation with Einstein.* It is interesting to note what happens in classical in distinction from quantum mechanics for a magnetically dilute material in which an elementary magnet of moment μ is subject to a potential $V(\theta, \varphi)$ (the analogue of the crystalline potential in quantum theory) and to an applied field H. The magnetic moment in the direction of H is now

$$M = NC\mu \int\int \cos(\mu, H) \exp[(-V + \mu \cdot H)/kT)] \, d\omega,$$

where $d\omega$ is an element of solid angle and

$$1/C = \int\int \exp[(-V + \mu \cdot H)/kT] \, d\omega.$$

If we neglect saturation effects and assume that V has bilateral symmetry, so that M vanishes when $H = 0$, the susceptibility in the z direction, which we can take as one of the principal axes, is given by

$$\chi_z = M/H = N\mu^2 k^{-1} T^{-1} C \int\int [\cos(z, H)]^2 \mathrm{e}^{-V/kT} \mathrm{d}\omega.$$

Since the sum of the squares of the direction cosines is 1, it follows immediately that:

$$\tfrac{1}{3}(\chi_x + \chi_y + \chi_z) = N\mu^2/3kT.$$

In other words the crystalline field is without effect on the powder magnetic susceptibility in classical theory, whereas we saw that this was only true of the $1/T^2$ term in quantum mechanics. As far as the writer knows this comparison was first noted in a monograph[2]) by him that appeared in 1946, but it's hard to believe that the simple classical result was not mentioned earlier somewhere. (It is, however, implicitly contained in the theories developed by Debye and by Fowler[20]) in 1935 for the reduction of the dielectric constant by unilateral fields.)

In this connection and in conclusion it is appropriate for me to recall a conversation which I had with Einstein in the hall or at breakfast at the time of the Solvay Congress on magnetism in 1930. In one of the previous sessions it had been suggested that crystalline fields would modify the susceptibility. He remarked that he could not understand how crystalline fields could give rise to a Δ in the formula $\chi = C/(T + \Delta)$. I remember his saying "ich habe es ausgerechnet" and he obtained $\Delta = 0$. I replied I felt confident that quantum mechanics would give rise to such a term. At that time I was not aware of the vanishing of the $1/T^2$ term for the powder in quantum mechanics, and I would have been right only if we were speaking of individual principal rather than powder susceptibilities. Due to interruptions or my limited understanding of German we did not become specific enough to define which case we were talking about. I am sure that Einstein would have agreed that there could be a $1/T^2$ term without the powder-type averaging, as this occurs even classically. Whether Einstein's calculation was classical or quantal no one will ever know. I would surmise the former. He could well have published a short paper or made some remarks in the formal conference proceedings, but he never did. With his remarkable intuition he was certainly right in detecting that the formula $\chi = C / (T + \Delta)$ was used by experimentalists under conditions not warranted by theory.

REFERENCES

1) Penney, J. C. and Schlapp, R., Phys. Rev. **41** (1932) 194; Schlapp, R. and Penney, J. C., *ibid.* **42** (1932) 666.
2) Van Vleck, J. H., Annales de l'Institut Henri Poincaré **10** (1947) 57, especially pp. 88–93.
3) Meijer, P. H. E., J. chem. Phys. Solids **32** (1971) 2163.

4) Gorter, C. J., Paramagnetische Eigenschaften von Salzen, Thesis, Leiden University, 1932.
5) Weiss, P., J. Phys. **6** (1907) 667.
6) Heisenberg, W., Z. Phys. **49** (1928) 619.
7) Van Vleck, J. H., The Theory of Electric and Magnetic Susceptibilities, Oxford University Press (Oxford, 1932) p. 348.
8) Néel, L., Ann. Physique **17** (1932) 64; **2** (1936) 255.
9) Bizette, H., Squire, C. F. and Tsai, B., CR Acad. Sci. **207** (1938) 449; Squire, C. F., Phys. Rev. **56** (1939) 922.
10) Stanley, H. E., Introduction to Phase Transitions and Critical Phenomena, Oxford University Press (Oxford, 1971), Chap. 9 C, or especially Paul, G. and Stanley, H. E., Phys. Rev. **B5** (1972) 3715.
11) Landoldt–Bornstein, Zahlenwerte und Funktionen aus Physik . . ., 6th Ed. II Band, 9 Teil, section 29 3.
12) Van den Handel, J., Metingen aan Paramagnetische Kristallen, Thesis, Leiden University, 1940.
13) Van Vleck, J. H., Phys. Rev. **29** (1927) 727 or Chap. VII of ref. 7.
14) Griffith, J. S., The Theory of Transition Metal Ions, Cambridge University Press (Cambridge, 1961) Chap. 10.
15) See, for instance, Griffith, J. S. [14]) or Van Vleck, J. H., Physica **26** (1960) 544.
16) Birgenau, R. J., Phys. Rev. Letters **19** (1967) 160 (quotes unpublished measurements by O'Leary and Wheeler).
17) Krishnan, K. S., Mookherji, A. and Bose, A., Phil. Trans. Roy. Soc. **238** (1939) 125. This article also gives measurements apparently confirming the $1/T^2$ term in $Gd_2(SO_4)_3 \cdot 8H_2O$, but later they were found to be unreliable, presumably because of chemical impurities; see Krishnan, K. S. and Banerjee, S., Phys. Rev. **59** (1941) 770; Lewis, W. D., *ibid* **57** (1940) 1088.
18) Hellwege, K. H., Schembs, W. and Schneider, B., Z. Phys. **167** (1962) 477.
19) Cooke, A. H., Lazenby, R. and Leask, M. J. M., Proc. Phys. Soc. London **85** (1965) 767.
20) Fowler, R. H., Proc. Roy. Soc. **149** (1935) 1; Debye, P., Phys. Z. **36** (1935) 100.

Physica **69** (1973) 193–217 © *North-Holland Publishing Co.*

SOME REFLECTIONS ON THE TWO-FLUID MODEL AND BOSE-EINSTEIN CONDENSATION

J. de BOER

Instituut voor Theoretische Fysica, Universiteit van Amsterdam, Amsterdam, Nederland

Received 19 April 1973

Synopsis

A survey is given of the essential concepts, occurring in Landau's excitation model and in the Penrose–Onsager theory of Bose–Einstein condensation in liquid helium. Its theoretical and experimental verifications are discussed. A study is made of the definition of the condensate wave function, requiring the introduction of quantum states with not exactly defined particle number, such as Glauber's coherent states. The Bogoliubov theory for the thermodynamic instability and the symmetry breaking which is connected with the transition of liquid helium into the superfluid state is discussed in detail.

1. *Introduction.* The invitation to contribute an article to this special issue dedicated to Professor Gorter was a great pleasure for me in view of the great appreciation which I have always felt for his scientific work. A great deal of his scientific activities were concentrated on the unravelling of the many problems in the field of superconductivity and superfluidity; I have therefore used this occasion to write an article of somewhat more didactical nature on the development and the present situation of our understanding of the equilibrium properties of the two-fluid model of liquid helium.

The discovery of the anomaly in the heat capacity at the transition point of liquid helium by Keesom and Clusius[1,2]) in 1932 and at the transition point into the superconductive state by Keesom, v. d. Ende and Kok[3,4]), both of which appeared to be phase transitions without a latent heat, induced Ehrenfest[5]) in 1933 to his well-known investigations on the thermodynamic classification of phase transitions based on the behaviour of the Gibbs free energy $G(p, T)$ as function of p and T. Of course $G(p, T)$ itself is a continuous function of p and T and the usual "first kind" phase transitions are characterized by a discontinuity in the first derivatives S and V. At the lambda point of liquid helium, however, also entropy S and volume V are continuous functions of p and T and a discontinuity seemed to occur in their second derivatives.

Now in the case of such a phase transition "of the second kind" a peculiar difficulty arises if we consider the metastable continuations of the low- and high-temperature phases, above and below the transition temperature. In ordinary phase transitions both continuations have a higher thermal potential $G(p, T)$ than the corresponding stable phases, as they should. For the transition of the second kind, however, the continuation of the low-temperature $G(p, T)$ curve above the transition point would have a smaller potential than the corresponding stable phase, because the two curves osculate at the transition temperature. This difficulty was taken so seriously that some investigators even drew the conclusion that phase transitions of the second kind cannot occur in nature. Here Gorter[6]) proposed a different solution which is deeply connected with the nature of the new type of transitions which were discovered: it may well be that the mathematical continuation of the $G(p, T)$ surface through the transition curve is physically meaningless. This became clearer in the thermodynamic "two fluid-model" which Gorter and Casimir[7,8]) in 1934 proposed for a superconductor, which in the absence of a magnetic field undergoes a true phase transition of the second kind. They introduced in the low-temperature superconducting phase a parameter ξ indicating a "degree of superconductivity" [9]), being the fraction of electrons which are in the superconductive state. At $T = 0$, $\xi = 1$ and with rising temperature ξ gradually decreases until ξ reaches the value $\xi = 0$ at the transition point, where superconductivity disappears. In principle at each temperature and pressure the equilibrium value of the internal parameter $\xi(p, T)$ is determined by minimizing the Gibbs free energy. Gorter and Casimir introduced a mathematical expression $G(p, T, \xi)$ which in fact gave a very satisfactory description of the properties of superconductors. The theory got the name of a two-fluid model because ξ appeared to be the fraction of electrons which are in the superconductive state, so that the whole phenomenon could be seen as a kind of equilibrium between two fluids.

This two-fluid model was a predecessor and example of the mathematical description of second-order phase transitions which Landau[10]) published in 1935. Two years later Landau[11]) extended the theory of second-order phase transitions by introducing the concept of symmetry breaking, replacing the internal variable ξ by the absolute square of some order parameter. This was already a precursor of the macroscopic wavefunction, which is considered in reality to be the complex "order parameter", characterizing the internal state of liquid helium II. We shall return to this matter in section 6. In 1938 London[12]) and Tisza[13]) introduced their kinetic two-fluid model to give a first explanation of the superfluid properties of liquid helium. London[14]) stressed very much the analogy between the phenomena in superfluid helium and those in a superconductor. Gorter[15]) then proposed a thermodynamic description for liquid helium II, which was very similar to the thermodynamic two-fluid model which had been given previously for superconductors. In the case of liquid helium II the superfluid fraction $\xi = \rho_s/\rho$ acts as the internal parameters which has to be determined as a function of p and T by minimizing the Gibbs free energy $G(p, T, \xi)$ and also here very satisfactory agreement with the experimental behaviour was obtained. The success of the two-fluid model stimulated Gorter and Mellink[16]) to propose equations of motion for the two fluids separately, which equations were very valuable for explaining many of the hydrodynamic properties of liquid helium. Gorter gave a derivation of the equation of motion for the two fluids by using what is often called the "pseudo-thermostatic" method, in which laws of equilibrium thermodynamics are applied on certain processes such as the thermomechanical and fountain effect, which are considered to be reversible, and where then irreversible processes connected with viscous friction and heat conduction are neglected. This stimulated De Groot, Jansen and Mazur[17]) in 1950 and Prigogine and Mazur[18]) in 1951 to apply the formalism of irreversible thermodynamics in a two-component mixture to this case, with the additional hypothesis that exchange of momentum between the two components is inhibited.

2. *The excitation model of Landau.* In the introduction we have tried to indicate, without going into detail, the role which Gorter's thermodynamic two-fluid models have played in increasing our understanding of the mechanism of second-order phase transitions and in developing the concept of a two-fluid model for explaining the properties of superconductors and superfluid liquid helium. These models, being "thermodynamic" models really abstained from going into the microscopic physical theories for the two-fluid model.

Several years before Gorter presented the thermodynamic two-fluid model for liquid helium, Tisza[13]) introduced the concept of a two-fluid model for liquid helium inspired by London's publication[12]) on Bose–Einstein condensation. Tisza was able to explain in principle the reversible thermomechanical effects and he predicted the possibility of the propagation of temperature waves, later called second sound after its experimental discovery by Peshkov[20]) in 1946.

A new and very different microscopic explanation for the two-fluid model of liquid helium was given by Landau[19]) in 1941.

Landau's theory has been improved and extended in particular by Khalatnikov (refs. 21,22, 25), Kramers[23]) and by Kronig[24]) and this theory up till now presents the most satisfactory treatment for the equilibrium and hydrodynamic phenomena in liquid helium.

The basic assumption is that the hamiltonian of the system can be transformed into the form

$$\begin{aligned} \mathbf{H} &= W_0 + \sum_k \varepsilon_k \boldsymbol{\beta}_k^\dagger \boldsymbol{\beta}_k + \text{interaction terms}, \\ \mathbf{G} &= \sum_k p_k \boldsymbol{\beta}_k^\dagger \boldsymbol{\beta}_k , \end{aligned} \tag{2.1}$$

where W_0 is the energy of the ground state and $\boldsymbol{\beta}_k^\dagger$ are $\boldsymbol{\beta}_k$ operators creating excitations of energy ε_k and momentum $p_k = \hbar k$ and $\mathbf{G} \equiv (\mathbf{G}_x, \mathbf{G}_y, \mathbf{G}_z)$ is the total-momentum operator. The system of excitations has properties very similar to the radiation gas. At low temperatures only a few excitations will be excited so that under these conditions the interaction can be neglected. For higher temperatures close to the λ-point this, however, no longer holds, and the picture looses its microscopic justification.

The system of excitations is then identified with the *normal fluid* of the two-fluid model and the background fluid in which the excitations are moving with the *superfluid*. The exact definition of the characteristic quantities like ρ_s, ρ_n, $\boldsymbol{v}_s$ and $\boldsymbol{v}_n$ of the two-fluid model in terms of the excitation model will be recalled below. We describe the liquid-helium system by an ensemble in which quasiparticles or excitations are moving with an average velocity $\boldsymbol{v}_n = \boldsymbol{v}$ and in which the background fluid is at rest ($\boldsymbol{v}_s = 0$).

The ensemble is represented by the probability function $\exp[-\beta(\mathbf{H} - \boldsymbol{v} . \mathbf{G})]$ where $\mathbf{H}$ and $\mathbf{G}$ are the total-energy and -momentum operators and $\boldsymbol{v}$ is the average velocity of the system of excitations. The partition function can then be written as

$$Z(T, \rho, V, \boldsymbol{v}) = e^{-\beta W_0} \sum_{\{\nu_k\}} \exp\left(-\beta \sum_k \nu_k(\varepsilon_k - \boldsymbol{v} \cdot \boldsymbol{p}_k)\right), \tag{2.2}$$

where ν_k are the occupation numbers of the excitations ε_k, *i.e.*, the eigenvalues of $\boldsymbol{\beta}_k^\dagger \boldsymbol{\beta}_k$. The average number of excitations ε_k, $\langle \nu_k \rangle$ is given by

$$\langle \nu_k \rangle = -\frac{\partial \ln Z}{\partial \beta \varepsilon_k} = \frac{1}{\exp \beta(\varepsilon_k - \boldsymbol{v} \cdot \boldsymbol{p}_k) - 1}. \tag{2.3}$$

The free-energy density $F = F_{\text{tot}}/V$ is given by

$$F(T, \rho, \boldsymbol{v}) = E_0 + (kT/h^3) \int d\boldsymbol{p} \ln\{1 - \exp[-\beta(\varepsilon - \boldsymbol{v} \cdot \boldsymbol{p})]\}, \tag{2.4}$$

where $\varepsilon = \varepsilon(p)$ and the ground-state energy density $E_0 = W_0/V$ may still be a function of the density ρ. The sum $\sum_k$ has been replaced by an integral $(V/h^3)\int d\boldsymbol{p}$. From this Helmholtz free-energy density $F(T, \rho, \boldsymbol{v})$ all thermodynamic quantities can be obtained using $dF = -S dT + \mu d\rho - \boldsymbol{g} \cdot d\boldsymbol{v}$ where $\boldsymbol{g} = \mathbf{G}/V$ is the excitation momentum density due to the excitations. The definition of the momentum density $\boldsymbol{g}$ defines in Landau's picture the *normal-fluid current density* in the reference frame in which the background fluid is at rest.

All these thermodynamic quantities can be expressed in terms of the distribution function for the excitations $f(\boldsymbol{p})$ defined by $\langle \nu_k \rangle / h^3 = f(\boldsymbol{p})$ or in terms of $f^0(p)$ (with $\boldsymbol{v} = 0$):

$$E = E_0 + \int d\boldsymbol{p} f^0(p) \varepsilon(p), \tag{2.5}$$

$$S = \frac{1}{T} \int d\boldsymbol{p} f^0(p) \left(\varepsilon + \tfrac{1}{3} p \frac{\partial \varepsilon}{\partial p}\right), \tag{2.6}$$

$$\mu = \mu_0 + \int d\boldsymbol{p} f^0(p) \frac{\partial \varepsilon}{\partial \rho}, \tag{2.7}$$

$$g = \int \mathrm{d}\boldsymbol{p} f(p)\boldsymbol{p} = -\tfrac{1}{3}\boldsymbol{v}\int \mathrm{d}\boldsymbol{p}\, \frac{\partial f^0(p)}{\partial \varepsilon}\, p^2 + \mathcal{O}(v^2). \tag{2.8}$$

Here E_0 and μ_0 are the thermodynamic quantities at $T = 0$, where $S_0 = 0$. All integrals represent the contributions of the excitation gas.

From the expression for the excitation momentum density $\boldsymbol{g}$ one obtains the excitation mass density, which is the definition of the *normal fluid density* ρ_n by dividing by $\boldsymbol{v}$, and neglecting terms $\mathcal{O}(v)$ giving

$$\rho_n = -\frac{1}{3}\int \mathrm{d}\boldsymbol{p}\, \frac{\partial f^0(p)}{\partial \varepsilon}\, p^2; \tag{2.9}$$

the *super fluid density* is then defined as $\rho_s = \rho - \rho_n$.

A slightly different derivation of the expression for the normal-fluid density uncovers an interesting relation with the fluctuations in the occupation number. Developing the general expression (2.2) in powers of $\boldsymbol{v}$ we obtain

$$g = \lim_{V\to\infty} \frac{1}{V}\, \frac{\partial \ln Z}{\partial \beta \boldsymbol{v}} = \lim_{V\to\infty} \frac{1}{V}\, \tfrac{1}{3}\beta \boldsymbol{v} \sum_{\boldsymbol{k}} (\langle \nu_{\boldsymbol{k}}^2\rangle - \langle \nu_{\boldsymbol{k}}\rangle^2) p_{\boldsymbol{k}}^2; \tag{2.10}$$

or, dividing by $\boldsymbol{v}$:

$$\rho_n = \tfrac{1}{3}\beta (1/h^3) \int \mathrm{d}\boldsymbol{p} (\langle \nu_p^2\rangle - \langle \nu_p\rangle^2) p^2. \tag{2.11}$$

This alternative expression for ρ_n shows that ρ_n is intimately connected with the fluctuations in the occupation numbers. These fluctuations can directly be obtained from (2.2) to be

$$\langle \nu_p^2\rangle - \langle \nu_p\rangle^2 = \frac{\partial^2 \ln Z}{\partial (\beta \varepsilon_p)^2} = -\frac{\partial \langle \nu_p\rangle}{\partial \beta \varepsilon_p} = \langle \nu_p\rangle^2 + \langle \nu_p\rangle, \tag{2.12}$$

in analogy with the radiation gas. After substituting in (2.11) and replacing $\langle \nu_p\rangle$ by $h^3 f(p)$ one obtains expression (2.9) for ρ_n.

The best empirical information about the excitations was obtained in the form of a dispersion curve from neutron scattering[26,27,28]). From this empirical dispersion curve, taking into account the empirical change with temperature, the thermodynamic quantities and in particular the heat capacity, the entropy and the normal-fluid density were calculated[29]) using computer methods. The excellent agreement with the existing experimental data shows that this Landau excitation model gives a very accurate explanation for the experimental facts.

We shall not consider here the hydrodynamics of the two-fluid model which is not very relevant in the present publication. This field has been treated most completely by Khalatnikov[22,25,67]) and in the literature[30,31]). For recent developments we may refer to Fröhlich[68,69]) and to Haug and Weiss[71,72]).

3. *Bose–Einstein condensation.* Clearly the direction in which Landau's excitation model has developed differs very much from the scope of London's original paper in 1938 on Bose–Einstein condensation. London had taken the view that, although liquid helium certainly cannot be treated as an ideal Bose–Einstein gas, the condensation phenomenon would still have to manifest itself in some distorted form and be made responsible for its superfluid properties: even in liquid helium a macroscopic fraction of the molecules should move into quantum states, represented by wave packets of macroscopic dimension in space, but corresponding to very narrow wave packets in momentum space. This ordering or condensation in momentum space had played already an important role in the case of superconductors when H. and F. London gave their explanation of the Meissner effect in 1934 and London was convinced that the superfluid effects in liquid helium had a similar origin. London and Tisza's original two-fluid model was constructed entirely on this basis: two interpenetrating fluids, the "superfluid" (the condensate in momentum space) being in one macroscopic quantum state and the "normal fluid" carrying all thermal disorder, *i.e.*, all the entropy of the liquid.

The further evolution of this two-fluid model into Landau's excitation model led to an important modification in the sense that at absolute zero, the superfluid includes the whole liquid and not the condensate in momentum space alone: the whole matter of the condensation in momentum space and the corresponding macroscopic quantum state was removed to the background. It was here that Penrose[32]) in 1951 and Penrose and Onsager[33]) in 1956 started their investigations on the condensation in momentum space in a real system like liquid helium II.

Their conjectures were placed in a much wider framework when Yang in 1962 introduced the concept of off-diagonal longe-range order (ODLRO) of the density matrix. Their calculations were based on the reduced one-particle density matrix, which in coordinate representation is defined by

$$\rho_1(\boldsymbol{r}, \boldsymbol{r}') = \langle\langle \psi^\dagger(\boldsymbol{r}')\psi(\boldsymbol{r})\rangle\rangle, \tag{3.1}$$

where $\langle\langle\ \rangle\rangle$ represents a canonical or grand canonical average and where $\psi^\dagger(\boldsymbol{r}')$ and $\psi(\boldsymbol{r})$ are the field operators for creation and annihilation of a particle at position $\boldsymbol{r}$. The diagonal element $n(\boldsymbol{r}) = \rho_1(\boldsymbol{r}, \boldsymbol{r})$ is equal to the local particle density. At absolute zero the ensemble average $\langle\langle\ \rangle\rangle$ becomes simply the expectation value $\langle\ \rangle$ in the ground state Φ_N such that

$$\begin{aligned}\rho_1(\boldsymbol{r}, \boldsymbol{r}') &= \langle \Phi_N | \psi^\dagger(\boldsymbol{r}')\psi(\boldsymbol{r}) | \Phi_N \rangle \\ &= N \int \mathrm{d}\boldsymbol{r}_2 \dots \mathrm{d}\boldsymbol{r}_N \Phi_N^*(\boldsymbol{r}'\boldsymbol{r}_2 \dots \boldsymbol{r}_N)\Phi_N(\boldsymbol{r}\boldsymbol{r}_2 \dots \boldsymbol{r}_N),\end{aligned} \tag{3.2}$$

where $\Phi_N(\boldsymbol{r}_1 \dots \boldsymbol{r}_N)$ is the normalized many-particle ground-state wave function.

Similarly the one-particle density matrix in momentum representation is given by

$$\rho_1(\boldsymbol{k}\boldsymbol{k}') = \langle\langle \mathbf{a}_{\boldsymbol{k}'}^\dagger \mathbf{a}_{\boldsymbol{k}} \rangle\rangle = (1/V) \int \mathrm{d}\boldsymbol{r}\, \mathrm{d}\boldsymbol{r}' \rho_1(\boldsymbol{r}\boldsymbol{r}') \mathrm{e}^{\mathrm{i}(\boldsymbol{k}'\boldsymbol{r}' - \boldsymbol{k}\boldsymbol{r})}, \tag{3.3}$$

where $\mathbf{a}_{\boldsymbol{k}}^\dagger$ and $\mathbf{a}_{\boldsymbol{k}}$ are construction operators for creating and annihilating a particle with momentum $\boldsymbol{p}=\hbar \boldsymbol{k}$. The diagonal elements $\bar{N}_{\boldsymbol{k}}=\rho_1(\boldsymbol{k}, \boldsymbol{k})$ are equal to the average occupation numbers of the state $\boldsymbol{k}$.

3.1. Spatially uniform systems. We first consider the simplest case of a spatially uniform system with periodic boundary conditions. In this case the density matrix in coordinate representation $\rho_1(\boldsymbol{r}\,\boldsymbol{r}')$ becomes a function of $|\boldsymbol{r}' - \boldsymbol{r}|$ only and the element $|\boldsymbol{r}' - \boldsymbol{r}| \to 0$ becomes equal to the constant particle density n. Consequently in momentum representation $\rho_1(\boldsymbol{k}, \boldsymbol{k}')$ becomes a diagonal matrix with diagonal elements $\rho_1(\boldsymbol{k}, \boldsymbol{k})$ equal to the average occupation number $\bar{N}_{\boldsymbol{k}}$ of the momentum state $\boldsymbol{k}$:

$$\langle\langle \psi^\dagger(\boldsymbol{r}')\psi(\boldsymbol{r})\rangle\rangle = \rho_1(|\boldsymbol{r}' - \boldsymbol{r}|), \tag{3.4}$$

$$\langle\langle \mathbf{a}_{\boldsymbol{k}'}^\dagger \mathbf{a}_{\boldsymbol{k}}\rangle\rangle = \bar{N}_{\boldsymbol{k}} \delta_{\boldsymbol{k}\boldsymbol{k}'} . \tag{3.5}$$

In this case (3.3) can be written as

$$\bar{N}_{\boldsymbol{k}} = \int \mathrm{d}(\boldsymbol{r}'-\boldsymbol{r})\rho_1(|\boldsymbol{r}'-\boldsymbol{r}|)\mathrm{e}^{i\boldsymbol{k}(\boldsymbol{r}'-\boldsymbol{r})}, \tag{3.6}$$

$$\rho_1(|\boldsymbol{r}'-\boldsymbol{r}|) = (1/V) \sum_{\boldsymbol{k}} \bar{N}_{\boldsymbol{k}} \mathrm{e}^{-i\boldsymbol{k}(\boldsymbol{r}'-\boldsymbol{r})}. \tag{3.7}$$

In analogy with the phenomenon of Bose–Einstein condensation for an ideal gas of non-interacting molecules Penrose and Onsager[33]) assumed that also for a system of interacting molecules there may exist below a certain temperature "Bose–Einstein condensation", which is then characterized by the existence of one particular momentum state $\boldsymbol{k} = \boldsymbol{k}_0$, which is usually taken $\boldsymbol{k} = 0$, for which in the thermodynamic limit $V \to \infty$ (with $N/V = n =$ constant) the condensate density remains a finite fraction of the number density n, *i.e.*,

$$\left.\begin{array}{l} \lim\limits_{V\to\infty} (1/V)\langle\langle \mathbf{a}_0^\dagger \mathbf{a}_0\rangle\rangle \\ \lim\limits_{V\to\infty} (1/V)\langle\langle \mathbf{a}_{\boldsymbol{k}_0}^\dagger \mathbf{a}_{\boldsymbol{k}_0}\rangle\rangle \end{array}\right\} = \lim_{V\to\infty} \frac{\bar{N}_0}{V} = n_0 = \alpha n, \tag{3.8}$$

where α is a finite fraction $0 < \alpha \leqq 1$. Performing the Fourier transform (3.7) we have

$$\langle\langle \psi^\dagger(\boldsymbol{r}')\psi(\boldsymbol{r})\rangle\rangle = n_0 \mathrm{e}^{-i\boldsymbol{k}_0(\boldsymbol{r}'-\boldsymbol{r})} + (1/V) \sum_{\boldsymbol{k}\neq\boldsymbol{k}_0}{}' \bar{N}_{\boldsymbol{k}} \mathrm{e}^{-i\boldsymbol{k}(\boldsymbol{r}'-\boldsymbol{r})}. \tag{3.9}$$

The second part is uncorrelated in the limit $|\boldsymbol{r}' - \boldsymbol{r}| \to \infty$, so that Bose–Einstein condensation is characterised by

$$\lim_{\boldsymbol{r}'-\boldsymbol{r}\to\infty} \langle\langle \psi^\dagger(\boldsymbol{r}')\psi(\boldsymbol{r})\rangle\rangle = \begin{cases} n_0, \\ n_0 \mathrm{e}^{-i\boldsymbol{k}_0(\boldsymbol{r}'-\boldsymbol{r})}. \end{cases} \tag{3.9'}$$

For $\boldsymbol{r} = \boldsymbol{r}'$ one obtains the relation $n = n_0 + V^{-1} \sum_{\boldsymbol{k}}' \bar{N}_{\boldsymbol{k}}$. The quantity

$\tilde{n} = V^{-1} \sum_k' \bar{N}_k$, being the particle density which has "depleted" in $\boldsymbol{k} \neq \boldsymbol{k}_0$ states as a result of the interaction, is called the depletion.

3.2. Spatially non-uniform systems. For a spatially non-uniform system, with arbitrary boundary conditions momentum is no longer a constant of motion so that condition (3.8) cannot be maintained. Penrose and Onsager therefore concentrated on the density matrix in coordinate representation $\langle\langle \psi^\dagger(\boldsymbol{r}')\psi(\boldsymbol{r})\rangle\rangle$ by considering its spectral resolution:

$$\langle\langle \psi^\dagger(\boldsymbol{r}')\psi(\boldsymbol{r})\rangle\rangle = \sum_\mu \lambda_\mu \psi_\mu^*(\boldsymbol{r}')\psi_\mu(\boldsymbol{r}) \tag{3.10}$$

in terms of the eigenvalues λ_μ and eigenfunctions $\psi_\mu(\boldsymbol{r})$ of the equation

$$\int \mathrm{d}\boldsymbol{r}' \rho_1(\boldsymbol{r}, \boldsymbol{r}')\psi_\mu(\boldsymbol{r}') = \lambda_\mu \psi_\mu(\boldsymbol{r}), \tag{3.11}$$

which now satisfy the boundary conditions of the system and which are normalized to 1. For a uniform system the eigenfunctions are $\psi_{\boldsymbol{k}}(\boldsymbol{r}) = V^{-\frac{1}{2}} \exp i\boldsymbol{k}\boldsymbol{r}$ and the eigenvalues $\lambda_{\boldsymbol{k}} = \bar{N}_{\boldsymbol{k}}$ in agreement with (3.6). Macroscopic occupation then corresponds to one macroscopic eigenvalue $\bar{N}_0 = \lambda_0$ or $\bar{N}_{\boldsymbol{k}_0} = \lambda_{\boldsymbol{k}_0}$. Penrose and Onsager then assumed that also in general the occurrence of Bose–Einstein condensation can be characterized by the existence of one macroscopic eigenvalue $\lambda_0 = \bar{N}_0$ which remains a finite fraction $\bar{N}_0 = \alpha N$ of N in the thermodynamic limit. The corresponding eigenfunction $\psi_0(\boldsymbol{r})$ will be called the condensate wave function. The spectral resolution of the one-particle density matrix can then be written as

$$\langle\langle \psi^\dagger(\boldsymbol{r}')\psi(\boldsymbol{r})\rangle\rangle = \bar{N}_0 \psi_0^*(\boldsymbol{r}')\psi_0(\boldsymbol{r}) + \tilde{\rho}_1(\boldsymbol{r}, \boldsymbol{r}'), \tag{3.12}$$

where, similar to eq. (3.9) for the uniform systems

$$\tilde{\rho}_1(\boldsymbol{r}, \boldsymbol{r}') = \sum_{\mu \neq 0}' \lambda_\mu \psi_\mu^*(\boldsymbol{r}')\psi_\mu(\boldsymbol{r}), \tag{3.13}$$

represents that part of the density matrix, which remains after separating off the macroscopic quantum state. The asymptotic behaviour is then given by

$$\lim_{\boldsymbol{r}'-\boldsymbol{r}\to\infty} \langle\langle \psi^\dagger(\boldsymbol{r}')\psi(\boldsymbol{r})\rangle\rangle = N_0 \psi_0^*(\boldsymbol{r}')\psi_0(\boldsymbol{r}), \tag{3.14}$$

whereas

$$\lim_{\boldsymbol{r}'-\boldsymbol{r}\to\infty} \tilde{\rho}_1(\boldsymbol{r}, \boldsymbol{r}') = 0. \tag{3.15}$$

The quantity $\tilde{n}(\boldsymbol{r}) = \tilde{\rho}_1(\boldsymbol{r}, \boldsymbol{r})$ is the depletion as before.

For future considerations it is more convenient to normalize the condensate wave function to $\bar{N}_0$, such that $\int \mathrm{d}\boldsymbol{r} \Psi^*(\boldsymbol{r})\Psi(\boldsymbol{r}) = \bar{N}_0$, which allows (3.12) to be written as

$$\langle\langle \psi^{\dagger}(\boldsymbol{r}')\psi(\boldsymbol{r})\rangle\rangle = \Psi^{*}(\boldsymbol{r}')\Psi(\boldsymbol{r})+\tilde{\rho}_1(\boldsymbol{r}, \boldsymbol{r}'). \tag{3.16}$$

For the special case of a uniform system the condensate wave function becomes either a constant $|\Psi(\boldsymbol{r})| = \Psi$ which, except for a phase factor, is now equal to $\Psi = n_0^{\frac{1}{2}}$ or becomes $\Psi(\boldsymbol{r}) = n_0^{\frac{1}{2}} \exp \mathrm{i}\boldsymbol{k}_0\boldsymbol{r}$ leading to (3.9).

This nonzero asymptotic limit for the one-particle density matrix in coordinate space, corresponding to the delta character of the one-particle density matrix in momentum space, was taken by Penrose and Onsager as a basic characteristic of Bose–Einstein condensation in an interacting Bose–Einstein system of molecules. Yang[34]) generalized this concept of non-vanishing one-particle density matrix $\rho_1(\boldsymbol{r}, \boldsymbol{r}')$ for distances $\boldsymbol{r}' - \boldsymbol{r} \to \infty$ far from the diagonal, to the concept of off-diagonal long-range order (ODLRO) as a criterion which is valid for superfluids as well as for superconductors. Girardeau[35,36]) gave a critical analysis of Penrose and Onsager's criterion (3.8) for Bose–Einstein condensation and suggested that in certain cases this "simple" type of Bose–Einstein condensation might not occur and would have to be replaced by a "generalized" type of Bose–Einstein condensation smeared out over a larger number of strongly occupied momentum states but all corresponding to macroscopic wavelengths.

On the basis of perturbation-theoretical considerations Girardeau then made the conjecture that in Bose–Einstein systems having an attractive interaction, this type of generalized Bose–Einstein condensation is realized.

As a conclusion to this section we may remark that London's original conjecture about the existence of a condensate characterized by a narrow range in momentum space and a macroscopic wave function in coordinate space has taken a definite shape in the Penrose-Onsager picture. If there is Bose–Einstein condensation at all, then for spatially uniform systems the condensate is characterized by a delta-type of singularity in momentum space in which a macroscopic fraction α of the particles of the system is concentrated and which corresponds to a macroscopic or condensate wave function $\Psi(\boldsymbol{r})$ in coordinate space.

4. *The condensate density in liquid helium.* Information about the existence and value of the condensate density n_0 has been drawn from theoretical evaluations of the N-particle ground-state wave function, obtained by variational procedures. MacMillan[36]) proposed a Bijl–Jastrov type of trial wave function

$$\Phi_N(\boldsymbol{r}_1 \ldots \boldsymbol{r}_N) = \prod_{i<j} \mathrm{e}^{-\frac{1}{2}u(r_{ij})}, \tag{4.1}$$

where $u(r_{ij})$ is a short-range function which accounts for the short-range correlations between helium atoms. The expectation value for the ground-state energy can then be written as

$$U = \frac{1}{\tilde{Q}_N}\langle\Phi_N|\mathbf{H}|\Phi_N\rangle = \tfrac{1}{2}Nn\int \mathrm{d}\boldsymbol{r}\, g(r)\left(\frac{-\hbar^2}{2m}\nabla^2 u(r)+v(r)\right), \tag{4.2}$$

where $v(r)$ is the intermolecular-potential field for two helium atoms and where $g(r)$ is the pair distribution function

$$g(r_{12}) = \frac{N(N-1)}{\tilde{Q}_N n^2} \int \mathrm{d}r_3 \ldots \mathrm{d}r_N |\Phi_N(r_1 \ldots r_N)|^2, \tag{4.3}$$

which two formulae in principle allow one to determine $u(r_{ij})$ by variational procedures by minimizing the expectation value U.

The one-particle density matrix $\langle \Phi_N | \psi^\dagger(r_1)\psi(r_0) | \Phi_N \rangle$ is given by eq. (3.2) as

$$\rho_1(r_{10}) = \frac{N}{\tilde{Q}_N} \int \mathrm{d}r_2 \ldots \mathrm{d}r_N \, \Phi_N^*(r_1 r_2 \ldots r_N) \Phi_N(r_0 r_2 \ldots r_N), \tag{4.4}$$

from which n_0 follows by taking the limit $n_0 = \lim_{r_{10} \to \infty} \rho_1(r_{10})$.

MacMillan[36]) used for $u(r)$ the trial function $u(r) = 2(b/r)^m$ introduced by Wu and Feenberg[45]) and determined the best values for b and m to be $b = 2.51$ Å and $m = 5$ using Monte-Carlo methods to compute (4.2) and (4.4). The results for the ground-state energy, the equilibrium density and the condensate number density are collected in table I.

TABLE I

Numerical estimates of the condensate density

	U^0/U^0_{exp}	ρ/ρ_{exp}	n_0/n
Penrose and Onsager[33])	—	—	0.08
MacMillan[36])	0.83 ±0.02	0.89±0.01	0.1 ±0.01
Schiff, Verlet[37])	0.833±0.03	0.9 ±0.01	0.105±0.005
Francis, Chester, Reatto[39])	0.88	0.970	0.131
Francis, Chester, Reatto[39]) (incl. phon.)	0.95	1.035	0.101

The analogy, which the expression for the pair distribution function $g(r_{12})$, after the substitution of the pair product wave function, shows with the pair distribution function for a classical gas having pair probability function $W(r_{ij}) = \exp[-u(r_{ij})]$, induced many authors to use methods borrowed from classical statistical mechanics to evaluate the integrals for $g(r)$ and $\rho_1(r)$.

Schiff and Verlet[37]) used the molecular-dynamics method developed by Alder and Wainwright[38]) to evaluate $g(r_{12})$ and Francis, Chester and Reatto[39]) used a modified type of hypernetted-chain approximation, used in theoretical calculations of the pair distribution function. Their results are also given in the table, showing a somewhat larger value for n_0.

It should be mentioned that already Penrose and Onsager[33]) derived a relation between the two quantities $g(r_{12})$ and $n(r_{01})$ which leads to a direct estimate of the condensation density. This point has been clarified further by Reatto and Chester[40]), Reatto[41]) and Feenberg[42]). Similar to the configurational partition function of a classical gas

$$Q_N = \int \mathrm{d}\boldsymbol{r}_1 \ldots \mathrm{d}\boldsymbol{r}_N \exp\left(-\beta \sum_{i>j}\sum v(r_{ij})\right), \tag{4.5}$$

we introduce the normalization integral

$$\tilde{Q}_N = \int |\Phi_N(\boldsymbol{r}_1 \ldots \boldsymbol{r}_N)|^2 \mathrm{d}\boldsymbol{r}_1 \ldots \mathrm{d}\boldsymbol{r}_N = \int \prod_{i>j} W(r_{ij}) \mathrm{d}\boldsymbol{r}_1 \ldots \mathrm{d}\boldsymbol{r}_N, \tag{4.6}$$

where $W(r_{ij}) = \exp[-u(r_{ij})]$. In terms of these quantities $W(r_{ij})$ the pair distribution function $g(r_{01})$ for a gas of $N+1$ molecules 0, 1, 2 . . ., N can be written as

$$g(r_{01}) = [N(N+1)/n^2](\tilde{Q}_{N-1}/\tilde{Q}_{N+1})\langle \prod_2^N W_{0i} W_{1i} \rangle W_{01}, \tag{4.7}$$

where

$$\langle X \rangle = \tilde{Q}_{N-1}^{-1} \int \mathrm{d}\boldsymbol{r}_2 \ldots \mathrm{d}\boldsymbol{r}_N X(\boldsymbol{r}_2 \ldots \boldsymbol{r}_N) |\Phi_{N-1}(\boldsymbol{r}_2 \ldots \boldsymbol{r}_N)|^2. \tag{4.8}$$

Similarly one can write

$$\rho_1(r_{01}) = N(\tilde{Q}_{N-1}/\tilde{Q}_N)\langle \prod_2^N W_{0i}^{\frac{1}{2}} W_{1i}^{\frac{1}{2}} \rangle. \tag{4.9}$$

In analogy again with the case of a classical gas of interacting molecules, one may introduce an "activity" z defined as $z = N\tilde{Q}_{N-1}/\tilde{Q}_N = (N+1)\tilde{Q}_N/\tilde{Q}_{N+1}$ (see for the classical system ref. 43) which makes it possible to write

$$g(r_{01}) = (Z^2/h^2) W_{01} \langle \prod_2^N W_{0i} W_{1i} \rangle, \quad \rho_1(r_{01}) = Z\langle \prod_2^N W_{0i}^{\frac{1}{2}} W_{1i}^{\frac{1}{2}} \rangle. \tag{4.10}$$

If now in addition it is assumed that $u(r)$ is represented by a hard-sphere potential, then $W_{ij} = W_{ij}^{\frac{1}{2}}$ and the two averages are the same. So one obtains Penrose and Onsager's formula[33])

$$n_0 = \lim_{r_{01}\to\infty} \rho_1(r_{01}) = (h^2/Z) \lim_{r_{01}\to\infty} g(r_{01}) = n^2/Z. \tag{4.11}$$

On the basis of numerical data for the hard-sphere gas and using a diameter $\sigma = 2.56$ Å for the helium atoms, Penrose and Onsager[33]) then calculated that at the liquid-helium density $z/n \approx 1/0.08$. This leads to the value for the condensate density of $n_0/n \approx 0.08$, which they published in 1956, a value remarkably close to the values obtained later.

It has already been pointed out by MacMillan[36]) that the liquid-structure function

$$S(k) = 1 + n \int [g(r) - 1] \mathrm{e}^{\mathrm{i}\boldsymbol{k}\cdot\boldsymbol{r}} \, \mathrm{d}\boldsymbol{r}, \tag{4.12}$$

which can be obtained from the calculated pair distribution function, does not behave properly for small k, where according to the analysis of Feynman $S(k)$ should behave like $\hbar k/2mc$. Instead, $S(k)$ seems to approach a very small constant value. Reatto and Chester[40]) have shown that this is due to the neglect of long-range correlations, due to the zero-point motions of long-wavelength phonons, in the trial wave function (4.1).

The appropriate classical normal coordinates for density waves are $\rho_k = m \sum_j \exp i\boldsymbol{k} \cdot \boldsymbol{r}_j$ with a certain cutoff wavelength $\lambda_c = 2\pi/k_c$, long compared to interatomic distances. In terms of these coordinates the ground-state wave function for the oscillator with frequency $\omega = ck$ becomes

$$\Phi_{\text{ph}}^{(k)} = \exp\left[-(c/2Nm\hbar k)\right]\rho_{\boldsymbol{k}}\rho_{-\boldsymbol{k}}. \tag{4.13}$$

The total phonon wave function can then be written as

$$\Phi_{\text{ph}} = \prod_{\boldsymbol{k}} \Phi_{\text{ph}}^{(\boldsymbol{k})} = \prod_{i>j} \exp\left[-\tfrac{1}{2}\chi(r_{ij})\right], \tag{4.14}$$

where, introducing a cutoff function $G(k, k_c) = \exp(-k/k_c)$

$$\chi(r_{ij}) = \frac{1}{N}\sum_{k} G(k, k_c)\frac{2mc}{\hbar k}\,e^{i\boldsymbol{k}\boldsymbol{r}_{ij}} = \frac{mc}{h\pi^2\hbar}\,\frac{1}{k_c^{-2}+r_{ij}^2}. \tag{4.15}$$

In this way Reatto and Chester[40]) showed that the long-range correlations due to long-wavelength phonons, could be taken into account by replacing $u(r)$ in the exponent by $u(r) + \chi(r)$. The asymptotic behaviour of $\chi(r) \propto 1/r^2$ then leads to a liquid-structure function $S(k) \approx \hbar k/2mc$ as required by Feynman[44]). The modified trial wave function has also been used by Francis, Chester and Reatto[39]) to obtain the condensate density. The wave function gave a considerable improvement of the ground-state energy and brought the condensate density back to the value 0.101 close to the values obtained by previous authors.

Jackson, Campbell and Feenberg[46,47]) have extended these investigations very much by constructing the phonon eigenfunctions for the excited states, leading to the result (2.1), where the excitation energies are given by $\varepsilon_k = \hbar^2k^2/2mS(k)$ and where $S(k)$ is the Fourier transform of the liquid-structure function (4.12), in agreement with Feynman[44]). For small k the function is $S(k) \approx \hbar k/2mc$, giving phonon type of excitations $\varepsilon_k = \hbar ck$. For large k, $S(k) \approx 1$ and one obtains particle type of excitations $\varepsilon_k = \hbar^2k^2/2m$. Feenberg[47]) also gave formal expressions for the phonon contribution to the single-particle density matrix and the depletion density, including Reatto and Chester's results in the limit $T = 0$, but numerical results have not yet been published. A further discussion falls, however, outside the scope of the present article.

Hohenberg and Platzman[48]) have pointed out that the existence of a condensate in liquid helium could be detected by neutron-scattering experiments for which the neutron momentum transfer would have to be so high that the scattering could be essentially single-particle scattering. In that case there would appear a smeared-out delta function superposed on a broader neutron-scattering curve. In this way Puff and Tenn[51]) discussing experiments of Cowley and Woods[49]) and Harling[50]) decided that there were indications of the existence of a condensate density $n_0/n \approx 0.06$. Mook, Scherm and Wilkinson[52]), however, found direct evidence for the existence of a zero-momentum state with a value of $n_0/n \approx 0.024$. These values are much smaller than the estimates on the basis of a theoretical analysis of the one-particle density matrix, but so far no solution for this discrepancy has been found. In any case, however, in particular these last experiments seem to have shown beyond doubt the existence of the condensate in the case of liquid helium.

5. *The condensate wave function.* In 1946 Bogoliubov[53]) in his pioneer contribution to the theory of the weakly interacting Bose–Einstein gas introduced what may be called the classical-quantity approximation, by assuming that in a uniform system the operators $\mathbf{a}_0^\dagger$ and $\mathbf{a}_0$ can be replaced by the corresponding classical quantities a_0^* and a_0. The justification is based on the fact that the expectation value of the occupation number $\mathbf{a}_0^\dagger \mathbf{a}_0$ of the zero-momentum state is a macroscopic quantity, so that the operators $\mathbf{a}_0^\dagger$ and $\mathbf{a}_0$, satisfying $\mathbf{a}_0 \mathbf{a}_0^\dagger - \mathbf{a}_0^\dagger \mathbf{a}_0 = 1$ nearly commute and behave as classical quantities with the absolute value $|a_0| = N_0^{\frac{1}{2}}$.

In the uniform system the field operators $\overline{\boldsymbol{\psi}} = V^{-\frac{1}{2}}\mathbf{a}_0$, where $\overline{\boldsymbol{\psi}} = V^{-1}\int d\boldsymbol{r}\boldsymbol{\psi}(\boldsymbol{r})$, may then be replaced by the corresponding classical quantity ψ with the absolute value $|\psi| = n_0^{\frac{1}{2}}$. Bogoliubov then replaced the particle field operator by $\boldsymbol{\psi}(\boldsymbol{r}) = \psi(\boldsymbol{r}) + \tilde{\boldsymbol{\psi}}(\boldsymbol{r})$, considered $\tilde{\boldsymbol{\psi}}(\boldsymbol{r})$ to be a first-order correction term, and was in this way able to solve the equation of motion for $\boldsymbol{\psi}(\boldsymbol{r})$ and to determine correctly the ground-state and excitation energies of the weakly interacting Bose–Einstein gas.

Beliaev[54]) argued that the "classical quantity" corresponding to $\mathbf{a}_0$ should really be identified with the matrix element $a_0 \approx \langle \Phi_{N-1}^0 | \mathbf{a}_0 | \Phi_N^0 \rangle = N_0^{\frac{1}{2}} \langle \Phi_{N-1}^0 | \Phi_{N-1}^0 \rangle = N_0^{\frac{1}{2}}$ between two ground states $|\Phi_N^0\rangle$ and $|\Phi_{N-1}^0\rangle$ differing only by one in the total number of particles.

Continuing this line of approach but generalizing to a not necessarily uniform system on the basis of Penrose and Onsager's characterization of Bose–Einstein condensation by a condensate wave function $\psi(\boldsymbol{r})$, Anderson[55, 56]) and Hohenberg and Martin[57]) made the conjecture that in general the condensate wave function $\psi(\boldsymbol{r})$ can be written as the mean value of the quantum-mechanical particle field operator

$$\psi(\boldsymbol{r}) = \langle\langle \boldsymbol{\psi}(\boldsymbol{r}) \rangle\rangle. \tag{5.1}$$

Again the basic idea is that $\boldsymbol{\psi}(\boldsymbol{r})$ is essentially an operator corresponding to a macroscopic dynamical variable, such that replacement of this field operator to first approximation by the corresponding classical field should be allowed. This classical field $\psi(\boldsymbol{r})$ is then defined by (5.1). Obviously for a non-uniform system this average is assumed to be a "local average" as is usually made in statistical mechanics when quantities like the temperature and the density vary in space.

Strictly speaking the "classical quantity", corresponding to the operator $\psi(\boldsymbol{r})$ should be defined, following Beliaev's argument, by the matrix element $\langle \Phi^0_{N-1}|\psi(\boldsymbol{r})|\Phi^0_N\rangle$ between two defined particle-number eigenstates differing by one particle. As long as only quantum states of well-defined particle number are considered the "average" (5.1) should therefore be replaced by this matrix element.

If one now develops the field operator with this classical field as the first term $\psi(\boldsymbol{r}) = \Psi(\boldsymbol{r}) + \tilde{\psi}(\boldsymbol{r})$ then one finds by substitution in the density matrix

$$\langle\langle \psi^\dagger(\boldsymbol{r}')\psi(\boldsymbol{r})\rangle\rangle = \Psi^*(\boldsymbol{r}')\Psi(\boldsymbol{r}) + \tilde{\rho}_1(\boldsymbol{r}, \boldsymbol{r}'), \tag{5.2}$$

where $\langle\langle \tilde{\psi}(\boldsymbol{r})\rangle\rangle = 0$ and where

$$\rho_1(\boldsymbol{r}\,\boldsymbol{r}') \equiv \langle\langle \tilde{\psi}^\dagger(\boldsymbol{r}')\tilde{\psi}(\boldsymbol{r})\rangle\rangle = \langle\langle \psi^\dagger(\boldsymbol{r}')\psi(\boldsymbol{r})\rangle\rangle - \langle\langle \psi^\dagger(\boldsymbol{r}')\rangle\rangle\langle\langle \psi(\boldsymbol{r})\rangle\rangle \tag{5.3}$$

now appears to be the contribution to the density matrix due to deviations from the average values of the field operator. This part really should vanish in the limit $\boldsymbol{r}' - \boldsymbol{r} \to \infty$ as expressed by (3.15). Comparison with (3.16) justifies that the mean value $\langle\langle \psi(\boldsymbol{r})\rangle\rangle$ has been identified with the condensate wave function as introduced in section 3. The separation (5.2) can be elucidated by considering for simplicity the system at absolute zero in the ground state $|\Phi^0_N\rangle$. Let a complete system of eigenstates be given by $|\Phi^i_N\rangle$, then

$$\begin{aligned}\langle \psi^\dagger(\boldsymbol{r}')\psi(\boldsymbol{r})\rangle &= \langle \Phi^0_N|\psi^\dagger(\boldsymbol{r}')\psi(\boldsymbol{r})|\Phi^0_N\rangle \\ &= \sum_i \langle \Phi^0_N|\psi^\dagger(\boldsymbol{r}')|\Phi^i_{N-1}\rangle\langle \Phi^i_{N-1}|\psi(\boldsymbol{r})|\Phi^0_N\rangle.\end{aligned} \tag{5.4}$$

The first term with $i = 0$ can then be identified with the product $\Psi^*(\boldsymbol{r}')\Psi(\boldsymbol{r})$ in (5.2). This leaves the following definition for $\tilde{\rho}_1(\boldsymbol{r}, \boldsymbol{r}')$:

$$\tilde{\rho}_1(\boldsymbol{r}\boldsymbol{r}') = \sum_{i\neq 0}{}' \langle \Phi^0_N|\psi^\dagger(\boldsymbol{r}')|\Phi^i_{N-1}\rangle\langle \Phi^i_{N-1}|\psi(\boldsymbol{r})|\Phi^0_N\rangle, \tag{5.5}$$

which should go to zero in the limit $\boldsymbol{r}' - \boldsymbol{r} \to \infty$ as the two factors are entirely uncorrelated in this limit.

As has already be remarked the definition of $\Psi(\boldsymbol{r})$ as an average expectation value of the field operator $\psi(\boldsymbol{r})$ needs further examination, because in every state of well-defined total number of particles this expectation value $\langle \Phi_N|\psi(\boldsymbol{r})|\Phi_N\rangle$ is zero. The same is true for the statistical average in a canonical and grand-canonical ensemble in which again all systems have well-defined particle number N, although N varies from one system to the other in the grand ensemble. A nonzero result for $\Psi(\boldsymbol{r})$ could only be obtained if the states of the system would not be quantum states of well-defined particle number, but composite quantum states obtained by superposing N-particle states with varying number of particles such that a wave packet in the number of particles results with a maximum at $N = \overline{N}$ and a small fluctuation round the maximum. It is then expected that such a state with unsharp particle number

$$|\bar{N}\rangle = \sum_N c_N |\Phi_N^0\rangle, \tag{5.6}$$

chosen in an appropriate way, might be a good description of situations in which averages of the type (5.1) are nonzero. The relative phase of the various states $|\Phi_N^0\rangle$ is chosen such that matrix elements $\langle\Phi_{N-1}^0|\Psi|\Phi_N^0\rangle$ turn out to be real. The coefficients, however, are complex and characterized by a phase χ on which also the compound state $|\bar{N}, \chi\rangle$ will depend. Sometimes such a composite state is referred to as a "coherent mixture", which is somewhat confusing because the state (5.6) is really a pure state and not a mixture.

Obviously the introduction of these states leads to the question about the physics behind the mathematical formalism, but before discussing this in section 6, we shall simply present two types of these unsharp particle-number states which have been used with success, *i.e.*, Anderson's "gaussian" states and Glauber's "coherent" states, taken from the theory of electromagnetic radiation.

5.1. Gaussian states. Anderson[56]) considered as an unsharp particle-number state a "wave packet" in N space with a gaussian distribution:

$$|\bar{N}, \chi\rangle = \frac{1}{2\pi \Delta N^{\frac{1}{2}}} \sum_N e^{-(N-\bar{N})^2/2\Delta N^2} e^{iN\chi} |\Phi_N^0\rangle. \tag{5.7}$$

The expectation value (5.1) in this state becomes equal to

$$\langle \bar{N}, \chi|\Psi(\boldsymbol{r})|\bar{N}, \chi\rangle = \sum_N c_{N-1}^* c_N \langle\Phi_{N-1}^0|\Psi(\boldsymbol{r})|\Phi_N^0\rangle. \tag{5.8}$$

For a uniform system one then obtains for the matrix elements

$$\langle\Phi_{N-1}^0|\bar{\Psi}||\Phi_N^0\rangle = V^{-\frac{1}{2}}\langle\Phi_{N-1}^0|\mathbf{a}_0|\Phi_N^0\rangle = n_0^{\frac{1}{2}}. \tag{5.9}$$

The coefficients may be written as $|c_{N-1}||c_N| \exp i\chi \approx |c_N|^2 \exp i\chi$. Carrying out the summation over N shows that to good approximation

$$\langle \bar{N}, \chi|\bar{\Psi}|\bar{N}, \chi\rangle = n_0^{\frac{1}{2}} \exp i\chi. \tag{5.10}$$

Using the mathematical analogy with the gaussian wave packet in coordinate space, where N, $\bar{N}$ and χ correspond to x, $\bar{x}$ and $\bar{p}$, respectively, one may transform from a wave packet in N space to a wave packet in χ space, showing that the uncertainty in the phase $\Delta\chi$, given by $\Delta\chi^2 = \overline{\chi^2} - \bar{\chi}^2$ is related to the uncertainty in the total particle number ΔN by the relation $\Delta N\, \Delta\chi \approx 1$. Phase and particle number appear here as conjugate variables in the quantum-mechanical sense. A well-defined particle number corresponds to complete uncertainty in phase, whereas narrowing down the uncertainty in the phase can only be done at the expense of an increasing uncertainty in the particle number[56]). There are known and valid objections (Susskind and Glasgower[58])) against treating the phase as a quantum-mechanical observable, but it can be assumed to be a valid picture as long as $\Delta\chi \ll 1$.

Assuming that this gaussian type of states applies to liquid helium, Anderson was able to discuss the equations of motion of the condensate and many interesting effects connected with the phase of the wave function (5.10), such as a macroscopic interference phenomenon in liquid helium following corresponding pictures in superconductors, but a discussion of these matters goes beyond the intention of the present article.

5.2. Glauber states or coherent states. A very promising possibility is to use Glauber's coherent states which have been used with very much success in the radiation theory[59]). In general these coherent states are eigenstates of the particle field operators $\boldsymbol{\psi}^{\dagger}(\boldsymbol{r})$ and $\boldsymbol{\psi}(\boldsymbol{r})$ or their Fourier transforms $\mathbf{a}_k^{\dagger}$ and $\mathbf{a}_k$. As these operators are non-hermitian one distinguishes right eigenstates of $\mathbf{a}_k$ and left eigenstates of $\mathbf{a}_k^{\dagger}$,

$$\mathbf{a}_k|a_k\rangle = a_k|a_k\rangle, \quad \langle a_k|\mathbf{a}_k^{\dagger} = a_k^*\langle a_k|, \tag{5.11}$$

where the eigenvalues a_k are in general complex. The states are approximately orthonormal and form a complete system provided the integration over states is carried out over the complex a_k plane. For any such momentum state $\boldsymbol{k}$ the coherent state $|a_k\rangle$ is a superposition of states with a different number of particles in the states $\boldsymbol{k}$:

$$|a_k\rangle = \mathrm{e}^{-\frac{1}{2}|a_k|^2} \sum_{N_k} \frac{a_k^{N_k}}{(N_k!)^{\frac{1}{2}}} |N_k\rangle. \tag{5.12}$$

The probability distribution for finding N_k particles in the state $|a_k\rangle$ is given by a Poisson distribution

$$\begin{aligned} |\langle N_k|a_k\rangle|^2 &= \mathrm{e}^{-|a_k|^2}|a_k|^{2N_k}/N_k! \\ &= \mathrm{e}^{-\overline{N}_k}\overline{N}_k^{N_k}/N_k! = \mathrm{e}^{N_k-\overline{N}_k}(\overline{N}_k/N_k)^{N_k}, \end{aligned} \tag{5.13}$$

round the average particle number $\overline{N}_k = |a_k|^2$. The variance of the number of particles round this average number is given by $\Delta N_k^2 = \overline{N_k^2} - \overline{N}_k^2 = \overline{N}_k^2 + \overline{N}_k$, such that for large $\overline{N}_k$ the variance $\Delta N_k \approx \overline{N}_k$, similar to the situation in a radiation gas. The eigenvalues a_k of eqs. (5.11) are thus complex quantities which can directly be expressed in terms of the average number of particles, $\overline{N}_k$, which occur in the eigenstate, *i.e.*,

$$a_k = \overline{N}_k^{\frac{1}{2}} \exp \mathrm{i}\chi_k. \tag{5.14}$$

Similarly to (5.7) there appears also in every term in the coherent state (5.12) a phase factor $\exp iN_k \chi_k$ and the coherent state as a whole can in analogy with (5.7) be written as $|a_k\rangle = |\bar{N}_k, \chi_k\rangle$.

It is quite possible to generalize these coherent states to the non-uniform case in which the field operator $\boldsymbol{\psi}(\boldsymbol{r})$ and its expectation values $\langle\langle\boldsymbol{\psi}(\boldsymbol{r})\rangle\rangle = \Psi(\boldsymbol{r})$ become the relevant quantities. Using the Fourier transform

$$\boldsymbol{\psi}(\boldsymbol{r}) = V^{-\frac{1}{2}} \sum_{\boldsymbol{k}} a_k \exp i\boldsymbol{kr}$$

one easily verifies that the product states $\prod |a_k\rangle$ act as coherent eigenstates of the operator $\boldsymbol{\psi}(\boldsymbol{r})$ such that

$$\boldsymbol{\psi}(\boldsymbol{r})|\psi(\boldsymbol{r})\rangle = \psi(\boldsymbol{r})|\psi(\boldsymbol{r})\rangle, \quad |\psi(\boldsymbol{r})\rangle = \prod_{\boldsymbol{k}} |a_k\rangle \equiv |\{a_k\}\rangle. \tag{5.15}$$

The eigenvalue or "eigenfield" $\psi(\boldsymbol{r})$ is in general complex and determined by the set of complex eigenvalues a_k:

$$\psi(\boldsymbol{r}) = V^{-\frac{1}{2}} \sum_{\boldsymbol{k}} a_k \exp i\boldsymbol{kr} = n_0(\boldsymbol{r})^{\frac{1}{2}} \exp i\chi(\boldsymbol{r}), \tag{5.16}$$

where $n_0(\boldsymbol{r})$ is the condensate density. This coherent state can thus be expressed in particle-number eigenstates $|\{N_k\}\rangle = \prod |N_k\rangle$ by

$$|\psi(\boldsymbol{r})\rangle = |n_0, \chi\rangle = \exp\left(-\tfrac{1}{2}\sum |a_k|^2\right) \sum_{\{N_k\}} \prod_{\boldsymbol{k}} \frac{a_k^{N_k}}{(N_k!)^{\frac{1}{2}}} |\{N_k\}\rangle. \tag{5.17}$$

The most important property of the coherent states is that any expectation value of the type $\langle\boldsymbol{\psi}^\dagger(\boldsymbol{r}')\boldsymbol{\psi}^\dagger(\boldsymbol{r}'')\ldots\boldsymbol{\psi}(\boldsymbol{r})\ldots\rangle$ when taken in a coherent state $|\psi(\boldsymbol{r})\rangle$ factorizes to the product $\psi^*(\boldsymbol{r}')\psi^*(\boldsymbol{r}'')\ldots\psi(\boldsymbol{r})\ldots$ and in particular also $\langle\psi^\dagger(\boldsymbol{r}')\psi(\boldsymbol{r})\rangle = \psi^*(\boldsymbol{r}')\psi(\boldsymbol{r})$. When the ground-state of liquid helium would be in a coherent state, any density matrix of the system would factorize completely. Conversely from the fact that this is not true, according to the calculation in section 4, one may conclude that the ground state of liquid helium is not a coherent state in the particle field operators. Glauber[59]) and Carruthers and Nieto[60]) have given a survey of the properties of these coherent states and have explored the utility of coherent states in connection with the transition to the classical limit. The coherent states seem to have been used in connection with superfluidity first by Cummings and Johnston[61]) and by Casher and Revzen[62]) and their usefulness for the present purpose has been explored in more detail by Langer[63]), Glassgold and Sauermann[64]) and by 't Hooft and De Boer[65]). It is, however, not our intention to give a presentation of their properties in the present publication. We limit ourselves to a discussion of the fundamental question *why* compound quantum states with unsharp particle number, such as the coherent states, have to be introduced in the theory of liquid helium.

6. *Broken symmetry*. The necessity to include states with unsharp particle

number in the field of statistical mechanics has proved to be a very useful and necessary extension of quantum statistical mechanics, where so far, even in the grand canonical ensemble, only states with definite particle number have been considered.

The physical reason that these composite states of indefinite particle number have been introduced in the theoretical treatment of liquid helium, is fundamentally connected with the fact that the lambda transition is an example of a whole class of phase transitions, such as those occurring in ferro- and antiferromagnetics, ferroelectrics, order–disorder systems and of course the transition into the superconducting state, which all have in common that below the transition point an order parameter exists which is zero above and different from zero below the transition point. The analogy among all these systems needs no further discussion, as this is an essential concept in the vast literature on phase transitions and the corresponding scaling phenomena. A brief remark should be made, however, on the concept of symmetry breaking, which is also common to all these phase transitions, but which is in particular relevant for understanding the situation in liquid helium. The fact that all second-order phase transitions have a connection with symmetry breaking, in the sense that below the transition point the thermodynamic state of the system does not exhibit the full symmetry of the hamiltonian, was recognized by Landau[10]) as early as 1937 (see section 1). Symmetry breaking has been introduced in the theory of Bose–Einstein condensation by Bogoliubov[66]). Often the situation in liquid helium is illuminated by comparing this with the situation in a Heisenberg model for a ferromagnet (*cf.* Anderson[55]).

In the isotropic Heisenberg model for a ferromagnet the total spin $\mathbf{S} \equiv (\mathbf{S}_x, \mathbf{S}_y, \mathbf{S}_z)$ is a constant of motion and commutes with $\mathbf{H}$. As always there is then also a symmetry group of transformations $\mathbf{H} \rightarrow \mathbf{U}^{\dagger}\mathbf{H}\mathbf{U}$, *i.e.*, those generated by the unitary operator $\mathbf{U}(\boldsymbol{\omega}) = \exp \mathrm{i}\boldsymbol{\omega} \cdot \mathbf{S}$, with $\boldsymbol{\omega} \equiv (\omega_x, \omega_y, \omega_z)$, which leaves the hamiltonian invariant. This reflects the fact that the hamiltonian has the symmetry property of being invariant under rotations in space. As a consequence the ground state of the system is degenerate and the ground-state vectors are transformed into each other by the unitary operator $\mathbf{U}(\boldsymbol{\omega})$ such that $|\Phi^0(\boldsymbol{\omega})\rangle = \mathbf{U}(\boldsymbol{\omega})|\Phi^0(0)\rangle$. These degenerate states can thus be labelled by the direction in space $\boldsymbol{\omega} \equiv (\omega_x, \omega_y, \omega_z)$.

The consequence of the rotational-symmetry property of the hamiltonian is that the statistical-mechanical average $\langle\langle \mathbf{S}_z \rangle\rangle$ is zero. Nevertheless there exists below the Curie temperature a physical situation in which the total spin is oriented in some direction in space, which evidently has *not* the symmetry of the hamiltonian and which therefore is not properly described by the statistical-mechanical canonical or grand-canonical ensemble. At $T = 0$, these unsymmetrical physical situations *can*, however, be described by choosing one particular state out of the various degenerate quantum-mechanical ground states, *e.g.* $|\Phi^0(\boldsymbol{\omega})\rangle$ which gives a nonzero result: $\langle \Phi^0(\boldsymbol{\omega})|\mathbf{S}_z|\Phi^0(\boldsymbol{\omega})\rangle \neq 0$. In the ensemble, however, an average is taken over all these states $|\Phi^0(\omega)\rangle$ with equal weight, giving a zero result.

As has been shown in particular by Bogoliubov[66]) this quantum-mechanical degeneracy leads to a kind of "instability" of the average values obtained from the statistical ensemble against small perturbations, which is very similar to the "instability" which a degenerate quantum state may have against small perturbations in perturbation theory. If one applies a small external magnetic field of strength H one breaks the symmetry of the hamiltonian by adding a term $-\, mH\mathbf{S}_z$. Then the partition function is given by

$$Z(T, V, H) = \mathrm{Tr}\, e^{-\beta(\mathbf{H} - mH\mathbf{S}_z)}, \tag{6.1}$$

from which the magnetization is obtained by

$$M(T, H) = \lim_{V\to\infty} \frac{m}{V} \langle\langle \mathbf{S}_z \rangle\rangle_H = \lim_{V\to\infty} \frac{1}{V} \frac{\partial \ln Z}{\partial \beta H}. \tag{6.2}$$

Obviously, when we are below the Curie temperature, $M(T, H)$ approaches a certain limit $M_0(T) = \lim_{H\to 0} M(T, H)$, such that $M(T, H) = M_0(T) + \mathcal{O}(H)$. Thus $M(T, H)$ jumps to $M_0(T)$ even for very small H and then rises further. This "instability" of the statistical average against an external field led Bogoliubov[66]) to the concept "quasi-average" being an average obtained by the following procedure

$$\begin{aligned} M_0(T) &= \lim_{H\to 0} M(T, H) = \lim_{H\to 0}\ \lim_{V\to\infty} (m/V)\langle\langle \mathbf{S}_z \rangle\rangle_H \neq 0 \quad (\text{for } T < T_c), \\ M_0(T) &= 0 \quad (\text{for } T > T_c), \end{aligned} \tag{6.3}$$

for which the order of the two limiting procedures is essential. On the other hand if one makes $H \to 0$ before taking the thermodynamic limit one obtains always zero

$$\langle\langle \mathbf{S}_z \rangle\rangle_{H=0} = \lim_{H\to 0} \langle\langle \mathbf{S}_z \rangle\rangle_H = 0. \tag{6.4}$$

This example shows very clearly that in cases where an order parameter occurs, which is only different from zero in states which have a lower symmetry than that of the original hamiltonian, the value of the order parameter can only be obtained as an average from the statistical-mechanical ensemble provided we follow the procedure indicated for defining a quasi-average (6.3) by Bogoliubov.

In liquid helium, *i.e.*, in a non-ideal Bose–Einstein system, the total number of particles of the system is a constant of motion, *i.e.*, the operator $\mathbf{N}$ commutes with $\mathbf{H}$. In this case there is the "gauge" group of transformations, generated by $\mathrm{U}(\chi) = \exp i\chi\mathbf{N}$, which leave the hamiltonian operator invariant: $\mathbf{H} = \mathbf{U}^\dagger\mathbf{H}\mathbf{U}$. This means that the hamiltonian operator has the property of being invariant under gauge transformations $\mathbf{a}_k \to \mathbf{U}^\dagger\mathbf{a}_c\mathbf{U} = \mathbf{a}_k \exp i\chi$ and $\mathbf{a}_k^\dagger \to \mathbf{a}_k^\dagger \exp -i\chi$, the number of creation operators and annihilation operators being equal. Consequently the ground state of the system is degenerate and the ground-state vectors are transformed into each other by the unitary operator $\mathbf{U}(\chi)$ such that $|\Phi^0(\chi)\rangle = \mathbf{U}(\chi)|\Phi^0(0)\rangle$. These degenerate states can thus be labelled by the phase χ.

The consequence of this symmetry property is that every thermodynamic average of the kind $\langle\langle \mathbf{a}_k^\dagger \ldots \mathbf{a}_l \ldots \rangle\rangle$ is zero, unless the number of creation operators equals the number of annihilation operators. In particular the average value $\langle\langle \boldsymbol{\psi}(\boldsymbol{r})\rangle\rangle$ which was introduced as the definition of the condensate wave function, is always zero. On the other hand we believe that below the condensation temperature T_0 there exists a physical situation which is characterized by a nonzero condensate wave function, just like the nonzero spontaneous magnetization in the ferromagnetic case. Such a situation, described by a complex condensate wave function with a definite phase χ, does not comply with the gauge invariance of the hamiltonian and is therefore not properly described by the statistical-mechanical ensemble theory. However, the expectation value in any of the degenerate states $|\Phi^0(\chi)\rangle$ separately may very well be different from zero, *i.e.*, $\langle\Phi^0(\chi)|\boldsymbol{\psi}(\boldsymbol{r})|\Phi^0(\chi)\rangle \neq 0$, such that at $T = 0$ these states may be useful to describe the physical situation with a condensate wave function different from zero. In the ensemble, however, the various degenerate states $|\Phi^0(\chi)\rangle$ have equal weight, so that the statistical average value $\langle\langle \boldsymbol{\psi}(\boldsymbol{r})\rangle\rangle$ becomes zero.

Following Bogoliubov[66]) the situation in a system of Bose–Einstein particles can again be described as an "instability" of the statistical average value $\langle\langle \boldsymbol{\psi}(\boldsymbol{r})\rangle\rangle$ against a small perturbation breaking the symmetry of the hamiltonian. The symmetry-breaking field for a uniform system with periodic boundary conditions is of the form of a "source" field $- V^{\frac{1}{2}}(\nu \mathbf{a}_0^\dagger + \nu^* \mathbf{a}_0)$ which may create or annihilate particles in the zero-momentum state. In the presence of this source field with strength $\nu \neq 0$ averages of the kind $\langle\langle \mathbf{a}_k^\dagger \ldots \mathbf{a}_l \ldots \rangle\rangle$, in which the number of creation operators minus the number of annihilation operators is equal to one, and in particular the average value of $\overline{\boldsymbol{\psi}} = V^{-1}\int \boldsymbol{\psi}(\boldsymbol{r})\mathrm{d}\boldsymbol{r} = V^{-\frac{1}{2}}\mathbf{a}_0$, *i.e.*, $\langle\langle \overline{\boldsymbol{\psi}}\rangle\rangle_\nu = V^{-\frac{1}{2}}\langle\langle a_0\rangle\rangle_\nu$ may be different from zero. In this case the partition function becomes

$$Z(T, V, \mu, \nu) = \mathrm{Tr}\, \mathrm{e}^{-\beta[\mathbf{H} - \mu\mathbf{N} - V(\nu\overline{\boldsymbol{\psi}}^\dagger + \nu^+\overline{\boldsymbol{\psi}})]}, \tag{6.5}$$

so that [compare (6.2)]

$$\Psi(T, \nu) = \lim_{V\to\infty} \frac{1}{V}\langle\langle \overline{\boldsymbol{\psi}}\rangle\rangle_\nu = \lim_{V\to\infty} \frac{1}{V}\frac{\partial \ln Z}{\partial \beta \nu^*}. \tag{6.6}$$

Above the transition temperature this so-obtained value of $\Psi(T, \nu)$ in the presence of a source field approaches zero continuously as a function of ν, but below the transition temperature the average value $\Psi(T, \nu)$ approaches a certain limit $\Psi_0(T)$ such that $\Psi(T, \nu) = \Psi_0(T) + \mathcal{O}(\nu)$, which shows the "instability" of the thermodynamic average in this case against an external source field. Thus we have to define a quasi average according to Bogoliubov[65]) so as to obtain below the transition temperature a nonzero result for the condensate wave function [compare (6.3)].

$$\Psi_0(T) = \lim_{\nu\to 0} \Psi_0(T, \nu) = \lim_{\nu\to 0} \lim_{V\to\infty} (1/V)\langle\langle\overline{\psi}\rangle\rangle_\nu \neq 0 \quad (\text{for } T < T_0),$$
$$\Psi_0(T) = 0 \quad (\text{for } T > T_0). \tag{6.7}$$

Essential in calculating this nonzero "quasi average" below T_0 is the fact that first a thermodynamic limit is taken. In this limit the energy perturbation between the degenerate states becomes proportional to V, which prevents the average over the various degenerate states to become zero.

The situation becomes very clear in the ideal Bose–Einstein gas (Casher and Revzen[62]), 't Hooft and de Boer[65])). Choosing for simplicity a uniform system with periodic boundary conditions, the hamiltonian occurring in the canonical ensemble, adding a symmetry-breaking field, becomes

$$\mathbf{H} - \mu\mathbf{N} = \sum_k (\varepsilon_k - \mu)\mathbf{a}_k^\dagger \mathbf{a}_k - V^{\frac{1}{2}}(\nu\mathbf{a}_0^\dagger + \nu^*\mathbf{a}_0), \tag{6.8}$$

where $\varepsilon_k = \hbar^2 k^2/2m$. This hamiltonian can be diagonalized by the substitution

$$b_k = a_k - V^{\frac{1}{2}}(\nu/\mu)\delta_{k,0}, \tag{6.9}$$

giving

$$\mathbf{H} - \mu\mathbf{N} = V|\nu|^2/\mu^2 + \sum_k (\varepsilon_k - \mu)\mathbf{b}_k^\dagger \mathbf{b}_k. \tag{6.10}$$

Then the partition function becomes

$$Z_{gr}(T, V, \mu, \nu) = \mathrm{e}^{-\beta V|\nu|^2/\mu^2} \sum_{\{N_k\}} \exp\left(-\beta \sum_k (\varepsilon_k - \mu)N_k\right), \tag{6.11}$$

where N_k, the eigenvalues of $N_k = \mathbf{b}_k^\dagger \mathbf{b}_k$, are the occupation numbers of the particle states $\boldsymbol{k}$. The condensate wave function $\Psi(T, \nu)$ is defined by (6.6) to be

$$\Psi(T, \nu) = \lim_{V\to\infty} \frac{1}{V} \frac{\partial \ln Z}{\partial \beta\nu^*} = \frac{\nu}{\mu} \tag{6.12}$$

and after taking the thermodynamic limit the thermodynamic potential μ is determined by the density through the relation

$$n = \lim_{V\to\infty} \frac{1}{V} \frac{\partial \ln Z}{\partial \beta\mu} = \frac{|\nu^2|}{\mu^2} + \int \mathrm{d}\boldsymbol{p} \frac{h^{-3}}{\exp \beta[\varepsilon(p) - \mu] - 1}$$
$$= |\nu|^2/\mu^2 + \lambda^{-3} g_{\frac{3}{2}}(\exp \beta\mu), \tag{6.13}$$

where $\lambda^2 = h^2/2\pi mkT$ and $g_{\frac{3}{2}}(z) = \sum_l z^l/l^{\frac{3}{2}}$ and where $|\nu|^2/\mu^2 = n_0(T, \nu)$ is equal to the particle number density in the zero-momentum state. Above the transition point $\mu < 0$, we always have $\Psi(T, \nu) \to 0$ for $\nu \to 0$ and $n_0(T) = 0$ for all $T > T_0$. Below the transition point and in the presence of an external source field, μ has a small negative value, proportional to $|v|$, which according to (6.13) for small $\beta\mu$ is given by $\mu(v, T) = -|v|/n_0(T)^{\frac{1}{2}}$, where $n_0(T) = n - \lambda^{-3} g_{\frac{3}{2}}(1)$. Substitution in (6.12) now gives for the condensate wave function (6.7):

$$\Psi_0(T) = \lim_{v \to 0} \Psi(T, v) = n_0(T)^{\frac{1}{2}} \exp i\chi, \tag{6.14}$$

where the sign has been absorbed in the phase. This example makes clear what happens in the symmetry breaking below the transition point.

The ground state $|\Phi_v^0\rangle$ at $T = 0$ in which the system is brought as a result of the applied source field $-V^{\frac{1}{2}}(v\mathbf{a}_0^\dagger + v^*\mathbf{a}_0)$ can easily be found. For $v > 0$ the potential μ is negative, therefore all quantities $\varepsilon_k - \mu$ in (6.8) are positive. Consequently the ground state in the external field is defined by the condition $b_k|\Phi^0\rangle = 0$ for all $\boldsymbol{k}$, so that, using (6.9):

$$\mathbf{a}_0|\Phi^0\rangle = V^{\frac{1}{2}}(v/\mu)|\Phi^0\rangle, \quad \mathbf{a}_k|\Phi^0\rangle = 0 \qquad (\boldsymbol{k} \neq 0). \tag{6.15}$$

This ground state $|\Phi^0\rangle = |\overline{N}_0(v), \chi\rangle$ therefore is a Glauber coherent state in the $\mathbf{a}_0$ operators with eigenvalue $a_0(v) = V^{\frac{1}{2}}v/\mu = V^{\frac{1}{2}}n_0(v)^{\frac{1}{2}} \exp i\chi = \overline{N_0(v)}^{\frac{1}{2}} \exp i\chi$, where $\overline{N_0(v)} = Vn_0(v)$. Thus

$$|\Phi^0\rangle = |a_0\rangle = e^{-\frac{1}{2}|a_0|^2} \sum_{N_0} \frac{a_0^{N_0}}{(N_0!)^{\frac{1}{2}}} |N_0\rangle,$$

where $|N_0\rangle$ is the ground state of an ideal Bose–Einstein gas at $T = 0$ with all particles in the condensate state. When now the field is switched off this ground state goes over smoothly into the coherent state $|\overline{N}_0, \chi\rangle$ of the unperturbed Bose–Einstein gas characterized by the nonzero condensate wave function (6.14), which state is just one of the various degenerate ground states $|\Phi^0(\chi)\rangle$, transforming into each other by the operator $\mathbf{U}(\chi)$.

The situation in an interacting Bose–Einstein gas, such as liquid helium, is not yet clear. In any case it seems true that the interacting Bose–Einstein gas cannot simply be brought into a coherent state in the particle field operators with an external symmetry-breaking field as is the case with the ideal Bose–Einstein system.

Cummings and Johnston[61]) have made the conjecture that the superfluid component, which in the picture of Landau's two-fluid model is identified with the ground state for the excitation gas, is a coherent state in the representation of the creation and annihilation operators for excitations of this excitation gas. In fact this excitation gas contains excitations of zero energy in the long-wavelength limit leading to a degeneracy of the ground state similar to that of an ideal Bose–Einstein gas of real particles below the transition point where $\mu = 0$. Application of a "source field" or symmetry-breaking field then removes this degeneracy and may bring the superfluid into a coherent state. As the claims were made on the basis of an approximate perturbation treatment of the nonideal Bose–Einstein gas the evidence unfortunately may not yet be convincing.

As a whole one may conclude that the status of the theory of the equilibrium statistical mechanics of liquid helium is still unsatisfactory.

On one hand there exists the Landau two-fluid model, with two well-defined quantities the superfluid density ρ_s and the normal-fluid density ρ_n, such that $\rho_n+\rho_s = \rho$, which gives a very satisfactory description of the equilibrium properties (as well as of the hydrodynamic properties) of liquid helium.

On the other hand there is the phenomenon of Bose–Einstein condensation in an interacting system of Bose–Einstein particles, according to Penrose and Onsager, characterized by a condensate density n_0 and a depletion $\tilde{n}$, such that $n = n_0+\tilde{n}$. Connected to this condensate is the existence of the condensate wave function on macroscopic wave functions, a classical field, which immediately suggests the necessity of introducing a Glauber type of coherent quantum states of which such classical fields may be the eigenvalues.

The connection between these two pictures is still not very clear, which is certainly due to the many difficulties encountered in the many-particle perturbation theory of an interacting Bose–Einstein gas which, even in the weak-interaction dilute-gas limit, make it very difficult to draw rigorous conclusions.

A very promising approach may be the use of response-function techniques and correlation functions introduced in the discussion of liquid helium by Pines and Nozières[73, 74, 75]), Kadanov and Martin[76]), and by Baym[77]), which relates the normal density to the response of a Bose–Einstein system to the Coriolis forces in a rotating bucket. A further discussion would go beyond the intention of the present article, so that reference is made to the existing literature.

Acknowledgement. The author is indebted to Drs. A. H. 't Hooft for many stimulating discussions during the preparation of this paper.

REFERENCES

1) Keesom, W. H. and Clusius, K., Proc. K. Ned. Akad. Wetensch. **35** (1932) 307; Commun. Kamerlingh Onnes Lab., Leiden, No. 219*e* (1932).
2) Keesom, W. H. and Keesom, A. P., Proc. K. Ned. Akad. Wetensch. **35** (1932) 736; Commun. Kamerlingh Onnes Lab., Leiden, No. 221*d* (1932).
3) Keesom, W. H. and Van de Ende, J. N., Proc. K. Ned. Akad. Wetensch. **35** (1932) 143; Commun. Kamerlingh Onnes Lab., Leiden, No. 219*b* (1932).
4) Keesom, W. H. and Kok, J. A., Proc. K. Ned. Akad. Wetensch. **35** (1932) 743; Commun. Kamerlingh Onnes Lab., Leiden, No. 221*e* (1932).
5) Ehrenfest, P., Proc. K. Ned. Akad. Wetensch. **36** (1933) 153; Commun. Kamerlingh Onnes Lab., Leiden Suppl. No. 75*b* (1933).
6) See Keesom, W. H., Helium, Elsevier (Amsterdam, 1942) p. 259.
7) Gorter, C. J. and Casimir, H. B. G., Phys. Z. **35** (1964) 963; Z. techn. Phys. **15** (1934) 539.
8) Gorter, C. J., Arch. Teyler **7** (1933) 387.
9) See Gorter, C. J., Rev. mod. Phys. **36** (1964) 5.

10) Landau, L., Phys. Z. Sowjet Union **8** (1935) 113.
11) Landau, L., Phys. Z. Sowjet Union **11** (1937) 26, 545.
12) London, F., Phys. Rev. **54** (1938) 947.
13) Tisza, L., Nature **141** (1938) 913; J. Phys. Radium **1** (1940) 165, 350.
14) London, F., Rev. mod. Phys. **17** (1945) 310.
15) Gorter, C. J., Physica **15** (1949) 523; Commun. Kamerlingh Onnes Lab., Leiden, Suppl. No. 99*a*; Progress low Temp. Phys. vol. I (1955) ch. 1.
16) Gorter, C. J. and Mellink, J. H., Physica **15** (1949) 285; Commun. Kamerlingh Onnes Lab., Leiden, Suppl. No. 98*a*.
Gorter, C. J., Kasteleijn, P. W. and Mellink, J. H., Physica **16** (1950) 113; Commun. Kamerlingh Onnes Lab., Leiden, Suppl. No. 100*b*.
17) De Groot, S. R., Jansen, L. and Mazur, P., Physica **16** (1950) 421, 691.
18) Prigogine, I. and Mazur, P., Physica **17** (1951) 661.
19) Landau, L., J. eksper. teor. Fiz. USSR **5** (1941) 71, **11** (1947) 9; Phys. Rev. **60** (1941) 356.
20) Peshkov, N., J. eksper. teor. Fiz. USSR **10** (1946) 389.
21) Landau, L. and Khalatnikov, I. M., J. eksper. teor. Fiz. USSR **19** (1949) 709, 637.
22) Khalatnikov, I. M., J. eksper. teor. Fiz. USSR **23** (1952) 8, 21.
23) Kramers, H. A., Physica **18** (1952) 653.
24) Kronig, R., Physica **19** (1953) 535.
25) Khalatnikov, I. M., Fortschr. Phys. **5** (1957) 211, 286.
26) Palevski, H., Otnes, K. and Larson, K. E., Phys. Rev. **112** (1958) 11.
27) Henshair, D. G. and Woods, A. D. B., Phys. Rev. **121** (1961) 1266.
28) Yarnell, J. L., Arnold, G. P., Bendt, P. J. and Kerr, E. C., Phys. Rev. **113** (1959) 1379.
29) Bendt, P. J., Cowan, R. D. and Yarnell, J. L., Phys. Rev. **113** (1959) 1386.
30) De Boer, J., Rendiconti della Scuola Internazionale di Fisica E. Fermi **21** (1961) 1;
De Boer, J., in Phonons and Phonon Interactions, Aarhus Summer School Lectures, T. A. Bak, ed.; Benjamin (New York, 1963).
31) Wilks, J. H., The properties of Liquid and Solid Helium, Clarendon Press (Oxford, 1967);
See also: Langer, S. S. and Reppy, J. D., in Progress in Low Temperature Physics, Vol. 5, C. J. Gorter, ed., North-Holland Publ. Co. (Amsterdam, 1970) p. 1.
32) Penrose, O., Phil. Mag. **42** (1951) 1373.
33) Penrose, O. and Onsager, L., Phys. Rev. **104** (1956) 576.
See also Chester, G. V., Rend. Sc. Int. Fis. E. Fermi **21** (1961) 51.
34) Yang, C. N., Rev. mod. Phys. **34** (1962) 694.
35) Girardeau, M., Phys. Fluids **5** (1962) 1468; J. math. Phys. **6** (1965) 1083.
Girardeau, M. and Arnowitt, R., Phys. Rev. **113** (1959) 755.
36) McMillan, W. L., Phys. Rev. **138** A (1965) 442.
37) Schiff, D. and Verlet, L., Phys. Rev. **160** (1967) 208.
38) Alder, B. S. and Wainwright, T. E., J. chem. Phys. **33** (1960) 1439.
39) Francis, W. P., Chester, G. V. and Reatto, L., Phys. Rev. **1** A (1970) 86.
40) Reatto, L. and Chester, G. V., Phys. Rev. **155** (1967) 88.
41) Reatto, L., Phys. Rev. **183** (1969) 334.
42) Feenberg, E., Amer. J. Phys. **38** (1970) 684.
43) De Boer, J., Rep. Progr. Phys. **12** (1948–49) 305.
44) Feynman, R. P., in Progress in Low Temperature Physics, Vol. 1, C. J. Gorter, ed., North-Holland Publ. Co. (Amsterdam, 1955) p. 17.
45) Wu, F. Y. and Feenberg, E., Phys. Rev. **122** (1961) 739.
46) Jackson, H. W. and Feenberg, E., Ann. Physics **15** (1961) 266.
Campbell, C. E. and Feenberg, E., Phys. Rev. **188** (1969) 396.
47) Feenberg, E., Ann. Physics **70** (1972) 133.
48) Hohenberg, P. C. and Platzman, P. M., Phys. Rev. **152** (1966) 198.
49) Cowley, R. A. and Woods, A. D. B., Phys. Rev. Letters **21** (1968) 787; Canad. J. Phys. **49** (1971) 177.
50) Harling, O. K., Phys. Rev. Letters **24** (1970) 1046; Phys. Rev. **3** A (1970) 1046.
51) Puff, R. D. and Tenn, J. S., Phys. Rev. **1** A (1970) 125.
52) Mook, H. A., Scherm, R. and Wilkinson, M. K., Phys. Rev. A **6** (1972) 2268.

53) Bogoliubov, N., J. Phys. USSR **11** (1947) 23.
54) Beliaev, S., Sowjet Physics JETP **7** (1958) 289.
55) Anderson, P. W., in Many Body Problem, vol. 2, Cajanello, ed., (Ravello, 1963).
56) Anderson, P. W., Rev. mod. Phys. **38** (1966) 298.
57) Hohenberg, P. C. and Martin, P. C., Ann. Physics **34** (1965) 291.
58) Susskind, L. and Glogower, J., Physics **1** (1964) 94.
59) Glauber, R. J., Phys. Rev. **131** (1963) 2766.
60) Carruthers, P. and Nieto, M. M., Rev. mod. Phys. **40** (1968) 411.
61) Cummings, F. W. and Johnston, J. R., Phys. Rev. **151** (1966) 105.
62) Casher, A. and Revzen, M., Ann. J. Phys. **35** (1967) 1154; Ann. Physics **48** (1968) 441.
63) Langer, J. S., Phys. Rev. **167** (1968) 183, 219.
64) Glassgold, A. E. and Sauermann, H., Phys. Rev. **182** (1969) 262, **188** (1969) 515.
65) 't Hooft, A. H. and De Boer, J., Proc. K. Ned. Akad. Wetensch. **B 73** (1970) 434, 446.
66) Bogoliubov, N. N., Physica **26** (1960) S 1; Phys. Abh. Sowjet Union **6** (1962) 1, 113, 229.
67) Khalatnikov, I. M., An Introduction to the Theory of Superfluidity, Benjamin (New York, Amsterdam, 1965).
68) Fröhlich, H., Physica **37** (1967) 215.
69) Fröhlich, H., Phys. kondens. Materie **9** (1969) 350.
70) Hijland, G. J. and Rowlands, P., Physica **54** (1971) 542.
71) Haug, H. and Weiss, K., Physica **59** (1972) 29.
72) Weiss, K. and Haug. H., to be published.
73) Pines, D., 1962 Cargese Lectures in Theor. Physics, p. 35.
74) Nozières, P. and Pines, D., Preprint, Theory of Quantum Liquids II.
75) Pines, D., Proceedings Int. Low Temp. Conf. 1964, p. 61.
76) Kadanov, L. P. and Martin, P. C., Ann. Physics **24** (1963) 419.
77) Baym, G., in Clark, R. C. and Derrick, G. H., Mathematical Methods in Solid State and Superfluid Theory, Oliver and Boyd (Edinburg, 1967) p. 121.

Physica **69** (1973) 218–244 © *North-Holland Publishing Co.*

EXPERIMENTAL PROPERTIES OF THE EXTRAORDINARY PHASES OF LIQUID ^{3}He AT MILLIKELVIN TEMPERATURES*

J. C. WHEATLEY

Department of Physics, University of California, San Diego, La Jolla, California 92037, USA

Received 20 June 1973

Synopsis

A critical review of experimental properties of the extraordinary phases of liquid ^{3}He is presented, including information on the phase diagram, thermal properties, nuclear magnetic resonance, flow properties as manifested in wire damping and heat-flow experiments, and propagation of collisionless sound.

1. *Introduction.* Although new results of both experimental and theoretical nature are rapidly emerging in the field of low temperature ^{3}He it is appropriate to pause at this stage to examine what we have learned thus far. In this paper we will restrict ourselves to a summary and a brief discussion of those experiments which characterize the remarkable properties of the *liquid* with the aim of presenting the known experimental facts as clearly as we can. We will generally not take a historical approach, except to note that *current experimental* activity began with the discovery by Osheroff, Richardson, and Lee[1]) of the "A" and "B" features on the ^{3}He pressure *vs. time* curve (pressurization curve) of ^{3}He contained in an adiabatic compressional cooling cell.

2. *Thermodynamic properties.* A phase diagram for zero external magnetic field of the new phases of liquid ^{3}He has been found by Greytak *et al.*[2]) and is shown in fig. 1. In this work the ^{3}He is cooled by adiabatic demagnetization of cerous magnesium nitrate (CMN) powder mixed with it so that the dependence on magnetic field cannot be determined. On the figure, we see two phase diagrams; one is referred to a magnetic temperature scale T^* actually measured and the other to a provisional absolute temperature scale T_{SOUND} which is inferred indirectly. This emphasizes at the outset one of the principal impediments to making quantitative measurements on the new phases: the absence of an accurate and precise absolute

* Work supported by the U.S. Atomic Energy Commission under Contract No. AT(04-3)-34, P.A. 143.

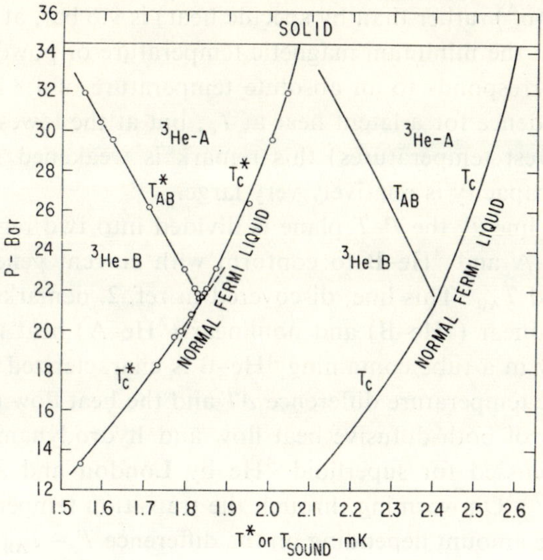

Fig. 1. Partial phase diagram in zero external magnetic field of ^{3}He. Both measured magnetic temperatures T^* and tentative absolute temperatures T_{SOUND} (from ref. 4) are shown.

temperature scale of *practical* use. This is such an important subject that it merits the present discussion; however, to avoid interfering with the main development we reserve our discussion for appendix A and restrict ourselves presently to several comments. 1) The existence of a P–T phase diagram in principle allows lines on the diagram to be determined accurately once. Pressure can then be used for secondary calibrations. 2) It is essential that any absolute thermometer used be put in excellent contact with the liquid ^{3}He. This probably means that thermal contact to the thermometer should be magnetic. 3) An alternative intermediary for a temperature scale may be some property of normal Fermi liquid ^{3}He which is more readily calibrated against absolute temperature.

Returning to the phase diagram we observe that the normal Fermi liquid is separated from liquid ^{3}He phases ^{3}He–A and ^{3}He–B by a line of second-order transitions which we tentatively call T_c in analogy to the similar thermal transition observed in superconductors. These transitions are second order in the sense of there being a discontinuity, but not a divergence, in the specific heat[3]). Actually, in all such specific heat transitions observed to date the transition width is about 10 μK or a few parts per thousand of T_c itself. On the other hand the rapid change of 5 MHz ultrasonic attenuation [4]) at T_c occurs in less than 0.1 % of T_c. The line of second-order transitions has either a discontinuity or a rapid change in slope in the vicinity of what may be a "polycritical" point (PCP) near $21\frac{1}{2}$ bar and 2.4 mK. Tentative values for dP_c/dT_c just above and just below the PCP are, respectively, 50 and 34 bar/mK. These are based on our tentative absolute temperature scale. The lowest pressure for which we have observed the transition T_c (and by ultrasonic attenuation[4]) rather than by specific heat) is 9.6 bar, at which pressure T_c^* was warmer than the minimum magnetic temperature of powdered CMN; we believe the latter corresponds to an absolute temperature of 1.8 mK[5]). Further, we have seen no evidence for a latent heat at T_c, but at the lowest pressure (and correspondingly lowest temperatures) this remark is weakened since the background CMN heat capacity is relatively very large.

To the left of the line T_c the P–T plane is divided into two regions, which we tentatively call ^{3}He–A and ^{3}He–B to conform with current general usage. The dividing line is called T_{AB}. This line, discovered in ref. 2, demarks the boundary between regions of linear (^{3}He–B) and nonlinear (^{3}He–A) heat flow. As we remark later heat flow in a tube containing ^{3}He–B is characterized by a linear relationship between the temperature difference ΔT and the heat flow $\dot{Q}$ which can be understood in terms of both diffusive heat flow and hydrodynamic heat flow of normal fluid as discussed for superfluid ^{4}He by London and Zilsel[6]) and by Gorter and Mellink[7]). On warming through the transition temperature T_{AB} (and with sufficient $\dot{Q}$, the amount depending on the difference $T_c - T_{AB}$ and decreasing as $T_c - T_{AB}$ decreases) the temperature difference required to drive $\dot{Q}$ suddenly increases. In the ^{3}He–A region the relationship between ΔT and $\dot{Q}$ was generally nonlinear, history dependent and showed critical velocity effects. We looked for but were unable to detect a change of entropy or specific heat associated with the T_{AB} transition, so it may reasonably be questioned why the T_{AB} line is placed on a phase diagram. Three observations suggest that it is appropriate. First, it is possible to *supercool* the liquid through T_{AB} by a substantial amount, a quality characteristic of first-order phase transitions in general and of the "B" feature in particular[1]). We know little quantitatively about the supercooling except to say that at 31.9 bar supercooling was the usual result; at 30.4 bar it occurred only once – and then when the temperature after demagnetization was higher than usual; and at lower pressures it was never observed at all. Further, unless ^{3}He–B were formed on cooling, no thermal shocking which we used was sufficient to cause it to form. Second, the line T_{AB} extrapolates to the melting curve to a temperature such that $(T_c - T_{AB})_m$ would be 0.5 to 0.6 mK, an amount reasonably expected[8]) for the difference of temperatures between the "A" and "B" features on the pressurization curve. Third, the line T_{AB} extrapolates into the line T_c in a region where the latter either is rapidly changing in slope or has a discontinuity in slope. The slope of the T_{AB} line (using the tentative absolute scale) is approximately -44 bar/mK near the PCP and -36 bar/mK near the melting line. If T_{AB} is indeed a line of first-order transitions and there is not a major change of slope very near T_c then both ΔS_{AB} and ΔV_{AB}, the entropy and volume change across the AB transition, must approach zero in the same way as the PCP is approached.

The specific heat of liquid ^{3}He at a variety of pressures was measured by Webb *et al.*[3]) using a mixture of ^{3}He and CMN powder. The CMN heat capacity always was larger than that of the ^{3}He in the region of interest, but its effect could be subtracted by taking the difference between the heat capacity under pressure and that at a ^{3}He pressure of 0.13 bar. Assuming that the heat capacity of liquid ^{3}He at 0.13 bar is known, then the total heat capacity can be determined. An example of the difference between the total cell heat capacity for 33.4 bar and that for 0.13 bar is shown in fig. 2. This figure shows both individual heat-capacity points obtained conventionally from the temperature change resulting from a known amount

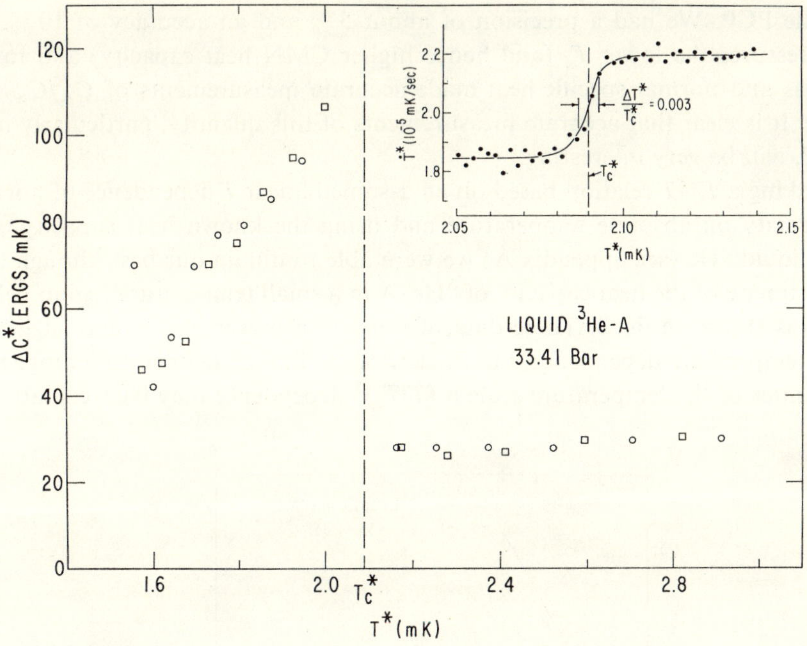

Fig. 2. Experimental difference between the total cell heat capacity for a liquid ^{3}He pressure of 33.41 bar and that for a pressure of 0.13 bar on a magnetic temperature scale T^*. The inset shows on an expanded magnetic scale the time rate of change $\dot{T}^*$ in the vicinity of the specific heat discontinuity.

of heat and the time rate of change of average cell temperature on an expanded scale near T_c^*. The latter illustrates how the specific heat changes rapidly in a small temperature range but does not diverge. T_c^* is chosen to be in the middle of the transition as shown. This temperature correlated well with the much sharper change in 5 MHz ultrasonic attenuation. Comparison of T_c^* for this pressure and that on fig. 1 shows a small displacement. This is because we are considering two different experiments with two different magnetic thermometers. We have observed, however, that in four different magnetic thermometers tested in various experiments the line T_c^* for one experiment is just laterally displaced by a nearly fixed amount from that for another experiment, departure from constancy being typically 10 μK over the range of temperature presently employed. This is as if the magnetic properties of the thermometer only differed by differences in the quantity Δ (see appendix A). This result extends reasonably well all the way to $T^*_{\min}$ and is an important simplifying feature in comparing experiments and developing temperature scales.

Although the specific heat itself depends on the temperature scale the ratio $C_</C_>$ of the ^{3}He heat capacity just below to just above T_c does not. We found this ratio to be about 2.85 at 34 bar decreasing to 2.55 near 23 bar, which is still above the PCP. We had a precision of about 5 % and an accuracy of 10 %. At lower pressures the lower T_c (and hence higher CMN heat capacity) and lower ^{3}He mass and normal specific heat made accurate measurements of $C_</C_>$ impossible. It is clear that accurate measurements of this quantity, particularly near the PCP, will be very interesting.

By making a T^*–T relation based on an assumed linear T dependence of normal heat capacity on absolute temperature and using the known heat capacity[9]) of normal liquid ^{3}He (see appendix A) we were able to obtain our best, though tentative, estimate of the heat capacity of ^{3}He–A in a small temperature region below T_c. This is shown in fig. 3. These data, if fitted to a power law, would suggest a $(T/T_c)^4$ temperature dependence, but in view of the limited temperature range and uncertainties of the temperature scale a $(T/T_c)^3$ dependence may be acceptable.

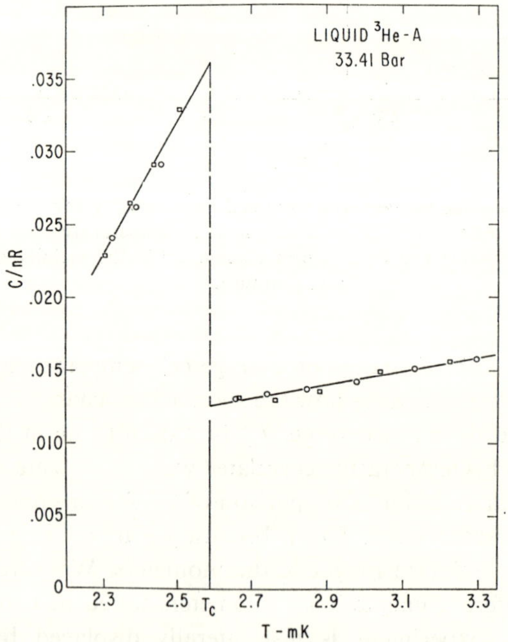

Fig. 3. Total molar heat capacity as a function of temperature of liquid ^{3}He at a pressure of 33.41 bar as deduced from the measurements and a T^*-T relation discussed in appendix A.

By making suitable assumptions about liquid expansion coefficients, compressibilities, solid thermal diffusivity, and cell properties it is possible to deduce liquid heat capacities by measuring pressure in an adiabatic compression cell. This was done by Anufriyev *et al.*[10]) and later, using a heat-pulse method, by Halperin *et al.*[11]). There seems to be some quantitative problem in ref. 10 as well as indication of a thermal precursor of the transition for $T > T_c$, but in ref. 11 rather good quantitative agreement is found with ref. 3 near T_c. Dundon *et al.*[12]) have found some rather puzzling specific-heat results using ^{3}He mixed with sintered copper in a nuclear cooling apparatus. They find a broad heat-capacity peak extending upward to over 3 mK but centered below 2 mK, and with little pressure dependence. Taken at face value the results suggest that the entropy of the normal Fermi liquid above the transition is substantially greater than expected. If true, this is a very important observation, but we feel that corroborating experiments are necessary.

Since the transition at T_c is second order in Ehrenfest's sense we may use his relations, the approximately known slope $\mathrm{d}P_c/\mathrm{d}T_c$, and the measured specific-heat change from ^{3}He–A to normal Fermi liquid ^{3}He to estimate both the isobaric expansion coefficient change $\alpha_{^3\text{He–A}} - \alpha_n$ and the isothermal compressibility change $\beta_{^3\text{He–A}} - \beta_n$. We find $\alpha_{^3\text{He–A}} - \alpha_n \simeq +4 \times 10^{-7}$ (mK)$^{-1}$ and $+2 \times 10^{-7}$ (mK)$^{-1}$, and $\beta_{^3\text{He–A}} - \beta_n = +8 \times 10^{-9}$ bar^{-1} and $+2 \times 10^{-9}$ bar^{-1} just above the PCP and near the melting curve, respectively. Since $\alpha_n \simeq -4 \times 10^{-7}$ (mK)$^{-1}$ and $\beta_n \simeq 6 \times 10^{-3}$ bar^{-1} the expected change in α is seen to be substantial, even including a possible change in sign; while the change in β is relatively very small. Accurate values of the specific-heat change between ^{3}He–B and normal Fermi liquid are not available at present.

The effect of a magnetic field on the features on the pressurization curve and on ultrasonic attenuation has been studied by Osheroff *et al.*[13]), Lawson *et al.*[14]) and Gully *et al.*[15]). Since measurements are made at melting pressure rather than constant pressure some results are obscured. Results are expressed in terms of measured pressure differences, although the corresponding temperature difference may be obtained from the approximately known slope of the melting curve. The B′ feature, which we tentatively believe to be the terminus at the melting curve of the T_{AB} line in fig. 1, is most profoundly affected by a magnetic field. It is found that[13]) $[P(\mathrm{B}') - P(\mathrm{A})]_{H_0} - [P(\mathrm{B}') - P(\mathrm{A})]_0 = +2.05 \times 10^{-9}\ H_0^2$ bar gauss^{-2}. Further, the "A" feature, which we believe to be the terminus at the melting curve of the T_c line in fig. 1, is split into two, called A_1 and A_2, with a pressure splitting[14, 15]) $\Delta P = 2.0 \times 10^{-7}\ H_0$ bar gauss^{-1}. There is a third feature A_3 with puzzling properties which we do not discuss but refer the reader to the original work[14, 15]). Finally, both the A_1 feature and the maximum pressure P_{max} are depressed in pressure by a field, the results being $P_{A_1}(H_0) - P_{A_2}(0) = -6.7 \times 10^{-11}\ H_0^2$ bar gauss^{-2} and $P_{max}(H_0) - P_{max}(0) = -1.95 \times 10^{-10} H_0^2$ bar gauss^{-2}. Owing to the effect of H_0 on melting pressure it is not known at present what the absolute effect of H_0 on T_{A_1} and T_{A_2} may be; only the splitting may be estimated, using a tentative value[8, 16]) of -35 mbar/mK for the slope of the melting curve in this region, to be $\Delta T_{A_1A_2} \simeq 5.7\times 10^{-6}\, H_0$ mK gauss^{-1}. On the other hand, the effect of H_0 on B′ may be seen from the above figures to be at least ten times its possible effect on the melting pressure or on the A transition. This will allow us, with suitable assumptions, to estimate the possible entropy and volume change at the AB transition near melting pressure. Thus, assuming that $(\partial T_{AB}/\partial H_0)_P$ is pressure independent over a small range and that the slope $(dP_M/dT_M)_0$ of the melting curve is field independent, then we have approximately that the measured pressure shift $\Delta P_{B'}$ with field change ΔH_0 is

$$\Delta P_{B'} \approx \left(\frac{\partial T_{AB}}{\partial H_0}\right)_P \left(\frac{dP_M}{dT_M}\right)_0 \Delta H_0 \approx \left|\frac{dP_M}{dT_M}\right|_0 \frac{\chi_A - \chi_B}{s_A - s_B} H_0 \Delta H_0, \tag{1}$$

where χ is the liquid nuclear susceptibility and s is the liquid entropy per unit volume. The static nuclear susceptibilities χ_A and χ_B have not yet been measured, but the NMR results[13]) suggest that χ_A is the same as that χ_n of the normal Fermi liquid (1.1×10^{-7} near the melting curve[17])) while χ_B is a fraction f_χ of χ_A, f_χ being estimated by $\frac{1}{2}$. If we define f_s such that $s_A - s_B = f_s s_c$, where s_c is the entropy per unit volume at T_c of the normal liquid near melting pressure[9]) (about 41 erg/cm^3 mK), then

$$\frac{f_\chi}{f_s} = \left(\frac{\Delta P_{B'}}{\Delta H_0}\right) s_c \Big/ \left|\frac{dP_M}{dT_M}\right|_0 \chi_n H_0 . \tag{2}$$

Putting in numerical values we find $f_\chi/f_s \approx 40$ to 50. With $f_\chi \simeq \frac{1}{2}$ we find $f_s \simeq 10^{-2}$, $\Delta s \approx \frac{1}{2}$ erg/cm^3 mK, and a latent heat of about 1 erg/cm^3 for $T_{AB} = 2$ mK on the melting curve. Furthermore, using the approximate slope near the melting line $(dP_{AB}/dT_{AB})_{H_0=0}$ given earlier together with the above entropy change we find a fractional volume change near the melting line of $(V_A - V_B)/V \approx -10^{-8}$. We were unable to prove either a volume or an entropy change at the AB transition. The above $\Delta V/V$ is beyond our sensitivity, but a latent heat of the size estimated above might have been observable as a reduction of the warm-up rate if the cell temperature inhomogeneity had been small. If this inhomogeneity were estimated by the usual *total* width ($\approx 20\ \mu$K) of the second-order transition then a latent heat of 1 erg/cm^3 would be very hard to distinguish. Furthermore, it is not known by how much the latent heat will have decreased by the pressure of our measurements.

3. *NMR.* The principle measurements thus far are those of Osheroff, Gully, Richardson, and Lee[13]). They constitute some of the most remarkable observations on the liquid, though all measurements have been at melting pressure. There is no need to paraphrase the original paper, so we will simply quote some of the results.

1) Observation of the nuclear magnetic resonance absorption in the liquid at melting pressure with the r.f. and static fields perpendicular to one another shows that in ^{3}He–A for a given magnetic field the liquid resonance frequency is shifted upward with respect to the solid resonance frequency by an amount

$$\nu_{\text{liq}}^2 - \nu_{\text{solid}}^2 = 4.89\times 10^{11} \Delta P \,\text{Hz}^2\,\text{bar}^{-1} - 5.79\times 10^{12}\,\Delta P^2\,\text{Hz}^2\,\text{bar}^{-2}, \tag{3}$$

where ΔP is the pressure shift along the melting curve. The effect probably depends only weakly on pressure at constant temperature, so the ΔP is more an experimental artifact representing the circumstance that although T cannot be measured well, pressure changes can be. If we use the tentative slope -35 mbar/mK for the melting curve and a temperature of 2.6 mK for T_c on the melting curve[8, 16]) we find

$$\nu_l^2 - \nu_s^2 \approx 4.5\times 10^{10}(1 - T/T_c)\,\text{Hz}^2; \quad T < T_c \tag{4}$$

as the shift for ^{3}He–A in the square of the resonance frequency near the second-order transition temperature T_c at melting pressure. This shift has been shown to depend on T but not on field over a range of fields from 31 G to 850 G. 2) Below 31 G the perpendicular field resonance shift seems to go away but details are obscure. 3) There are no major changes of the amplitude of the NMR signal in ^{3}He–A. 4) There is no perpendicular field resonance shift in ^{3}He–B, although the amplitude of the resonance decreased typically by 40 to 60 % and was history dependent.

All the above observations are made difficult by the presence of a variable amount of high susceptibility solid. Halperin *et al.*[11]) have also observed a small change of total cell static nuclear susceptibility at T_{AB} in a compressional cooling cell, but this too is difficult to interpret owing to the effect of solid.

4. *Flow experiments.* Two experiments have been performed at this writing on the flow properties of ^{3}He–A and ^{3}He–B. The first is the wire damping[18, 19]) experiment of Alvesalo *et al.*[20]) and the second is the heat-flow experiment of Greytak *et al.*[2]). The wire damping experiment was performed at melting pressure in an adiabatic compression cell where the formation of solid could alter or terminate the measurements, although apparently it did not in many of the cooling runs. The heat-flow experiments were performed at a variety of pressures below melting pressure. We shall discuss the two separately and then make a comparison.

In the wire damping experiments a stretched *superconducting* wire was caused to vibrate in ^{3}He in a compressional cooling cell by means of a longitudinal oscillating current in a transverse magnetic field. Motion of the wire in the field caused a Faraday EMF across its terminals. In the experiments the drive frequency was swept through resonance; the amplitude on resonance was the prime experimental datum. Measurements were made while the temperature was changing very rapidly, and this may have had some effect on the results, which are as follows: After compressional cooling started near 15 mK, the amplitude decreased rapidly with decreasing temperature – more rapidly than expected from the T^{-2} law expected in the present temperature range on the basis of vibrating-wire experiments quoted in Lawson *et al.*[14]) and ultrasonic attenuation measurements of Paulson *et al.*[4]). As the temperature decreased through the "A" feature the resonant amplitude started to increase again to a value which was history dependent. At the "B" feature the resonant amplitude increased suddenly. Subsequent *increase* of temperature showed a rapid but apparently continuous increase of damping at the "B′" feature. Cooling in ^{3}He–B produced further dramatic changes in amplitude. At the lowest temperature the melting pressure was about 50 mbar greater than that at the "A" feature. If dP_m/dT_m had remained constant at -35 mbar/mK this would correspond to a lowest temperature 1.4 mK below T_c, or about 1.2 mK. It is likely that the minimum temperature is even lower.

Wire-damping experiments in normal liquid ^{3}He have been interpreted[19]) in terms of the viscous penetration depth $\delta = (\eta/\rho\omega)^{\frac{1}{2}}$, where η is viscosity, ρ is density, and ω is angular frequency. At low T near melting pressure we have[4, 14]) $\eta \simeq 0.95\ (1\ \text{mK}/T)^2$ poise and $\rho = 0.118\ \text{g/cm}^3$, so at the resonant frequency of 1225 Hz and at $T_c = 2.6$ mK we calculate $\delta = 1.25\times 10^{-2}$ cm, which is the same as the radius of the wire. For such a large penetration depth Stokes[21]) has argued that his solution of the problem is no longer applicable, so we prefer to use as a fiducial point the amplitude in the liquid near the starting temperature. This particular difficulty illustrates one of the interesting properties of liquid ^{3}He, which is the very high viscosity of the normal liquid. At 2.6 mK, as indicated above, the normal-liquid viscosity is about 0.14 poise, or about that of a light machine oil. Even at a temperature of 12.6 mK, corresponding to the left side of the amplitude data graph (fig. 2 in ref. 20) and near the starting temperature, the viscosity of normal liquid ^{3}He is 0.006 poise, or 60 % of the viscosity of water at 20 °C. Since at temperatures well below the B′ feature the wire amplitude has not yet returned to its value at 12.6 mK the effective viscosity of even ^{3}He–B is like that of water. This is a profound difference from the normal viscosity of superfluid ^{4}He, which is[22]) 10 to 20 μpoise in the range from 1 to 2 K. The viscosity of ^{4}He at the lambda point is 10^4 times less than the viscosity of ^{3}He–A at T_c.

Although the wire-damping experiments probably cannot be interpreted readily either in normal liquid at high damping as indicated above or in ^{3}He–A owing to history dependence, they possibly may be interpreted in terms of an "effective" viscosity in ^{3}He–B. The effective viscosity is that value predicted by the standard formulas[18, 19]) for ordinary liquids. To make this analysis we will take as starting point the amplitude at 12.6 mK and use the normal-liquid viscosity given above. Just below B′, where $T/T_c \approx 0.75$ to 0.8, the amplitude is about half its value at 12.6 mK. This corresponds to an effective viscosity of 0.04 poise or 0.3 of the calculated viscosity of normal fluid at 2.6 mK. On the other hand at the lowest temperature, which may correspond to $T/T_c \simeq 0.4$, the amplitude is $2\frac{1}{2}$ times its value at 12.6 mK. This gives an effective viscosity of about 0.001 poise. This is a factor 1.4×10^2 less than that calculated for normal fluid at T_c. We have more confidence in the above numbers, which rest on amplitudes in normal liquid near the starting temperature and in ^{3}He–B where damping is not very high, than on those based on the observed amplitudes in the normal liquid on cooling and at high damping. For further understanding quantitative discrepancies must be understood; in particular resonance widths and shifts and a study of nonlinearities would be desirable.

It would be tempting to interpret the above results in terms of a two-fluid model, in which for low enough damping we expect[18, 19]) the amplitude to vary as $[\rho_n k'(m)]^{-1}$, where ρ_n is normal-fluid density and k' is a function calculated by Stokes[21]) of the quantity $m = a/2\delta$, with a the wire radius and $\delta = (\eta_n/\rho_n\omega)^{\frac{1}{2}}$. Here η_n is normal-fluid viscosity. For low damping this leads to an amplitude proportional to $(\rho_n\eta_n)^{-\frac{1}{2}}$, but this limit is not reached for most of the experiment. Before proceeding some proof of the two-fluid model would be required; with that might come the ρ_n or the η_n needed to begin the analysis.

The heat-flow experiments of Greytak *et al.* represent another attempt to detect unusual flow properties of the extraordinary phases of liquid ^{3}He. They are analogous to the measurements of Brewer and Edwards[22, 23]) of heat flow in capillary tubes containing superfluid ^{4}He, where heat flows both diffusively and hydrodynamically. The relationship between hydrodynamic heat flow and the two-fluid model was worked out by London and Zilsel[6]) and by Gorter and Mellink[7]). If a small temperature difference ΔT is imposed across a column of length l and diameter d then a fountain pressure difference $\Delta p = s\Delta T$ is developed, where s is entropy per unit volume. For laminar flow there is a corresponding volume rate of flow $\dot{V}_n$ of normal fluid given by

$$\dot{V}_n = \Delta p / Z\eta_n, \tag{5}$$

where η_n is the viscosity of the normal fluid and $Z = 128l/\pi d^4$. The corresponding hydrodynamic heat flow $\dot{Q}_h$ is $Ts\,\dot{V}_n$ or

$$\dot{Q}_h = \frac{d^2}{32}\frac{Ts^2}{\eta_n}\left(\frac{\pi d^2}{4l}\right)\Delta T. \tag{6}$$

There is also a parallel heat flow due to diffusive conduction given by

$$\dot{Q}_d = \kappa_d \frac{\pi d^2}{4l}\Delta T, \tag{7}$$

where κ_d is the diffusive conductivity. The diffusive heat flow was not important for the Brewer–Edwards experiments. In the present experiments, as interpreted using a two-fluid model, at least near T_c both κ_d and η_n are relatively very large compared with these quantities near T_λ in ^{4}He. This results from the very long mean free paths of quasiparticles in a normal Fermi liquid at very low temperatures. So the diffusive heat flow can be very important in our experiments. The total heat flow is then proportional to ΔT and to a conductivity

$$\kappa = \kappa_h + \kappa_d , \tag{8}$$

where

$$\kappa_h = \frac{d^2}{32} \frac{Ts^2}{\eta_n} . \tag{9}$$

The Brewer–Edwards measurements were used to obtain η_n.

The present experiments provided a number of surprises, not the least of which was the thermal resistance discontinuity at T_{AB} already mentioned. A schematic diagram of the cell is given at the top of fig. 4. A mass of 13.6 g CMN powder is both refrigerant and lower magnetic thermometer T_1^* of the heat-flow cell. A second magnetic thermometer T_2^* of 10 mg CMN powder is at the top of a column

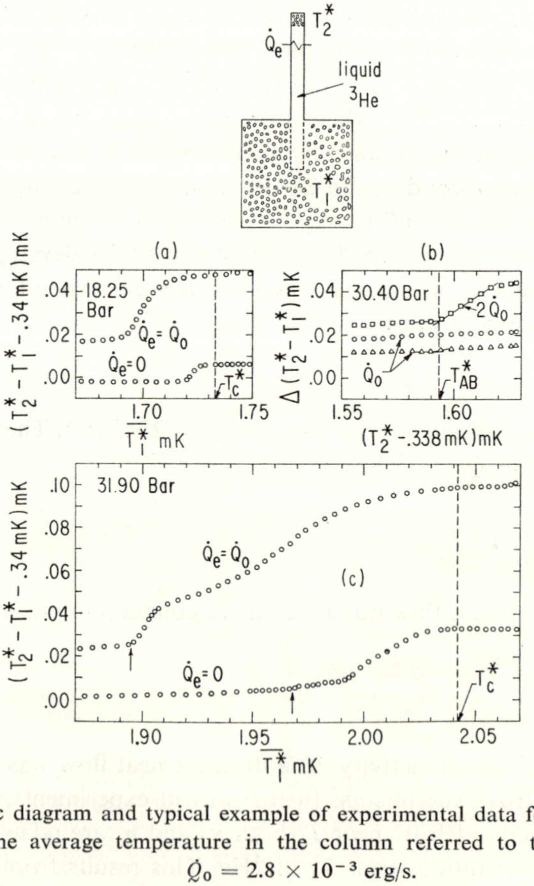

Fig. 4. Schematic diagram and typical example of experimental data for the heat-flow experiments. $\overline{T_1^*}$ is the average temperature in the column referred to the lower thermometer. $\dot{Q}_0 = 2.8 \times 10^{-3}$ erg/s.

of liquid ^{3}He. A hole is drilled into the main CMN to facilitate dissipation of the heat $\dot{Q}_e$ provided by the column heater. The column and hole are 2.0 mm diam; the former extends 18 mm below the heater and the latter penetrates 11 mm into the CMN. Liquid ^{3}He fills the interstices between the CMN grains. Owing to different shape and packing different magnetic thermometers read differently for the same temperature. However, by intercomparing the T_c^* line for different experiments[3, 4]), including the present one, we have found that in the present range different T^* scales are displaced from one another by essentially constant amounts. In the present experiment the T_2^* and T_1^* scales are displaced from one another by about 0.34 mK. The difference is a weak function of temperature, even very close to the minimum magnetic temperature. In these measurements we kept $\dot{Q}_e$ constant during the drift under residual heat leak after demagnetizational cooling, excepting at the lowest and highest temperatures when we set $\dot{Q}_e = 0$ for comparing with background drift. We found that the temperature difference varied linearly with $\dot{Q}_e$ above T_c^* and in the ^{3}He–B region except very near T_c^*; however, the response was complicated in ^{3}He–A and at T_{AB}^*. In fig. 2a typical measurements in ^{3}He–B near T_c^* are shown. The important qualitative result is the *rise* in $T_2^* - T_1^*$ on warming near T_c^*. Even for $\dot{Q}_e = 0$ a rise is seen; this results from residual heat leak down the column. Thermal resistance starts to increase before T_2^* has reached T_c^*. This onset temperature depends on $\dot{Q}_e$. Typical results in ^{3}He–A near T_c^* are shown in fig. 2c for the same values of $\dot{Q}_e$ as above. Although the thermal transition T_c^* is not broadened, the resistive transition is broad, history dependent (not shown), and shows a reproducible onset temperature feature (arrows). Typical dependence of $\Delta(T_2^* - T_1^*)$ on $\dot{Q}_e$ near T_{AB}^* is shown in fig. 2b. The upper and lower curves show both the linear dependence of $\Delta(T_2^* - T_1^*)$ on $\dot{Q}_e$ below T_{AB}^* and the $\dot{Q}$ dependent resistance which develops when T_2^* reaches T_{AB}^*. For points just to the right of T_{AB}^*, T_2^* is increasing rapidly with time; the ramp reflects transient, not steady state, response. The middle curve corresponds to a higher than usual minimum temperature and shows no A to B transition, illustrating both supercooling and the history-dependent resistance of ^{3}He–A.

Owing to probable difficulties with the temperature scale we reduced the resistance data at pressure P by dividing the measured resistance, $R^*(P) \equiv \Delta(T_2^* - T_1^*)/\Delta\dot{Q}_e$, by that measured at 0.05 bar. The latter has also been measured[24]) in a similar apparatus, and in the present temperature range one expects $R(0.05 \text{ bar}) \propto T$. These ratios for three pressures (our lowest, our highest, and the highest for which we have only ^{3}He–B below T_c^*) are shown in fig. 5. No *resistances* are quoted in the region near T_c where there is evidence (see fig. 4) for nonlinear critical behavior or where two phases are in the column. The resistance ratios are curiously only weakly temperature dependent and rather close to 1; we regard the latter as being coincidental. Extrapolation of the resistance ratios into T_c is not too uncertain, allowing a quantitative attempt to test for hydrodynamic heat flow using knowledge from the normal state and the assumption that neither the viscosity nor the

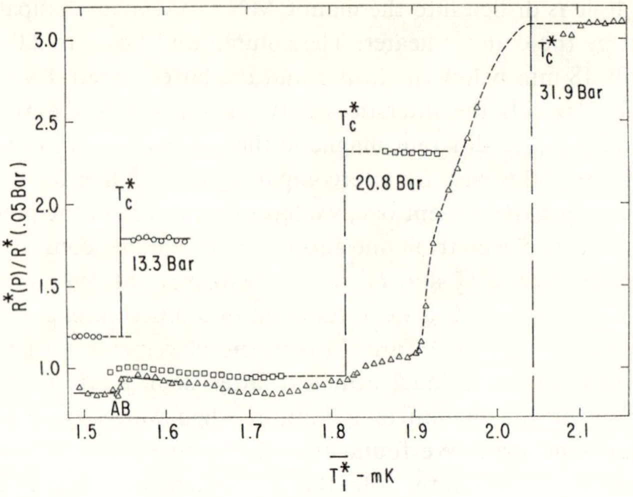

Fig. 5. Thermal resistances at three pressures reduced using the measured resistance of normal Fermi liquid ^3He at 0.05 bar. $\overline{T_1{}^*}$ is the average temperature in the column referred to the lower thermometer. In the region near $T_c{}^*$ there are two phases in the column.

diffusive conductivity changes discontinuously at T_c. Carrying through the extrapolation of $R^*(P)/R^*$ (0.05 bar) into T_c^* from both $T^* < T_c^*$ and $T^* > T_c^*$, we can find the ratio $(R^*_>/R^*_<)_{\text{expt.}}$ of the measured resistance just above to just below T_c^*. These ratios are shown in table I. If we have both diffusive and hydrodynamic heat flow but no critical-velocity effect below T_c and only diffusive heat flow above T_c then we have

$$\frac{R^*_>}{R^*_<} = 1 + \frac{\kappa_h}{\kappa_d} = 1 + \frac{d^2}{32}\frac{T_c s_c^2}{\eta\kappa_d}, \tag{10}$$

where $s_c = \gamma T_c$ is the entropy per unit volume at T_c and η and κ_d are the normal viscosity and thermal conductivity at T_c. Putting in the expected temperature

TABLE I

Analysis of thermal resistance data using a two-fluid model

P (bar)	$R^*_>/R^*_<$ Expt.	$R^*_>/R^*_<$ Calc.	T_c (mK)	γ (10^7 erg/cm³ K²)	ηT^2 (10^{-6} poise K²)	$\kappa_d T$ (erg/s cm)
13.3	1.5	1.5	2.14	1.09	1.4	20
18.2	2.0	2.3	2.31	1.21	1.3	17
19.9	2.3	2.7	2.36	1.25	1.2	16
20.8	2.4	3.0	2.39	1.27	1.2	15
23.0	2.8[a]	3.6	2.44	1.32	1.2	15
31.9		8.6	2.58	1.52	0.9_5	12

[a] Extrapolated through ^3He–A phase.

dependences of these quantities we find

$$\frac{R^*_>}{R^*_<} = 1 + \frac{T_c^6 \gamma^2 d^2}{32(\eta T^2)(\kappa_d T)} . \tag{11}$$

Calculated values of this ratio using approximate experimental values for the quantities in (11) are also given in table I. Fair quantitative agreement is obtained, especially when one considers the sixth-power dependence on T_c, possible uncertainties in the quantities, and uncertainty in the extrapolation into T_c. Owing to the high impedance factor for the packed CMN powder, heat flow in the main CMN is probably diffusive. This does not cause more than a few percent error near T_c in interpreting $\Delta(T_2^* - T_1^*)$ as the change in the temperature difference across the *column* due to $\dot{Q}_e$. However, well below T_c we suspect that κ_d decreases substantially while κ_h increases (roughly as T^{-1}). Particularly at high pressure where κ_h is large and κ_d small anyway, the measured value of $R^*(P)/R^*(0.05 \text{ bar})$ in ^{3}He–B could be systematically high compared to what it should be for the column only, as a result of an excessive diffusive resistance within the main CMN.

Perhaps the most common suggestion for the increase of conductivity as the temperature decreases through T_c is that one should consider the well-known diffusive heat conductivity equation $\kappa = \frac{1}{3}cv\lambda$, where c is the heat capacity of excitations of velocity v and mean free path λ. Then as c jumps at the second-order transition, so does κ, assuming no discontinuous changes in either v or λ. In discussing the merits of this suggestion experimentally we note from ref. 3 that the specific heat increases by a factor of 2.6 near the PCP and has a weak and uncertain pressure dependence, in quantitative disagreement with the results in table I. A somewhat more subtle observation is that (refer to fig. 4a) on warming the resistive transition anticipates – takes place before – the thermal second-order transition, again suggesting a hydrodynamic description. Aside from the above, it is not at all clear to us that the above simple formula should hold for heat flow near this second-order transition.

If we make the assumption that below the transition heat flow is mainly hydrodynamic then a hydrodynamic resistance approximately linear in T would suggest that $\kappa_h T$ is constant or, referring to (9), that for ^{3}He–B η has the same temperature dependence as $(Ts)^2$ below T_c, where it has the same value as for the normal fluid. We do not believe the temperature dependence of s is known very well, but it is possible that it depends roughly on the third or fourth power of T. Hence very roughly one might write that near T_c one has $\eta_n \approx \eta_c\ (T/T_c)^a$, where a is in the range 8 to 10. This is very different from the behavior[22]) of the normal viscosity of superfluid ^{4}He.

As we discussed above the heat flow in ^{3}He–A shows a history dependence, a nonlinear dependence on $\dot{Q}_e$, and critical velocity effects. We have not proved that we have found any region of ^{3}He–A where there is subcritical behavior. However, near T_{AB} at the highest pressures we find (see fig. 4b, bottom curve) very little resistance change at T_{AB} for small enough $\dot{Q}_e$. For the same $\dot{Q}_e$, however, we do see at a higher temperature near T_c a reproducible feature which may be described as the onset of additional thermal resistance. Whereas the T_{AB} feature always occurs, for given P, at the *same* value of T_2^*, the onset feature (arrows in fig. 4c) occurs at a temperature $T_{crit.}$ which is correlated with total heat flow $\dot{Q}$ and temperature displacement $(T_c - T_{crit.})$ from T_c such that $(T_c - T_{crit.})$ is approximately proportional to $\dot{Q}$. This suggests the interpretation of the onset in terms of a *superfluid* critical velocity $v_{s_{crit.}}$. If one has $\rho_s v_s + \rho_n \bar{v}_n = 0$ connecting superfluid density ρ_s and velocity v_s with normal-fluid density ρ_n and average velocity $\bar{v}_n$; and if, as for superconductors[25]), near T_c one has $\rho_s = \rho(1 - T/T_c)$, then

$$v_s \approx \bar{v}_n/(1 - T/T_c). \tag{12}$$

The normal velocity, if it results from laminar flow, is just proportional to the heat flow $\dot{Q}$. Hence near T_c the superfluid velocity is proportional to the ratio $\dot{Q}/(1 - T/T_c)$. If there is a superfluid critical velocity $v_{s_{crit}}$ then, on warming toward T_c, when T reaches the critical value $T_{crit.}$ for a given $\dot{Q}$ the resistance will suddenly increase, as observed in our experiments. Further the ratio $\dot{Q}/(T_c - T_{crit.})$ should be constant, also approximately as observed. Using $\dot{Q} = Ts\,\dot{V}_n$, we find an average normal-fluid velocity by dividing $\dot{V}_n$ by column area. Substituting this into (12) with $T = T_{crit.}$ we find $v_{s_{crit.}} \simeq 10^{-1}$ cm/s in ^{3}He–A. Critical velocities in ^{3}He–B must be substantially higher since their effect is seen only incipiently near T_c. One substantial defect of our measurements of critical-velocity phenomena is that for the heat fluxes we are required to use to obtain adequate sensitivity in $\Delta(T_2^* - T_1^*)$, the displacement $(T_c - T_{crit.})$ is comparable to the temperature difference across the column (see fig. 4).

It is instructive to compare the wire damping and the heat-flow experiments. The authors of ref. 20 suggest that the history-dependent damping in ^{3}He–A is caused by slow thermal relaxation in the liquid. Our heat-flow experiments tend not to support this but rather to suggest that in ^{3}He–A the damping may reflect a supercritical behavior. It is also suggested in ref. 20 that the A–B transition reflects a discontinuous change of superfluid density. Our experiments suggest that the rapid increase of damping near B′ may rather reflect a change from subcritical to supercritical behavior. It would be very helpful to know more about the linearity of response of the wire. In ref. 20 it is suggested that both the viscosity and the superfluid density change at B, the former profoundly. We do not understand the basis for these conclusions, nor for the assumption that the normal-fluid density decreases rapidly in ^{3}He–B with decreasing temperature. Our heat-flow experiments suggest that in the limited temperature below T_c of our measurements the normal viscosity is decreasing rapidly. Further, both the approximate linear dependence of the displacement of onset temperature from T_c on heat flux in ^{3}He–A and the linear dependence of $v_1^2 - v_s^2$ on $(T - T_c)$, eq. (4), suggest that condensate density may vary approximately as $(1-T/T_c)$ near T_c or normal-fluid density as T/T_c, which is a rather slow variation. This is speculative, of course, but it suggests that in the range down to $T/T_c \simeq 0.75$, where comparison of wire damping and heat-flow experiments can be made, that the damping of a wire is influenced primarily by viscosity changes and not much by the two-fluid model. On the other hand, the existence of hydrodynamic heat flow depends directly on the validity of a two-fluid model. It is clear that both types of measurements need to be refined. In particular, independent experiments which allow measurements of ρ_s, such as fourth-sound[26]) measurements, are important.

5. *Propagation of ultrasound.* Propagation of ultrasound in the extraordinary phases of liquid ^{3}He has been studied by Lawson *et al.*[14]) and by Paulson *et al.*[4]). The former experiments were performed in a compressional cooling device, and solid in the sound cell unfortunately prevented quantitative velocity and attenuation measurements over an extended temperature range. They were important in showing an attenuation peak at the "A" feature which is split in two by an applied magnetic field. However, we will confine our discussion primarily to the results of ref. 4, which were obtained at pressures below melting pressure.

Ultrasonic measurements in the extraordinary phases so far have been confined to the propagation of collisionless sound, or zero sound[27, 28]) in the normal Fermi liquid. Typical quasiparticle collision times for viscosity are $(1\ \mathrm{mK/T})^2\ \mu\mathrm{s}$, so that in the present temperature range relatively low frequencies would be necessary to be in a clear hydrodynamic regime. Readily available ultrasonic frequencies (we used 5, 15 and 25 MHz in our work) will all lead to collisionless propagation below 3 mK, so this is a motivation for studying collisionless propagation. A perhaps stronger motivation for us was that since, at least for normal zero sound, attenuation in the "collisionless" regime increases with increasing interquasiparticle collisions but is independent of frequency, we might be sensitive to more microscopic events than would be the case for hydrodynamic attenuation.

Measurements were made extensively at only two pressures, 33.16 bar and 19.61 bar, and before the phase diagram of fig. 1 was discovered. We believe that the measurements at 33.16 bar probably supercooled through the T_{AB} transition so that at this pressure we have purely ^{3}He–A behavior. On the other hand, 19.61 bar is below the PCP, so at this pressure we have behavior for ^{3}He–B only. Since a velocity decrease of about 1 % for the A → B transition was reported in ref. 14, it would be very interesting to look into this in an extension to intermediate pressure of our work.

The results of the experiments are shown in figs. 6 and 7. The amplitude attenuation coefficient is presented logarithmically since it varies over such a wide range below T_c. Velocity data are presented as the difference of measured velocity from measured first sound velocity relative to first sound velocity. Data are presented in figs. 6a and 7a as actual measured attenuation and relative velocity *vs.* the mag-

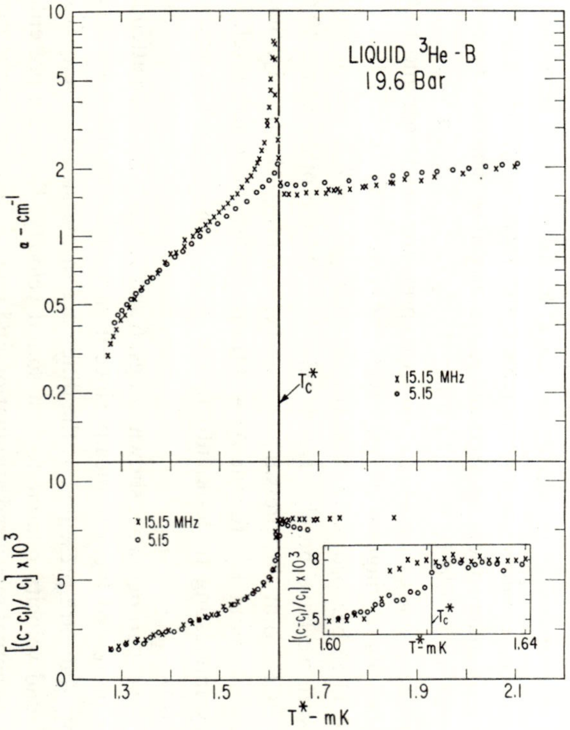

Fig. 6a. The logarithm of the amplitude attenuation coefficient α and the fractional velocity change relative to the first sound velocity c_1 for liquid ^{3}He–B and normal Fermi liquid at 19.6 bar for several frequencies as a function of the magnetic temperature of a powdered CMN thermometer. $c_1 = 354$ m/s.

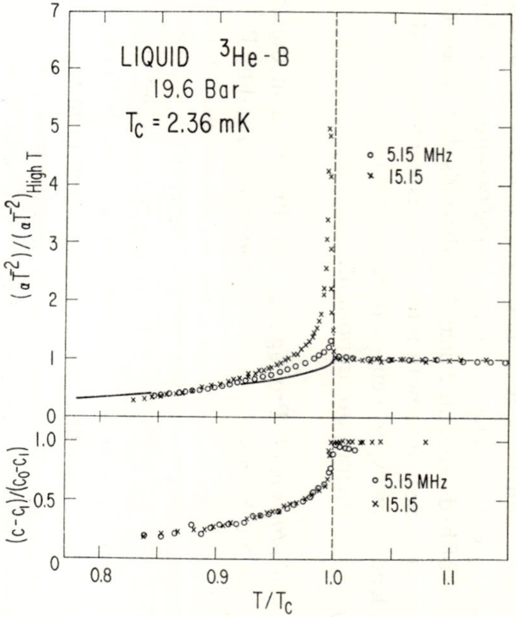

Fig. 6b. The reduced amplitude attenuation $(\alpha T^{-2})/(\alpha T^{-2})_{\text{High } T}$ and reduced velocity $(c - c_1)/(c_0 - c_1)$ as a function of the reduced temperature T/T_c for liquid ^{3}He–B and normal Fermi liquid at 19.6 bar. Temperatures are determined as discussed in appendix A.

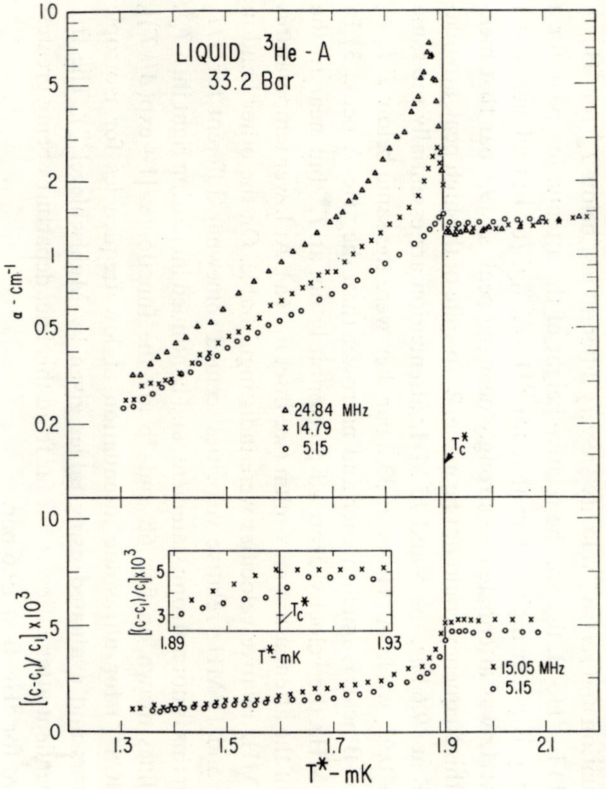

Fig. 7a. The logarithm of the amplitude attenuation coefficient α and the fractional velocity change relative to the first sound velocity c_1 for liquid ^{3}He–A and normal Fermi liquid at 33.2 bar for several frequencies as a function of the magnetic temperature T^* of a powdered CMN thermometer. $c_1 = 417$ m/s.

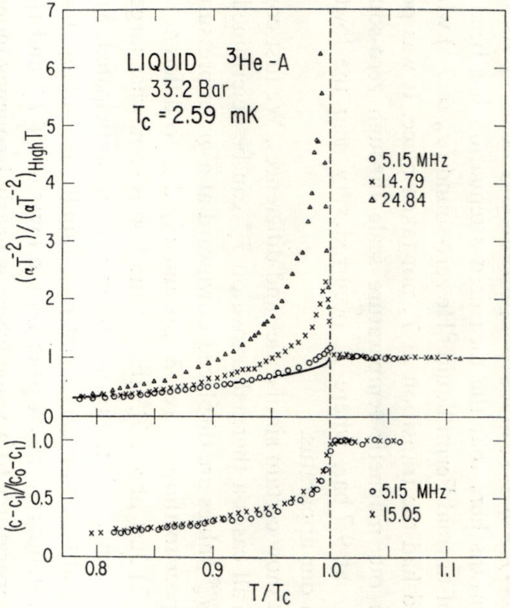

Fig. 7b. The reduced amplitude attenuation coefficient $(\alpha T^{-2})/(\alpha T^{-2})_{\mathrm{High\ T}}$ and reduced velocity $(c - c_1)/(c_0 - c_1)$ as a function of reduced temperature T/T_c for liquid ^{3}He–A and normal Fermi liquid at 33.2 bar. Temperatures are determined as discussed in appendix A.

netic temperature scale of the measurements. This scale is displaced by almost a constant amount from that used in other experiments[2, 3]). The relative attenuation and velocity are shown in figs. 6b and 7b on a relative absolute temperature scale (see appendix A), where T_c at a given pressure may be found from fig. 1. Relative attenuation means here that the measured attenuation has been divided by the attenuation of normal Fermi liquid ^{3}He zero sound ($\alpha_0 \propto T^2$) which would have been observed had the transition at T_c not taken place. It was possible to know the latter on our magnetic temperature scale through zero-sound attenuation measurements at 9.7 bar, where T_c occurred very near the lowest temperature obtainable in our apparatus.

The results show certain similarities and differences. We first comment on similarities: 1) In all cases a thermal transition T_c^* can be determined precisely as in ref. 3. These T_c^* values are displaced downward at a given pressure by about 0.18 mK with respect to those of ref. 3, presumably due to different CMN geometry and packing. 2) Just above T_c^* the attenuation is somewhat larger than that for ordinary zero sound, as if the transition were being anticipated. 3) Just at T_c^* and on cooling the attenuation coefficient rises rapidly, essentially discontinuously at 5 MHz. The attenuation has a peak on the low side of T_c^* and then decreases at the lowest temperatures to a value which is nearly frequency independent. 4) The relative velocity drops rapidly near T_c^* and becomes frequency independent at the lowest temperatures, possibly approaching zero, corresponding to the velocity of first sound. 5) The small frequency dependence of zero-sound attenuation above T_c^* is thought to be an experimental effect. The frequency effect on relative velocity above T_c may reflect incomplete development of zero sound at 5 MHz.

Both attenuation and relative velocity are very different just below T_c^* for ^{3}He–A and ^{3}He–B. 1) In ^{3}He–B, fig. 6b, the relative height of the attenuation peak for a given frequency is much higher than that for ^{3}He–A, fig. 7b. Indeed the sound signal at 25 MHz was attenuated so strongly near the peak at 19.6 bar that measurements at this frequency could not be made. 2) In spite of the high peak attenuation in ^{3}He–B at 19.6 bar, the 5 and 15 MHz attenuation are essentially the same below $T/T_c \simeq 0.93$, while in ^{3}He–A at 33.2 bar they were the same below $T/T_c \approx 0.87$. The ^{3}He–B peak is much higher and narrower than the ^{3}He–A peak. 3) In ^{3}He–B at 15 MHz the velocity dropped precipitously not at T_c^* but near to the temperature of the attenuation maximum (see inset fig. 6a). At lower temperatures the 5 and 15 MHz relative velocities were indistinguishable. On the other hand in ^{3}He–A the 5 and 15 MHz relative velocities seemed somewhat different for $T/T_c > 0.9$, though this is not a strong statement, and continued increasing right into T_c^*.

The solid lines drawn on figs. 6b and 7b are the function $2/[1+\exp(\Delta/kT)]$, derived by BCS[29]) for ultrasonic attenuation at low frequencies for isotropic superconductors and evaluated using tables given by Muhlschlegel[30]). The frequency-independent attenuation is not far from this line, departures being greatest and downward for ^{3}He–B at 19.6 bar.

The ultrasonic phonon energy quantum in these experiments is not small. The value of $h\nu/k$ is 0.24 mK, 0.72 mK, and 1.20 mK at 5, 15, and 25 MHz, respectively. These are to be compared with T_c, which is of order $2\frac{1}{2}$ mK. In ^{3}He–A both $(T_c - T_{max})/T_c$ and $\alpha_{max}/\alpha_0(T_c) - 1$, where α_{max}, T_{max} are the value and temperature of the maximum attenuation and $\alpha_0(T_c)$ is the zero-sound attenuation at T_c, tend to increase somewhat more rapidly than the square of the frequency. However, the experimental determination is crude.

Both Patton[31]) and Wölfle[32]) have attempted to discuss the attenuation peak in terms of phonon absorption by a condensed pair in a BCS-like state. For an isotropic gap function Δ which varies with temperature near T_c as $(1 - T/T_c)^{\frac{1}{2}}$, in agreement with the suggestion that $\rho_s \simeq \rho(1 - T/T_c)$, then it is expected that as T decreases below T_c the attenuation increases until $\Delta = \hbar\omega/2$. For lower temperatures the attenuation would drop sharply since attenuation due to this mechanism would cease. Further, for the above temperature dependence of Δ one might expect $1 - (T_{max}/T_c) \propto \omega^2$, which is not far from what is observed. However, the attenuation does not drop precipitously below T_{max} but rather has a tail. The tail extends to considerably lower relative T for ^{3}He–A than it does for ^{3}He–B and no doubt reflects important differences between the two states.

6. *Conclusions.* We believe that there is now no doubt concerning the existence of extraordinary phases of liquid ^{3}He over a wide range of pressure below temperatures extending up to about 2.6 mK at pressures near the melting line. The partial phase diagram of fig. 1 will no doubt, on the basis of measurements at melting pressure, show even more interesting behavior when the effect of a magnetic field can be included. This will be particularly true near the PCP when the magnetic field dimension is included.

The relationship of the new phases to those predicted years ago by Pitaevskii[33]); Brueckner, Soda, Anderson, and Morel[34]); Emery and Sessler[35]); and Thouless[36]) has yet to be proved; but most current theoretical work on low-temperature liquid ^{3}He seems to be based on these original ideas and on those on anisotropic superfluids by Anderson and Morel[37]) and Balian and Werthamer[38]). The relationship between known flow properties and those initially predicted by Glassgold and Sessler[39]) is also not yet clear. The above theories have a BCS-like[29]) structure but depend on pairing in non-zero relative orbital angular momentum states, where advantage may be taken of the attractive Van der Waals interaction between the ^{3}He atoms. For odd angular momentum pairing the spin state will be symmetric and lead to interesting new effects as discussed recently by Leggett[40]), Anderson[41]) and Ambegaokar and Mermin[42]).

The thermal properties of liquid ^{3}He in the vicinity of T_c at zero field are most analogous to those of superconductors in zero field. The transition is second order in Ehrenfest's sense. There is no evidence down to the admittedly large temperature displacement of 2×10^{-3} T_c of a divergence in the heat capacity. Hence liquid ^{3}He is more like a superconductor than superfluid ^{4}He in this regard.

Whether or not liquid ^{3}He–A or ^{3}He–B are superfluids *at least* depends on what we mean by the term. If we think in a context of superfluid ^{4}He then we imagine[43]) two interpenetrating fluids of densities ρ_n and ρ_s such that $\rho_n+\rho_s = \rho$, the total fluid density, with two velocity fields v_n and v_s. The superfluid velocity field may have $\nabla\times v_s = 0$, in which case the superfluid will flow as if it had zero viscosity; while the normal fluid will be characterized by a normal viscosity η_n and possibly other coefficients. Also, in pure superfluid flow there is no entropy transport. Above some critical velocity $v_{s,\,crit}$ the superfluidity is destroyed, but below this velocity persistent currents should be observable. In light of the above we see no compelling reason to postulate superfluidity to explain the wire-damping experiments. If indeed the normal viscosity was known to be rather temperature independent, as it is for superfluid ^{4}He, then there would be reason to introduce a rapidly changing normal-fluid density to explain the results; but this is not known, and furthermore the heat-flow experiments suggest that η_n does decrease rapidly below T_c in ^{3}He–B. The heat-flow experiments do not demonstrate a persistent circulating current, but they can be explained by hydrodynamic heat flow in ^{3}He–B and by critical flow velocities in ^{3}He–A, both of which are based on the two-fluid model. The heat-flow experiments thus suggest that a two-fluid model is valid in both ^{3}He–A and ^{3}He–B.

The microscopic nature of ^{3}He–A and ^{3}He–B has been elucidated best so far by the NMR experiments, by the effect of magnetic field on the "A" and "B" features on the pressurization curve, and by the experiments on propagation of collisionless sound. The temperature independence of NMR absorption in ^{3}He–A, the frequency shift as semi-quantitatively deduced by Leggett[40]) and Anderson[41]), the splitting of the "A" feature by magnetic field as understood in ref. 42, and the transition from ^{3}He–B to ^{3}He–A as pressure increases along the T_c line as anticipated by Anderson and Brinkman[44]) all support the parallel spin pairing state of Anderson and Morel[37]) as being important for ^{3}He–A. On the other hand, although ^{3}He–B has been discussed as manifesting the Balian–Werthamer[38]) state, this has not been shown experimentally. No conclusive identification of either ^{3}He–A or ^{3}He–B has yet been made. The ultrasonic attenuation is not yet quantitatively understood, but the excess frequency-dependent attenuation at temperatures below the peak, particularly in ^{3}He–A, may reflect the anisotropic gap function of Anderson and Morel[37]). Further, the observation that at low T the velocity approaches that of first sound is consistent with the discussion by Leggett[45]) of the propagation of a density fluctuation mode in a superfluid neutral Fermi fluid similar to the Bogolyubov–Anderson[46, 47]) mode in a superconductor.

Acknowledgements. I wish to acknowledge my co-workers Dr. T. J. Greytak, Dr. R. T. Johnson, Mr. D. N. Paulson, and Dr. R. A. Webb with whom I have spent many stimulating months during the past year in studying the remarkable properties of liquid ^{3}He. I have also had several helpful discussions with Dr. S. Putterman, particularly in the relationship of the present experiments to the properties of superfluid ^{4}He.

APPENDIX A

Temperature scales. In work along the melting curve the pressure is used as a thermometric indicator; in our work at lower pressures we use the magnetic temperature T^* of powdered CMN. According to refs. 8 and 16 the melting-curve slope changes little in the vicinity of the "A" and "B" features and is approximately -35 mbar/mK. This figure is tentative, but has been used to convert pressure changes to temperature changes in this paper. Our magnetic temperature scales are in all cases for powdered CMN thermometers calibrated to better than 1 % accuracy using a calibrated germanium resistance thermometer in the range 0.5 to 2 K. These thermometers all have a minimum temperature $T^*_{\min}$, which we believe[5]) occurs at 1.8 mK. The magnetic temperatures T_i^* and T_j^* of different thermometers i and j in the same or different experiments but at the same temperature (as known for example by corresponding to the same *pressure* along the T_c line) differ from one another by an amount $T_i^* - T_j^* = \Delta_{ij}$, where Δ_{ij} is only weakly dependent on temperature (variation of order 10–20 μK) down to $T^*_{\min}$.

Our temperature scale is based on unpublished Johnson noise thermometer measurements T_J of the "A" and "B" features on the melting curve by Paulson, Johnson, and myself. We found $T_J = 2.81$ mK at point A and $T_J = 2.37$ mK at point B′. It has been found by Webb *et al.*[16]) that a noise generating resistor of the sort we have will register a temperature greater than that of the surrounding ^{3}He owing, it is thought, to a very small heat leak directly to the resistor. Furthermore the difference $T_J^4 - T_3^4$, where T_3 is the absolute temperature of the ^{3}He, is nearly constant; as it would be for a constant residual heat leak to the thermometer and a T^{-3} thermal boundary resistance. We used this knowledge together with an assumed, though consistent, value of 2.0 mK for $T_{B'}$ to determine T_A. That is, we assumed that

$$T_A^4 = T_{J_A}^4 - (T_{J_{B'}}^4 - T_{B'}^4), \tag{A.1}$$

with values of temperatures on the right side of (A1) given above, to find $T_A = 2.6$ mK. This temperature was also consistent with the later measurements of Johnson *et al.*[8]) provided we used the $T^* - T_G$ correction found for the magnetic thermometer of ref. 16. For the purpose of obtaining temperature differences precisely we have set $T_A = 2.6000$ mK. We hope that in the not too distant future accurate values of P_c on an absolute scale will become available, but until that time comes we have to be satisfied with the above.

In all our experiments the $T_c^* - P_c$ line is determined, so that value T^*_{cm} corresponding to the intersection with the melting pressure of the T_c^* line is known. We can then find a tentative absolute scale in the vicinity of T^*_{cm} if we make assumptions about the absolute temperature, T, dependence of certain quantities for the normal Fermi liquid. For example, we assume a temperature dependence[27, 28]) T^2 for the attenuation coefficient α_0 of zero sound and have measurements in normal

Fermi liquid of $\alpha_0(T^*)$ as function of magnetic temperature, including the attenuation $\alpha_0(T^*_{cm})$ at the temperature T^*_{cm}. The temperature T_{SOUND} corresponding to magnetic temperature T^* is then given by

$$T_{SOUND} = 2.6 \text{ mK}[\alpha_0(T^*)/\alpha_0(T^*_{cm})]^{\frac{1}{2}}. \tag{A.2}$$

Or in heat-capacity experiments we can measure a difference heat capacity ΔC^*, the heat capacity with respect to magnetic temperature differences, as function of T^* in the normal Fermi liquid. We assume that ΔC, the heat capacity based on absolute temperature differences, is given by $\Delta C = \gamma T$, where γ is known. Then with $\Delta C = \Delta C^*$ $(\mathrm{d}T^*/\mathrm{d}T)$ we have the T–T^* relation determined by

$$\int_T^{2.6 \text{ mK}} \gamma T \, \mathrm{d}T = \int_{T^*}^{T^*_{cm}} \Delta C^* \, \mathrm{d}T^*. \tag{A.3}$$

APPENDIX B

The experimental properties of normal Fermi liquid ^{3}He are important in considering those of the extraordinary phases. We give below tables II and III which

TABLE II

Summary of experimental data for normal Fermi liquid ^{3}He under pressure (1 atm = 1.01325 bar = 14.696 psi)

P (bar)	V/n [a] (cm^3/mole)	C/nRT [b] (K^{-1})	c_1 [c] (m/s)	T^* [d] (K)	ηT^2 [c] (dyne s mK^2/cm^2)	κT [e] (erg/s cm)
9	30.76	3.6_1	286.8	0.256	1.6_7	$24._0$
12	29.71	3.7_8	308.1	0.238	1.5_4	$21._2$
15	28.86	3.9_5	327.1	0.224	1.4_2	$18._9$
18	28.13	4.1_0	345.0	0.212	1.3_2	$17._1$
21	27.56	4.2_4	360.5	0.205	1.2_2	$15._6$
24	27.06	4.3_7	375.1	0.198	1.1_5	$14._3$
27	26.58	4.5_1	389.3	0.191	1.0_7	$13._2$
30	26.14	4.6_4	403.0	0.185	0.9_9	$12._3$
33	25.71	4.7_8	415.9	0.179	0.9_2	$11._5$
34.36 [f]	25.54	4.8_5	421.7	0.177	0.8_8	$11._1$

[a] Wheatley, J. C., in Quantum Fluids, D. F. Brewer, ed., North-Holland Publishing Co. (Amsterdam, 1966), p. 183.
Grilly, E. R., J. low Temp. Phys. **4** (1971) 615.

[b] Anderson, A. C., Reese, W. and Wheatley, J. C., Phys. Rev. **130** (1963) 495.
Abel, W. R., Anderson, A. C., Black, W. C. and Wheatley, J. C., Phys. Rev. **147** (1966) 111. (C/nRT) is determined at 5 mK.

[c] Paulson, D. N., Johnson, R. T. and Wheatley, J. C., unpublished.

[d] Ramm, H., Pedroni, P., Thompson, J. R. and Meyer, H., J. low Temp. Phys. **2** (1970) 539. Here T^* is the effective magnetic temperature; see ref. [a] for definition.

[e] Greytak, T. J., Johnson, R. T., Paulson, D. N. and Wheatley, J. C., unpublished.
Abel, W. R., Johnson, R. T., Wheatley, J. C. and Zimmermann, Jr., W., Phys. Rev. Letters **18** (1967) 737.

[f] Melting pressure.

TABLE III

Summary of derived parameters[a] for normal Fermi liquid ^{3}He under pressure using data from table II

P (bar)	$(1/V)(\partial\tau/\partial\varepsilon)_\mu$ (10^{38} (erg cm^3)$^{-1}$)	p_F (10^{-20} g cm/s)	m^*/m	v_F (10^3 cm/s)	F_1	F_0	Z_0	$\tau_\eta T^2$ (10^{-6} s mK^2)	$\tau_\kappa T^2$ (10^{-6} s mK^2)
9	1.5_6	8.7_9	4.0_9	4.2_9	9.2_7	31.7_5	-2.8_8	1.1_3	0.4_0
12	1.6_9	8.8_9	4.3_8	4.0_5	10.1_5	38.5_8	-2.9_0	1.0_5	0.3_7
15	1.8_1	8.9_8	4.6_7	3.8_4	11.0_1	45.6_2	-2.9_2	0.9_9	0.3_4
18	1.9_3	9.0_6	4.9_3	3.6_7	11.7_9	52.8_3	-2.9_4	0.9_3	0.3_2
21	2.0_4	9.1_2	5.1_7	3.5_2	12.5_1	59.7_8	-2.9_4	0.8_7	0.3_0
24	2.1_4	9.1_8	5.3_9	3.4_0	13.1_8	66.8_1	-2.9_5	0.8_3	0.2_8
27	2.2_5	9.2_3	5.6_3	3.2_7	13.9_0	74.3_8	-2.9_5	0.7_8	0.2_6
30	2.3_5	9.2_8	5.8_6	3.1_6	14.5_8	82.1_3	-2.9_6	0.7_3	0.2_5
33	2.4_6	9.3_4	6.1_0	3.0_5	15.3_1	90.1_7	-2.9_6	0.6_9	0.2_4
34.36 [b]	2.5_2	9.3_6	6.2_2	3.0_0	15.6_6	94.1_3	-2.9_6	0.6_6	0.2_3

[a] For definition see ref. a of table II.

[b] Melting pressure.

are summaries of properties of the normal liquid under pressure. The most uncertain entry in table II is (C/nRT), where we resorted to very early data. This quantity is then reflected throughout table III of derived quantities. The latter gives quantities defined in ref. a of table II. Reference a also gives data on spin diffusion under pressure.

REFERENCES

1) Osheroff, D. D., Richardson, R. C. and Lee, D. M., Phys. Rev. Letters **28** (1972) 885.
2) Greytak, T. J., Johnson, R. T., Paulson, D. N. and Wheatley, J. C., submitted for publication.
3) Webb, R. A., Greytak, T. J., Johnson, R. T. and Wheatley, J. C., Phys. Rev. Letters **30** (1973) 210.
4) Paulson, D. N., Johnson, R. T. and Wheatley, J. C., Phys. Rev. Letters **30** (1973) 829 and unpublished work.
5) Fisher, R. A., Hornung, E. W., Brodale, C. E. and Giauque, W. F., to be published.
6) London, F. and Zilsel, P. R., Phys. Rev. **74** (1948) 1148.
7) Gorter, C. J. and Mellink, J. H., Physica **15** (1949) 285.
8) Johnson, R. T., Paulson, D. N., Pierce, C. B. and Wheatley, J. C., Phys. Rev. Letters **30** (1973) 207.
9) Wheatley, J. C., in Prog. in Low Temp. Phys. VI, C. J. Gorter, ed., North-Holland Publishing Co. (Amsterdam, 1970) p. 77.
Wheatley, J. C., in Quantum Fluids, D. F. Brewer, ed., North-Holland Publishing Co. (Amsterdam, 1966), p. 183.
Johnson, R. T., Lounasmaa, O. V., Rosenbaum, R., Symko, O. G. and Wheatley, J. C., J. low Temp. Phys. **2** (1970) 403.
10) Anyfriyev, Yu. D., Alvesalo, T. A., Collan, H. K., Opheim, N. T. and Wennerström, P. Phys. Letters **43A** (1973) 175.
11) Halperin, W. P., Buhrman, R. A. and Richardson, R. C., Bull. Am. Phys. Soc. **18** (1973) 642.
12) Dundon, J. M., Stolfa, D. L. and Goodkind, J. M., Phys. Rev. Letters **30** (1973) 843.
13) Osheroff, D. D., Gully, W. J., Richardson, R. C. and Lee, D. M., Phys. Rev. Letters **29** (1972) 920.
14) Lawson, D. T., Gully, W. J., Goldstein, S., Richardson, R. C. and Lee, D. M., Phys. Rev. Letters **30** (1973) 541.
15) Gully, W. J., Osheroff, D. D., Lawson, D. T., Richardson, R. C. and Lee, D. M., preprint.
16) Webb, R. A., Giffard, R. P. and Wheatley, J. C., to be submitted.
17) Ramm, H., Pedroni, P., Thompson, J. R. and Meyer, H., J. low Temp. Phys. **2** (1970) 539.
18) Tough, J. T., McCormick, W. D. and Dash, J. G., Rev. Sci. Instr. **35** (1964) 1345.
19) Black, M. A., Hall, H. E. and Thompson, K., J. Phys. C., Proc. Phys. Soc. (London) **4** (1971) 129.
20) Alvesalo, T. A., Anufriyev, Yu. D., Collan, H. K., Lounasmaa, O. V. and Wennerström, P., Phys. Rev. Letters **30** (1973) 962.
21) Stokes, G. G., Mathematical and Physical Papers, Cambridge University Press (London, 1922), Vol. III, p. 38.
22) Brewer, D. F. and Edwards, D. O., Proc. Roy. Soc. **A251** (1959) 247.
23) Brewer, D. F. and Edwards, D. O., Phil. Mag. **6** (1961) 775.
24) Abel, W. R., Johnson, R. T., Wheatley, J. C. and Zimmermann, Jr., W., Phys. Rev. Letters **18** (1967) 737.
25) De Gennes, P. G., Superconductivity of Metals and Alloys, W. A. Benjamin, Inc. (New York, 1966), p. 172.
26) Shapiro, K. A. and Rudnick, I., Phys. Rev. **137** (1965) A1383.
27) Landau, L. D., Zh. eksper. teor. Fiz. **32** (1957) 59 [transl.: Soviet Phys.-JETP **5** (1957) 101].
28) Abel, W. R., Anderson, A. C. and Wheatley, J. C., Phys. Rev. Letters **17** (1966) 74.

29) Bardeen, J., Cooper, L. N. and Schrieffer, J. R., Phys. Rev. **108** (1957) 1175.
30) Muhlschlegel, B., Z. Phys. **155** (1959) 313.
31) Patton, B. R., preprint.
32) Wölfle, P., Phys. Rev. Letters **30** (1973) 1169.
33) Pitaevskii, L. P., Zh. eksper. teor. Fiz. **37** (1959) 1794 [transl.: Soviet Phys.-JETP **10** (1960) 1267].
34) Brueckner, K. A., Soda, T., Anderson, P. W. and Morel, P., Phys. Rev. **118** (1960) 1442.
35) Emery, V. J. and Sessler, A. M., Phys. Rev. **119** (1960) 43.
36) Thouless, D. J., Ann. Phys. **10** (1960) 553.
37) Anderson, P. W. and Morel, P., Phys. Rev. **123** (1961) 1911.
38) Balian, R. and Werthamer, N. R., Phys. Rev. **131** (1963) 1553.
39) Glassgold, A. E. and Sessler, A. M., Nuovo Cimento **19** (1961) 723.
40) Leggett, A. J., Phys. Rev. Letters **29** (1972) 1227.
41) Anderson, P. W., Phys. Rev. Letters **30** (1973) 368.
42) Ambegaokar, V. and Mermin, D., Phys. Rev. Letters **30** (1973) 81.
43) See, for example, Keller, W. E., Helium-3 and Helium-4, Plenum Press (New York, 1969), p. 276.
44) Anderson, P. W. and Brinkman, W. F., Phys. Rev. Letters **30** (1973) 1108.
45) Leggett, A. J., Phys. Rev. **147** (1966) 119.
46) Bogolyubov, N. N., Tolmachev, V. V. and Shirkov, D. N., New Method in the Theory of Superconductivity [English transl.: Consultants Bureau Enterprises, Inc. (New York, 1959)].
47) Anderson, P. W., Phys. Rev. **112** (1958) 1900.

Physica **69** (1973) 245–250 © *North-Holland Publishing Co.*

MUTUAL FRICTION AND SECOND SOUND

H. C. KRAMERS, T. M. WIARDA and G. VAN DER HEIJDEN

Kamerlingh Onnes Laboratorium der Rijksuniversiteit Leiden, Leiden, Nederland

(Commun. Suppl. No. 129)

Received 25 June 1973

Synopsis

The attenuation of second sound is investigated in flow conditions in a capillary. In particular results for "pure" superfluid flow and "pure" normal flow are given and compared.

1. *Introduction.* The idea of Gorter and Mellink to ascribe the peculiar flow resistance, occurring in liquid helium II, to a mutual force or "friction" between the counterparts of the two-fluid system has been a very fruitful one. Further, the fundamental work of Onsager and Feynman and the subsequent study of Hall and Vinen have allowed for a deeper physical insight into its nature by explaining it as an interaction between the thermal excitations of the normal fluid and the quantized vortex lines or rings essentially moving with the superfluid. In particular the picture of vortex lines parallel to the axis of rotation in a rotating liquid-filled bucket could satisfactorily be analysed by observing the attenuation of second sound, *i.e.*, of a periodic relative motion of the two fluids[1]).

On the other hand, notwithstanding a wealth of experiments and of theoretical studies, no complete quantitative understanding of the resistance phenomena occurring in the flow through tubes or channels can be claimed at the present time. Neither the exact form of the vortex-excitation interaction, nor the conditions of creation and annihilation of vortices are satisfactorily understood. From an experimental point of view a big problem still is the acquisition of sufficiently well-defined physical conditions; therefore, contradictory results are a rather common feature of this field.

In our laboratory an extensive study has been made of adiabatic flow through metal tubes with diameters around 1 mm. Some of the results have been published[2]), other results can only be found in the theses of two of the present authors[3,4]). In the present paper some peculiar features of second-sound attenuation results will be discussed.

2. *The model.* In order to describe the experimental results, it is necessary to summarize the general picture which, of course, is based on the two-fluid model. Mutual friction may occur above certain critical values of either the superfluid velocity v_s or the relative velocity $v_n - v_s$; its magnitude may further depend on the normal-fluid velocity v_n as well.

The superfluid is supposed to "carry" a certain amount of vorticity (vortex lines) or "turbulence", the density of which may in general depend on $\bar{v}_n$, $\bar{v}_s$ and T. The bars indicate values averaged over the region of the tube or channel and over an appropriate time, connected with the build-up of the vortices.

In general the normal fluid might also be turbulent or turbulence might be a condition of the liquid as a whole. However, in the present study, which is limited to velocities of the order of 10 cm/s, there has been found rather strong evidence for simultaneous laminar properties of the normal fluid and "turbulent" properties of the superfluid. This has been discussed elsewhere[4]).

In the present paper discussion will be limited to measurements of the attenuation of second sound as a function of $\bar{v}_n$, $\bar{v}_s$ and T. Observations of the gradients of temperature and the chemical potential have to be referred to other papers[5, 6]).

The attenuation of second sound was always found to be linear, *i.e.*, independent of the amplitude. Therefore, it seems to be reasonable to use linearized quasi-equations of motion for the analysis of the results. It should be emphasized that, though these equations show a close resemblance to the Landau equations of motion, the mutual-friction terms are insufficiently founded from a theoretical point of view. The equations can be written as

$$\frac{\partial v_s}{\partial t} = -\frac{1}{\rho}\,\text{grad}\,p + S\,\text{grad}\,T + \frac{G}{\rho_s}(v_n - v_s), \tag{1}$$

$$\frac{\partial v_n}{\partial t} = -\frac{1}{\rho}\,\text{grad}\,p - \frac{\rho_s}{\rho_n}S\,\text{grad}\,T - \frac{G}{\rho_n}(v_n - v_s) + \frac{\eta}{\rho_n}\Delta v_n. \tag{2}$$

Subtraction gives the "equation of motion" for the relative velocity:

$$\frac{\partial(v_n - v_s)}{\partial t} = -\frac{\rho}{\rho_n}\,\text{grad}\,T - G\frac{\rho}{\rho_n\rho_s}(v_n - v_s) + \frac{\eta}{\rho_n}\Delta v_n \tag{3}$$

from which, by combination with the equations of conservation of mass and entropy (valid in this linearized approximation), the attenuation and velocity of second sound can be deduced. The velocities v_n and v_s are the time-dependent velocities in the second-sound wave; the mutual-friction parameter G may depend on the average steady-flow velocities $\bar{v}_n$ and $\bar{v}_s$ and on T. In the original Gorter–Mellink form of the friction force, G was set equal to $A\rho_n\rho_s\overline{(v_n - v_s)}^2$ which form is, however, not compatible with the present experimental results. The value of G is, clearly, a measure for the vortex density of the superfluid, if the suggested model is accepted. The last term of eqs. (2) and (3) is the ordinary viscosity term, mainly responsible for the attenuation in zero steady flow.

3. *The experiment.* The method used to produce at will any steady-flow condition in a capillary, *i.e.*, any combination of $\bar{v}_n$ and $\bar{v}_s$, has been described in ref. 3. Second-sound attenuation was determined by measuring the damping of a second-sound resonator of the "double" Helmholtz type connected in series with the capillary (see fig. 1). Its resonant frequency corresponded with

$$\nu_r^2 = (v_{II}^2/4\pi^2)(O/l)[(1/V_1) + (1/V_2)], \tag{4}$$

with O, l, V_1 and V_2 indicating the effective cross section and length of the connecting tube and the two "capacitive" volumes; v_{II} is the second-sound velocity, given by

$$v_{II}^2 = (\rho_s/\rho_n)S^2T/C. \tag{5}$$

The main contributions to the attenuation are:
a) the viscous damping of the normal fluid motion which can be written as an appropriate width of the resonance curve

$$\Delta\nu_\eta = \nu_r(\rho/\rho_s)\delta/r, \tag{6}$$

with r, the radius of the tube and δ, the viscous penetration depth. The latter can be written as $\delta = (\eta_n/\pi\nu\rho_n)^{\frac{1}{2}}$.
b) the damping due to the mutal friction if steady flow is present, its resonance width corresponds to

$$\Delta\nu_m = (\rho/\rho_n\rho_s)G. \tag{7}$$

A discussion of other (smaller) contributions to the damping will be omitted here. Further, as will be suggested in the following, the two main contributions may not always be additive.

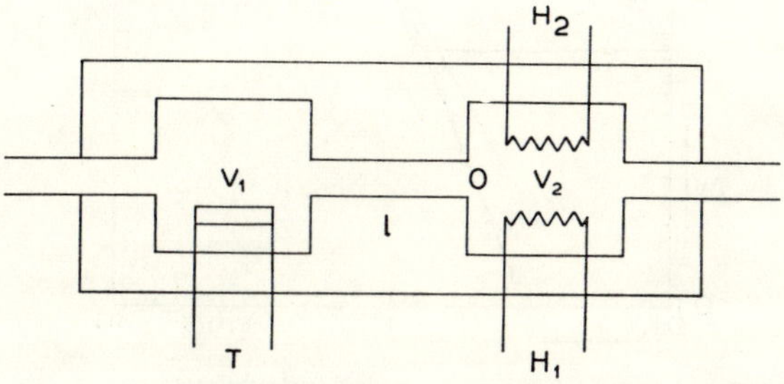

Fig. 1. Double Helmholtz resonator for second sound ($\nu \approx 100$ Hz). H_1 H_2: heaters; T: thermometer detector; connecting tube: length 8 mm, diameter 0.51 mm.

4. *Results.* Fig. 2 gives a review of the measurements at $T = 1.5$ K. Plotted are values of the observed resonance width Δv divided by its magnitude without steady flow $(\Delta v)_0$, as a function of the average *relative* steady velocity. Fully drawn lines indicate loci of constant $\bar{v}_n$, dotted lines loci of constant $\bar{v}_s$. It is clear that the original Gorter–Mellink formula containing a quadratic dependence on the relative velocity is not sufficient for a description of the results.

Most promising for a better understanding are the curves for $\bar{v}_n = 0$ and $\bar{v}_s = 0$. Due to the rather large cross section of the tube, no critical velocity can be observed for pure superfluid flow. Pure normal-fluid flow shows, however, an extended region of absence of mutual friction, *i.e.*, an apparent vortex-free region. Careful

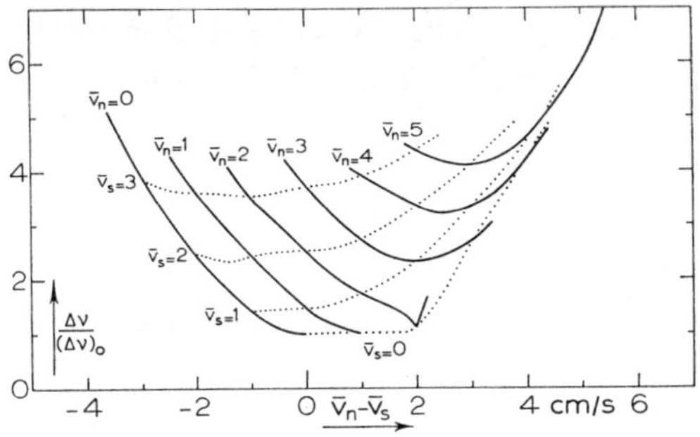

Fig. 2. Damping of second sound at $T = 1.5$ K against the relative velocity $\bar{v}_n - \bar{v}_s$. Fully-drawn lines: loci of constant $\bar{v}_n$; dotted lines: loci of constant $\bar{v}_s$.

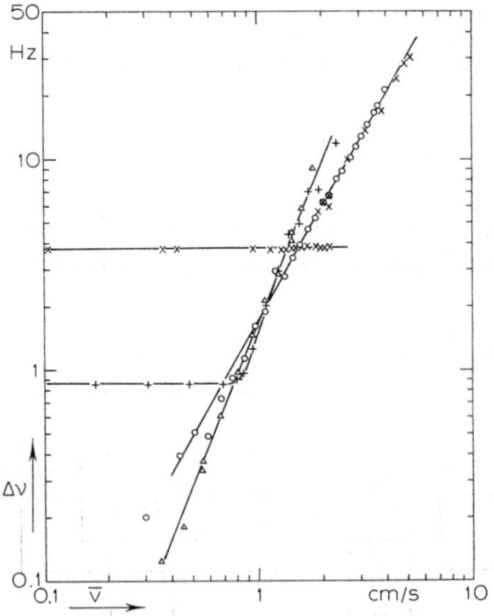

Fig. 3. Resonance width for some cases against $\bar{v}_n$ and $\bar{v}_s$. $T = 1.5$ K. o: $\bar{v}_n = 0$ plotted is $\Delta v - \Delta v_\eta$; ×: $\bar{v}_s = 0$ plotted is Δv. $T = 2.0$ K. △: $\bar{v}_n = 0$ plotted is $\Delta v - \Delta v_\eta$; +: $\bar{v}_s = 0$ plotted is Δv.

measurements show that this situation is limited to within a very small critical value of $\bar{v}_s$.

For two temperatures the double-logarithmic drawing of fig. 3 gives in one graph Δv for pure normal flow together with $\Delta v - \Delta v_\eta$ for pure superflow. The peculiar outcome is that, by plotting in this way, the turbulent parts of both curves apparently coincide, *i.e.*, the straight mutual-friction curve for $\bar{v}_n = 0$ is joined by the $\bar{v}_s = 0$ line at exactly the point where it cuts the horizontal laminar stretch of the latter. As is clear, in particular for the lower temperature ($T = 1.5$ K), this laminar part can be extended to the right if sufficient care is taken. Actually there is a small region of instability or rather bistability.

The noted correlation between the $\bar{v}_s = 0$ curve and the $\bar{v}_n = 0$ curve is not yet understood. It is perhaps not surprising that the two contributions to the attenuation are additive if the average value of v_n is zero; the amount of vorticity (strength of turbulence) in the superfluid may then be expected to depend only on v_s and the profiles involved are practically flat. The situation for a pure steady normal flow may be more complicated. For instance the profile for v_n has a tendency to be parabolic, though the shortness of the resonator tube makes a fully developed Poiseuille profile improbable. In what way this can influence the energy dissipation of the second-sound wave is not clear.

The conclusion must be that, for pure normal flow, energy loss of the second-sound wave initially takes place by the viscous process only; above the crossing point, however, the number of vortices is adjusted in such a way that dissipation in pure normal flow corresponds to the one effected by mutual friction only, as is found in pure superfluid motion of the same magnitude. It appears rather as if the viscous dissipation completely drops out for the pure normal flow as soon as the mutual friction becomes effective, but this seems rather improbable.

This result was obtained at all temperatures, provided sufficient care was taken to allow for establishment of equilibrium. The slope of the turbulent curve does not agree with a quadratic dependence as was suggested by Gorter and Mellink. The power dependence on the temperature is given in table I.

TABLE I

Power dependence on temperature

T (K)	1.3	1.4	1.5	1.6	1.7	1.8	1.9	2.0
Power	1.66	1.69	1.84	1.90	1.97	2.20	2.30	2.64

The conclusion of this may be that it might be profitable to try to understand the two types of flow with their peculiar interrelation as discussed here, before attempts are made to explain more complicated flow conditions. Perhaps one may suggest that the flow condition most frequently studied, *i.e.*, that of zero-mass flow or "pure heat conduction", may belong to the more complicated class.

REFERENCES

1) Progress in Low Temperature Physics, C. J. Gorter, ed., vol. I, North-Holland Publ. Comp. (Amsterdam, 1955), chap. I and II; vol. III (1961), chap. I. See for further references other volumes of this series and Wilks, J., The Properties of Liquid and Solid Helium, Clarendon Press (Oxford, 1967).
2) Kramers, H. C., Superfluid Helium, J. F. Allen, ed., Academic Press (London and New York 1966) p. 199.
3) Wiarda, T. M., Thesis (Leiden, 1967).
4) Van der Heijden, G., Thesis (Leiden, 1972).
5) Van der Heijden, G., De Voogt, W. J. P. and Kramers, H. C., Physica **59** (1972) 473 (Commun. Kamerlingh Onnes Lab., Leiden No. 392a).
6) Van der Heijden, G., Giezen, J. J. and Kramers, H. C., Physica **61** (1972) 566 (Commun. Kamerlingh Onnes Lab., Leiden No. 394c).
7) Van der Heijden, G., Van der Boog, A. G. M. and Kramers, H. C., Physica, to be published.

Physica **69** (1973) 251–258 © *North-Holland Publishing Co.*

APPLICATION DES MESURES DE TEMPS DE RELAXATION A L'INTERACTION ENTRE DIFFÉRENTS IONS

G. RAOULT

Laboratoire de Radioélectricité et Théorie du Solide, B.P. 45,
63 170 – Aubière, France

Reçu le 17 mai 1973

Sommaire

Les études de temps de relaxation peuvent conduire à la mise en évidence d'ions dont il n'est pas facile en général de déceler la présence par les moyens classiques de R.P.E. Différents résultats de mesure sont donnés et des réflexions sont faites sur la définition des temps de relaxation eux-mêmes.

1. *Introduction.* Les temps de relaxation ont été introduits par Casimir et Dupré[1]), Gorter[2]), Bloch[3]) à partir de notions légèrement différentes. Nous dirons quelques mots de ce problème, en suivant un raisonnement de Spaposhnikov[4]).

La mesure que nous effectuons consiste à saturer par impulsions une raie de résonance paramagnétique dans un champ B_0 directeur et à une température θ, et d'observer, avec une très faible interrogation, la réapparition exponentielle du signal. L'ion dont nous mesurons le temps de relaxation est l'ion Cr^{3+} dans une maille d'alumine cristallisée (corindon) et nous observons les variations de ce temps en présence d'ions "d'impuretés" ajoutés intentionnellement dans la maille. Nous avons plus particulièrement étudié V^{3+}, Fe^{3+}, Ni^{3+}, Fe^{2+}. La direction du champ B_0 par rapport aux axes cristallins est un facteur de variation important, les courbes représentant les variations de T_1 avec la position de B_0 présentent des extremums (en général des minimums) dus à certains ions, souvent non détectables par les méthodes classiques de R.P.E. ou dont les raies sont extrêmement faibles. Les variations de T_1 avec la température fournissent aussi des informations sur ces ions et les processus de relaxation.

2. *Matériaux utilisés.* Les cristaux de corindon dopés au chrome sont fabriqués par différentes méthodes, la plupart par la méthode de Verneuil, mais nous en avons étudié certains, dans notre laboratoire, qui avaient été obtenus par tirage. Les poudres servant à la fabrication sont des mélanges d'alumine, d'oxyde de

chrome et éventuellement "d'impuretés". Les concentrations sont déterminées par différentes méthodes (méthodes spectrographiques, fluorescence X, activation, R.P.E., R.P.A.) sur les cristaux eux-mêmes, dont une partie est quelquefois sacrifiée. Cette détermination est malheureusement assez peu précise et dans certains cas 10 % est une limite qui n'est atteinte que difficilement.

3. *Conditions expérimentales.* Dans un premier temps nous avons étudié avec soin la dépendance du temps de relaxation avec l'orientation pour un certain nombre de rubis "purs" c'est à dire dont la concentration en ions autres que Cr^{3+} est la plus faible possible. Ces mesures sont faites en bande X (environ 10 GHz) aux températures de l'hélium liquide: soit en équilibre avec sa vapeur saturante à la pression atmosphérique, c'est à dire 4,2 K, soit en pompant de manière à faire descendre la température jusque vers 1,2 K.

Le cristal est taillé en forme de parallélépipède rectangle placé sur un support dont la position peut être variée régulièrement en le maintenant dans le cryostat. L'électroaimant est alimenté par une source stabilisée (10^{-5}) construite au laboratoire et la forme de ses pièces polaires a été étudiée de manière à rendre le champ très homogène (10^{-5}) dans l'étendue du cristal[5]). Si maintenant nous traçons les mêmes courbes avec des rubis dopés, aux points de croisement des diagrammes des ions Cr^{3+} et de l'impureté considérée, il se produit souvent des minimums très prononcés du temps de relaxation.

4. *Travaux antérieurs.* Zverev, Prokhorov et Schevchenko[6]) ont observé une diminution du temps T_1 de Cr^{3+} dans un monocristal d'alumine dopé au chrome et au vanadium, mais ils n'ont pas trouvé de minimum aux croisements des raies de Cr^{3+} et V^{3+}. Nisida[7]) a obtenu des minimums pour des cristaux comportant du titane, et ceci aux points de croisement des raies de Cr^{3+} et Ti^{3+}. Larson et Jeffries[8]) ont observé des phénomènes de cross-relaxation analogues dans les sels de terres rares dopés avec deux ions. Pour expliquer leurs résultats, Nisida et Larson et Jeffries ont écrit des équations d'évolution des populations des niveaux des deux systèmes de spins en tenant compte de la relaxation avec le réseau et de la cross-relaxation.

5. *Etudes de cross-relaxation.* a) Cr^{3+} et V^{3+}. Nos premières études ont été faites sur des rubis dopés au vanadium[9,10]). A 4,2 K, les temps de relaxation de Cr^{3+} dans un rubis pur est de l'ordre de quelques centaines de millisecondes suivant les transitions et les orientations considérées. Pour l'ion V^{3+} il est de l'ordre de 50 μs. On observe des minimums à l'intersection des raies de Cr^{3+} avec les huit composantes hyperfines de V^{3+}, dans tous nos échantillons (fig. 1).

Les variations avec la température du temps de relaxation sont voisines de exp $(10/\theta)$; ceci peut s'expliquer en considérant que la population des niveaux de

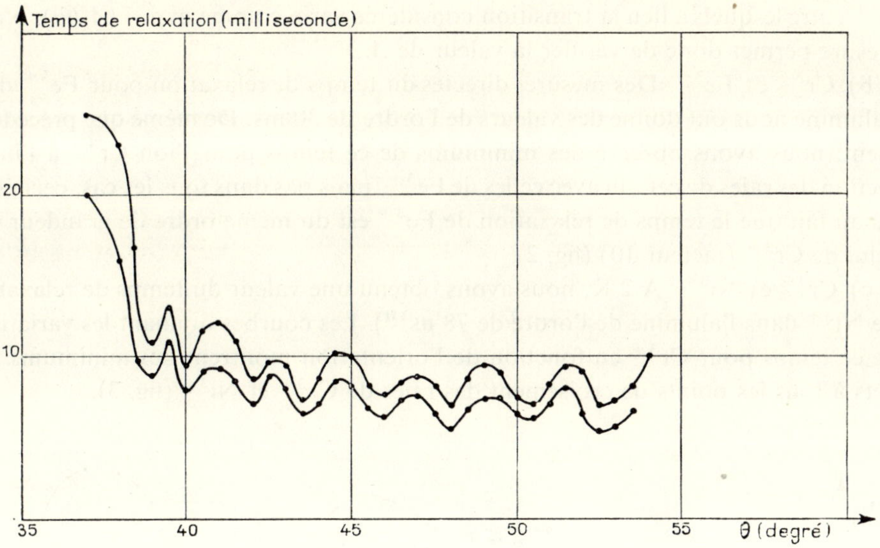

Fig. 1. Temps de relaxation de Cr^{3+} dans une région où les raies de Cr^{3+} et V^{3+} se croisent.

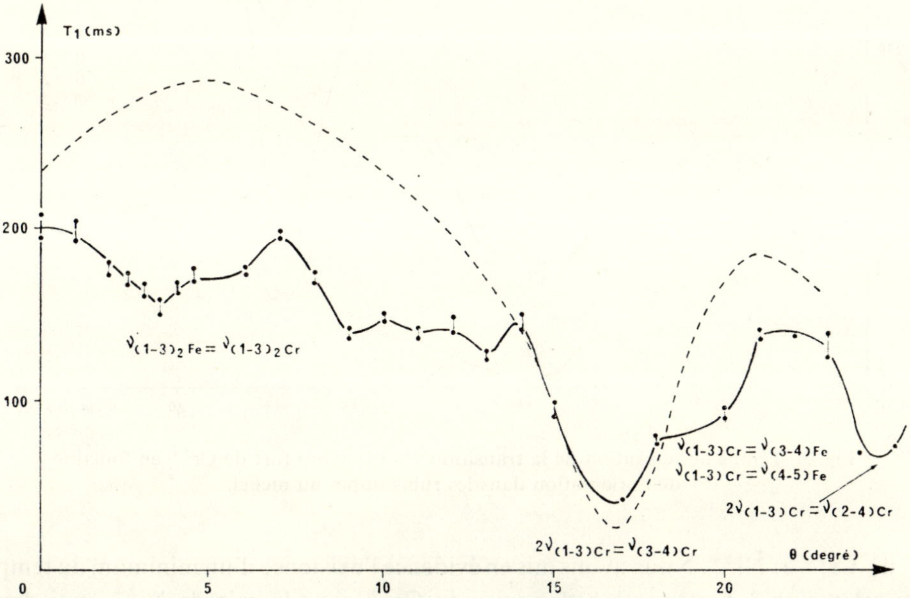

Fig. 2. Comparaison des courbes représentant les variations du temps de relaxation de Cr^{3+} avec l'orientation pour un rubis pur et un rubis dopé au fer de concentrations en chrome voisines de 200×10^{-6}, la concentration en fer du dernier étant faible. Transition (1–3) champ fort de Cr^{3+}: —, Rubis dopé au fer no. 1: Concentration en Cr^{3+}: 185×10^{-6}, Concentration en Fe^{3+}: 35×10^{-6}. - - - Rubis pur: Concentration en Cr^{3+}: 250×10^{-6}.

V^{3+} entre lesquels a lieu la transition considérée varie comme exp $-(\Delta/k\theta)$. Notre mesure permet donc de vérifier la valeur de Δ.

b) Cr^{3+} et Fe^{3+}. Des mesures directes du temps de relaxation pour Fe^{3+} dans l'alumine nous ont donné des valeurs de l'ordre de 30 ms. De même que précédemment, nous avons observé des minimums de ce temps pour l'ion Cr^{3+} à l'intersection des raies de cet ion avec celles de Fe^{3+}, mais pas dans tous les cas, ceci étant dû au fait que le temps de relaxation de Fe^{3+} est du même ordre de grandeur que celui de Cr^{3+} (facteur 10) (fig. 2).

c) Cr^{3+} et Ni^{3+}. A 2 K, nous avons obtenu une valeur du temps de relaxation de Ni^{3+} dans l'alumine de l'ordre de 78 μs[10]). Les courbes donnant les variations de ce temps pour Cr^{3+} en fonction de l'orientation montrent des minimums très nets à tous les points de croisement des raies de Cr^{3+} et Ni^{3+} (fig. 3).

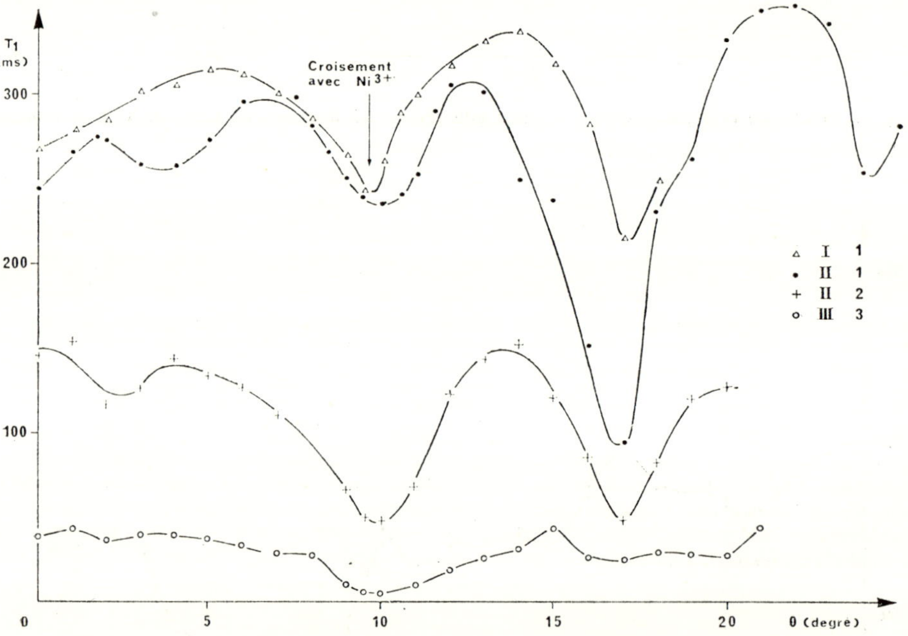

Fig. 3. Temps de relaxation de la transition (1–3) champ fort de Cr^{3+} en fonction de l'orientation dans les rubis dopés au nickel.

d) Cr^{3+} et Ni^{2+}. Nous avons mis en évidence l'existence d'un minimum du temps de relaxation à l'intersection des raies de Cr^{3+} avec la raie de Ni^{2+}, ceci dans différents échantillons.

e) Fe^{3+} et V^{3+}. On observe toujours des minimums du temps de relaxation de Fe^{3+} très sensibles aux points de croisement de cet ion avec les composantes hyperfines de V^{3+}.

f) Introduction d'ions non paramagnétiques. Pour changer éventuellement la valence des ions par compensation de charge, nous avons fabriqué des cristaux dopés avec des ions Mg^{2+}, ou Si^{4+}. Dans le premier cas, les rubis prennent une couleur orange due à la présence de Cr^{4+}, mais nous n'avons pu observer de minimum aux points de croisement. Dans le deuxième cas, il y a eu apparition d'ions Fe^{2+}. Nous avons effectivement mesuré des minimums très sensibles aux points de croisement des raies de Cr^{3+} et Fe^{2+}.

6. *Détection et étude de l'ion Fe^{2+} dans l'alumine.* Jusqu'ici il n'avait pas été possible d'obtenir directement la R.P.E. de l'ion Fe^{2+}, mais seulement la résonance paramagnétique acoustique[12, 13]). En mesurant les temps de relaxation des ions Cr^{3+} dans des rubis dopés au fer et au silicium, nous avons obtenu des minimums très nets aux intersections des raies de Cr^{3+} avec la transition $\Delta M_{s'} = 2$ de Fe^{2+} [14]). Ce qui est remarquable est la forme dissymétrique de la raie de Fe^{2+} qui se retrouve comme en R.P.A. Récemment cette raie dissymétrique a été détectée par une méthode thermique[15]) (fig. 4a).

Dans des cristaux dopés uniquement au fer, nous avons pu ainsi observer les minimums correspondant aux croisements entre les raies de Fe^{3+} et Fe^{2+} [16, 17]).

Ces résultats posent le problème de la cross-relaxation avec un ion non-Kramers ayant une valeur de $g_\perp$ nulle tel que Fe^{2+}. En effet, l'interaction magnétique dipolaire n'a pas d'élément de matrice entre les niveaux de Fe^{2+}, aussi la cross-relaxation habituellement envisagée ne peut expliquer les phénomènes. Bates et Steggles ont recherché un autre mécanisme (article à paraître).

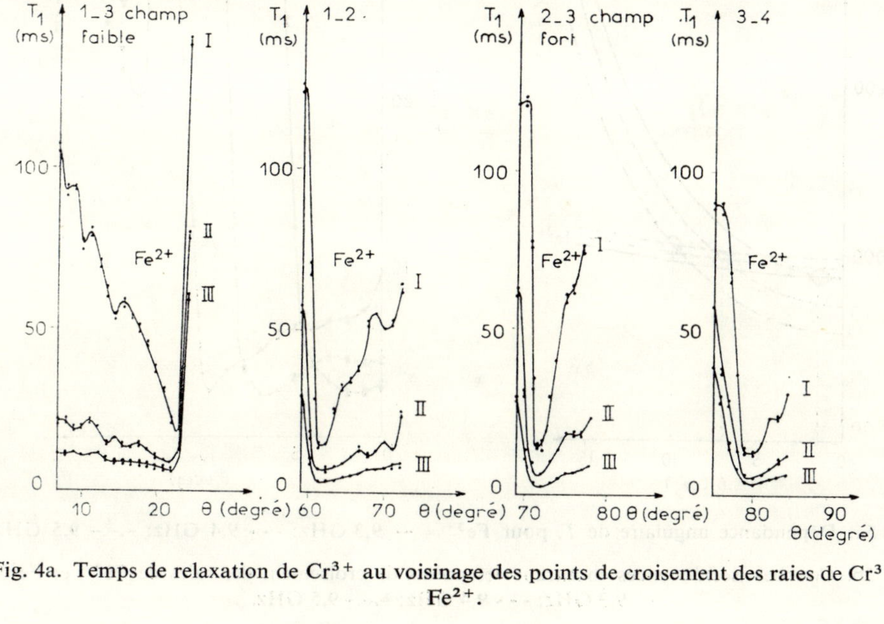

Fig. 4a. Temps de relaxation de Cr^{3+} au voisinage des points de croisement des raies de Cr^{3+} et Fe^{2+}.

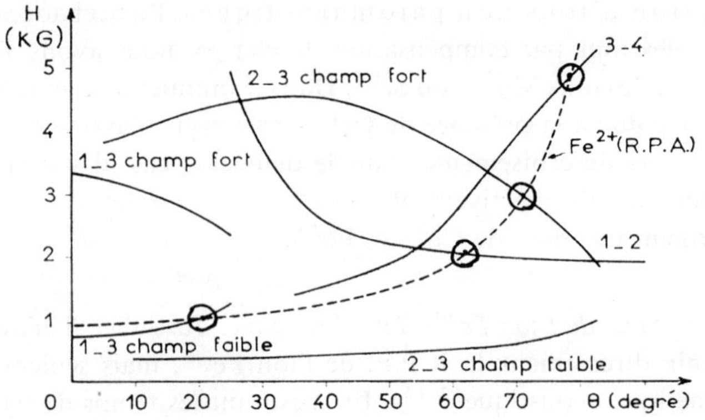

Fig. 4b. Courbes isofréquences montrant les points de croisement des raies de Cr^{3+} et Fe^{2+}.

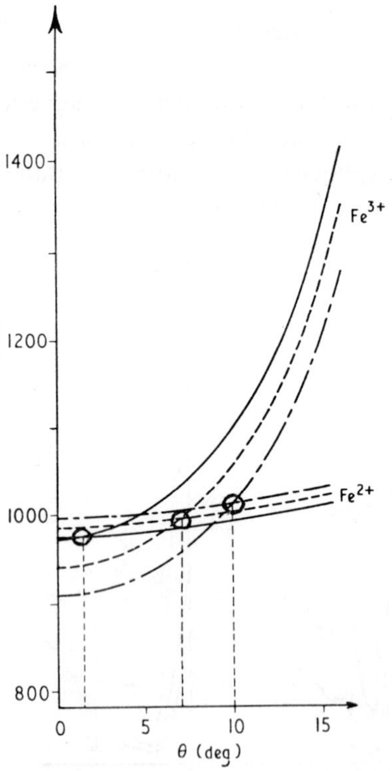

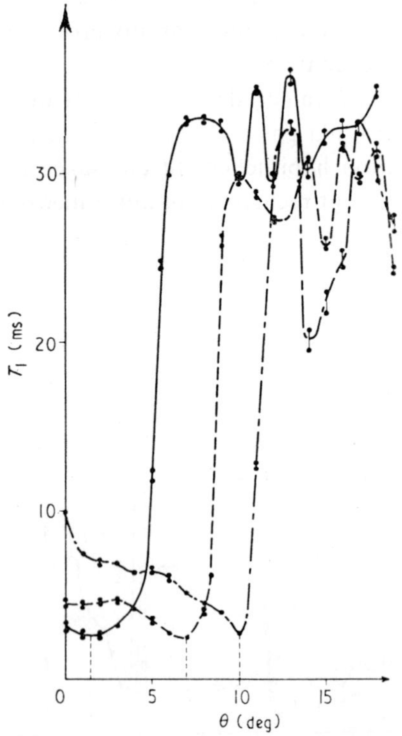

Fig. 5a. Dépendance angulaire de T_1 pour Fe^{3+}. — 9,3 GHz; - - - 9,4 GHz; –.–.– 9,5 GHz.

Fig. 5b. Courbes isofréquences montrant les points de croisement des raies de Fe^{3+} et Fe^{2+}. — 9,3 GHz; - - - 9,4 GHz; –.–.– 9,5 GHz.

7. *Réflexion sur les définitions des temps de relaxation.* Les temps de relaxation τ spin–réseau de Casimir et Dupré et τ' spin–spin de Gorter ont été assimilés aux temps T_1 et T_2 longitudinal et transversal de Bloch. Il semble bien que cette façon de voir ne soit pas rigoureusement exacte. Dans une étude très soignée Shaposhnikov[4]) a montré qu'il y aurait lieu d'appeler T_2 transversal, τ longitudinal d'équilibre, T_1 longitudinal isothermique et τ' longitudinal adiabatique.

Suivant la méthode utilisée pour la mesure, les résultats permettent de calculer des temps qui sont des fonctions de différents temps de relaxation définis plus haut.

Ainsi, dans un cas particulier[18]) des expériences sur des sulfates de gadolinium et de manganèse ammonium en poudre ont montré que les quantités T_1 et τ étaient très différentes: $\tau(2000\,\text{gauss}\,300\,\text{K}) = 4 \times 10^{-8}$ et $T_1(300\,\text{K}) = 2 \times 10^{-11}$ s.

Dans notre cas précis, puisque nous étudions la réapparition du signal après qu'une impulsion ait égalisé les populations, nous mesurons la constante de temps du retour à l'équilibre thermique.

Cette constante de temps que nous appelons par commodité T_1 est en réalité due aux interactions entre l'ion et le réseau et aussi entre l'ion et les ions voisins analogues au d'impureté, sans compter les phénomènes de cross-relaxation harmonique. Dans certains cas simples, il a été possible de calculer directement les constantes de temps, sans faire intervenir aucune des définitions précédentes. Donoho[19]) a fait cela pour Cr^{3+} dans la maille d'alumine et a trouvé ainsi plusieurs temps de relaxation pour les différentes transitions.

8. *Conclusion.* De ce très bref exposé d'un certain nombre de travaux sur les temps de relaxation, il apparaît que cette étude permet la détection d'ions que l'on ne pourrait atteindre directement par les méthodes classiques de R.P.E., ainsi que de permettre la recherche des interactions dans les mailles des ions paramagnétiques. Ces travaux sont un hommage rendu au travail de pionnier de Gorter dans ce domaine qui se révèle un champ immense et d'une portée considérable pour la physique atomique et moléculaire.

RÉFÉRENCES

1) Casimir, H. B. G. et Dupré, F., Physica **5** (1938) 507.
2) Gorter, C. J., Paramagnetic Relaxation, Elsevier (Amsterdam, 1947).
3) Bloch, F., Phys. Rev. **70** (1946) 460.
4) Shaposhnikov, Gr., Conférences à l'Université d'Alger (1972).
5) Raoult, G., Adamski, J., Cueille, J. P., Laval, C. et Roux, R., J. Phys. appl. **23** (1962) 47A (Champs homogènes).
6) Zverev, G. M., Prokhorov, A. M. et Schevchenko, A. K., Soviet Physics – Solid State **4** (1963) 2297.
7) Nisida, Y., J. Phys. Soc. Japan **20** (1965) 1390.
8) Larson, G. H. et Jeffries, C. D., Phys. Rev. **145** (1966) 311.
9) Raoult, G. et Duclaux, A. M., CR Acad. Sci. **263** (1966) 391.
10) Duclaux, A. M., Ann. Physique **3** (1968) 89.

11) Gavaix, A., Vasson, A. M., Vasson, A. et Raoult, G., Proc. XVIth Congress Ampère Ed. URSU Publ. Ac. Soc. Rep. Romania (1971) 611.
12) Lewiner, J., Maijer, P. H. E. et Wigmore, J. K., Phys. Rev. **185** (1969) 546.
13) Ganapol'skii, E. M., Soviet Physics – Solid State **12** (1971) 2095.
14) Raoult, G., Gavaix, A., Vasson, A. et Vasson, A. M., Phys. Rev. **B4** (1971) 3849.
15) Bates, Moore et Al-Sharbati, à paraître aux Phys. Rev. Letters.
16) Raoult, G., Gavaix, A., Vasson, A. et Vasson, A. M., J. Phys. C. (Solid State Phys.) **4** (1971) 3297.
17) Gavaix, A., Raoult, G., Vasson, A. et Vasson, A. M., Proc. XVIIth Congress Ampère, Turku (1972), ed. V. Hovi, North-Holland Publ. Comp. (Amsterdam).
18) Kacimi, X. et Shaposhnikov, I. G., Dep. Theoretical Physics University of Perm USSR Proc. (1972) XVIIth Congress Ampère, Turku (1972), North-Holland Publ. Comp. (Amsterdam).
19) Donoho, P. L., Phys. Rev. **133A** (1964) 1080.

Physica **69** (1973) 259–272 © *North-Holland Publishing Co.*

TIME CORRELATION FUNCTIONS IN THE a-CYCLIC *XY* MODEL. I

P. MAZUR and TH. J. SISKENS

Instituut-Lorentz, Rijksuniversiteit te Leiden, Leiden, Nederland

Received 22 June 1973

Synopsis

Explicit expressions for the time correlation functions of the z components of two spins and the time autocorrelation function of the z component of the magnetization are derived both for the c-cyclic and the c-anticyclic XY model.

1. *Introduction.* The time correlation functions of the z components of two spins and the time autocorrelation function of the z component of the magnetization have been derived previously by Niemeijer[1]) for the so-called c-cyclic anisotropic XY model. These correlation functions only represent correctly the corresponding correlation functions of the cyclic spin XY model (the so-called a-cyclic XY model[2])) in the limit of an infinite number of spins. The purpose of the present paper and a subsequent one is to calculate these correlation functions for the finite a-cyclic model with the aim of studying later the ergodic properties of this model, which is somewhat more physical than the finite c-cyclic model.

Since the hamiltonian of the a-cyclic problem has the property that it acts in a subspace of the space of states, as if it were the c-cyclic hamiltonian, and in the orthogonal complement of this subspace, as if it were the c-anticyclic hamiltonian, we shall first, in this paper, calculate the correlation functions for the c-cyclic and the c-anticyclic hamiltonian as if these were valid in the whole space of states. In a forthcoming paper we shall combine these results in order to obtain the correct expressions for the correlation functions for the a-cyclic problem.

The method used in this paper differs from Niemeijer's approach and does not require an explicit diagonalization of the hamiltonians and calculation of their eigenvectors. In section 2 we formulate the problem and give the form of the c-cyclic and the c-anticyclic hamiltonian. In section 3 we introduce hermitian operators α_i and β_i ($i = 1, \ldots, N$) which are linear combinations of the fermion creation and annihilation operators. In terms of these operators the dynamical problem is solved for both models. In section 4 we evaluate the z component of the magnetization and the internal energy for both models. The expressions for these quantities reduce to traces of functions of cyclic and anticyclic matrices. The cyclic/anticyclic nature of these matrices enables one to express these quantities in a simple way in terms of the parameters of the system. Finally, in section 5, we derive in a similar way explicit expressions for the various time correlation functions for the c-cyclic and the c-anticyclic model.

2. *Formulation.* We consider a linear chain of N spins $\frac{1}{2}$ subjected to an external magnetic field B along the z axis. The spins have nearest-neighbour interactions. The hamiltonian of the system (the so-called XY model) is

$$H = \sum_{j=1}^{N} [(1 + \gamma)S_j^x S_{j+1}^x + (1 - \gamma)S_j^y S_{j+1}^y - BS_j^z], \tag{1}$$

where periodic boundary conditions have been taken. Performing the transformation

$$S_j^x = (a_j^\dagger + a_j)/2, \quad S_j^y = (a_j^\dagger - a_j)/2\mathrm{i}, \quad S_j^z = a_j^\dagger a_j - \tfrac{1}{2} \quad (j = 1, \ldots, N), \tag{2}$$

and subsequently the transformation

$$\begin{aligned} a_j^\dagger &= \exp\left(\mathrm{i}\pi \sum_{k=1}^{j-1} c_k^\dagger c_k\right) c_j^\dagger \quad (j = 2, \ldots, N), \qquad a_1^\dagger = c_1^\dagger, \\ a_j &= \exp\left(-\,\mathrm{i}\pi \sum_{k=1}^{j-1} c_k^\dagger c_k\right) c_j \quad (j = 2, \ldots, N), \qquad a_1 = c_1, \end{aligned} \tag{3}$$

the hamiltonian becomes (*cf.* refs. 1, 2)

$$\begin{aligned} H = {} & \tfrac{1}{2}NB - B\sum_{j=1}^{N} c_j^\dagger c_j + \tfrac{1}{2}\sum_{j=1}^{N} [(c_j^\dagger c_{j+1} + \gamma c_j^\dagger c_{j+1}^\dagger) + \text{h.c.}] \\ & - \tfrac{1}{2}[(c_N^\dagger c_1 + \gamma c_N^\dagger c_1^\dagger) + \text{h.c.}] \left[\exp\left(\mathrm{i}\pi \sum_{j=1}^{N} c_j^\dagger c_j\right) + 1\right]. \end{aligned} \tag{4}$$

The c operators are fermion operators. Thus the operators $c_j^\dagger c_j$ ($j = 1, \cdots, N$) are occupation-number operators having eigenvalues 0 or 1. Therefore the operator P, defined as

$$P = \exp\left(\mathrm{i}\pi \sum_{j=1}^{N} c_j^\dagger c_j\right), \tag{5}$$

has eigenvalues -1 or $+1$, and can also be written as

$$P = \prod_{j=1}^{N} (1 - 2c_j^\dagger c_j). \tag{6}$$

It follows immediately that

$$P^2 = 1 \quad \text{(unit operator).} \tag{7}$$

Since P is hermitian, it is easily seen that the space of states can be decomposed into two orthogonal subspaces, one belonging to the eigenvalue $+1$ of P, and one belonging to the eigenvalue -1. It can furthermore be checked that H and P commute:

$$[H, P] = 0. \tag{8}$$

It follows that in the subspace belonging to the eigenvalue $+1$ of P, the hamiltonian can effectively be described by

$$H = H_{+1} = \tfrac{1}{2}NB - B\sum_{j=1}^{N} c_j^\dagger c_j + \tfrac{1}{2}\sum_{j=1}^{N-1} [(c_j^\dagger c_{j+1} + \gamma c_j^\dagger c_{j+1}^\dagger) + \text{h.c.}]$$
$$- \tfrac{1}{2}[(c_N^\dagger c_1 + \gamma c_N^\dagger c_1^\dagger) + \text{h.c.}]. \tag{9}$$

and in the subspace belonging to the eigenvalue -1 by

$$H = H_{-1} = \tfrac{1}{2}NB - B\sum_{j=1}^{N} c_j^\dagger c_j + \tfrac{1}{2}\sum_{j=1}^{N} [(c_j^\dagger c_{j+1} + \gamma c_j^\dagger c_{j+1}^\dagger) + \text{h.c.}]. \tag{10}$$

The problem corresponding with the hamiltonian (4) is the so-called a-cyclic problem (*cf.* ref. 2). If the hamiltonian (4) is replaced by the hamiltonian H_{-1} [eq. (10)] in the *whole* space of states, one is dealing with the so-called c-cyclic problem. However, when dealing with the a-cyclic problem one has to realize that H and H_{-1} are effectively identical only in a subspace of the space of states, *viz.* the one belonging to the eigenvalue -1 of P. If the hamiltonian (4) is replaced by H_{+1} [eq. (9)] in the *whole* space of states, one is dealing with, what we shall call, the c-anticyclic problem. The validity of H_{+1} for the a-cyclic problem is restricted to the subspace belonging to the eigenvalue $+1$ of P.

The purpose of this paper is to compute spin–spin correlation functions and the autocorrelation function of the magnetization for the models characterized by the hamiltonians H_{-1} and H_{+1}, respectively, as if these hamiltonians were valid in the whole space of states.

In a forthcoming paper we shall separate in the expressions thus obtained the contributions from the two subspaces belonging to the two different eigenvalues of P, and subsequently combine the relevant parts (for H_{+1} the part produced by the subspace belonging to the eigenvalue $+1$ of P, and for H_{-1} the part produced by the subspace belonging to the eigenvalue -1) in order to obtain the correlation functions for the a-cyclic model.

3. *Solution of the dynamical problem for the c-cyclic and the c-anticyclic hamiltonian.* The hamiltonians H_{+1} and H_{-1} [*cf.* eqs (9) and (10)] can be expressed as follows:

$$H_\sigma = \sum_{j,k=1}^{N} \{c_j^\dagger (\mathsf{A}_\sigma)_{jk} c_k + [c_j^\dagger (\mathsf{D}_\sigma)_{jk} c_k^\dagger + \text{h.c.}]\} + \tfrac{1}{2}NB \quad (\sigma = -1, +1), \tag{11}$$

where the $N \times N$ matrices A_σ $(\sigma = -1, +1)$ are symmetric and the $N \times N$ matrices D_σ $(\sigma = -1, +1)$ are antisymmetric. Furthermore A_{-1} and D_{-1} are cyclic, and A_{+1} and D_{+1} are anticyclic (*cf.* appendices A and B). The elements of the matrices A_σ and D_σ are given by

$$(\mathsf{A}_\sigma)_n = -B\delta_{n,0} + \tfrac{1}{2}(\delta_{n,1} + \delta_{n,-1} - \sigma\delta_{n,1-N} - \sigma\delta_{n,N-1}) \quad (\sigma = -1, +1) \tag{12}$$

and

$$(\mathsf{D}_\sigma)_n = \tfrac{1}{2}\gamma(\delta_{n,1} - \delta_{n,-1} - \sigma\delta_{n,1-N} + \sigma\delta_{n,N-1}) \quad (\sigma = -1, +1), \tag{13}$$

where n (which equals the difference of the indices) runs from $1-N$ to $N-1$ and where δ_{ij} denotes Kronecker delta. Now we introduce new operators α_j and β_j $(j = 1, \ldots, N)$, defined by

$$\alpha_j = \frac{1}{\sqrt{2}}(c_j + c_j^\dagger), \quad \beta_j = -\frac{\mathrm{i}}{\sqrt{2}}(c_j - c_j^\dagger) \qquad (j = 1, \ldots, N). \tag{14}$$

It is easily seen that the α and β operators are hermitian

$$\alpha_j^\dagger = \alpha_j, \quad \beta_j^\dagger = \beta_j \qquad (j = 1, \ldots, N), \tag{15}$$

and obey the following anticommutation rules

$$\{\alpha_i, \alpha_j\} = \{\beta_i, \beta_j\} = \delta_{ij}, \quad \{\alpha_i, \beta_j\} = 0 \qquad (i, j = 1, \ldots, N). \tag{16}$$

In terms of the α and β operators the hamiltonians (11) read

$$H_\sigma = \mathrm{i} \sum_{j,k=1}^{N} \alpha_j (\mathsf{S}_\sigma)_{jk} \beta_k \quad (\sigma = -1, +1), \tag{17}$$

where the matrices S_σ are defined by

$$\mathsf{S}_\sigma = \mathsf{A}_\sigma - \mathsf{D}_\sigma \quad (\sigma = -1, +1). \tag{18}$$

It is easily seen that S_{-1} is cyclic and S_{+1} is anticyclic. If $\tilde{\mathsf{S}}_\sigma$ is the transpose of S_σ $(\sigma = -1, +1)$, the hamiltonians can also be written as

$$H_\sigma = -\mathrm{i} \sum_{j,k=1}^{N} \beta_j (\tilde{\mathsf{S}}_\sigma)_{jk} \alpha_k \quad (\sigma = -1, +1). \tag{19}$$

The equations of motion of the α and β operators are

$$\dot{\alpha}_k = \mathrm{i}[H_\sigma, \alpha_k], \quad \dot{\beta}_k = \mathrm{i}[H_\sigma, \beta_k] \qquad (\sigma = -1, +1; k = 1, \ldots, N). \tag{20}$$

With (17) and using the anticommutation rules (16), we obtain

$$\dot{\alpha}_k = \sum_{l=1}^{N} (\mathsf{S}_\sigma)_{kl} \beta_l \quad (\sigma = -1, +1; k = 1, \ldots, N), \tag{21}$$

and in a similar way

$$\dot{\beta}_k = -\sum_{l=1}^{N} (\tilde{\mathsf{S}}_\sigma)_{kl} \alpha_l \quad (\sigma = -1, +1; k = 1, \ldots, N). \tag{22}$$

Introducing the matrices M_σ ($\sigma = -1, +1$) defined as

$$\mathsf{M}_\sigma = \mathsf{S}_\sigma \tilde{\mathsf{S}}_\sigma = \tilde{\mathsf{S}}_\sigma \mathsf{S}_\sigma = \mathsf{A}_\sigma^2 - \mathsf{D}_\sigma^2, \tag{23}$$

(the M_σ are symmetric; M_{-1} is cyclic and M_{+1} anticyclic), the solution of the equations of motion is given by

$$\alpha_j(t) = \sum_{k=1}^{N} [(\cos \mathsf{M}_\sigma^{\frac{1}{2}} t)_{jk} \alpha_k + (\mathsf{S}_\sigma \mathsf{M}_\sigma^{-\frac{1}{2}} \sin \mathsf{M}_\sigma^{\frac{1}{2}} t)_{jk} \beta_k] \qquad (\sigma = -1, +1; j = 1, \ldots, N), \tag{24}$$

$$\beta_j(t) = \sum_{k=1}^{N} [(\cos \mathsf{M}_\sigma^{\frac{1}{2}} t)_{jk} \beta_k - (\tilde{\mathsf{S}}_\sigma \mathsf{M}_\sigma^{-\frac{1}{2}} \sin \mathsf{M}_\sigma^{\frac{1}{2}} t)_{jk} \alpha_k] \qquad (\sigma = -1, +1; j = 1, \ldots, N). \tag{25}$$

The correlation functions to be computed in the following sections, will be expressed in terms of the elements of matrices which are functions of the matrices S_{-1}, $\tilde{\mathsf{S}}_{-1}$ and M_{-1}, and S_{+1}, $\tilde{\mathsf{S}}_{+1}$ and M_{+1} for the two models, respectively. These elements can, due to the cyclic/anticyclic nature of the matrices S_σ, S_σ and M_σ, easily be expressed in terms of the eigenvalues of these matrices. These eigenvalues can, in their turn, easily be expressed in terms of the elements of S_σ, $\tilde{\mathsf{S}}_\sigma$ and M_σ, *i.e.*, in terms of γ and B. Using the properties given in the appendices A and B it follows that the eigenvalues $\lambda_{\sigma,k}$ of $\mathsf{S}_{\sigma,k}$ are given by

$$\lambda_{\sigma,k} = (\cos \phi_{\sigma,k} - B) + \mathrm{i}\gamma \sin \phi_{\sigma,k} \quad (\sigma = -1, +1; k = 1, \ldots, N), \tag{26}$$

where

$$\phi_{-1,k} = k 2\pi/N \quad (k = 1, \ldots, N) \tag{27}$$

and

$$\phi_{+1,k} = (k - \tfrac{1}{2}) 2\pi/N \quad (k = 1, \ldots, N). \tag{28}$$

It follows immediately that the eigenvalues $\tilde{\lambda}_{\sigma,k}$ of $\tilde{S}_\sigma$ are given by

$$\tilde{\lambda}_{\sigma,k} = (\cos\phi_{\sigma,k} - B) - \mathrm{i}\gamma\sin\phi_{\sigma,k} = \lambda^*_{\sigma,k}$$
$$(\sigma = -1, +1;\ k = 1, \ldots, N), \quad (29)$$

and the eigenvalues $\Lambda^2_{\sigma,k}$ of M_σ by

$$\Lambda^2_{\sigma,k} = \lambda_{\sigma,k}\tilde{\lambda}_{\sigma,k} = (\cos\phi_{\sigma,k} - B)^2 + \gamma^2\sin^2\phi_{\sigma,k}$$
$$(\sigma = -1, +1;\ k = 1, \ldots, N). \quad (30)$$

4. *The z component of the magnetization and the internal energy*. The z component of the spin at site j reads in terms of the c operators

$$S^z_j = \tfrac{1}{2}(c^\dagger_j + c_j)(c_j - c^\dagger_j), \quad (31)$$

and in terms of the α and β operators

$$S^z_j = \mathrm{i}\alpha_j\beta_j. \quad (32)$$

The z component of the magnetization operator reads

$$M^z = \mathrm{i}\sum_{j=1}^{N}\alpha_j\beta_j. \quad (33)$$

The canonical average of M^z is thus given by

$$\langle\rho_\sigma M^z\rangle = \mathrm{i}\sum_{j=1}^{N}\langle\rho_\sigma\alpha_j\beta_j\rangle \quad (\sigma = -1, +1), \quad (34)$$

where $\langle\cdots\rangle$ stands for quantum-mechanical trace and where ρ_σ is defined as

$$\rho_\sigma = \exp(-\beta H_\sigma)/\langle\exp(-\beta H_\sigma)\rangle \quad (\sigma = -1, +1;\ \beta = 1/kT). \quad (35)$$

In appendix C it is shown that

$$\langle\rho_\sigma\alpha_j\beta_k\rangle = \tfrac{1}{2}\mathrm{i}(S_\sigma M_\sigma^{-\frac{1}{2}}\tanh\tfrac{1}{2}\beta M_\sigma^{\frac{1}{2}})_{jk} \quad (\sigma = -1, +1;\ j, k = 1, \ldots, N), \quad (36)$$

$$\langle\rho_\sigma\alpha_j\alpha_k\rangle = \langle\rho_\sigma\beta_j\beta_k\rangle = \tfrac{1}{2}\delta_{jk} \quad (\sigma = -1, +1;\ j, k = 1, \ldots, N). \quad (37)$$

For the z component of the magnetization we obtain

$$\begin{aligned}\langle\rho_\sigma M^z\rangle &= \mathrm{i}\sum_{j=1}^{N}\langle\rho_\sigma\alpha_j\beta_j\rangle = -\tfrac{1}{2}\,\mathrm{Tr}\,(S_\sigma M_\sigma^{-\frac{1}{2}}\tanh\tfrac{1}{2}\beta M_\sigma^{\frac{1}{2}})\\ &= -\tfrac{1}{4}\,\mathrm{Tr}\,[(S_\sigma + \tilde{S}_\sigma)M_\sigma^{-\frac{1}{2}}\tanh\tfrac{1}{2}\beta M_\sigma^{\frac{1}{2}}]\\ &= -\tfrac{1}{2}\sum_{p=1}^{N}\frac{(\cos\phi_{\sigma,p} - B)}{\Lambda_{\sigma,p}}\tanh\tfrac{1}{2}\beta\Lambda_{\sigma p} \quad (\sigma = -1, +1),\end{aligned} \quad (38)$$

where the sign of the $\Lambda_{\sigma,p}$ is arbitrary and chosen positive. In the thermodynamic limit we obtain for the magnetization per spin

$$\lim_{N\to\infty} \frac{1}{N} \langle \rho_\sigma M^z \rangle = -\frac{1}{4\pi} \int_0^{2\pi} \mathrm{d}\phi \frac{(\cos\phi - B)}{\Lambda(\phi)} \tanh \tfrac{1}{2}\beta\Lambda(\phi) \quad (\sigma = -1, +1) \tag{39}$$

where

$$\Lambda(\phi) = [(\cos\phi - B)^2 + \gamma^2 \sin^2\phi]^{\frac{1}{2}}. \tag{40}$$

Thus, in the thermodynamic limit the magnetization per spin is the same for the c-cyclic and the c-anticyclic case. For the internal energy E_σ we obtain

$$\begin{aligned} E_\sigma \equiv \langle \rho_\sigma H_\sigma \rangle &= \mathrm{i} \sum_{j,k=1}^{N} \langle \rho_\sigma \alpha_j (S_\sigma)_{jk} \beta_k \rangle = \mathrm{i} \sum_{j,k=1}^{N} (\tilde{S}_\sigma)_{kj} \langle \rho_\sigma \alpha_j \beta_k \rangle \\ &= -\tfrac{1}{2} \sum_{j,k=1}^{N} (\tilde{S}_\sigma)_{kj} (S_\sigma M_\sigma^{-\frac{1}{2}} \tanh \tfrac{1}{2}\beta M_\sigma^{\frac{1}{2}})_{jk} = -\tfrac{1}{2} \operatorname{Tr} (M_\sigma^{\frac{1}{2}} \tanh \tfrac{1}{2}\beta M_\sigma^{\frac{1}{2}}) \\ &= -\tfrac{1}{2} \sum_{p=1}^{N} \Lambda_{\sigma,p} \tanh \tfrac{1}{2}\beta\Lambda_{\sigma,p} \quad (\sigma = -1, +1). \end{aligned} \tag{41}$$

In the thermodynamic limit the internal energy per spin is given by

$$\lim_{N\to\infty} (E_\sigma/N) = -(1/4\pi) \int_0^{2\pi} \mathrm{d}\phi\, \Lambda(\phi) \tanh \tfrac{1}{2}\beta\Lambda(\phi), \tag{42}$$

both for the c-cyclic and the c-anticyclic model.

5. *The time-dependent correlation functions of the z components of two spins and the autocorrelation function of the z component of the magnetization.* For arbitrary j and k ($j, k = 1, \ldots, N$) the correlation function $\langle \rho_\sigma S_j^z S_k^z(t) \rangle$ can be written as [*cf.* (32)]

$$\langle \rho_\sigma S_j^z S_k^z(t) \rangle = -\langle \rho_\sigma \alpha_j \beta_j \alpha_k(t) \beta_k(t) \rangle \quad (\sigma = -1, +1). \tag{43}$$

With (24) and (25) we obtain

$$\begin{aligned} \langle \rho_\sigma S_j^z S_k^z(t) \rangle = -\sum_{l,m=1} &[(\cos M_\sigma^{\frac{1}{2}} t)_{kl} (\cos M_\sigma^{\frac{1}{2}} t)_{km} \langle \rho_\sigma \alpha_j \beta_j \alpha_l \beta_m \rangle \\ &- (\cos M_\sigma^{\frac{1}{2}} t)_{kl} (\tilde{S}_\sigma M_\sigma^{-\frac{1}{2}} \sin M_\sigma^{\frac{1}{2}} t)_{km} \langle \rho_\sigma \alpha_j \beta_j \alpha_l \alpha_m \rangle \\ &+ (S_\sigma M_\sigma^{-\frac{1}{2}} \sin M_\sigma^{\frac{1}{2}} t)_{kl} (\cos M_\sigma^{\frac{1}{2}} t)_{km} \langle \rho_\sigma \alpha_j \beta_j \beta_l \beta_m \rangle \\ &- (S_\sigma M_\sigma^{-\frac{1}{2}} \sin M_\sigma^{\frac{1}{2}} t)_{kl} (\tilde{S}_\sigma M_\sigma^{-\frac{1}{2}} \sin M_\sigma^{\frac{1}{2}} t)_{km} \langle \rho_\sigma \alpha_j \beta_j \beta_l \alpha_m \rangle]. \end{aligned} \tag{44}$$

In appendix D the elements of the tetradics $\mathbf{X}_\sigma^{(\varepsilon)}$, defined by

$$(\mathbf{X}_\sigma^{(1)})_{jklm} \equiv \langle \rho_\sigma \alpha_j \alpha_k \alpha_l \alpha_m \rangle, \qquad (\mathbf{X}_\sigma^{(2)})_{jklm} \equiv \langle \rho_\sigma \beta_j \alpha_k \alpha_l \alpha_m \rangle,$$
$$(\mathbf{X}_\sigma^{(3)})_{jklm} \equiv \langle \rho_\sigma \beta_j \alpha_k \alpha_l \beta_m \rangle, \qquad (\mathbf{X}_\sigma^{(4)})_{jklm} \equiv \langle \rho_\sigma \alpha_j \beta_k \beta_l \beta_m \rangle,$$
$$(\mathbf{X}_\sigma^{(5)})_{jklm} \equiv \langle \rho_\sigma \beta_j \beta_k \beta_l \beta_m \rangle, \qquad (\sigma = -1, +1; j, k, l, m = 1, \ldots, N), \tag{45}$$

are computed explicitly. In terms of the elements of the tetradics $\mathbf{X}_\sigma^{(\varepsilon)}$ the correlation function (44) reads

$$\begin{aligned}\langle \rho_\sigma S_j^z S_k^z(t) \rangle = \sum_{l,m=1}^{N} [&(\cos M_\sigma^{\frac{1}{2}} t)_{kl} (\cos M_\sigma^{\frac{1}{2}} t)_{km} (\mathbf{X}_\sigma^{(3)})_{jjlm} \\ &- (\cos M_\sigma^{\frac{1}{2}} t)_{kl} (\tilde{S}_\sigma M_\sigma^{-\frac{1}{2}} \sin M_\sigma^{\frac{1}{2}} t)_{km} (\mathbf{X}_\sigma^{(2)})_{jjlm} \\ &- (S_\sigma M_\sigma^{-\frac{1}{2}} \sin M_\sigma^{\frac{1}{2}} t)_{kl} (\cos M_\sigma^{\frac{1}{2}} t)_{km} (\mathbf{X}_\sigma^{(4)})_{jjlm} \\ &+ (S_\sigma M_\sigma^{-\frac{1}{2}} \sin M_\sigma^{\frac{1}{2}} t)_{kl} (\tilde{S}_\sigma M_\sigma^{-\frac{1}{2}} \sin M_\sigma t)_{km} (\mathbf{X}_\sigma^{(3)})_{jjml}],\end{aligned} \tag{46}$$

where use has been made of the anticommutation rules (16). Substituting the explicit expressions for the elements of $\mathbf{X}_\sigma^{(2)}$, $\mathbf{X}_\sigma^{(3)}$ and $\mathbf{X}_\sigma^{(4)}$ obtained in appendix D, into eq. (46), we obtain after performing the summations and appropriate rearrangements

$$\begin{aligned}\langle \rho_\sigma S_j^z S_k^z(t) \rangle = \langle \rho_\sigma S_j^z \rangle \langle \rho_\sigma S_k^z \rangle &+ \tfrac{1}{4} (\cos M_\sigma^{\frac{1}{2}} t + \mathrm{i} \tanh \tfrac{1}{2}\beta M_\sigma^{\frac{1}{2}} \sin M_\sigma^{\frac{1}{2}} t)_{kj}^2 \\ &- \tfrac{1}{4} [(\mathrm{i} \sin M_\sigma^{\frac{1}{2}} t + \tanh \tfrac{1}{2}\beta M_\sigma^{\frac{1}{2}} \cos M_\sigma^{\frac{1}{2}} t) \tfrac{1}{2}(S_\sigma + \tilde{S}_\sigma) M_\sigma^{-\frac{1}{2}}]_{kj}^2 \\ &+ \tfrac{1}{4} [(\mathrm{i} \sin M_\sigma^{\frac{1}{2}} t + \tanh \tfrac{1}{2}\beta M_\sigma^{\frac{1}{2}} \cos M_\sigma^{\frac{1}{2}} t) \tfrac{1}{2}(S_\sigma - \tilde{S}_\sigma) M_\sigma^{-\frac{1}{2}}]_{kj}^2 \\ &\qquad (\sigma = -1, +1).\end{aligned} \tag{47}$$

For the autocorrelation function $R_\sigma(t)$ of the z component of the magnetization we obtain

$$\begin{aligned}R_\sigma(t) &\equiv (1/N)(\langle \rho_\sigma M^z M^z(t) \rangle - \langle \rho_\sigma M^z \rangle^2) \\ &= \sum_{j,k=1}^{N} (\langle \rho_\sigma S_j^z S_k^z(t) \rangle - \langle \rho S_j^z \rangle \langle \rho S_k^z \rangle) \\ &= (1/4N) \operatorname{Tr} (\cos M_\sigma^{\frac{1}{2}} t + \mathrm{i} \tanh \tfrac{1}{2}\beta M_\sigma^{\frac{1}{2}} \sin M_\sigma^{\frac{1}{2}} t)^2 \\ &\quad - (1/4N) \operatorname{Tr} [(\mathrm{i} \sin M_\sigma^{\frac{1}{2}} t + \tanh \tfrac{1}{2}\beta M_\sigma^{\frac{1}{2}} \cos M_\sigma^{\frac{1}{2}} t)^2 \tfrac{1}{4}(S_\sigma + \tilde{S}_\sigma)^2 M_\sigma^{-1}] \\ &\quad - (1/4N) \operatorname{Tr} [(\mathrm{i} \sin M_\sigma^{\frac{1}{2}} t + \tanh \tfrac{1}{2}\beta M_\sigma^{\frac{1}{2}} \cos M_\sigma^{\frac{1}{2}} t)^2 \tfrac{1}{4}(S_\sigma - \tilde{S}_\sigma)^2 M_\sigma^{-1}] \\ &\qquad (\sigma = -1, +1).\end{aligned} \tag{48}$$

And after straightforward calculations we get

$$\begin{aligned}R_\sigma(t) = (1/4N) &\operatorname{Tr} [\tfrac{1}{4}(S_\sigma + \tilde{S}_\sigma)^2 M_\sigma^{-1} \cosh^{-2} \tfrac{1}{2}\beta M_\sigma^{\frac{1}{2}}] \\ &- (1/4N) \operatorname{Tr} [\tfrac{1}{4}(S_\sigma - \tilde{S}_\sigma)^2 M_\sigma^{-1} (1 + \tanh^2 \tfrac{1}{2}\beta M_\sigma^{\frac{1}{2}}) \cos 2M_\sigma^{\frac{1}{2}} t] \\ &- (\mathrm{i}/2N) \operatorname{Tr} [\tfrac{1}{4}(S_\sigma - \tilde{S}_\sigma)^2 M_\sigma^{-1} \tanh \tfrac{1}{2}\beta M_\sigma^{\frac{1}{2}} \sin 2M_\sigma^{\frac{1}{2}} t] \\ &\qquad (\sigma = -1, +1).\end{aligned} \tag{49}$$

In terms of the eigenvalues we obtain instead of (47)

$$\langle\rho_\sigma S_j^z S_k^z(t)\rangle = \langle\rho_\sigma S_j^z\rangle\langle\rho_\sigma S_k^z\rangle + \frac{1}{4}\left(\frac{1}{N}\sum_{p=1}^{N}[(\cos\Lambda_{\sigma,p}t + \mathrm{i}\tanh\tfrac{1}{2}\beta\Lambda_{\sigma,p}\sin\Lambda_{\sigma,p}t)\exp\mathrm{i}\,(j-k)\phi_{\sigma,p}]\right)^2$$
$$- \frac{1}{4}\left[\frac{1}{N}\sum_{p=1}^{N}\left((\mathrm{i}\sin\Lambda_{\sigma,p}t + \tanh\tfrac{1}{2}\beta\Lambda_{\sigma,p}\cos\Lambda_{\sigma,p}t)\times\frac{(\cos\phi_{\sigma,p} - B)}{\Lambda_{\sigma,p}}\exp\mathrm{i}(j-k)\phi_{\sigma,p}\right)\right]^2$$
$$- \frac{1}{4}\left[\frac{1}{N}\sum_{p=1}^{N}\left((\mathrm{i}\sin\Lambda_{\sigma,p}t + \tanh\tfrac{1}{2}\beta\Lambda_{\sigma,p}\cos\Lambda_{\sigma,p}t)\times\frac{\gamma\sin\phi_{\sigma,p}}{\Lambda_{\sigma,p}}\exp\mathrm{i}(j-k)\phi_{\sigma,p}\right)\right]^2 \quad (\sigma = -1, +1), \tag{50}$$

and instead of (49)

$$R_\sigma(t) = \frac{1}{4N}\sum_{p=1}^{N}\left(\frac{(\cos\phi_{\sigma,p} - B)^2}{\Lambda_{\sigma,p}^2}\cosh^{-2}\tfrac{1}{2}\beta\Lambda_{\sigma,p}\right) + \frac{1}{4N}\sum_{p=1}^{N}\left(\frac{\gamma^2\sin^2\phi_{\sigma,p}}{\Lambda_{\sigma,p}^2}(1 + \tanh^2\tfrac{1}{2}\beta\Lambda_{\sigma,p})\cos 2\Lambda_{\sigma,p}t\right)$$
$$+ \frac{\mathrm{i}}{2N}\sum_{p=1}^{N}\left(\frac{\gamma^2\sin^2\phi_{\sigma,p}}{\Lambda_{\sigma,p}^2}\tanh\tfrac{1}{2}\beta\Lambda_{\sigma,p}\sin 2\Lambda_{\sigma,p}t\right) \quad (\sigma = -1, +1). \tag{51}$$

The expression for the autocorrelation function of the z component of one arbitrary spin follows immediately from (50) by putting $j = k$. The last term on the r.h.s. of (50) then vanishes for reasons of symmetry.

In the thermodynamic limit we obtain the well-known expressions derived by Niemeijer[1]) for the c-cyclic case. It is clear that the results for the c-cyclic and the c-anticyclic case are the same in this limit.

6. *Final remark*. In a forthcoming paper we shall combine the relevant parts of the correlation functions for the c-cyclic and the c-anticyclic model in order to obtain the correlation functions for the a-cyclic model (*cf.* section 2). From the discussion in this paper it is already clear, that in the thermodynamic limit the results for the a-cyclic model will be equal to the results obtained in this paper for the c-cyclic and the c-anticyclic model.

Acknowledgment. The authors are grateful to Professor S. K. Kim for valuable discussions.

APPENDIX A

1. *Definition*. The $N \times N$ matrix A is called cyclic, if

$$A_{ij} = A_{j-i} \quad (i, j = 1, \ldots, N) \tag{A.1}$$

and

$$A_n = A_{n-N} \quad (n = 1, \ldots, N-1). \tag{A.2}$$

2. *Properties*. 1) If A is a cyclic $N \times N$ matrix, and U is a unitary $N \times N$ matrix, defined by

$$U_{jk} = (1/\sqrt{N}) \exp(-2\pi i jk/N) \quad (j, k = 1, \ldots, N), \tag{A.3}$$

we have

$$(\mathsf{U}^\dagger \mathsf{A} \mathsf{U})_{jk} = \lambda_k \delta_{jk} \quad (j, k = 1, \ldots, N), \tag{A.4}$$

with

$$\lambda_k = \sum_{n=0}^{N-1} A_n \exp(-2\pi i nk/N) \quad (k = 1, \ldots, N). \tag{A.5}$$

By inversion of (A.5) it follows that

2) $$A_n = (1/N) \sum_{k=1}^{N} \lambda_k \exp(2\pi i nk/N) \quad (n = 1 - N, \ldots, N-1). \tag{A.6}$$

3) If A and B are cyclic $N \times N$ matrices, AB is cyclic, and A and B commute.
4) If $\mathsf{A}, \mathsf{B}, \ldots$ are cyclic $N \times N$ matrices with eigenvalues $\lambda_k, \mu_k, \ldots$ $(k = 1, \ldots, N)$ respectively [*cf.* (A.5)], and if f is an analytic function, we have

$$[f(\mathsf{A}, \mathsf{B}, \ldots)]_n = (1/N) \sum_{k=1}^{N} f(\lambda_k, \mu_k, \ldots) \exp(2\pi i kn/N) \quad (n = 1 - N, \ldots, N-1). \tag{A.7}$$

APPENDIX B

1. *Definition*. The $N \times N$ matrix A is called anticyclic, if

$$A_{ij} = A_{j-i} \quad (i, j = 1, \cdots, N) \tag{B.1}$$

and

$$A_n = -A_{n-N} \quad (n = 1, \ldots, N-1). \tag{B.2}$$

2. *Properties*. 1) If A is an anticyclic $N \times N$ matrix, and U a unitary $N \times N$

matrix, defined as

$$U_{jk} = (1/\sqrt{N}) \exp[-2\pi i j(k - \tfrac{1}{2})/N] \quad (j, k = 1, \ldots, N), \tag{B.3}$$

we have

$$(U^{\dagger}AU)_{jk} = \lambda_k \delta_{jk} \quad (j, k = 1, \ldots, N), \tag{B.4}$$

with

$$\lambda_k = \sum_{n=0}^{N-1} A_n \exp[-2\pi i n(k - \tfrac{1}{2})/N] \quad (k = 1, \ldots, N). \tag{B.5}$$

From inversion of (B.5) it follows that

2) $$A_n = (1/N) \sum_{k=1}^{N} \lambda_k \exp[2\pi i n(k - \tfrac{1}{2})/N] \quad (n = 1 - N, \ldots, N - 1). \tag{B.6}$$

3) If A and B are anticyclic $N \times N$ matrices, AB is anticyclic and A and B commute.
4) If A, B, ... are anticyclic $N \times N$ matrices with eigenvalues $\lambda_k, \mu_k, \ldots$ ($k = 1, \ldots, N$), respectively [*cf.* (B.5)], and if f is an analytic function, we have

$$[f(\mathsf{A}, \mathsf{B}, \ldots)]_n = (1/N) \sum_{k=1}^{N} f(\lambda_k, \mu_k, \ldots) \exp[2\pi i n(k - \tfrac{1}{2})/N]$$
$$(n = 1 - N, \ldots, N - 1). \tag{B.7}$$

APPENDIX C

In this appendix we shall compute the elements of the matrices X, Y and Z, defined as

$$X_{jk} = \langle \rho \alpha_j \beta_k \rangle, \quad Y_{jk} = \langle \rho \alpha_j \alpha_k \rangle, \quad Z_{jk} = \langle \rho \beta_j \beta_k \rangle$$
$$(j, k = 1, \ldots, N). \tag{C.1}$$

(For simplicity of notation we omit the subscript σ.) It is easily seen, using the anticommution rules (16) and the invariance of traces under cyclic permutation, that

$$X_{jk} = \tfrac{1}{2}\langle [\rho, \alpha_j] \beta_k \rangle, \tag{C.2}$$

$$Y_{jk} = \tfrac{1}{2}\delta_{jk} + \tfrac{1}{2}\langle [\rho, \alpha_j] \alpha_k \rangle, \tag{C.3}$$

$$Z_{jk} = \tfrac{1}{2}\delta_{jk} + \tfrac{1}{2}\langle [\rho, \beta_j] \beta_k \rangle \quad (j, k = 1, \ldots, N). \tag{C.4}$$

Using the well-known equality

$$\langle [\rho, \alpha_j] \beta_k \rangle = i \int_0^{\beta} \langle \rho \dot{\alpha}_j(-i\lambda) \beta_k \rangle d\lambda, \tag{C.5}$$

we have, using (21) and (25),

$$
\begin{aligned}
X_{jk} &= \tfrac{1}{2}\mathrm{i} \int_0^{\beta} \langle \rho \dot{\alpha}_j(-\mathrm{i}\lambda)\beta_k \rangle \mathrm{d}\lambda = \tfrac{1}{2}\mathrm{i} \sum_{l=1}^{N} S_{jl} \int_0^{\beta} \langle \rho \beta_l(-\mathrm{i}\lambda)\beta_k \rangle \mathrm{d}\lambda \\
&= \tfrac{1}{2}\mathrm{i} \sum_{l,m=1}^{N} S_{jl} \int_0^{\beta} [\cos(-\mathrm{i}\lambda M^{\frac{1}{2}})]_{lm} \mathrm{d}\lambda \langle \rho \beta_m \beta_k \rangle \\
&\quad - \tfrac{1}{2}\mathrm{i} \sum_{l,m=1}^{N} S_{jl} \int_0^{\beta} [\tilde{S} M^{-\frac{1}{2}} \sin(-\mathrm{i}\lambda M^{\frac{1}{2}})]_{lm} \mathrm{d}\lambda \langle \rho \alpha_m \beta_k \rangle \\
&= \tfrac{1}{2}\mathrm{i} \sum_{l,m=1}^{N} S_{jl} \int_0^{\beta} [\cosh \lambda M^{\frac{1}{2}}]_{lm} \mathrm{d}\lambda\, Z_{mk} \\
&\quad - \tfrac{1}{2} \sum_{l,m=1}^{N} S_{jl} \int_0^{\beta} [\tilde{S} M^{-\frac{1}{2}} \sinh \lambda M^{\frac{1}{2}}]_{lm} \mathrm{d}\lambda\, X_{mk} \\
&= \tfrac{1}{2}\mathrm{i} \sum_{l,m=1}^{N} S_{jl} (M^{-\frac{1}{2}} \sinh \beta M^{\frac{1}{2}})_{lm} Z_{mk} \\
&\quad - \tfrac{1}{2} \sum_{l,m=1}^{N} S_{jl} [\tilde{S} M^{-1} (\cosh \beta M^{\frac{1}{2}} - U)]_{lm} X_{mk},
\end{aligned} \tag{C.6}
$$

where $U = N \times N$ unit matrix. In matrix notation we obtain

$$X = \tfrac{1}{2}\mathrm{i}(SM^{-\frac{1}{2}} \sinh \beta M^{\frac{1}{2}}) \cdot Z - \tfrac{1}{2}(\cosh \beta M^{\frac{1}{2}} - U) \cdot X. \tag{C.7}$$

In a similar way we find

$$Y = \tfrac{1}{2}U - \tfrac{1}{2}\mathrm{i}(SM^{-\frac{1}{2}} \sinh \beta M^{\frac{1}{2}}) \cdot \tilde{X} - \tfrac{1}{2}(\cosh \beta M^{\frac{1}{2}} - U) \cdot Y \tag{C.8}$$

and

$$Z = \tfrac{1}{2}U - \tfrac{1}{2}\mathrm{i}(\tilde{S}M^{-\frac{1}{2}} \sinh \beta M^{\frac{1}{2}}) \cdot X - \tfrac{1}{2}(\cosh \beta M^{\frac{1}{2}} - U) \cdot Z. \tag{C.9}$$

From (C.7) it follows that

$$X = \mathrm{i}[(\cosh \beta M^{\frac{1}{2}} + U)^{-1} SM^{-\frac{1}{2}} \sinh \beta M^{\frac{1}{2}}] \cdot Z. \tag{C.10}$$

Inserting (C.10) into (C.9) we obtain

$$Z = \tfrac{1}{2}\, U. \tag{C.11}$$

Substituting (C.11) into (C.10) we have

$$X = \tfrac{1}{2}\, \mathrm{i} SM^{-\frac{1}{2}} \tanh \tfrac{1}{2}\beta M^{\frac{1}{2}}; \tag{C.12}$$

and finally, by inserting (C.12) into (C.8), we find

$$Y = \tfrac{1}{2}\, U. \tag{C.13}$$

APPENDIX D

In this appendix we shall compute the elements of the tetradics $\mathbf{X}^{(1)}$, $\mathbf{X}^{(2)}$, $\mathbf{X}^{(3)}$, $\mathbf{X}^{(4)}$ and $\mathbf{X}^{(5)}$, defined as

$$X^{(1)}_{jklm} = \langle \rho\alpha_j \alpha_k \alpha_l \alpha_m \rangle, \quad X^{(2)}_{jklm} = \langle \rho\beta_j \alpha_k \alpha_l \alpha_m \rangle,$$
$$X^{(3)}_{jklm} = \langle \rho\beta_j \alpha_k \alpha_l \beta_m \rangle, \quad X^{(4)}_{jklm} = \langle \rho\alpha_j \beta_k \beta_l \beta_m \rangle,$$
$$X^{(5)}_{jklm} = \langle \rho\beta_j \beta_k \beta_l \beta_m \rangle, \quad (j, k, l, m = 1, \ldots, N). \tag{D.1}$$

(For simplicity of notation we omit the subscript σ.) Using the anticommutation rules (16), the invariance of traces under cyclic permutation, and furthermore using the results of appendix C, we have

$$X^{(1)}_{jklm} = \tfrac{1}{2}\langle [\rho, \alpha_j]\alpha_k \alpha_l \alpha_m \rangle + \tfrac{1}{4} I_{jklm}, \tag{D.2}$$

where the tetradic $\mathbf{I}$ is defined by

$$I_{jklm} = \delta_{jk}\delta_{lm} - \delta_{jl}\delta_{km} + \delta_{jm}\delta_{kl}, \tag{D.3}$$
$$X^{(2)}_{jklm} = \tfrac{1}{2}\langle [\rho, \beta_j]\alpha_k \alpha_l \alpha_m \rangle, \tag{D.4}$$
$$X^{(3)}_{jklm} = \tfrac{1}{2}\langle [\rho, \beta_j]\alpha_k \alpha_l \beta_m \rangle + \tfrac{1}{4}\delta_{jm}\delta_{kl}, \tag{D.5}$$
$$X^{(4)}_{jklm} = \tfrac{1}{2}\langle [\rho, \alpha_j]\beta_k \beta_l \beta_m \rangle, \tag{D.6}$$
$$X^{(5)}_{jklm} = \tfrac{1}{2}\langle [\rho, \beta_j]\beta_k \beta_l \beta_m \rangle + \tfrac{1}{4} I_{jklm} \quad (j, k, l, m = 1, \ldots, N). \tag{D.7}$$

Along the lines of appendix C it is easily found that

$$\mathbf{X}^{(1)} = \tfrac{1}{2}\mathrm{i}(SM^{-\frac{1}{2}} \sinh \beta M^{\frac{1}{2}}) \cdot \mathbf{X}^{(2)} - \tfrac{1}{2}(\cosh \beta M^{\frac{1}{2}} - U) \cdot \mathbf{X}^{(1)} + \tfrac{1}{4}\mathbf{I} \tag{D.8}$$

and

$$\mathbf{X}^{(2)} = -\tfrac{1}{2}\mathrm{i}(\tilde{S}M^{-\frac{1}{2}} \sinh \beta M^{\frac{1}{2}}) \cdot \mathbf{X}^{(1)} - \tfrac{1}{2}(\cosh \beta M^{\frac{1}{2}} - U) \cdot \mathbf{X}^{(2)}. \tag{D.9}$$

From (D.9) it follows that

$$\mathbf{X}^{(2)} = -\mathrm{i}(\tilde{S}M^{-\frac{1}{2}} \tanh \tfrac{1}{2}\beta M^{\frac{1}{2}}) \cdot \mathbf{X}^{(1)}. \tag{D.10}$$

Inserting (D.10) into (D.8) we obtain

$$\mathbf{X}^{(1)} = \tfrac{1}{4}\mathbf{I}, \tag{D.11}$$

and it follows immediately that

$$\mathbf{X}^{(2)} = -\tfrac{1}{4}\mathrm{i}(\tilde{S}M^{-\frac{1}{2}} \tanh \tfrac{1}{2}\beta M^{\frac{1}{2}}) \cdot \mathbf{I}. \tag{D.12}$$

In a similar way we have from (D.6) and (D.7)

$$\mathbf{X}^{(5)} = \tfrac{1}{4}\mathbf{I} \tag{D.13}$$

and

$$\mathbf{X}^{(4)} = \tfrac{1}{4}\mathrm{i}(SM^{-\frac{1}{2}} \tanh \tfrac{1}{2}\beta M^{\frac{1}{2}}) \cdot \mathbf{I}. \tag{D.14}$$

Along the lines of appendix C we have for $\mathbf{X}^{(3)}$:

$$\begin{aligned} X^{(3)}_{jklm} &= \tfrac{1}{4}\delta_{jm}\delta_{kl} - \tfrac{1}{2}\mathrm{i}\sum_{p=1}^{N}(\tilde{S}M^{-\frac{1}{2}} \sinh \beta M^{\frac{1}{2}})_{jp}\langle\rho\alpha_p\alpha_k\alpha_l\beta_m\rangle \\ &\quad - \tfrac{1}{2}\sum_{p=1}^{N}(\cosh \beta M^{\frac{1}{2}} - U)_{jp}\langle\rho\beta_p\alpha_k\alpha_l\beta_m\rangle \\ &= \tfrac{1}{4}\delta_{jm}\delta_{kl} + \tfrac{1}{2}\mathrm{i}\sum_{p=1}^{N}(\tilde{S}M^{-\frac{1}{2}} \sinh \beta M^{\frac{1}{2}})_{jp} X^{(2)}_{mpkl} \\ &\quad - \tfrac{1}{2}\sum_{p=1}^{N}(\cosh \beta M^{\frac{1}{2}} - U)_{jp} X^{(3)}_{pklm}. \end{aligned} \tag{D.15}$$

It is easily seen that

$$\tfrac{1}{2}\sum_{p=1}^{N}(\cosh \beta M^{\frac{1}{2}} + U)_{jp} X^{(3)}_{pklm} = \tfrac{1}{4}\delta_{jm}\delta_{kl} + \tfrac{1}{2}\mathrm{i}\sum_{p=1}^{N}(\tilde{S}M^{-\frac{1}{2}} \sinh \beta M^{\frac{1}{2}})_{jp} X^{(2)}_{mpkl} \tag{D.16}$$

or,

$$\begin{aligned} &\sum_{p=1}^{N}(\cosh^2 \tfrac{1}{2}\beta M^{\frac{1}{2}})_{jp} X^{(3)}_{pklm} \\ &\quad = \tfrac{1}{4}\delta_{jm}\delta_{kl} + \mathrm{i}\sum_{p=1}^{N}(\tilde{S}M^{-\frac{1}{2}} \sinh \tfrac{1}{2}\beta M^{\frac{1}{2}} \cosh \tfrac{1}{2}\beta M^{\frac{1}{2}})_{jp} X^{(2)}_{mpkl}. \end{aligned} \tag{D.17}$$

And finally we obtain

$$\begin{aligned} X^{(3)}_{nklm} &= \tfrac{1}{4}\sum_{j=1}^{N}(\cosh^{-2} \tfrac{1}{2}\beta M^{\frac{1}{2}})_{nj}\delta_{jm}\delta_{kl} \\ &\quad + \mathrm{i}\sum_{j,\,p=1}^{N}(\cosh^{-2} \tfrac{1}{2}\beta M^{\frac{1}{2}})_{nj}(\tilde{S}M^{-\frac{1}{2}} \sinh \tfrac{1}{2}\beta M^{\frac{1}{2}} \cosh \tfrac{1}{2}\beta M)_{jp} X^{(2)}_{mpkl} \\ &= \tfrac{1}{4}(\cosh^{-2} \tfrac{1}{2}\beta M^{\frac{1}{2}})_{nm}\delta_{kl} + \mathrm{i}\sum_{p=1}^{N}(\tilde{S}M^{-\frac{1}{2}} \tanh \tfrac{1}{2}\beta M^{\frac{1}{2}})_{np} X^{(2)}_{mpkl} \\ &= \tfrac{1}{4}(\cosh^{-2} \tfrac{1}{2}\beta M^{\frac{1}{2}})_{nm}\delta_{kl} \\ &\quad + \tfrac{1}{4}\sum_{p,\,q=1}^{N}(\tilde{S}M^{-\frac{1}{2}} \tanh \tfrac{1}{2}\beta M^{\frac{1}{2}})_{np}(\tilde{S}M^{-\frac{1}{2}} \tanh \tfrac{1}{2}\beta M^{\frac{1}{2}})_{mq} I_{qpkl} \\ &\qquad (n, k, l, m = 1, \ldots, N). \end{aligned} \tag{D.18}$$

REFERENCES

1) Niemeijer, Th., Physica **36** (1967) 377.
2) Lieb, E., Schultz, T. and Mattis, D., Ann. Physics **16** (1961) 407.

Physica **69** (1973) 273–285 © *North-Holland Publishing Co.*

NOTES ON PARAMAGNETIC RELAXATION IN COBALTOUS SALTS

T. HASEDA, K. AMAYA, N. YAMASHITA and S. IKEDA

Department of Material Physics, Faculty of Engineering Science, Osaka University, Toyonaka, Osaka, Japan

and

Y. TOKUNAGA

Department of Physics, Faculty of Science, Kyoto University, Kyoto, Japan

Received 22 May 1973

Synopsis

Spin–lattice relaxation of Co^{2+} and cross-relaxation among Co^{2+} and Ni^{2+} in some cobaltous salts are studied in detail by a.c. susceptibility measurements at the liquid-^{4}He temperature. The anomaly of the spin–lattice relaxation of Co^{2+} in (Co, Zn)$(NH_4)_2(SO_4)_2 6H_2O$ is attributed to a very small amount of Ni^{2+} contained in the sample. In the mixed crystal of (Co, Ni, Zn) $(NH_4)_2(SO_4)_2 6H_2O$, various cross-relaxation processes are found, which have a definite effect on the spin–lattice relaxation of Co^{2+}. In some cases Ni^{2+} spins are found in partial thermal equilibrium with Co^{2+} spins by the cross-relaxation. The spin–lattice relaxation time of Co^{2+} at high fields ($H \gtrsim 10$ kOe), where cross-relaxation does not take place, is, in all the cobaltous salts observed, both size- and concentration-dependent; it has a weaker field dependence than predicted by theory.

1. *Introduction.* In our previous papers[1,2]), we studied cross-relaxation (CR) phenomena among unlike spins, such as Co^{2+} and Ni^{2+} in their mixed crystals. A qualitative explanation for the anomalous magnetic-field dependence of the spin–lattice relaxation (SLR) in cobalt ammonium tutton salt (Co–ATS), which was observed by Haseda and Kanda[3]), and Van den Broek *et al.*[4]), was briefly presented there from the viewpoint of Co^{2+}–Ni^{2+} CR.

Wharmby and Gill[5]) studied the magnetic-field dependence of the SLR time of diluted Co–ATS by resonance experiments and concluded the anomaly to be due to a Ni^{2+} impurity in the salt. In contrast with the resonant type, the present non-resonant type of experiment enables us to investigate CR and SLR in a wide range of magnetic fields and concentrations.

In section 2 of this paper, we report in detail the cross-relaxation phenomena in concentrated and diluted (Co, Ni)–ATS through a.c. susceptibility measurements.

CR including up to a 5-spin process of Co^{2+}–Ni^{2+} and a 2-spin process of Ni^{2+}–Ni^{2+} is observed in magnetic fields up to 10 kOe. The SLR time becomes short at some special values of the magnetic field where a CR process takes place[6]). The adiabatic susceptibility of the mixed crystal is found to be characterized with a large effective internal field, which is well explained by the existence of Ni^{2+} with large crystal-field splittings in the salt.

In section 3, SLR of Co^{2+} is studied in a wide range of external fields including some other cobaltous salts such as Co–acetate, Co–silicofluoride, and Co–Cs tutton salt. The anomalies of relaxation in low magnetic fields, which are attributed to a Co^{2+}–Ni^{2+} CR effect, are found to be common in all the salts observed. At high magnetic fields, above 6 kOe, Co^{2+}–Ni^{2+} CR processes are not expected to take place on the basis of the level splittings of both ions. Relaxation times become short with increasing field strength. Agreement with theoretical prediction for the direct process SLR[7, 8]) is not so satisfactory, but it is found that they depend on crystal size and concentration suggesting the importance of the phonon-bottleneck effect[9]).

2. *Cross relaxation in (Co, Ni, Zn)–ATS.* 2.1. Samples. Measurements are performed on single crystals of the following three mixed samples.

$Co_{0.87}Ni_{0.13}(NH_4)_2(SO_4)_2 6H_2O$ (sample A)

$Co_{0.39}Ni_{0.09}Zn_{0.52}(NH_4)_2(SO_4)_2 6H_2O$ (sample B)

$Co_{0.089}Ni_{0.0025}Zn_{0.908}(NH_4)_2(SO_4)_2 6H_2O$ (sample C)

Ni^{2+} in Ni–ATS is described by the following spin hamiltonian[10]):

$$\mathscr{H} = -DS_z^2 - E(S_x^2 - S_y^2) + g\mu_B \boldsymbol{H} \cdot \boldsymbol{S}, \quad S = 1, \tag{1}$$

where $D = 1.99\ \text{cm}^{-1}$, $E = 0.486\ \text{cm}^{-1}$ and $g = 2.25$.

The ground state of Co^{2+} in Co–ATS is a simple Kramers doublet ($S' = \frac{1}{2}$) with splitting factors given by[11])

$$g_{K_1} = 5.70, \quad g_{K_2} = 3.06 \quad \text{and} \quad g_{K_3} = 4.36, \tag{2}$$

where K_1, K_2 and K_3 denote the susceptibility principal axes.

The ion axis (z) in expression (1) has almost the same direction as the principal K_1 axis in pure Ni–ATS. The angles between K_1 and the crystallographic c axis are $\psi = -43°$ for Co^{2+} salt[4]) and $\psi = -14°$ for the Ni^{2+} salt[10]), respectively. In most of the experiments, the external field H was applied parallel to the K_1 direction of Co^{2+}($H // K_1^{Co}$). $g_{K_1} = 5.70$ for Co^{2+} was assumed in the mixed crystals throughout.

As for the Ni^{2+} ion, the ion axis (z) is assumed 29° away from H. Previous experiments on Ni–ATS[1,10]) have shown that expression (1) and the approximation of $z \approx K_1$ hold well at the liquid ^{4}He temperature both in the concentrated and the diluted salt. The numerical computation was made using (1) and (2). The results are illustrated as a function of magnetic field in fig. 1.

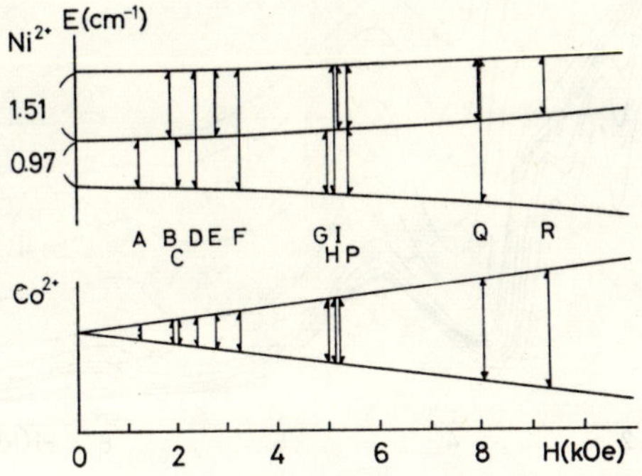

Fig. 1. Energy-level splittings of Ni^{2+} and Co^{2+} in (Co, Ni)–ATS, $H//K_1^{Co}$. Arrows show CR determined according to experimental results.

CR will be expected to take place at special field values (H_{cr}) where the level separations of Co^{2+} and Ni^{2+} are in integer ratio to each other as are shown in fig. 1. The H_{cr} thus obtained are compared with the experimental results in table 1. The numbers of Co^{2+} ions and Ni^{2+} ions which participate in several processes are also listed in the table. The agreement between the calculated H_{cr} values and the experimental ones is rather reasonable.

TABLE I

Calculated and observed values of the magnetic field for CR processes A–R. In CR A–I the number of Co^{2+} spins for a single Ni^{2+} spin is given

CR process	Number of Co spins	$H_{calc.}$ (kOe)	$H_{obs.}$ (kOe)
A	3	1.25	1.42
B	3	1.86	1.85
C	2	1.94	
D	4	2.38	2.47
E	2	2.74	2.70
F	3	3.23	3.09
G	1	4.96	
H	2	5.10	5.06
I	1	5.16	
P	Ni2	5.34	
Q	Co2Ni2	8.03	8.10
R	Co1Ni2	9.30	8.90

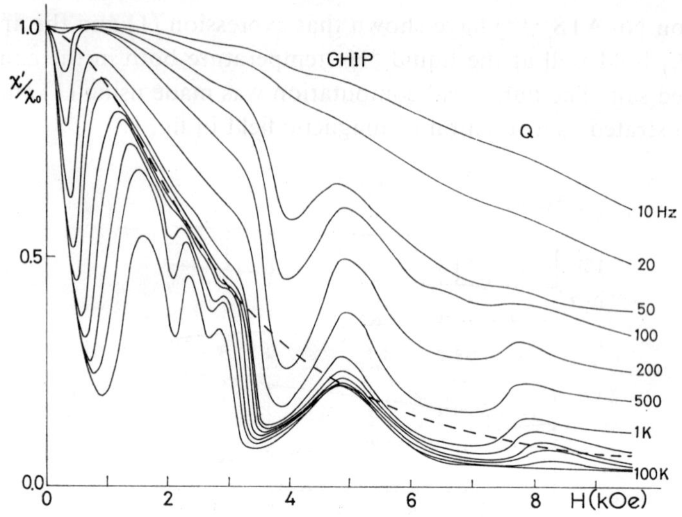

Fig. 2. χ' *vs.* H curves for sample A, $H//K_1^{\mathrm{Co}}$, $T = 4.2$ K. The dotted line gives the calculated adiabatic susceptibility, χ_S.

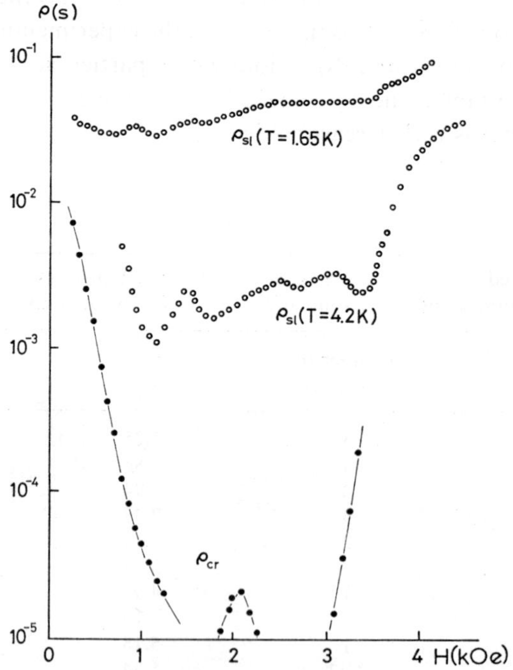

Fig. 3. Magnetic-field dependence of relaxation times ρ at $T = 1.65$ K and $T = 4.2$ K for sample A, $H//K_1^{\mathrm{Co}}$. CR time ρ_{cr} is temperature independent.

2.2. Experimental results. 2.2.1. Sample A: $Co_{0.87}Ni_{0.13}$–ATS. The dispersion signal $\chi'(\nu)$ *versus* H curves of sample A at $T = 4.2$ K are shown in fig. 2.

In the curve measured at high frequency ($\nu \geqq 10^4$Hz), the maxima observed at several values of the magnetic field are identified as due to CR's among Co^{2+} and Ni^{2+} or Ni^{2+} and Ni^{2+}. Referring to table 1, we interpreted these maxima as those involving concecutively two or three CR processes. That at $H \approx 8$ kOe can be attributed to process Q. In the frequency range of 10^3 Hz $\geqq \nu \geqq 10^4$ Hz, the susceptibility maxima overlap each other at magnetic fields from 1 kOe to 3 kOe forming a smooth slope there. This observed slope (corresponding to a stationary plateau in the $\chi'(H)$ *versus* ν curve as in fig. 5) are found to agree well with the adiabatic susceptibility (χ_S) calculated for the present two-spin system. Our calculation of χ_S is based on the assumption that the total entropy of the two-spin system is invariant, which is expressed as follows,

$$\chi_S = \chi_T - \left(\frac{\partial M}{\partial T}\right)_H^2 \bigg/ \left(\frac{\partial S}{\partial T}\right)_H , \tag{3}$$

where

$$\left(\frac{\partial M}{\partial T}\right)_H = \sum_{i=1,2} N_i \left(\frac{\partial M_i}{\partial T}\right)_H , \quad \left(\frac{\partial S}{\partial T}\right)_H = \sum_{i=1,2} N_i \left(\frac{\partial S_i}{\partial T}\right)_H . \tag{4}$$

χ_T, M and S are the isothermal susceptibility, magnetization, and entropy, respectively. The indices 1 and 2 in expression (4) denote Co^{2+} and Ni^{2+}, respectively. The results are shown in fig. 2 with a dotted line which is in good agreement with experiment. A qualitative explanation of the effect of Ni^{2+} ions on χ_S is that the large specific heat of the Ni^{2+} spin system through D and E terms of the crystalline field induces a large effective internal field $H_i((b/C)^{\frac{1}{2}})$ in the (Co, Ni) mixed system. Rough estimation of expression (3) gives

$$H_i \propto (1/g_{K_1}\mu_B)[(N_2/N_1)(D^2 + 3E^2)]^{\frac{1}{2}}. \tag{5}$$

The experimentally determined values are $H_i = 2.5$ kOe and 1.9 kOe at $T = 4.2$ K and $T = 1.65$ K, respectively. The CR times obtained were temperature independent down to 1.6 K. At frequencies lower than 10^3 Hz, we could determine the SLR time from the dispersion curve of χ'. The magnetic field dependence of the relaxation times are plotted in fig. 3.

2.2.2. Sample B: $Co_{0.39}Ni_{0.09}Zn_{0.52}$–ATS. CR processes and the effect of Ni^{2+} ions on SLR are made much clearer with magnetic dilution by 52 % of non-magnetic Zn^{2+} ions. The dispersion signals are shown in fig. 4.

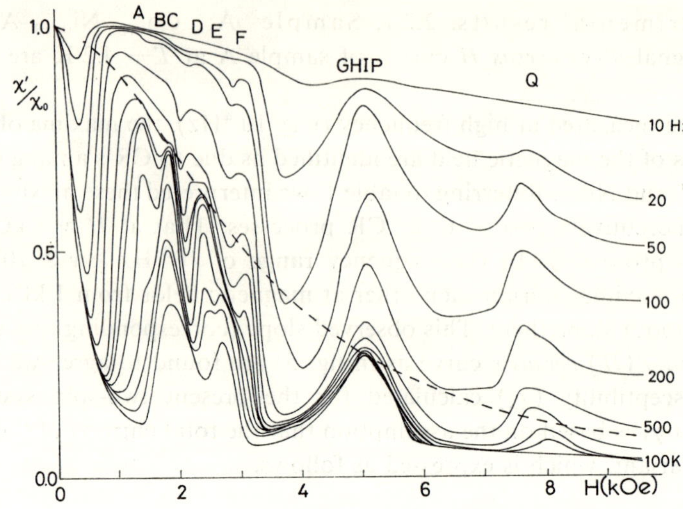

Fig. 4. χ' *vs.* H curves for sample B, $H//K_1^{\mathrm{Co}}$, $T = 4.2$ K. The dotted line shows the calculated adiabatic susceptibility, χ_S.

The dotted line shows χ_S calculated as above and H_i gives 2.9 kOe at $T = 4.2$ K. We notice that another new stationary point does exist on the $\chi'(H)$ *versus* ν curve for CR process E, suggesting a partial equilibrium[12]) between the Co^{2+} ion levels and only the two upper levels of the Ni^{2+} ions. We can calculate the adiabatic susceptibility (χ'_S) in such a case as well as χ_S, excepting the contribution of the lowest level of Ni^{2+} in expressions (3) and (4). Fig. 5 shows dispersion curves

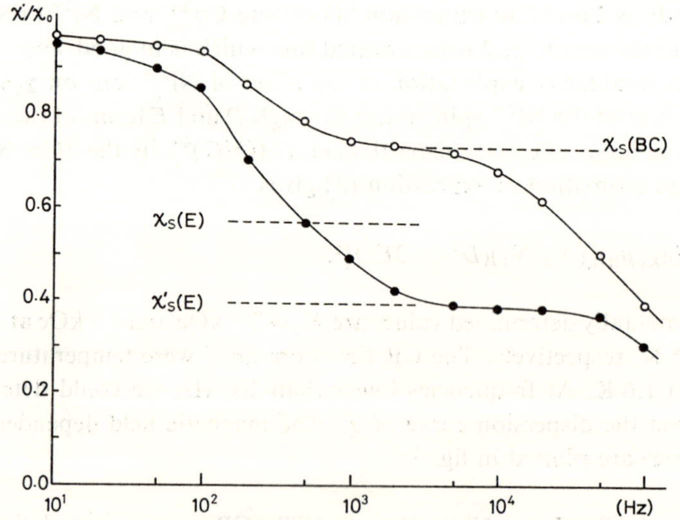

Fig. 5. χ' *vs.* ν curves at H_{cr}(BC) and H_{cr}(E) for sample B, $H//K_1^{\mathrm{Co}}$, $T = 4.2$ K. χ_S(BC) and χ_S(E) show the adiabatic susceptibility at H_{cr}(BC) and H_{cr}(E). χ'_S(E) is the susceptibility in partial equilibrium.

plotted against ν, at a fixed magnetic field of H_{cr}(E) and H_{cr}(BC) where CR processes E and BC are observed.

Apparently, spin thermal equilibrium at $H = H_{cr}$(E) is expressed by χ'_S, and by χ_S at $H = H_{cr}$(BC). The relaxation times are given in fig. 6. Shortening of the SLR time due to the existence of CR processes is observed to spread over the field strength from 1.5 kOe to 3.5 kOe and there are some CR processes (*e.g.*, E) for which the shortening does not appear distinctly. The effect of CR on SLR becomes obscure with decreasing temperature[13]). The CR time is also temperature independent as in case 2.2.1.

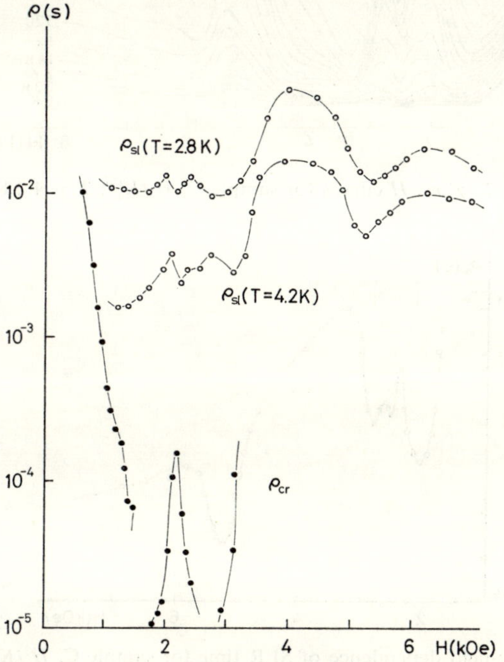

Fig. 6. Magnetic-field dependence of relaxation times ρ at $T = 2.8$ K and $T = 4.2$ K for sample B, $H//K_1^{Co}$. The CR time ρ_{cr} is temperature independent.

2.2.3. Sample C: $Co_{0.089}Ni_{0.0025}Zn_{0.908}$–ATS. We can see in the diluted cobaltous salt how the Ni^{2+} ions are effective in the relaxation phenomena. In fig. 7, the dispersion signal of this diluted crystal, in which the Ni^{2+} to Co^{2+} ratio is 0.028, is shown.

Shortening of SLR due to a CR mechanism is much more distinctly observed. Where there is no fast CR process, SLR is found to be very slow. Fig. 8 shows that the SLR time has a sharp minimum at $H = 2.07$, 2.55 and 2.85 kOe. Around 5.4 kOe, three CR processes overlap each other and a somewhat broad minimum is observed. Each minimum of the relaxation time is temperature dependent and

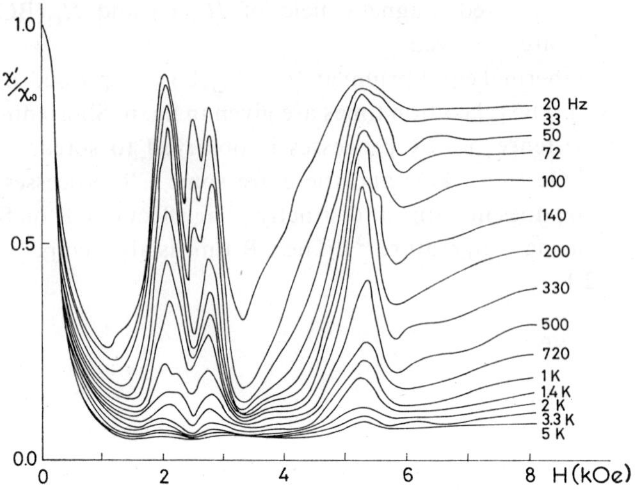

Fig. 7. χ' *vs.* H curves for sample C, $H//K_1^{\mathrm{Co}}$, $T = 4.2$ K.

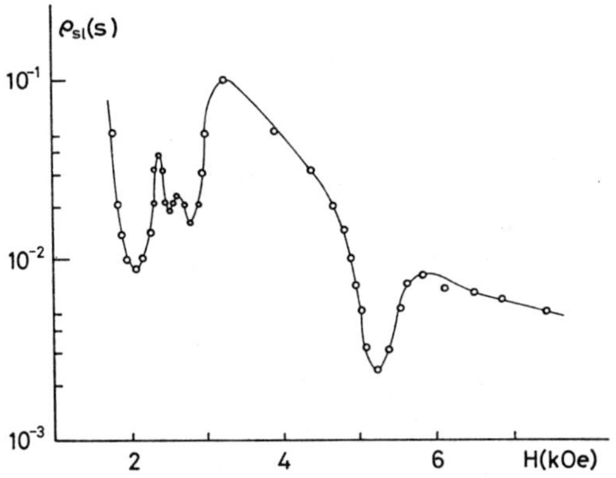

Fig. 8. Magnetic-field dependence of SLR time for sample C, $H//K_1^{\mathrm{Co}}$, $T = 4.2$ K.

nearly proportional to T^{-1}. Apart from the shortening due to CR, we recognize that the SLR time of Co^{2+} becomes rapidly short with an increasing magnetic field above 3 kOe. At magnetic fields higher than 6 kOe, the SLR time is short enough so as to compete or overcome the shortest CR, even if it has to be taken into account.

2.3. Discussion. In the concentrated sample A, adiabatic susceptibility is accounted for by the response of the magnetization, assuming the total entropy in the mixed spin system to be invariant. In the diluted sample B, however, the spin thermal equilibrium is found to be attained partially at a certain magnetic field. This partial equilibrium state is expected to be realized in general by the CR process in the 2-spin system, when either spin has multiple spin levels. The most diluted sample C shows no apparent stationary point in the dispersion curve. The observed relaxation time is attributed to that of SLR which shows several distinct minima corresponding to the Co^{2+} –Ni^{2+}CR processes. Shortening of SLR due to the existence of the rapid CR process is easily explained if we assume that the SLR of Ni^{2+} is relatively short[13]). Thus, the so-called anomaly of Co–ATS is well explained by the Ni^{2+} impurities in the salt. Detailed study of the magnetic-field dependence of SLR of Ni^{2+} in Ni–ATS has not yet been completed but concentrated and diluted Ni–Tl tutton salt has been found to show rapid SLR at low field strength and to become rather slow with increasing field strengths at liquid ^{4}He temperature[13]).

Concerning the anisotropy of the SLR anomaly of Co–ATS, not much is known besides some detailed work at Leiden[4]). The fact that the characteristic field value was proportional to the inverse g value may nicely be explained if the level splitting of the Ni^{2+} impurity is effectively constant at weak fields because of the large D and E.

3. *Relaxation phenomena in cobaltous salts.* 3.1. Relaxations in some other cobaltous salts. Although the anomalous SLR behaviour in Co–ATS below 6 kOe has now been explained by a CR process with Ni^{2+}, the field dependence of intrinsic SLR of Co^{2+} still remains in some ambiguous situation. We studied relaxations in some other cobaltous salts to find some of the characteristic and common patterns of behaviour.

The first salt we investigated is Co-acetate[14]), in which the crystalline-field parameters of Ni^{2+} are large enough[15]) and in which there are no rapid CR processes below 5 kOe. The result gives the expected 3-spin and 2-spin CR process in Co^{2+} and Ni^{2+} around 5.5 kOe and 12 kOe, respectively *. The field dependences of SLR are $\rho \propto H^{-1}$ in a single crystal and $\rho \propto H^{-2}$ in a powdered sample at a field range of 2 kOe $\leqq H \leqq$ 20 kOe. The field dependence of SLR found in this salt shows a size effect even at low field ($H <$ 5 kOe) where Ni^{2+} is no more effective as a rapid relaxing impurity, so long as it is taken into account through a CR process. This size effect is considered to be the phonon bottleneck effect mentioned earlier. It is noteworthy that the Gorter anomaly is not found down to $H \approx$ 2 kOe in this salt.

In other cobaltous salts, such as single crystals of Co–CsTS[16]) and Co-silicofluoride[17]), rapid CR processes of Co^{2+}–Ni^{2+} are found at 5 kOe ($H // K_1^{Co}$) and 1.2 kOe ($H // c$), respectively. CR effects due to a Ni^{2+} impurity in the concentrated crystals, including the above rapid process, were not avoidable at low fields. The SLR time, for example in Co-silicofluoride, is also size dependent,

* A two-spin CR process in Ni^{2+} ions in a Ni-acetate single crystal has been observed at $H \approx$ 10 kOe.

giving $\rho \propto H^{-1}$ for powdered samples and a weaker field dependence for the single crystal.

3.2. Spin–lattice relaxation of (Co, Zn)–ATS in strong fields. The experiments were performed on the following concentrated and diluted samples. (i) 5 % Co–ATS: relative concentrations of Co, Ni, and Zn in the sample are 4.215, 0.029 and 95.76 in per cent, respectively. We denote hereafter the ratio as (4.215, 0.029, 95.76). (ii) 10 % Co–ATS: (10.56, 0.04, 89.4). (iii) 50 % Co–ATS: (52.5, 0.069, 47.5). (iv) 100 % Co–ATS: (99.7, 0.2, 0.04). Single crystals are shaped cylindrically and powdered samples have a grain size of the order of 0.01 mm diameter. To find the characteristic and common behaviour of relaxation of Co^{2+} in the strong-field region, we assume that the relaxation time ρ is written in the following form,

$$\rho^{-1} \propto c^{\alpha} H^{\beta} T^{\gamma}, \tag{6}$$

where c is the concentration of Co^{2+} ions.

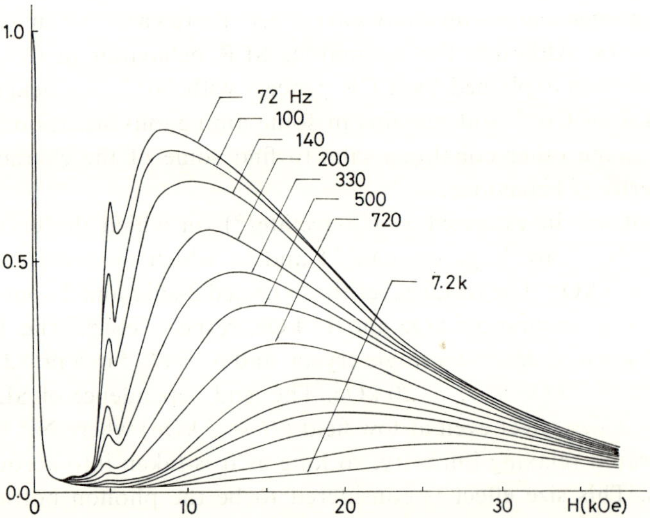

Fig. 9. χ' *vs.* H curves for 5 % Co–ATS, $H // K_1^{Co}$, $T = 4.2$ K.

Fig. 9 shows the dispersion signal of a single crystal of 5 % Co–ATS. Apparently, in 5 % Co–ATS, the SLR time decreases with increasing field and no effect of CR on SLR is observed above 6 kOe. The magnetic-field dependences of SLR are plotted in fig. 10a for single crystals and in fig. 10b for powdered samples. As shown in fig. 10a, in the case of single crystals, β increases with dilution from $\beta \approx 1$ to $\beta \approx 2$. The same tendency holds also in powdered samples showing $\beta \approx 2$ (100 %) and $\beta = 3$ (10 %). The size effect is thus clearly demonstrated. The concentration

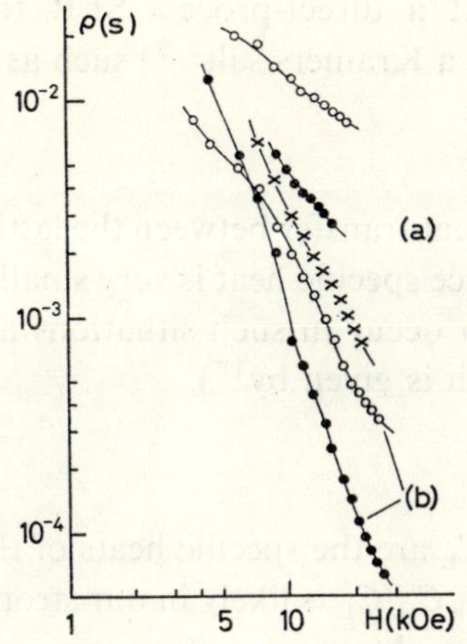

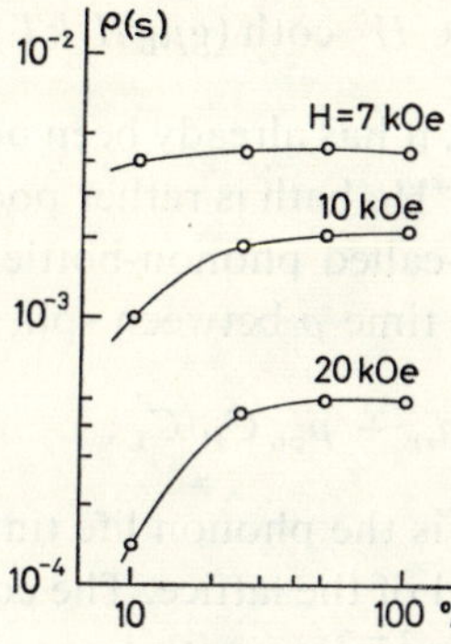

Fig. 10. Magnetic-field dependence of relaxation time ρ, $T = 4.2$ K. (a) single crystals of 5 % (×), 10 % (●), and 50 % (○) Co–ATS, $H // K_1^{\mathrm{Co}}$. (b) powdered samples of 10 % (●), and 100 % (○) Co–ATS.

Fig. 11. Concentration dependence of relaxation time ρ for powdered Co–ATS, $T = 4.2$ K.

dependence of ρ is given in fig. 11 in the case of a powdered sample. ρ is weakly c dependent at weak fields, but the c dependence becomes strong at high fields and at lower concentrations. In the case of a single crystal, ρ is roughly proportional to $c^{0.5}$. This is consistent with the prediction of the phonon-bottleneck theory in the case of a direct process.

The temperature dependence of ρ at a fixed magnetic field is also observed in the powdered samples and plotted in figs. 12a and b. The theory predicts $\rho^{-1} \propto T^1$ ($\gamma = 1$) in the case of a direct-process SLR. The results show that $\gamma \approx 1$ at low field strengths and slightly increases towards higher fields in the case of 10 % as well as a 100 % Co–ATS powdered sample.

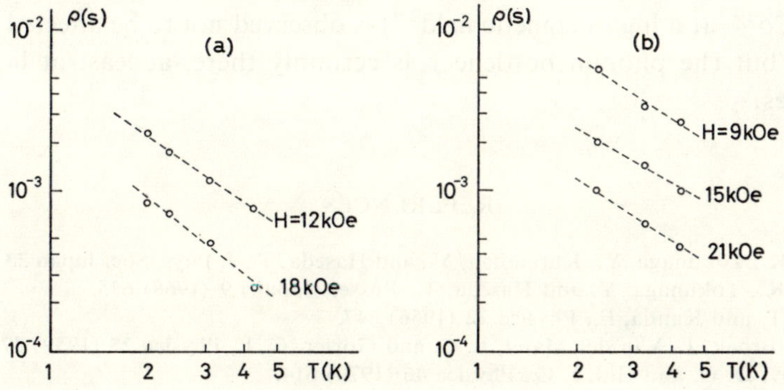

Fig. 12. Temperature dependence of relaxation time ρ for powdered samples. (a) 10 % Co–ATS. (b) 100 % Co–ATS.

3.3. Discussion. The theory predicts that a direct-process SLR time ρ_{sl} becomes very short at strong magnetic fields. In a Kramers salt[7,8]) such as Co^{2+},

$$\rho_{sl}^{-1} \propto H^5 \coth(g\mu_B H/kT). \qquad (7)$$

Moreover, it has already been pointed out that heat transfer between the lattice and the liquid ^{4}He bath is rather poor. Also, the lattice specific heat is very small below 4.2 K. So-called phonon-bottleneck phenomena occur in such situations and the relaxation time ρ between spin and thermal bath is given by[18]),

$$\rho = \rho_{sl} + \rho_{ph} C_H/C_L, \qquad (8)$$

where ρ_{ph} is the phonon life time, and C_H and C_L are the specific heats of the spin system and of the lattice. The condition $\rho_{sl} < \rho_{ph} C_H/C_L$ is likely in our strong-field case for Co^{2+} ions with large g values. Then, we obtain

$$\rho^{-1} \propto c^{-\frac{1}{2}} T^2 \qquad (9)$$

assuming that the width of the spin-energy levels is proportional to $c^{-\frac{1}{2}}$ as is reported elsewhere[19]). Therefore the relaxation rate to be observed will be $\rho^{-1} \propto H^4 T$ at weak fields and $\rho^{-1} \propto c^{-\frac{1}{2}} T^2$ at the high-field limit, so long as one is not concerned with, for example, lattice imperfections. All the experimental results both on single crystals and powdered samples are qualitatively in agreement with these predictions although the quantitative results still lag behind.

4. *Concluding remarks.* It has been verified experimentally that a small amount of Ni^{2+} ions are very effective on the paramagnetic relaxation in cobaltous salts. A typical behaviour of CR between Co^{2+} and Ni^{2+} is commonly found in several cobaltous salts under magnetic fields of 10 kOe or so. Also it has been pointed out that Ni^{2+} spins happen to be partially in equilibrium in concentrated mixed salts through CR with Co^{2+} ions.

SLR of Co^{2+} at a high magnetic field[20]) is observed not to be affected by Ni^{2+} impurities, but the phonon bottleneck is certainly there, at least at liquid ^{4}He temperatures.

REFERENCES

1) Amaya, K., Tokunaga, Y., Kuramitsu, Y., and Haseda, T., J. Phys. Soc. Japan **33** (1972) 49.
2) Amaya, K., Tokunaga, Y. and Haseda, T., Bussei (Japan) **9** (1968) 635.
3) Haseda, T. and Kanda, E., Physica **22** (1956) 647.
4) Van den Broek, J., Van der Marel, L. C. and Gorter, C. J., Physica **25** (1959) 371.
5) Wharmby, D. O. and Gill, J. C., Physica **46** (1970) 614.
6) Von Klot, R. and Weber, G., Z. Phys. **209** (1968) 380.
7) Van Vleck, J. H., Phys. Rev. **57** (1940) 426.
8) Orbach, R., Proc. Roy. Soc. **A264** (1961) 458.

9) Van Vleck, J. H., Phys. Rev. **59** (1941) 724.
Gorter, C. J., Van der Marel, L. C. and Bölger, B., Physica **21** (1955) 103.
10) Griffiths, J. H. E. and Owen, J., Proc. Roy. Soc. **A213** (1952) 459; Proc. Phys. Soc. **A64** (1951) 583.
11) Bleany, B. and Ingram, D. J. E., Proc. Roy. Soc. **A208** (1951) 143.
12) Kötzler, J., J. Phys. C.: Solid State Physics **5** (1972) 1876.
13) Tokunaga, Y., Ikeda, S., Ito, K. and Haseda, T. (to be published).
14) Friedberg, S. A. and Schriempf, J. T., J. appl. Phys. **35** (1964) 1000.
15) Polgar, L. G. and Friedberg, S. A., Phys. Rev. **B6** (1972) 3497.
16) Van der Marel, L. C., Bots, G. J. C. and Blaisse, B. S., Proc. of Colloque Ampère XV, North-Holland Publ. Co. (Amsterdam, 1969). Poolman, P. J., Wever, J. J., Van der Marel, L. C., Bots, G. J. C. and Blaisse, B. S., Proc. of Colloque Ampère XIV, North-Holland Publ. Co. (Amsterdam, 1967).
17) Ohtsubo, A., J. Phys. Soc. Japan **20** (1965) 82.
Bleaney, B. and Ingram, D. J. E., Proc. Roy. Soc. **A208** (1951) 143.
18) Stoneham, A. M., Proc. Phys. Soc. **86** (1965) 1163.
19) See, for example, Abragam, A., Principles of Nuclear Magnetism, Oxford University Press (New York, 1960).
20) Roest, J. A., thesis, Leiden, 1972.

Physica **69** (1973) 286–292 © *North-Holland Publishing Co.*

MAGNETORESISTANCE ANISOTROPY IN SINGLE CRYSTALS OF CADMIUM AND VERY DILUTE CADMIUM ALLOYS *

D. A. LILLY and A. N. GERRITSEN

Department of Physics, Purdue University, West Lafayette, Indiana, USA

Received 17 April 1973

Synopsis

Angular-dependence measurements on the magnetoresistance of pure Cd, Cd–Ag and Cd–In alloys with solute concentrations of the order 25 ppmw and less over the temperature range 1.4 K to 10 K in fields up to 23 kG confirm the anisotropic temperature dependence for field directions in the $(11\bar{2}0)$ plane. Evidence is obtained that inter-sheet scattering does not seem to affect the magnetoresistance in the basal plane.

1. *Introduction.* The transport properties of hexagonal metals (and cadmium in particular) have received renewed interest in the last decade due to progress – experimental and theoretical – in determining Fermi-surface topologies**. Magnetic breakdown effects have been observed in these metals in rather different experiments; in all cases these effects have been related to the multi-sheet character of their respective Fermi surfaces at special points in the Brillouin zone.

The correlation of magneto-transport phenomena with the accepted Fermi surface is not always straightforward, however. Measurements usually determine only an effective $\omega\tau$ ($\omega = eH/m^*c$ = cyclotron frequency, τ = average carrier scattering time), whereas the value of ω for a particular orbit may deviate considerably from the effective one, depending on details of the Fermi surface. Certainly, the concept of a single scattering parameter is too simplistic; the large observed deviations from Kohler's rule [$\Delta R/R_0 = F(H/\rho)$, $H/\rho \propto \omega\tau$] are evidence of this.

In cadmium $\Delta R/R_0 \propto H^n$, $n \approx 2$, up to very large values of $\omega\tau$ (exceeding 3×10^3), in apparent agreement with the expected H^2 dependence for a compensated metal, when $\omega\tau \gg 1$ and all cyclotron orbits are closed. For $\boldsymbol{H} \| [0001]$ (the c axis) this field dependence is surprising, in view of the fact that Hall-resistivity data for this field orientation exhibit temperature- and field-dependent

* Supported by Grant GP12633 from the National Science Foundation.

** For statements of a general character in this section the reader is referred to the more detailed discussion and bibliography in ref. 1.

carrier discompensation. A discompensation would normally lead to a magnetoresistance which saturates for $\omega\tau \gg 1$ and closed cyclotron orbits.

A semi-quantitative explanation has been used to account for this general behavior, and, in particular, for the observed sign reversal of the Hall resistivity to negative values below 6 K. It was shown[2, 3, 4]) that discompensation could result if hole orbits tunelled into electron orbits in the basal plane of the 1st Brillouin zone between segments of the second-zone hole surface (at the tips of these segments, fig. 1). This process, called inter-sheet scattering, formally resembles magnetic breakdown, but differs in that the probability for inter-sheet scattering (for a hole to "become" an electron) *decreases* with increasing field strength.

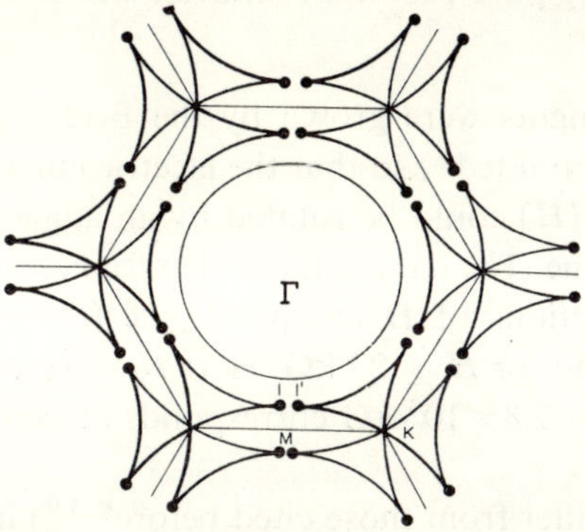

Fig. 1. Sections of the Fermi surface of cadmium in the basal (ΓKM) plane. The triangles are the hole sheets in the second zone, and the circle around Γ is the third-zone electron lens. Inter-sheet scattering occurs at the tips of the triangles, between points such as 1 and 1′.

The effects of small amounts of impurities on inter-sheet scattering is especially interesting: it follows from the Hall-resistivity data that concentrations of 0.5 at. % and less of zinc enhance such scattering, while amounts of 25 ppmw of silver or indium inhibit it[5]). It is uncertain why the inhibition should occur, but the overall behavior of the Hall resistivity (for $T \lesssim 10$ K) in Cd–Ag or Cd–In alloys can be qualitatively understood in a simple model which uses different scattering times for holes and for electrons, varying as T^3 and T^5, respectively[6]). Such temperature dependences have been observed in size-dependent oscillatory magnetoresistance measurements[7]).

The observed[8]), anomalous behavior of the transverse magnetoresistance, $R(H, T, \theta)$, (for $\omega\tau \gg 1$, $\theta \equiv \,< \boldsymbol{H}$, [0001]) has led to an interpretation in terms of anisotropic electron–phonon scattering. Young[9]) calculated $R(H, T, \theta)$ explicitly for a model Fermi surface (a hole-like undulating cylinder) on which anisotropic scattering was concentrated in a "hot-band" of orbits, centered at the bulging areas of the cylinder. Hole scattering outside the "hot-bands" and electron scattering on a compensating electron sphere were assumed to be isotropic and identical. A seven-parameter fit to data obtained on a very pure sample of cadmium was argued to be limited only by the geometry of the model Fermi surface employed. Young conceded, however, that Fermi-surface effects only could produce the deviations from Kohler's rule that were observed. This possibility was emphasized by the indication[10]) that orbits subject to inter-sheet scattering might contribute most strongly to this anisotropic scattering.

The angular dependence of the transverse magnetoresistance and the influence of temperature and impurities on it remains worth considering, in particular, with regard to the contribution to the anomalous behavior by inter-sheet scattering. In this note, such data obtained on single-crystal samples of Cd–Ag (silver concentrations 25 ppmw and 1 ppmw), Cd–In (indium concentration 10 ppmw) and two samples representing pure-cadmium behavior will be presented and discussed*.

2. *Results*. Crystal ingots were grown by the Bridgeman method from which samples were cut and mounted[6]) so that the electric current was along $[11\bar{2}0]$ and that the magnetic field ($\boldsymbol{H}$) could be rotated by an angle $\theta \pm 0.5°$ with respect to [0001] in the $(11\bar{2}0)$ plane. The data indicate that for $r_T H \gtrsim 1 \times 10^4$ kG, $\Delta R/R_0 \propto H^{1.95 \pm 0.05}$ in all directions of $\boldsymbol{H}$ except $\boldsymbol{H} \perp c$ ($\theta = 90°$), in the temperature range 1.4 K to 10 K, and for $H \leqq 23$ kG. Here r_T = resistance (273 K)/resistance (T); the product $r_T H = 2.8 \times 10^3$ kG corresponds in cadmium[4]) to $(\omega\tau)_f = 1$ for free electrons.

The measurements differ from those cited before[8, 10]) in that (1) data were also acquired in the temperature range 4.2 K $< T <$ 10 K, and (2) the $(11\bar{2}0)$ instead of the $(10\bar{1}0)$ plane was chosen as the plane of rotation. $R(H, \theta)$ for the $(11\bar{2}0)$ plane of rotation differs markedly from $R(H, \theta)$ for the field rotated in the $(10\bar{1}0)$ plane near $\theta = 50°$. This difference, which is an apparent shift by approximately 7° in the minimum in $R(H, \theta \approx 50°)$ for rotation in the $(10\bar{1}0)$ plane, is clearly illustrated for the case of two pure cadmium samples in fig. 2. This minimum can be associated[8]) with the onset of orbits which span two Brillouin zones, and appears experimentally in $R(H, \theta)$ between 55° and 60° for rotation in the $(11\bar{2}0)$ plane.

It is possible to correlate this shift with measurements on the de Haas–Van Alphen effect[11]) and cyclotron resonance[12]). Such measurements show that extremal areas ($\mathrm{d}A/\mathrm{d}k_H = 0$) and extremal effective masses ($\mathrm{d}m^*/\mathrm{d}k_H = 0$) are present in the $(11\bar{2}0)$ plane (the plane of rotation here) and not in the $(10\bar{1}0)$ plane. The orbits enclosing these extremal areas are designated β_2-type (ref. 11, fig. 1).

The minimum in $R(H, \theta)$ near 50° for rotation in the $(10\bar{1}0)$ plane is attributed to extremal orbits at 42.5° (β_1-type orbits) for which $m^* \to \infty$ and $\omega \to 0$. Since

* The preparation of these samples will be discussed in a forthcoming paper on the Hall-resistivity data[6]). They have been chosen for this discussion as representative for the magnetoresistance in an extensive $\omega\tau$ range. The sample enriched with ^{116}Cd was of importance in the Hall-resistivity investigation, but no different behavior with other pure cadmium samples was observed. The most complete set of data for $R(H, \theta)$ were taken with this specimen.

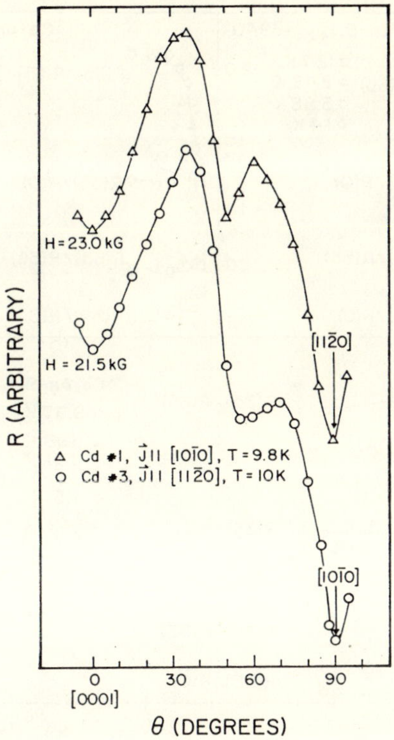

Fig. 2. The angular dependence of the transverse magnetoresistance for $\boldsymbol{H}$ rotated in the two high-symmetry planes: (11$\bar{2}$0), (10$\bar{1}$0).

in the (11$\bar{2}$0) plane the β_2-type orbits appear[11]) at 43.5°, the β_1 minimum is not observed but is followed by the β_2 cutoff at 58°. It should be noted, however, that an exact correlation between the observed magnetoresistance and the dHvA data has not been found.

The variation of $R(H, \theta_1, T)/R(H, \theta_2, T)$ with $r_T H$ at *extremal positions* in the rotation diagrams (θ near 35°, 55°, 65°) is presented in fig. 3. The measured ratios have experimental accuracy $\pm 2\%$; the $r_{4.2\,\mathrm{K}}$ value listed is a measure of sample purity. In the range 1.4 K $< T <$ 4.2 K, the ratios confirm the general anomalous temperature dependence, which decreases with decreasing temperature. Effects of impurities and magnetic field (especially for $r_T H < 2 \times 10^4$ kG) are also evident. Specific trends are as follows:

(i) The ratio $R(65)/R(55) \approx 1$ and varies within $\pm 6\,\%$ with temperature for all samples.

(ii) The ratio $R(35)/R(65)$ initially increases with increasing $r_T H$ for all samples. For the alloys this ratio approaches a nearly temperature-independent value ($\approx 2.20 \pm 5\,\%$) for $r_T H > 2 \times 10^4$ kG, $(\omega\tau)_{\mathrm{f}} > 7$. By contrast, $R(35)/R(65)$ is strongly temperature dependent in the purest samples: it saturates to a value that decreases by 15 % for a factor 4 in decreasing temperature.

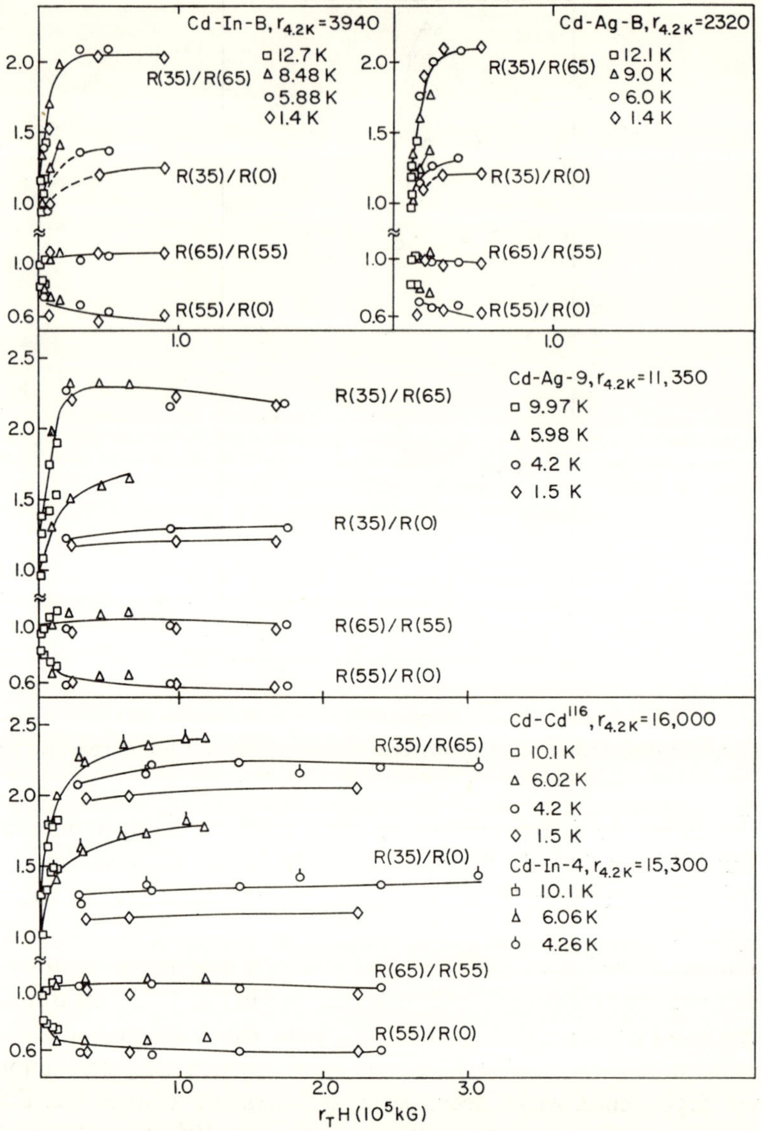

Fig. 3. The magnetoresistance ratios $R(H, \theta_1, T)/R(H, \theta_2, T)$ *versus* $r_T H$ for θ near extrema in $R(H, \theta)$.

(iii) The ratio $R(35)/R(0)$ also initially increases with increasing $r_T H$, but remains for all samples strongly temperature dependent (of the order 40 % between 6 K and 1.5 K). For the two purest samples, $R(35)/R(0)$ for $T \leqq 4.2$ K reaches a value independent of H that decreases with decreasing temperature.

(iv) The ratio $R(55)/R(0)$ is approximately constant ($\approx 0.62 \pm 5\,\%$) for $r_T H > 2 \times 10^4$ kG.

3. *Discussion.* The effects of phonon and impurity scattering on the magnetoresistance can be deduced from (i)–(iv) described above. The large field dependence evident in $R(35)/R(65)$ and $R(35)/R(0)$ for $r_T H < 2 \times 10^4$ kG indicates, whatever the causes, that the high-field condition is reached for different values of $r_T H$ in different directions.

The approximately Kohler behavior of $R(35)/R(65)$ in the alloys indicates that $\tau_{35°} \approx \tau_{65°}$ for controlled impurity concentrations exceeding 1 ppmw (as in sample Cd–Ag-9, $r_{4.2\,K} = 1.1 \times 10^4$). For smaller impurity concentrations, temperature effects on $R(35)/R(65)$ dominate (as in sample Cd–^{116}Cd, $r_{4.2\,K} = 1.6 \times 10^4$) and indicate the presence of anisotropic phonon scattering. However, an increasing impurity concentration has little (or no) effect on $R(35)/R(0)$, evidently due to stronger temperature effects. In fact, plots of $R(H, \theta)/R(H, 0)$ against $r_T H$ show that for increasing θ, the deviations from Kohler's rule rise rapidly to a maximum near $\theta = 35°$, and virtually disappear for $\theta = 55°$ (as seen in fig. 3). This indicates that the anisotropic phonon scattering has a greater influence on orbits confined to the 1st Brillouin zone ($\theta \leqq 43°$) than on larger angle orbits. Such behavior of $R(H, \theta, T)$ is consistent with the "hot-band" model[9]), in which phonon effects are strongest for small angles.

The question arises whether the temperature dependence of $R(35)/R(0)$ is in any way connected to inter-sheet scattering. It should be noted that the Hall resistivity of the alloy samples was observed to remain positive and to reverse sign in sample Cd–In-4 ($\approx$2 ppmw In) and (as expected) in sample Cd–^{116}Cd. This was taken as an indication for the inhibition of inter-sheet scattering by small impurity concentrations (in the 1 ppmw range). At the same time, the $R(35)/R(0)$ curves displayed here exhibit a strong similarity to those obtained for the dilute Cd–Zn alloys, in which the occurrence of inter-sheet scattering was observed. This indicates clearly that inter-sheet scattering, whether present or not, does not qualitatively affect the magnetoresistance for the 35° orientation, and perhaps the other orientations as well.

In conclusion, it has been confirmed that anisotropic electron–phonon scattering contributes to the temperature anomalies in the magnetoresistance in cadmium. Impurity effects are noticeable, but tend to produce, rather than destroy, Kohler behavior [as in $R(35)/R(65)$]. Further, the similarity between rotation diagrams for alloy samples in which inter-sheet scattering operates and those in which it is inhibited, argues against strong inter-sheet effects in the transverse magnetoresistance in cadmium for field directions in a plane containing the hexagonal axis.

REFERENCES

1) Hurd, C. M., The Hall Effect in Metals and Alloys, Plenum Press (New York, 1972).
2) Katyal, O. P., Gerritsen, A. N., Ruvalds, J., Young, R. A. and Falicov, L. M., Phys. Rev. Letters **21** (1968) 694.
3) Young, R. A., Ruvalds, J. and Falicov, L. M., Phys. Rev. **178** (1969) 1043.

4) Katyal, O. P. and Gerritsen, A. N., Phys. Rev. **178** (1969) 1037.
5) Lilly, D. A. and Gerritsen, A. N., Hall Resistivity in Dilute Crystals of Cd–In and Cd–Ag: An Impurity Problem for Inter-sheet Scattering, Proceedings of the 13th International Low Temperature Conference.
6) Lilly, D. A., Ph.D. Thesis, Purdue University. Results to be published in Phys. Rev.
7) Hambourger, P. D., Electronic Mean Free Paths in Cadmium, Proceedings of the 13th International Low Temperature Conference.
8) Tsui, D. C. and Stark, R. W., Phys. Rev. Letters **19** (1967) 1317.
9) Young, R. A., Phys. Rev. **183** (1969) 611.
10) Katyal, O. P. and Gerritsen, A. N., Phys. Rev. **185** (1969) 1017.
11) Tsui, D. C. and Stark, R. W., Phys. Rev. Letters **16** (1966) 19.
12) Shaw, M. P., Eckland, T. G. and Zych, D. A., Phys. Rev. **142** (1966) 406.

Physica **69** (1973) 293–307 © *North-Holland Publishing Co.*

ANOMALOUS AMPLITUDES AND PHASES IN THE DE HAAS–VAN ALPHEN EFFECT

D. SHOENBERG* and I. M. TEMPLETON

Division of Physics, National Research Council of Canada, Ottawa, Canada

Received 13 June 1973

Synopsis

In the usual theoretical treatment of the De Haas–Van Alphen effect is it assumed that the area A of cross section of the Fermi surface varies as κ^2 with distance κ in k space away from the extremal cross section. The consequences of the more general assumption that the variation includes a term in κ^4 are examined and compared with some experimental results on the variation of oscillation amplitude in copper in the neighbourhood of an orientation where $d^2A/d\kappa^2$ changes sign. The qualitative agreement found can be somewhat improved by using a more realistic variation with κ based on the actual Fermi surface. An attempt to verify the theoretically predicted phase of the oscillations proved unsuccessful.

1. *Introduction.* As is well known, the amplitude and phase of the oscillatory field dependence of magnetic properties (De Haas–Van Alphen effect) can be derived by first calculating the oscillatory variation for a section of the Fermi surface (FS) of thickness $d\kappa$ and then integrating this over κ, the component of the wave vector along the field direction. Thus the final result contains a factor of the form

$$A = \int w(\kappa) \cos (2\pi\{[F(\kappa)/H] - \gamma\}) \, d\kappa, \tag{1}$$

where $F(\kappa)$ is a frequency which is proportional to the area $a(\kappa)$ of cross section of the Fermi surface, γ is a constant ($\frac{1}{2}$ for a free-electron gas) and the limits are to be taken from one side of the FS to the other; $w(\kappa)$ is a weighting factor which can normally be set equal to unity. The standard method of dealing with (1) is to note that the phase F/H is usually much greater than unity, so that the only appreciable contribution to the integral comes from a narrow region of κ around the value κ_0 for which $F(\kappa)$ is an extremum. If we choose the origin of κ to make

* Permanent address: Cavendish Laboratory, Cambridge, England.

$\kappa_0 = 0$, and expand $F(\kappa)$ around this origin as

$$F(\kappa) = F_0 + \tfrac{1}{2}F''\kappa^2 + \tfrac{1}{24}F^{\mathrm{IV}}\kappa^4 + etc., \tag{2}$$

where

$$F_0 = F(0), \quad F'' = \left(\frac{\partial^2 F}{\partial \kappa^2}\right)_0, \quad F^{\mathrm{IV}} = \left(\frac{\partial^2 F}{\partial \kappa^4}\right)_0,$$

it is usually an excellent approximation to retain only the first two terms on the r.h.s. of (2) and to put $w(\kappa) = 1$. Eq. (1) then reduces to

$$A = \mathscr{R}\left(\mathrm{e}^{2\pi\mathrm{i}[(F_0/H)-\gamma]}\int_{-\infty}^{\infty} \mathrm{e}^{\pi\mathrm{i}F''\kappa^2/H}\,\mathrm{d}\kappa\right). \tag{3}$$

It is because of the high phase of the argument of the exponent in the integral for even relatively small values of κ that the higher-order terms in (2) can be ignored and the limits of integration taken as $\pm\infty$. The result (3) can be expressed more conveniently in terms of the Fresnel integral as

$$A(|F''|/2H)^{\frac{1}{2}} = \mathscr{R}\left(\mathrm{e}^{2\pi\mathrm{i}[(F_0/H)-\gamma]}\int_{0}^{\infty} \mathrm{e}^{\pm\frac{1}{2}\mathrm{i}\pi u^2}\,\mathrm{d}u\right), \tag{4}$$

where

$$u = (2|F''|/H)^{\frac{1}{2}}\kappa,$$

or

$$A(|F''|/2H)^{\frac{1}{2}} = (1/\sqrt{2})\cos\{2\pi[(F_0/H) - \gamma] \pm \pi/4\}, \tag{5}$$

and the + or − sign is chosen according as F'' is + (*i.e.* minimum of F) or − (maximum of F). The integration can of course be represented graphically by the Cornu spiral and the approximation implied in (3), (4) or (5) is that deviations from the exact Cornu spiral occur only for such high values of u that the spiral has effectively converged on its limiting point.

Although (5) is normally an entirely adequate approximation it can fail in special circumstances of two kinds: (a) where the Fermi surface is such that F'' becomes very small for particular field directions and the higher-order terms in (2) become relevant, and (b) where $w(\kappa)$ varies appreciably over the significant range of κ. In this paper we shall mostly be concerned with an example of (a) which occurs in copper for a narrow range of field directions around $23\frac{1}{4}°$ from ⟨100⟩ in the (110) plane, over which F'' changes sign as the angle is varied (Halse[1]), Coleridge, Scott and Templeton[2])). We shall show that a calculation based on including the F^{IV} term in (2) provides a fair qualitative description of the observed behaviour illustrated in fig. 1, though the detailed behaviour cannot be completely accounted for by this extra term alone. A rather better interpretation can be given in terms

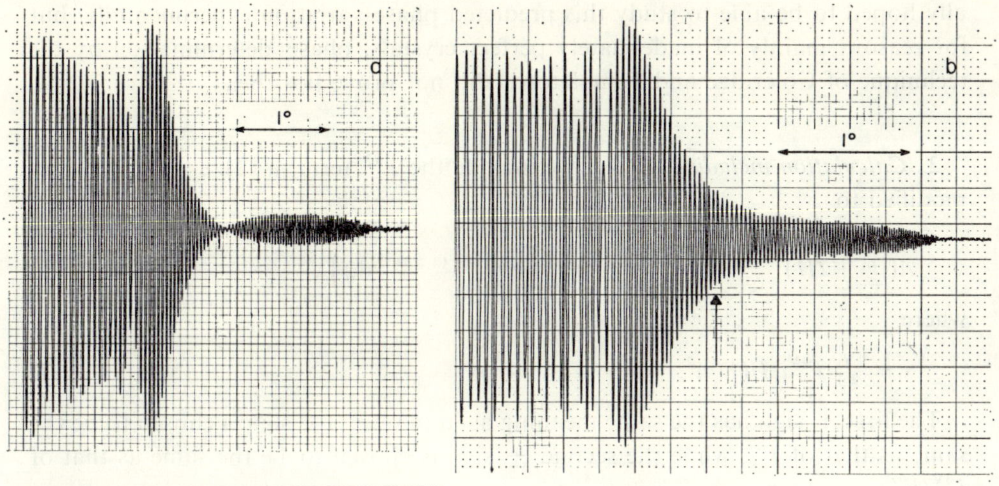

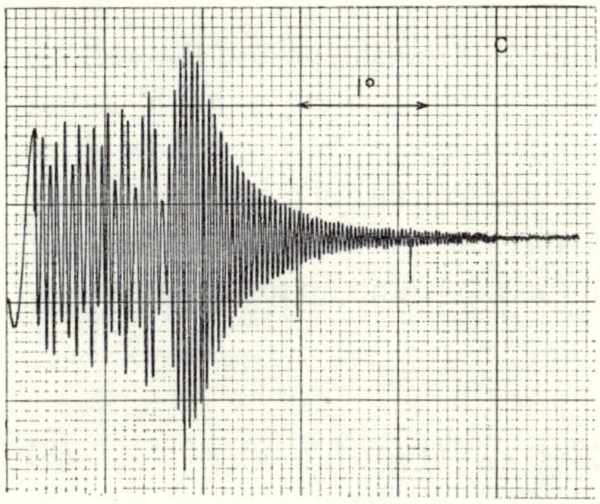

Fig. 1. Observed De Haas–Van Alphen oscillations with angle in the neighbourhood of $23\frac{1}{4}$ ° from ⟨100⟩ in a (110) plane: (a) pure Cu, (b) Cu + 6 ppm Fe, (c) Cu + 10 ppm Fe [(a) and (b) from Coleridge, Scott and Templeton[2]), (c) unpublished data by same authors]. The measured quantity is proportional to d^2M/dH^2 and the data were taken at $T = 1.2$ K and $H = 50.5$ kG.

of the detailed specification of the FS, but since the observed behaviour is very sensitive to specimen perfection and moreover the effects of (b) above also prove relevant, these refinements are somewhat illusory. The effects (b) can be important if some of the amplitude-determining properties such as the cyclotron mass and the spin factor are rapid functions of κ or if the integration has to be truncated because the relevant section of the Fermi surface becomes no longer closed for a value of κ for which the Cornu spiral has not nearly reached its limiting point.

We shall first calculate the amplitude and phase when the F^{IV} term in (2) is included and show how this calculation reproduces some features of the observed results. We then describe some more elaborate computations based on the actual FS of copper as described by Halse[1]), and also consider how introduction of a realistic weighting factor $w(\kappa)$ modifies the results. One feature of all the calculated predictions is that the phase of the oscillation should vary in a complex manner as the direction of the field is varied through the direction for which F'' vanishes. At exactly this orientation [about $23\frac{1}{4}$° from ⟨100⟩ in a (110) plane] the oscillatory factor in (5) should become modified to cos $\{2\pi[(F_0/H)-\gamma]\pm\pi/8\}$. It was originally hoped to be able to study this predicted phase variation experimentally, but for reasons mainly of inadequately perfect crystals, phase determination by the technique of Coleridge and Templeton[3]) did not prove possible.

2. *Calculation including* F^{IV}. If we include the F^{IV} term in (2), eq. (4) becomes modified to

$$A(|F''|/2H)^{\frac{1}{2}} = \mathscr{R}\left(e^{2\pi i[(F_0/H)-\gamma]}\int_0^\infty e^{\pm\frac{1}{2}i\pi u^2(1\pm\alpha u^2)}\,du\right), \tag{6}$$

where

$$\alpha = \tfrac{1}{24}|F^{IV}|H/(F'')^2. \tag{7}$$

The first $\pm$ sign has the same meaning as in (4), *i.e.*, the sign is chosen to be the same as that of F'', while the second $\pm$ sign is chosen to be the same as that of F^{IV}/F''.

From the explicit expression for the integral in (6) (Gradshteyn and Rhyzhik[4])) the amplitude and phase of (6) may be readily computed for any value of α, but before discussing the results of this computation it is instructive to consider three limiting cases where appropriate approximations lead to relatively simple formulae. For each case we give an expression analogous to (5) for the amplitude and phase; in these expressions terms up to α^2 are retained for $\alpha \ll 1$ and up to $1/\alpha$ for $\alpha > 1$.

2.1. $\alpha \ll 1$, F^{IV}/F'' positive.

$$A(|F''|/2H)^{\frac{1}{2}} = (1/\sqrt{2})(1 - 12\alpha^2/\pi^2)\cos\{2\pi[(F_0/H) - \gamma] \pm \varphi\}, \tag{8}$$

where

$$\varphi = (\pi/4) - (3\alpha/2\pi). \tag{9}$$

The sign is chosen to be the same as that of F'', and in the limit $\alpha = 0$, (8) and (9) of course reduce to (5).

2.2. $\alpha \ll 1$, F^{IV}/F'' negative. The result is most meaningfully expressed as the sum of *two* periodic terms:

$$A\left(\frac{|F''|}{2H}\right)^{\frac{1}{2}} = \frac{1}{\sqrt{2}}\left(1 - \frac{12\alpha^2}{\pi^2}\right)\left\{\cos\left[2\pi\left(\frac{F_0}{H} - \gamma\right) \pm \varphi\right]\right.$$
$$\left. + \sqrt{2}\cos\left[2\pi\left(\frac{F_0}{H} - \gamma\right) \pm \left(\frac{\pi}{8\alpha} - \varphi\right)\right]\right\}, \tag{10}$$

where

$$\varphi = (\pi/4) + (3\alpha/2\pi). \tag{11}$$

The sign is chosen to be the same as that of F''.

We can also combine the two terms into a single oscillatory term of the form

$$A\left(\frac{|F''|}{2H}\right)^{\frac{1}{2}} = \frac{1}{\sqrt{2}}\left(1 - \frac{12\alpha^2}{\pi^2}\right) \times \left[3 + 2\sqrt{2}\sin\left(\frac{\pi}{8\alpha} - \frac{3\alpha}{\pi}\right)\right]^{\frac{1}{2}} \cos\left[2\pi\left(\frac{F_0}{H} - \gamma\right) + \varphi'\right], \quad (12)$$

where ϕ' is given by

$$\tan\varphi' = \pm \frac{\sqrt{2}\sin[(\pi/8\alpha) - \varphi] + \sin\varphi}{\sqrt{2}\cos[(\pi/8\alpha) - \varphi] + \cos\varphi}, \quad (13)$$

and ϕ is as defined by (11). This emphasizes the beat-like character of both the amplitude and the phase of the sum of the two periodic terms in (10). The 'amplitude' of the right-hand side of (10) or (12), in fact oscillates approximately between $(\sqrt{2}+1)/\sqrt{2}$ and $(\sqrt{2}-1)/\sqrt{2}$.

2.3. $\alpha > 1$. The expansion is now in powers of $(1/\alpha)^{\frac{1}{2}}$ and the result is

$$A\left(\frac{|F''|}{2H}\right)^{\frac{1}{2}} = \frac{0.8096}{\alpha^{\frac{1}{4}}}\left(1 \mp \frac{0.2995}{\alpha^{\frac{1}{2}}} + \frac{0.0449}{\alpha}\right)\cos\left[2\pi\left(\frac{F_0}{H} - \gamma\right) + \varphi\right], \quad (14)$$

where

$$\varphi = \pm\left(\frac{\pi}{8} \pm \frac{0.2995}{\alpha^{\frac{1}{2}}} - \frac{0.1066}{\alpha}\right). \quad (15)$$

The upper or lower sign inside the brackets of (14) and (15) is chosen accordingly as of F^{IV}/F'' is positive or negative and the $\pm$ outside the bracket of (15) follows the sign of F^{IV}.

3. *Discussion of amplitude and phase.* The amplitudes and phases computed from the exact formula and also from the various asymptotic approximations, are shown graphically in figs. 2 and 3. Since over the range of interest F'' varies rapidly with angle and passes through zero, while F^{IV} varies only gradually, it is convenient to note that

$$(|F''|/2H)^{\frac{1}{2}} = (|F^{IV}|/96H)^{\frac{1}{4}}\alpha^{-\frac{1}{4}}, \quad (16)$$

and to plot the right-hand sides of (6), (8), (12) and (14), multiplied by $\alpha^{\frac{1}{4}}$ rather than as they stand. If we had plotted the right-hand side of (14) just as it stands, we should have produced a zero result for $1/\alpha = 0$. All amplitudes are plotted against $s\alpha^{-\frac{1}{2}}$ where s is the sign of F^{IV}/F''; this emphasizes the continuity as we pass through $1/\alpha = 0$, (where F'' changes sign) and also helps to compress a wider range of $1/\alpha$ into the diagram.

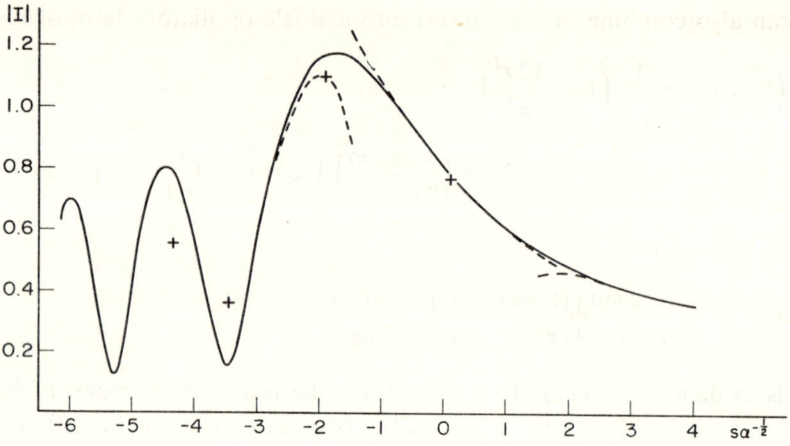

Fig. 2. Plot of $|I|$ against $s\alpha^{-\frac{1}{2}}$ where $I = \alpha^{\frac{1}{2}} \int_0^\infty e^{\frac{1}{2}i\pi u^2(1 \pm \alpha u^2)}\, du$ and s is the $\pm$ sign chosen. The broken lines indicate the various asymptotic expressions discussed in the text in the regions where they diverge appreciably from the exact values of $|I|$. The points + are computed from the actual FS, as explained in the text.

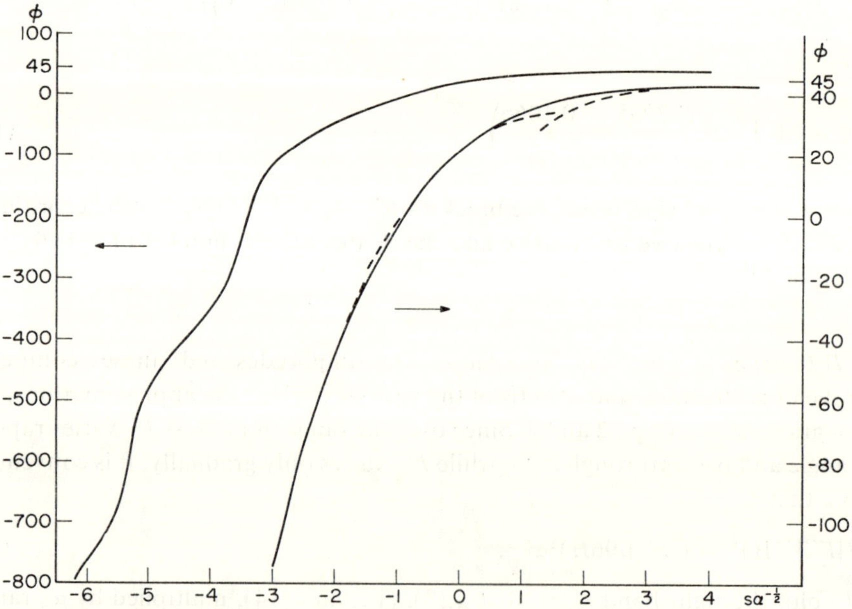

Fig. 3. Plot of $\phi = \tan^{-1} s[\mathrm{Im}(I)/\mathrm{Re}(I)]$ against $s\alpha^{-\frac{1}{2}}$. The right-hand curve is an expanded version of the plot and the broken curves indicate the various asymptotic expressions. This definition of ϕ implies that F'' is positive for s positive, as is appropriate for copper in the range of interest. If F'' is negative for s positive the sign of ϕ must be reversed. The values of $\tan^{-1}$ are chosen to produce a continuously decreasing value of ϕ as $1/\alpha$ increases for s negative; this corresponds to the continuous change of $\pi/8\alpha$ in the second term of (10).

It can be seen at once that the asymptotic formulae represent the exact calculation very well and they are usually entirely adequate for semiquantitative purposes. The following points should be noted.

1) As has already been pointed out by Bosacchi, Ketterson and Windmiller[5]), the amplitude of A when $F'' = 0$, *i.e.*, $1/\alpha = 0$, is governed by $(H/|F^{IV}|)^{\frac{1}{4}}$ and the phase becomes $\pm\pi/8$ instead of the usual $\pm\pi/4$. Eqs. (14) and (15) show how the amplitude and phase vary on either side of this point and we see that the phase changes particularly rapidly as $s\alpha^{-\frac{1}{2}}$ changes from $+1$ to -1. We shall see later that in practice this happens over a very narrow range of angles (about $\frac{1}{4}^{\circ}$).

2) The beats that occur for F^{IV}/F'' negative have a very simple interpretation, namely that F then has not only an extremum for $\kappa = 0$ but also two extrema of the opposite kind on either side of $\kappa = 0$. Thus, in terms of the more convenient u notation, $\frac{1}{2}\pi u^2(1-\alpha u^2)$ has a minimum for $u = 0$ and maxima at $u = \pm(1/2\alpha)^{\frac{1}{2}}$. The $\pi/8\alpha$ which appears in (10) is simply the difference between the minimum (or maximum) and maximum (or minimum) values of $\pm\frac{1}{2}\pi u^2(1-\alpha u^2)$, while the change of the sign of ϕ (whose value is approximately $\pi/4$) between the two periodic terms reflects the fact that the first term comes from the central minimum (or maximum) but the second comes from the noncentral maxima (or minima). The factor $\sqrt{2}$ in the second periodic term is accounted for by the different curvatures of the central and noncentral extrema and the fact that there are two of the latter. It should be noticed that the phase difference $\pi/8\alpha$ is proportional to $1/H$ and so should really be thought of as a frequency difference if H is varied. Finally it should be emphasized that the formula which gives the beats is not likely to apply for too small values of α since then the subsidiary extrema come so far away from the central extremum that higher-order terms in the expansion (2) of F must become relevant. This will be discussed in more detail later.

3) The biggest amplitude does not occur exactly at $\alpha^{-\frac{1}{2}} = 0$, but appreciably away, at $s\alpha^{-\frac{1}{2}} = -1.7$. This can also be understood qualitatively in terms of the beats just discussed. In terms of (10) (which of course is beginning to become invalid for this value of α), the phases of the two terms in (10) become just equal when $\pi/8\alpha = 2\phi$ [this is also apparent from (12)]; this occurs for $s\alpha^{-\frac{1}{2}} = -2.13$, which is indeed not far off the maximum position*.

4) It should be remembered that since α is proportional to H the graph of fig. 2 can also be regarded as a graph of the field dependence of the amplitude times $H^{-\frac{1}{4}}$ at any given orientation.

4. *Comparison with experiment.* Most of the experimental results available for comparison with the calculations were obtained for other purposes and so are not precise or extensive enough for a thorough check of the theory. However, it is

* The position of the maximum is of course slightly biassed by the factor $\alpha^{\frac{1}{4}}$ which is included in the quantity actually plotted in fig. 2.

evident that the results shown in fig. 1 do resemble, at least qualitatively, the predicted variations of amplitude shown in fig. 2. As already mentioned, an attempt to study the phase variation proved unsuccessful but it is convenient to defer discussion of this experiment until later.

The first step in making a closer comparison between experiment and theory as regards amplitude is to establish the angular dependence of α. This was done by computation from a variant of Halse's formula[1]) (see appendix for details) for the Fermi surface of copper. For each of a number of orientations in the critical region between 22.5° and 23.8° from $\langle 100 \rangle$ in a (110) plane, the value of F was computed as a function of z, a distance proportional to κ, and relative values of F'' and F^{IV} could be derived from the intercept and initial slope of a plot of $\Delta F/z^2$. It was found that these plots usually depart appreciably from the initial linearity, *i.e.*, it is *not* usually entirely adequate to restrict the expansion of F to the quartic term. This can be seen in the examples shown in fig. 4, where it is evident that the

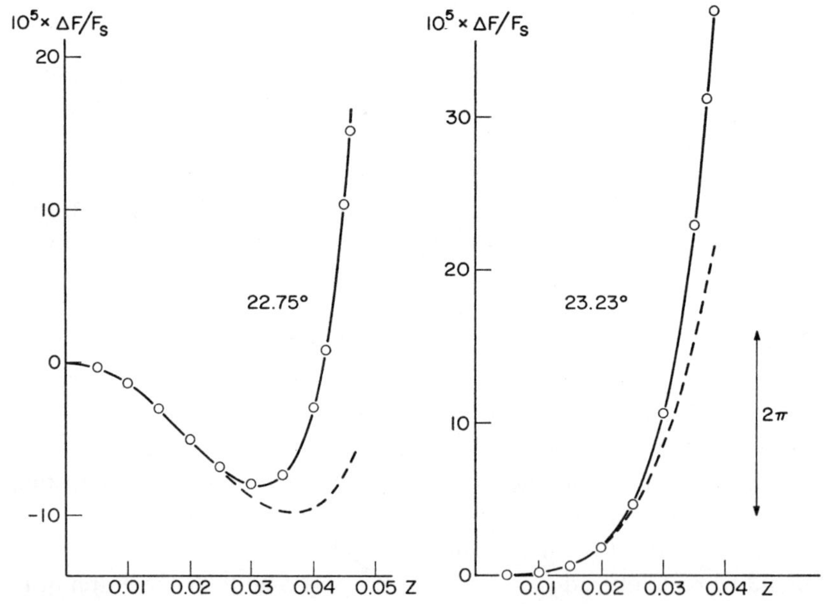

Fig. 4. Variation of $\Delta F/F_s$ with z [defined as $\kappa/(1.18\kappa_s)$, where κ_s is the free-electron sphere radius] computed from the 5-term Halse formula at 22.75 ° and 23.23 ° from $\langle 100 \rangle$ in a (110) plane. The broken lines represent the continuations of the quartic formulae which fit the computed curves in the limit of low z. As indicated by the arrows, 12×10^{-5} change in $\Delta F/F_s$ corresponds to a phase change of 2π, for $H = 50.5$ kG.

continuation of the curve of ΔF against z based on the quartic approximation departs appreciably from the actually computed curve, even where the corresponding phase difference $\Delta\psi$ $(= 2\pi\Delta F/H)$ is still only a fraction of 2π.

The computed variation of $s\alpha^{-\frac{1}{2}}$ with orientation is shown in fig. 5 for $H =$ 50.9 kG. To check the sensitivity of the curve to the FS model, computations were made also with a different variant of Halse's formula (7-term instead of 5-term) and these gave a curve which was almost identical in form but shifted to higher

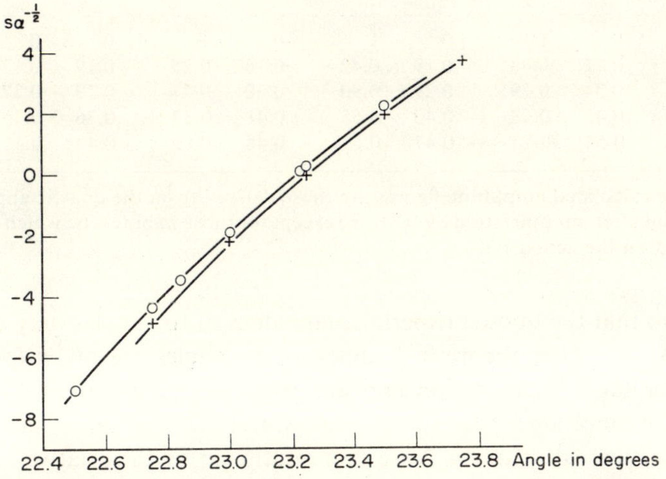

Fig. 5. Plot of $s\alpha^{-\frac{1}{2}}$ against angle from ⟨100⟩ in (110) plane: ○ 5-term formula, + 7-term formula.

angles by about 0.05°. It should be noticed that most of the variation of $\alpha^{-\frac{1}{2}}$ over the critical 1° region is due to the change of F'' rather than F^{IV}; thus between 22.5° and 23.5° F'' goes through zero, while $|F^{\mathrm{IV}}|^{\frac{1}{2}}$ increases by a factor of less than 2. To appreciate the magnitudes involved it is useful to consider $a''/2\pi$ (which is -1 for a spherical FS), rather than F'' (which is proportional to it); in fact between 22.5° and 23.5°, $a''/2\pi$ changes from about -0.07 to $+0.04$. For comparison we may note that for the ⟨100⟩ belly and ⟨111⟩ neck in copper, respectively, $a''/2\pi$ is about -1.27 and 2.57, while $\alpha^{-\frac{1}{2}}$ is 130 and 340. For such 'normal' situations, then, there is certainly no need to worry about the F^{IV} term: the Cornu spiral has effectively reached its limiting point before the parabolic approximation begins to fail.

We now compare the details of the experimental oscillations of fig. 1 with the predictions of the calculation as regards, 1), the positions and 2), the depths of the various features of the beat pattern. Since absolute angular measurement (from, say, ⟨100⟩) was not as reliable as the measurement of angular differences, the position of the principal maximum ("0 max") was used as a local origin and table 1 shows the angles from it of the easily identifiable features, namely the first and second maxima and minima of the beats (denoted by 1 max, 2 max, 1 min, 2 min, respectively). The angular calibration was not very certain and the determination from the record of the positions of maxima and minima is also a bit

TABLE I

	Pure Cu		Cu + 6 ppmFe		Cu + 10 ppmFe		Calculation			
	Angle (deg.)	Ampl.	Angle (deg.)	Ampl.	Angle (deg.)	Ampl.	Angle (deg.) 5-term	Angle (deg.) 7-term	Ampl.	
0 max	0	1	0	1	0	1	0	0	1	(1)
1 min	0.22	0.48	0.19	0.42	0.18	0.25	0.19	0.17	0.14	(0.35)
1 max	0.34	0.79	0.29	0.90	0.30	0.77	0.29	0.27	0.75	(0.44)
2 min	0.45	0.63	0.40	0.55	0.41	0.33	0.36	0.35	0.12	
2 max	0.54	0.75	0.47	0.69	0.48	0.69	0.43	0.41	0.68	

Note: The calculated amplitude figures are those derived from the quartic approximation (*i.e.* as in fig. 2, but after multiplication by $|F^{IV}|^{-\frac{1}{4}}$) except for those in brackets, which refer to the calculation based on the actual FS.

rough, so that the quoted experimental values of the angles may be in error by as much as 10 %. The theoretical values of the angles are taken from figs. 2 and 5 using graphical interpolation and are probably reliable to $\pm 0.01°$. In the comparison of amplitudes the central maximum is taken as unity, but the ordinates of the theoretical curve of fig. 2 are first multiplied by the relative values of $(F^{IV})^{-\frac{1}{4}}$ to make them comparable to the experimental data.

It can be seen that the positions of the beat minima and maxima are reasonably well represented by the quartic approximation, though there appears to be a definite tendency for the experimental positions of the higher extrema to be further off than the positions predicted by the quartic approximation. This tendency is consistent with the sense of the deviation illustrated in fig. 4, of the actual ΔF against z curve from the curve of the quartic approximation. The difference between the central and noncentral extremal values of F changes more rapidly with angle for the quartic approximation than for the real FS, which means that the beat maxima and minima will be more crowded together.

The situation concerning the amplitudes of the beats is much less satisfactory than that concerning their angular positions. Thus it is evident that the results vary considerably from one sample to another and that none of them show beat minima as deep as predicted by the quartic approximation. These discrepancies may be due to a combination of causes, partly experimental and partly due to inadequacies of the quartic approximation, and we shall now discuss these briefly.

4.1. Experimental causes. 1) Probably the most serious experimental cause is the "phase smearing" due to sample imperfections, such as bending or mosaic structure, which would be expected to make the beats less pronounced. It is puzzling, however, why the sample with a little added iron should show so much more pronounced beats (there should be a small effect connected with the g-factor discussed below, but it is insufficient to account for the difference). Possibly there is some metallurgical influence of the added iron which improves the perfection of the sample.

2) Because there are very few oscillations per beat it is rather difficult to establish the true maximum and minimum amplitudes of a beat unless measurements are made over a small range of fields at each angle. The tendency is to underestimate the amplitude of a beat maximum and overestimate that of a beat minimum.

3) Extremely slow sweeping of angle is essential if the record is not to be smeared out by the time constant of the recording equipment. It is not certain if in fact adequate care was always taken in this respect.

4) The sensitivity of the modulation method of detection may depend on the sample resistivity and this can vary appreciably with angle.

4.2. Theoretical causes. 1) The most important point is that the quartic approximation is not really adequate to describe the beat amplitudes quantitatively. This will be considered in more detail below.

2) The factor $w(\kappa)$ which has been ignored hitherto does in reality vary appreciably; this too will be discussed below.

3) The amplitude depends on the De Haas–Van Alphen frequency F, the cyclotron mass m, the g-factor and the Dingle temperature x, as well as on the geometrical effects we have considered. The most serious effect is the variation of gm; pure copper has a spin-zero [*i.e.*, cos $(\frac{1}{2}\pi gm/m_0)$ vanishes] at 24.05°, which is close to the angular range studied and consequently the factor $\cos(\frac{1}{2}\pi gm/m_0)$ varies rather rapidly with angle in this range. If we suppose that gm/m_0 varies linearily with angle away from the spin-zero (at which it has the value 3), it follows that the amplitude must vary proportionally to the difference of the angle from 24.05 °. This would increase the theoretical relative amplitudes by factors of 1.18, 1.28, 1.35 and 1.41 for 1 min, 1 max, 2 min and 2 max, respectively. These corrections, however, should not be relevant (or at least not so relevant) for the samples containing iron, for which the spin-zero is suppressed and this indeed makes them rather more suitable for comparison with theory.

The other changes, due to variations of F, m and x with angle are a good deal less serious. The change in F is only of order 0.2 % per degree and can be ignored; m and x have more effect because they enter in the exponential exponent and might increase the relative amplitude by as much as 10 % per degree in the same sense as does the spin factor.

5. *More realistic discussion of amplitudes.* The most important cause of the inability of the quartic approximation to give a good account of the beat amplitudes can be seen from fig. 4. It is that the noncentral minimum of F is in reality much sharper than that of the quartic approximation. Thus, if we think of the beats as

due to the interference of two periodic terms [such as in (10)], associated with the central maximum and the noncentral minima on either side, the relative amplitude due to the latter would be appreciably less than indicated in (10) and consequently the beats would be less deep, as observed. With a good deal of computing effort it proved possible to put this qualitative argument on a more quantitative basis. Because of the effort involved, computations were made for only 4 orientations: at 23.23 °, 23.00 °, 22.84 ° and 22.75 ° (respectively, approximately the position where F'' vanishes, and close to the positions of 0 max, 1 min and 1 max as predicted by the 5-term formula and the quartic approximation). For each of these orientations the computed values of $\Delta F(z)$ were converted into values of $\Delta\psi(z)$, where $\Delta\psi = 2\pi\Delta F/H$ for $H = 50.5$ kG; then, using a suitable interpolation procedure to give $\Delta\psi(z)$ at sufficiently close values of z, the values of

$$C = \int_0^{z_{\max}} \cos \Delta\psi \, dz \quad \text{and} \quad S = \int_0^{z_{\max}} \sin \Delta\psi \, dz,$$

were computed. The exact values of $z_{\max}$, the "cutoff" value (beyond which a closed orbit no longer exists) were not very precisely established and this uncertainty probably produced uncertainties of a few percent in the amplitudes $(C^2+S^2)^{\frac{1}{2}}$ and of a few degrees in the phase angles $\tan^{-1}S/C$. It is easily shown that if $(C^2+S^2)^{\frac{1}{2}}$ is multiplied by λ, where $\lambda = (1/6H)(\partial^4F/\partial z^4)^{\frac{1}{4}}$, the answer is directly comparable to the quantity plotted in fig. 2, and the 4 values of $\lambda(C^2+S^2)^{\frac{1}{2}}$ are indicated in fig. 2. This calculation strongly suggests that the beats should indeed be appreciably less pronounced than on the quartic approximation. The true first minimum and first maximum beat amplitudes cannot, however, be reliably assessed from the computed points, since, as has already been pointed out, the true positions of these may be slightly different from those of the quartic approximation. The question could be settled by more extensive computing, but this seemed hardly worthwhile in view of the uncertainties of the experimental data available for comparison. The main point brought out by the computations is that the quartic approximation is certainly not adequate for getting anything more than a qualitative picture of the beat amplitudes. It should be noticed, however, that the quartic approximation works reasonably well at 23.23 °, close to the position for which F'' vanishes.

An additional excuse for not going much further with the computing of C and S, was that we have up to now ignored the effect of the weighting factor $w(\kappa)$. In reality, each slab $d\kappa$ has a cyclotron mass m and a g-factor and since m varies rather rapidly as we approach the cutoff value of κ, the value of $\cos(\frac{1}{2}\pi gm/m_0)$ can pass through a spin-zero in the relevant range of κ, even if g is treated as constant. To get an idea of the possible importance of $w(\kappa)$ a calculation was made in which $m(\kappa)$ [in practice $m(z)$] was computed from the cross-sectional areas of two constant-energy surfaces closely on either side of the FS (see appendix) and the effect of $m(z)$, through both the exponential and the $\cos(\frac{1}{2}\pi g m/m_0)$ factors, was then evaluated to produce a $w(z)$ of plausible form.

Finally the integrals

$$C' = \int_0^{z_{max}} w(z) \cos \Delta\psi \, dz \quad \text{and} \quad S' = \int_0^{z_{max}} w(z) \sin \Delta\psi \, dz,$$

were computed and treated in the same way as the C and S of the previous calculation. Because of lack of time this was done for only a single orientation (23.23°). The result (not shown in fig. 2) is an amplitude about 7 % lower than that of the unweighted calculation. It is quite likely that the weighting might have a more drastic effect at orientations in the beat region.

6. *Attempts to measure the phase.* As already mentioned, an attempt to measure the phase of the oscillations in the region where it should be an "anomalous" $\pi/8$ rather than the "conventional" $\pi/4$, was not successful. Samples prepared by techniques which were quite good enough to permit phase measurement at symmetry orientations proved to be inadequate at the relevant orientation (close to 23.23 °) where F'' is expected to vanish. The trouble is that at this orientation F varies rapidly with orientation, so even the slightest variation of orientation over the sample (which would not matter at a symmetry direction) is enough to cause appreciable interference effects between one part of the sample and another. The consequence is that the effective average of the phase $2\pi[(F/H)-\gamma] + \phi$ is no longer quite linearly dependent on $1/H$, and the method of Coleridge and Templeton [3]) fails. In fact in each of two separate attempts it proved to be impossible to apply the method. The reason became apparent when the field dependence of amplitude was studied, and it was found that the appropriate logarithmic plot of field dependence of amplitude (designed to give a straight line whose slope is is determined by the Dingle temperature) was in fact something like a sine curve, as illustrated in fig. 6a. The long period of this dependence seemed to vary from one sample to another, but to be relatively insensitive to change in sample orientation; the "adjusted" amplitude (*i.e.*, the quantity whose logarithm is plotted) varies by a factor of between $1\frac{1}{2}$ and 3 or so. Because the effect varied from one sample to another, the most probable cause is very slight bending or perhaps mosaic structure of the sample but another possible cause needs brief consideration.

This is that the nature of the weighting function $w(\kappa)$ and the fact that the integration over κ is truncated, might cause an appreciably oscillatory character in the field dependence of the amplitude even at the position where $\alpha^{-\frac{1}{2}} = 0$. Thus in diagrams such as those of fig. 4, the scale of $\Delta\psi$ is field dependent and it would not be too surprising if truncation at a fixed κ produced an oscillatory field variation of amplitude. To test this suggestion a number of computations were made.

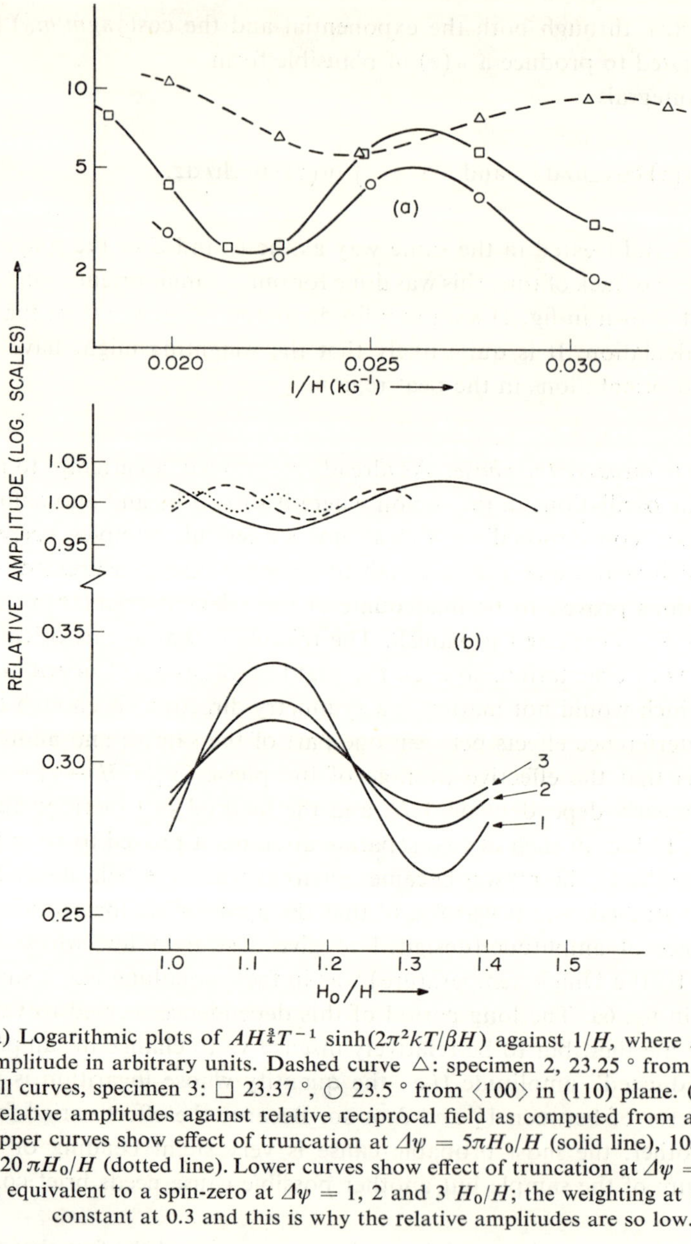

Fig. 6. (a) Logarithmic plots of $AH^{\frac{3}{4}}T^{-1}$ $\sinh(2\pi^2kT/\beta H)$ against $1/H$, where A is the experimental amplitude in arbitrary units. Dashed curve △: specimen 2, 23.25 ° from ⟨100⟩ in (110) plane. Full curves, specimen 3: □ 23.37 °, ○ 23.5 ° from ⟨100⟩ in (110) plane. (b) Logarithmic plots of relative amplitudes against relative reciprocal field as computed from a simple quartic model. Upper curves show effect of truncation at $\Delta\psi = 5\pi H_0/H$ (solid line), $10\pi H_0/H$ (dashed line) and $20\,\pi H_0/H$ (dotted line). Lower curves show effect of truncation at $\Delta\psi = 5\,\pi H_0/H$ with weighting equivalent to a spin-zero at $\Delta\psi = 1$, 2 and 3 H_0/H; the weighting at $\kappa = 0$ was kept constant at 0.3 and this is why the relative amplitudes are so low.

First of all both the weighted and unweighted computations at 23.23 ° were repeated at 40.4 kg and 30.3 as well as at 50.5 kg, but it was found that the departures from the expected $H^{\frac{1}{4}}$ dependence of the computed amplitudes were only of order 5 % rather than factors of $1\frac{1}{2}$ to 3 as observed. Secondly some computations were made on the behaviour of idealized models in which $\Delta\psi$ varied as κ^4, but the integrals were truncated at fixed κ; the integrals were computed both weighted to have a spin-zero in the relevant range and unweighted. Once again, beats in the field dependence both of amplitude and phase were produced, but although the spin-zero weighting did increase the beat amplitude, the beat amplitudes for plausible values of the parameters were always much less than those observed. Some typical results are shown in fig. 6b. It is clear that if it should later prove possible to make meaningful phase measurements by taking greater care in sample preparation and handling, it will be essential to take account of the modifications to the idealized theoretical predictions due to the real properties of the FS.

Acknowledgements. We should like to thank Dr. P. T. Coleridge for generous help in the experiments as well as for a number of valuable suggestions; one of us (D.S.) would like to thank the Division of Physics, N.R.C. Ottawa for hospitality during September 1972, when most of this work was carried out.

APPENDIX

Coefficients used in model computations. Most of the computations were based on a modification of Halse's[1]) 5-term formula (his table 6, Cu5) similar to that given by Coleridge and Templeton[3]) (their table 6, Cu5VI), but weighted to give a somewhat better fit to the neck. These coefficients are listed in table II as Cu5VI3.

TABLE II

	C_0	C_{200}	C_{211}	C_{220}	C_{310}	C_{222}	C_{321}
Cu5VI3	1.6 913 140	0.0 058 026	−0.4 280 209	−0.0 175 523	−0.0 348 530		
Cu76	3.349 228	0.191 001	0.126 891	−0.007 918	−0.087 210	−0.188 372	−0.061 040
Cu5P	1.691 578	0.006 923	−0.425 039	−0.017 087	−0.037 874		
Cu5M	1.691 762	0.006 937	−0.424 980	−0.016 494	−0.037 567		

The 7-term fit referred to in the text is listed as Cu76: this is the direct analogue of Cu5VI. The calculations of effective mass were made from the two constant-energy surfaces represented by the coefficients Cu5P and Cu5M used by Coleridge *et al.*[2]) and listed in their table 1(b). For the sake of completeness these coefficients, which are based directly on Halse's[1]) Cu5, but with only one tenth of the energy spread used by Halse in Cu5+ and Cu5−, are repeated here.

REFERENCES

1) Halse, M. R., Phil. Trans. Roy. Soc. **A265** (1969) 507.
2) Coleridge, P. T., Scott, G. B. and Templeton, I. M., Canad. J. Phys. **50** (1972) 1999.
3) Coleridge, P. T. and Templeton, I. M., J. Phys. F. **2** (1972) 643.
4) Gradshteyn, I. S. and Rhyzhik, I. M. Tables of Integrals, Series and Products, 4th Ed., Academic Press (New York and London) p. 398.
5) Bosacchi, B., Ketterson, J. B. and Windmiller, L. R., Phys. Rev. **B4** (1971) 1197.

Physica **69** (1973) 308–316 © *North-Holland Publishing Co.*

SUPERCONDUCTIVITY IN TERNARY ALLOYS OF TRANSITION METALS

A. R. MIEDEMA and M. H. VAN MAAREN

Philips Research Laboratories, Eindhoven, Nederland

Received 28 Juni 1973

Synopsis

Predictions are made on the concentration dependence of the transition temperature for superconductivity, T_c, in ternary solid solutions of transition metals.

Use is made of a model which has recently been shown to give a fair account of properties of binary transition-metal alloys; the metals in an alloy are considered to contribute individually to the density of states at the Fermi level.

It is found that in ternary disordered alloy systems T_c values do not exceed the highest value of one of the three corresponding binary systems. A number of examples is given from which it can be seen that considerable variations in T_c are possible in ternary alloys for which the average number of electrons per atom, Z_{av}, is kept constant.

1. *Introduction.* Whereas the superconducting and thermal properties of binary solid solutions of transition metals have been the subject of numerous experimental investigations, the information on ternary disordered alloy systems is very limited. One of the reasons for this is that, because of the enormous increase in the number of ternary systems relative to that of binary ones, a systematic investigation of ternary alloys is hardly possible. What one needs in this field is some sort of a guideline by means of which one can select the relatively more interesting ternary alloy systems. It is the aim of the present paper to provide such a guideline.

Until recently the only more nearly systematic approach to superconductivity possible is the one along the lines of Matthias's empirical rule[1]) for the occurrence of high and low transition temperatures for superconductivity, T_c. The rule states that the average number of valence electrons per atom, Z_{av}, is an important quantity the knowledge of which provides a qualitative expectation of the occurrence of high and low T_c values. In a sense Matthias's empirical rule is related to the rigid-band model for the electronic heat capacities of alloys of transition metals; within the rigid-band model it is assumed that in an alloy different metal atoms share their valence electrons thus making Z_{av} a quantity by means of which many alloy properties can be characterized. In addition there is a characteristic curve for the coefficient of the linear term in the electronic heat capacity, γ, which relates this quantity to Z_{av}. The γ *vs.* Z_{av} curve, and by definition also Matthias's relation between T_c and Z_{av}, will pass through the data points for the pure elements.

As mentioned above, Matthias's rule is not meant to be really quantitative in predicting T_c values of alloys, while the rigid-band model[2,3]) is difficult to apply to alloys of metals which are far apart in the periodic table or belong to different rows of this table.

Recently we showed[4,5]) that the extensive set of experimental data on γ and T_c for binary solid solutions of transition metals can be accurately described by means of a relatively simple model. This empirical description can be looked upon as being the counterpart of the rigid-band model. The constituting metals in a binary alloy are assumed to contribute individually to γ or to the electronic density of states at the Fermi energy, $N(0)$. In the field of superconductivity this implies individual contributions of the metals in an alloy to $\ln (T_c/\theta_D)^{-1}$.

In this paper we apply these ideas to predict the superconducting transition temperatures in units of the Debye temperature, θ_D, for ternary solid solutions of transition metals. We introduce the parameters needed to apply the model in section 2; these are not discussed or justified in the present paper, but are presented simply as a prescription to predict T_c/θ_D or γ values. Readers interested in the details are referred to earlier papers[4-6]); the model finds its justification in the fact that it accounts quantitatively for practically all experimental data on γ and T_c/θ_D available at present for binary-alloy systems.

2. *Formulae and empirical parameters.* The basic assumption in the present description of transition-metal alloys is that the metals in an alloy contribute individually to the density of states

$$N(0)_{\text{alloy}} = \sum_i c_i N(0)_i . \tag{1}$$

Here c_i is the concentration of metal i. Secondly it is assumed that the contributions to $N(0)$ are determined by the individual number of electrons per atom, Z_i, *i.e.*, $N(0)$ is taken to be of atomic origin rather than being determined by crystal-structure effects. In order to know Z_i it is not sufficient to know the position of element i in the periodic table (Z_i^0). One has to know in addition the transfer of electrons that takes place upon alloying.

$$Z_i = Z_i^0 + \Delta Z_i . \tag{2}$$

The latter correction can be quite large (of the order of one electron per atom) and can be calculated from the scale of the electro-negativities, ϕ^*, of transition metals which is presented in table I. The scale is closely related to that of the experimental work functions of pure metals as well as approximately proportional to Pauling-

TABLE I

The electro-negativity parameter for transition metals. The parameter ϕ^* is, in principle, proportional to the chemical potential for electrons in pure metals measured relative to the vacuum. Values have been derived from heat of formation data of alloys[6]).

Element	ϕ^* (V)	Element	ϕ^* (V)	Element	ϕ^* (V)
Sc	3.0	Y	2.95	Lu	2.8
Ti	3.4	Zr	3.15	Hf	3.3
V	4.25	Nb	4.0	Ta	4.05
Cr	4.65	Mo	4.65	W	4.8
Mn	4.75	Tc	5.3	Re	5.6
Fe	4.93	Ru	5.55	Os	5.55
Co	5.1	Rh	5.4	Ir	5.55
Ni	5.35	Pd	5.75	Pt	5.55

type[7]) electro-negativities. ϕ^* has been derived in such a way as to produce an accurate description of the stability (heat of formation) of binary alloys of transition metals[6]). The electron transfer ΔZ is proportional to the electro-negativity difference, $\Delta\phi^*$, as well as the relative concentration of the metals. In an analysis of a.o. magnetic properties[6]) the proportionality constant has been found to be 1.2, the resulting expression for ΔZ_i being (for three metals i, j and k)

$$\Delta Z_i = (1.2)(c_j \Delta\varphi^*_{ij} + c_k \Delta\varphi^*_{ik}). \tag{3}$$

Neglecting enhancement effects* the additivity of contributions to the density of states at the Fermi energy is equivalent to the additivity of γ.

$$\gamma_{\text{alloy}} = \sum_{i=1,2,3} c_i \gamma_i. \tag{4}$$

Having determined (empirically) a curve for γ as a function of Z one can simply read the three individual contributions, γ_i, from the curve after having calculated the three values for Z_i by means of relations (2), (3) and the table of electro-negativity values (table I). We show the two γ *versus* Z curves for the 4d and 5d series in fig. 1, the numerical values have been tabulated in ref. 4.

Within the original theory of Bardeen, Cooper and Schrieffer[8]) T_c is related to the electronic density of states at the Fermi level, E_F, by the formula

$$T_c = \theta_D \exp(-1/g); \qquad g = N(0)V, \tag{5}$$

where V is the net attractive interaction and θ_D the Debye temperature. Assuming that the interaction parameter V is an average value of those of the constituent

* In ref. 5 the influence of phonon enhancement on the heat capacity and the corresponding renormalization effects in the BCS parameter have been discussed in some detail. It is found that for all practical cases the present description is sufficiently accurate. This has to do with the fact that the enhancement/renormalization factor $1 + N(0)V_{ph}$ for the alloys is quite close to the weighted average of the enhancement factors for the individual contributions.

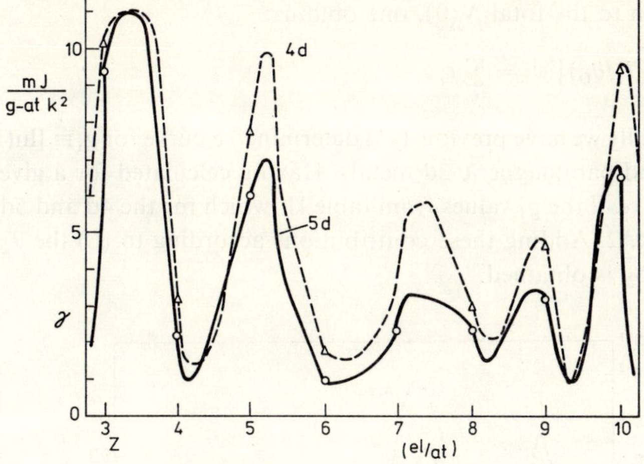

Fig. 1. The relation[4]) between the coefficient of the linear term in the electronic heat capacity, γ, and the number of valence electrons per atom Z for the 4d and 5d transition metals.

TABLE II

The interaction parameter $g \equiv N(0)V$ in the formalism $T_c/\theta_D = \exp(-1/g)$ as a function of the number of electrons per atom, Z

Z	3d	4d	5d	Z	4d	5d
3.2	0.220	0.175	0.20	6.6	0.145	0.115
3.4	0.265	0.23	0.24	6.8	0.18	0.135
3.6	0.28	0.28	0.23	7.0	0.245	0.182
3.8	0.265	0.305	0.22	7.1	0.275	0.255
3.9	0.225	0.245	0.19	7.4	0.275	0.24
4.0	0.143	0.156	0.126	7.6	0.25	0.225
4.1	0.085	0.08	0.07	7.8	0.195	0.195
4.4	0.085	0.10	0.085	8.0	0.142	0.151
4.6	0.095	0.155	0.13	8.1	0.12	0.12
4.8	0.15	0.235	0.19	8.2	0.105	0.11
5.0	0.230	0.292	0.246	8.4	0.11	0.14
5.2	0.24	0.36	0.30	8.6	0.12	0.15
5.4	0.235	0.39	0.28	8.8	0.13	0.15
5.6	0.215	0.345	0.25	9.0	$\simeq$ 0.076	0.120
5.8	0.145	0.25	0.225	9.2		0.095
6.0		0.160	0.096			
6.2	(0.095)	0.105	0.090			
6.4	(0.14)	0.115	0.10			

metals which is made up by weighting the individual contributions according to their contribution to the total $N(0)$, one obtains:

$$g_{\text{alloy}} \equiv [\ln (T_c/\theta_D)]^{-1} = \sum_i c_i g_i . \tag{6}$$

Again empirically we have previously[5]) determined a curve for $g_i \equiv [\ln(T_c/\theta_D)]^{-1}$ for the 4d, 5d and paramagnetic 3d metals. Having calculated for a given ternary alloy Z_i one can read the g_i values from table II, which for the 4d and 5d metals is also shown in fig. 2. Adding these contributions according to (6) the T_c/θ_D value for a ternary alloy is obtained.

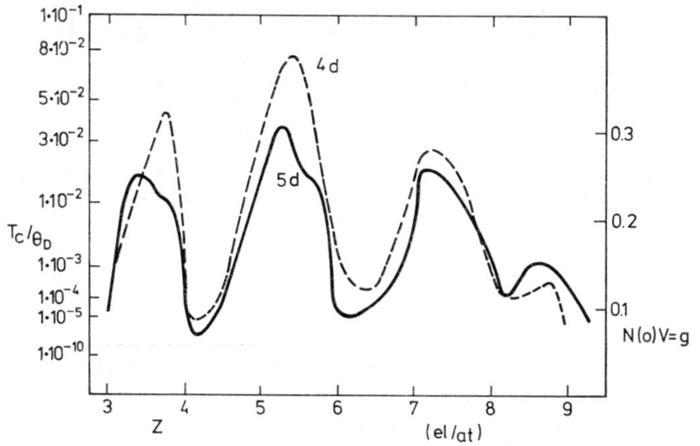

Fig. 2. Relation between T_c/θ_D and Z for 4d and 5d transition metals[5]). The values of the transition temperature in units of the Debye temperature are plotted in such a way that $[\ln(T_c/\theta_D]^{-1}$ is on a linear scale. Note that the 4d series is the more favourable for superconductivity.

Note that by definition the curves of figs. 1 and 2 pass through the data points for pure elements at values of Z = 3, 4, 5, 6, 7, 8, 9, 10. In that sense they agree with rigid-band ideas; however, the position of the maxima near the middle of the series is completely different. As already mentioned, the extensive data on γ and T_c/θ_D of binary solid solutions of transition metals are quite accurately accounted for by the present prescription. It is also found that isoelectronic systems (the minimum of T_c and γ in Nb–V, the maxima in Ti–Zr) can be described, while in contradistinction to the rigid-band model, the present "atomic model" can be equally well applied to near neighbours, as to elements which are far apart in the periodic table.

3. *Predictions for ternary alloys.* The interest in ternary alloys is twofold. Firstly one may wish to know whether or not ternary alloys offer the possibility of higher transition temperatures than those that occur in binary solid solutions of the same

metals. Secondly, ternary alloys make a simple confrontation of the present "atomic"-like description with the Z_{av} concept possible. Among ternary alloys and within one series of transitions metals (say the 5d series) one can change the consitution of the alloy without changing the average number of electrons per atom, for instance when alloying an element with equal atomic percentages of its two neighbours in the periodic table. In the rigid-band model or from Matthias's Z_{av} rule no large change in T_c is to be expected, whereas in the "atomic picture" in principle large changes are possible whether Z_{av} is constant or not. As discussed in ref. 6 Z_{av} = constant no longer implies a special case, apart from the fact that a linear relation between ϕ^* and Z^0 for the pure metals (existing in fact over a certain region of the periodic table) may result in an apparent rigid-band behaviour for dilute alloys.

By means of relations (2), (3) and (6) and tables I and II we have calculated T_c/θ_D for all relevant ternary solid solutions. It was not considered whether or not solid solutions do exist over the full range of concentrations; all T_c values given in the following do in principle apply to mixed crystals in which the atoms are statistically distributed over the lattice positions. For the more interesting ternary systems T_c/θ_D has been calculated at 10 atomic percent intervals in concentration; in all other cases the intervals amounted to 20 atomic percent.

A first result common to all ternary systems which have been considered (all permutations based on Sc, Ti, V, Cr–Y, Zr, Nb, Mo, Tc, Ru, Rh, Pd–Lu, Hf, Ta, W, Re, Os, Ir, Pt) is that there are no T_c/θ_D values within the ternary range that are larger than those occurring within one of the binary systems.

Considering ternary systems individually some interesting observations can be made. As a first example we present in fig. 3, results for alloys of W, Re and Os, metals which are nearest neighbours in the periodic table. Fig. 3 presents T_c/θ_D values as a function of concentration. The solid lines represent lines of equal T_c/θ_D. It is found that the highest T_c/θ_D value occurs near the binary alloy $Re_{80}W_{20}$. The calculated T_c/θ_D values show a complicated structure which does not at all indicate that Z_{av} is a relevant quantity for determining T_c. This is made clear in fig. 3 by drawing lines of equal Z_{av} (dashed lines, Z_{av} = 6.8, 7.0 and 7.2, respectively). For example, starting from pure Re for which $T_c/\theta_D = 4 \times 10^{-3}$ and adding equal amounts of its nearest neighbours in the same row of the periodic table W and Os, the transition temperature rises to $T_c/\theta_D = 17 \times 10^{-3}$ for $Re_{80}W_{10}Os_{10}$ and starts decreasing again at higher W and Os concentrations. This behaviour is not restricted to alloys for which $Z_{av} = 7.0$. Also starting from $Re_{80}Os_{20}$ an increase is predicted for T_c/θ_D when adding equal amounts of W and Os (increase to $T_c/\theta_D \simeq 1 \times 10^{-2}$ for $Re_{60}W_{10}Os_{30}$).

Fig. 4 shows the reverse situation. In alloys of Nb, Zr and Mo the transition temperature of Nb decreases considerably upon adding equal amounts of Zr and Mo.

One might suggest that the effects pointed to here, *viz.*, an increase for a metal

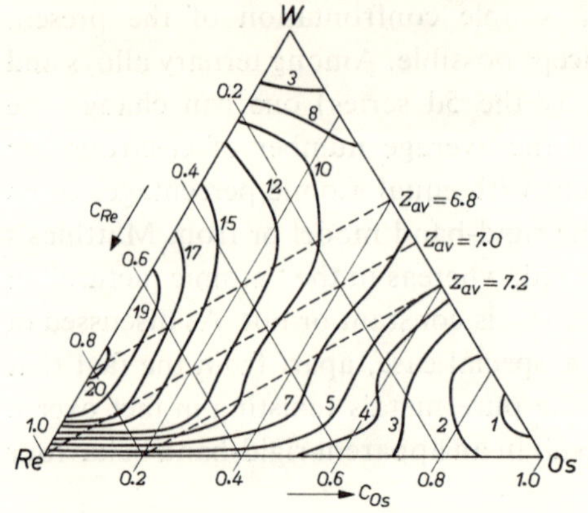

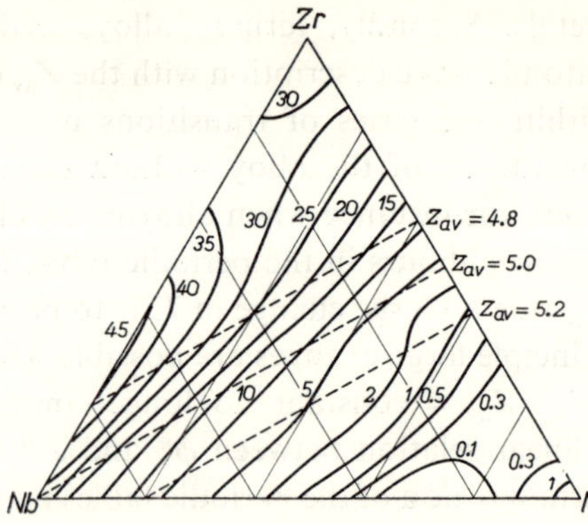

Fig. 3. Model values for T_c/θ_D in ternary solid solutions of W, Re and Os. Thick solid lines are lines of equal T_c/θ_D [numbers refer to $10^3 \times (T_c/\theta_D)$]; dashed lines correspond to constant values for the average number of conduction electrons per atom.

Fig. 4. Predicted values for $(T_c/\theta_D) \times 10^3$ for random alloys based on Zr, Nb and Mo.

(Re) having a low T_c and a decrease in T_c for a metal (Nb) having a high T_c for a series of alloys of constant Z_{av} is in fact trivial and equivalent to a smearing out of the density-of-states curve. However, there are examples of metals with low T_c which are predicted to remain low upon alloying and metals having a relatively high T_c which becomes higher upon alloying under the condition of constant Z_{av}. Such examples are given in figs. 5a and 5b. In alloys of Mo with its neighbours Nb and Tc the low transition temperature of Mo is predicted to remain practically unchanged on adding equal amounts Nb and Tc. Note that in fig. 5a lines of equal T_c/θ_D are identical to lines of equal Z_{av} over a large concentration range, so that for this particular case the atomic description cannot be distinguished from a Matthias-type description. Since the element Tc is unattractive from an experi-

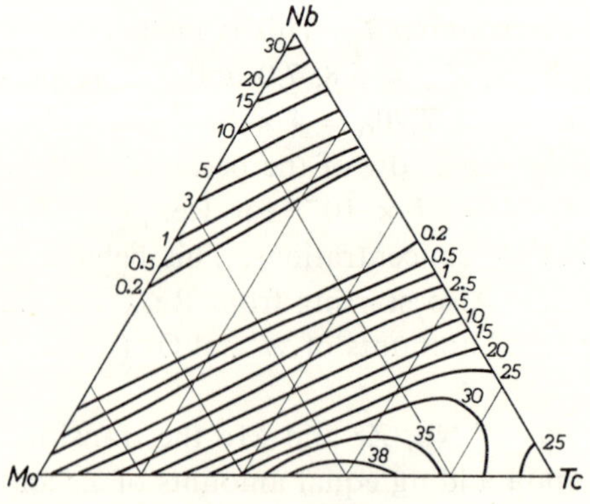

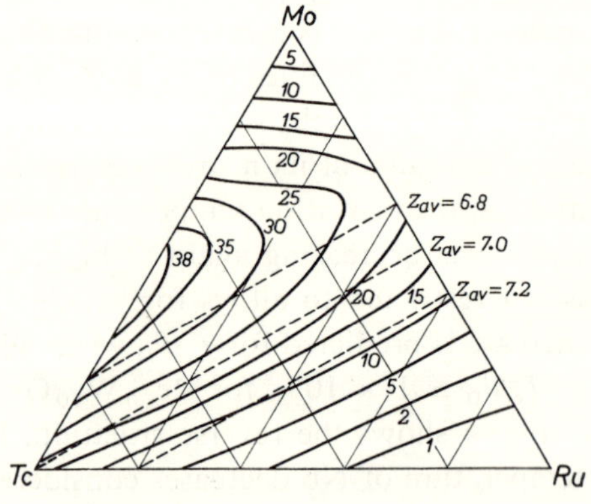

Fig. 5a, b. Apparent rigid-band model behaviour for Nb–Mo–Tc and Mo–Tc–Ru alloys. Solid lines are lines of equal $(T_c/\theta_D) \times 10^3$ (calculated), dashed lines correspond to equal Z_{av}.

mental point of view we mention the fact that the ternary system Mo–Ta–Re produces a very similar picture.

In fig. 5b we treat the case of a high T_c which increases when alloying with equal amounts of its neighbours in the periodic table (Tc with Mo and Ru). It is predicted that in the Ru-rich region of the diagram lines of constant T_c/θ_D coincide with lines of constant Z_{av}. This is not the case in the region rich in molybdenum. Starting from pure technecium an increase of 30 percent in T_c/θ_D is predicted when going to $Tc_{70}Mo_{15}Ru_{15}$.

4. *Comparison with experiments.* As already mentioned there is not much experimental information on superconducting transition temperatures in ternary solid solutions. The only system which has been investigated extensively is Ti–V–Nb. For this system Bellin, Sadagopan and Gatos[9]) measured T_c at 10 percent concentration differences.

The calculated T_c/θ_D values are given in fig. 6. The calculated diagram is not easily compared with the experimental results because the experiments give T_c values whereas we calculate T_c/θ_D. Since in this case T_c differences are small over a wide range of concentrations, while the metals alloyed have quite different θ_D

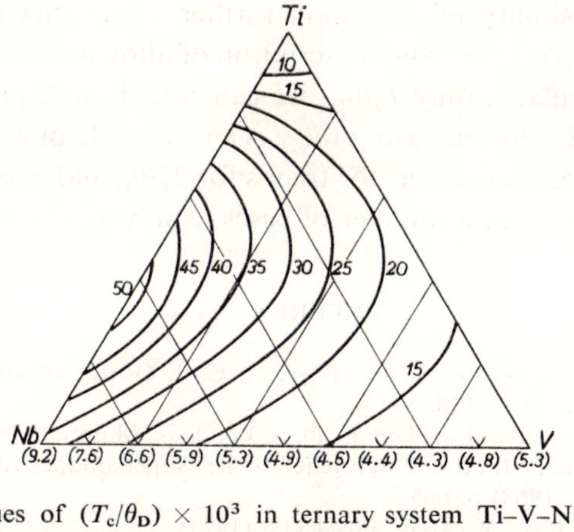

Fig. 6. Calculated values of $(T_c/\theta_D) \times 10^3$ in ternary system Ti–V–Nb. The values between brackets for the binary system Nb–V represent T_c values calculated from T_c/θ_D and experimental values for θ_D. There is a minimum for T_c, which is absent for T_c/θ_D.

values one can have a rather different behaviour for T_c and T_c/θ_D. The experiments do agree in that the highest T_c value is found along the Nb–Ti axis. The experimental minimum for T_c along the Nb–V axis is present in calculated T_c values [refs. 10, 11] but it is absent in T_c/θ_D itself. Note that for the other alloy systems discussed so far the variation in T_c/θ_D is sufficiently pronounced to make θ_D variations relatively unimportant.

Sadogopan *et al.*[12]) have reported T_c values for seven ternary alloys in the system Nb–Ti–Mo. The experimental diagram for T_c does correlate with the calculated one for T_c/θ_D, but without knowing θ_D a quantitative comparison is not possible.

Since the effect of adding equal amounts of W and Os to Re is quite spectacular (fig. 1) we performed some experiments in this system. Studying alloys $Re_{100-2x}Os_xW_x$ with x up to 20 we indeed found that there is a steep rise in T_c (of the order of a factor 3) at quite low x. A detailed comparison with calculated values is not possible since θ_D has not yet been measured and the width of the superconducting transition was quite broad in our samples (according to X-ray data the alloys were single phase).

5. *Conclusions.* We suggest on the basis of a model which accounts quantitatively for experimental data for binary alloys that no new high-temperature superconductors are to be expected among ternary solid solutions of transition metals, as compared to their binary alloys. This result applies to solid solutions only; the connection with the occurrence of superconductivity in ternary compounds or alloys of transition metals and non-transition metals (hydrogen) is not made.

In spite of the above negative statement experiments on ternary alloys may be interesting as a possibility of obtaining further arguments favouring either an "atomic" or a "collective electron" description of alloy properties. Note that while in this paper we calculated only T_c/θ_D, we can equally well predict the behaviour of γ for ternary solid solutions using the γ *versus* Z table of ref. 4. A combination of these data produces predictions for trends for T_c/θ_D and γ, respectively, through systems of alloys which, in a number of cases, can have the opposite sign.

REFERENCES

1) Matthias, B. T., Progress low Temp. Phys. II, C. J. Gorter editor, North-Holland Publ. Comp. (Amsterdam, 1957) 138.
2) Heiniger, F., Bucher, E. and Muller, J., Phys. kondens. Materie **5** (1966) 342.
3) Gladstone, C., Jensen, M. A. and Schrieffer, J. R., Superconductivity, R. D. Parks, editor, Dekker (New York, 1968) p. 665.
4) Miedema, A. R., J. Phys. F (Metal Physics) **3** (1973).
5) Miedema, A. R., J. Phys. F (Metal Physics) **3** (1973).
6) Miedema, A. R., J. less-common Metals **32** (1973) 117.
7) Pauling, L., The Nature of the Chemical Bond, Ithaca Cornell Univ. Press (1939) third ed. (1960).
8) Bardeen, J., Cooper, L. N. and Schrieffer, J. R., Phys. Rev. **108** (1957) 1175.
9) Bellin, P. H., Sadagopan, V. and Gatos, H. C., J. appl. Phys. **40** (1969) 3982.
10) Corsan, J. M. and Cooke, A. J., Phys. Status solidi **40** (1970) 657.
11) Ishikawa, M. and Toth, L. E., Phys. Rev. **B3** (1971) 1856.
12) Sadagopan, V., Gatos, H. C. and Olson, G., J. appl. Phys. **41** (1970) 1874.

Physica **69** (1973) 317–329 © *North-Holland Publishing Co.*

ENHANCED NUCLEAR MAGNETISM

B. BLEANEY

Clarendon Laboratory,
Oxford, England

Received 13 June 1973

Synopsis

In an electronic paramagnetic substance with "Van Vleck" temperature-independent susceptibility, interactions with the nuclear magnetic moment are enhanced through the magnetic hyperfine structure. These interactions include the effect of an external magnetic field, and the "pseudo-nuclear electric quadrupole interaction", together with magnetic-dipole and exchange interactions between neighbouring nuclear dipoles. The limits to the degree of enhancement are explored for "non-Kramers" ions of the lanthanide group, with particular reference to enhanced nuclear cooling, by examination of some special configurations of low-lying electronic energy levels. These are theoretically possible, but have not yet been realised experimentally.

1. *Introduction.* In the field of cryomagnetics the traditional type of paramagnetic working substance has been one whose susceptibility closely follows Curie's law. This may either be an electronic paramagnet, with $\chi^{E} \sim 1/T$ per gram ion, whose use for magnetic cooling was proposed by Debye[1]) and Giauque[2]); or a nuclear paramagnet, with $\chi^{N} \sim 10^{-6}/T$, whose use for magnetic cooling to much lower temperatures was suggested by Gorter[3]) and Kurti and Simon[4]).

A quite different class of paramagnetic substances comprises those where the electronic ground state of the magnetic ion is a singlet. Such a state can have no permanent magnetic moment, but when a magnetic field is applied, excited states are mixed in and the ion acquires an "induced" dipole moment whose size is proportional to the magnetic field. At temperatures sufficiently low that only the singlet state is occupied, the electronic susceptibility is independent of temperature, a phenomenon often referred to as "Van Vleck paramagnetism". The singlet state has zero electronic entropy, and by itself is useless for magnetic cooling or magnetic thermometry. If, however, the nucleus of the ion has a spin I, there is a nuclear entropy of $R \log (2I + 1)$, and a nuclear susceptibility which increases as the temperature is lowered.

Amongst substances of this type, we shall be particularly concerned with those which possess (a) a large magnetic hyperfine interaction, and (b) low-lying excited electronic states. In practice this means paramagnetic ions with an even number of electrons in a partly filled shell, whose energy levels are split by interactions arising from the crystal ligand field and the spin–orbit coupling. Provided that matrix elements of the electronic Zeeman interaction exist between the ground state and one (or more) low-lying excited state, the Van Vleck paramagnetic susceptibility will be large, since an external magnetic field can induce a large electronic magnetic moment in the ground state. This induced moment then interacts with the nuclear magnetic moment through the magnetic hyperfine interaction to give a "pseudo-nuclear" Zeeman interaction which may be orders of magnitude greater than the true nuclear Zeeman interaction. This is the phenomenon of "enhanced nuclear magnetism", and the degree of enhancement depends on the size of the magnetic field at the nucleus produced by the electrons. This, together with the actual nuclear magnetic moment, determines the size of the splitting of the nuclear levels.

The use of such nuclear splittings for "enhanced nuclear cooling" was suggested by Al'tshuler[5]), and experimental investigation of the field has been due mainly to Andres and Bucher[6,7]). Another possible application lies in magnetic thermometry using nuclear resonance techniques, where the transition probability is enhanced in a manner closely similar to that in ENDOR. Magnetic-dipole and exchange interactions between the nuclear moments are enormously increased, and it may well be that the most interesting development will lie in exploration of the cooperative magnetic phase. For enhanced nuclear magnetism this sets in at millidegrees kelvin, instead of the microdegrees needed for simple nuclear moments. In this paper we shall merely examine a few examples where the degree of enhancement is potentially very high in order to explore the limits to such enhancement.

2. *Enhanced magnetism of lanthanide nuclei*. The magnetic field at the nucleus produced by electrons in a partly filled shell increases with the nuclear charge, and ions of the 4f shell generally offer the most attractive possibilities. In the prevalent tripositive state, the interesting ions with an even number of electrons are fortunately those with odd nuclear charge; they possess a single stable isotope which, except

TABLE I

Nuclear properties of the lanthanide ions with an even number of electrons in the tripositive state (omitting Eu, $4f^6$, $J = 0$)

Mass		I	μ_I (nuclear magneton)	Q (barn)	A_J (MHz)
141	Pr	5/2	+4.25	−0.059	+1093
159	Tb	3/2	+2.00	+1.12	+ 530
165	Ho	7/2	+4.03	+2.4	+ 812
169	Tm	1/2	−0.231	—	− 394

in the case of ^{169}Tm, has a large nuclear magnetic moment. Their nuclear properties are summarized in table I.

For the purposes of analysis they have the additional advantage of a fairly simple hamiltonian. For the majority of lanthanide ions (the exceptions being $4f^5$, $4f^6$, $4f^7$) it is sufficient to take as a starting point the hamiltonian

$$\mathscr{H} = \mathscr{H}_X + g_J \mu_B(\boldsymbol{B} \cdot \boldsymbol{J}) + A_J(\boldsymbol{J} \cdot \boldsymbol{I}) - g_I \mu_B(\boldsymbol{B} \cdot \boldsymbol{I}) + \mathscr{H}_Q, \tag{1}$$

where $\mathscr{H}_X$ denotes the interaction with the ligand field, and the next term the Zeeman interaction for an ion with electronic angular momentum $J\hbar$. The last three terms represent, respectively, the magnetic hyperfine interaction with a nucleus of angular momentum $I\hbar$; the nuclear Zeeman interaction, with the nuclear moment expressed in Bohr magnetons, so that $g_I \sim 10^{-3}$; and the nuclear electric quadrupole interaction. We assume that $\mathscr{H}_X$ produces a singlet ground state $|G\rangle$, with a low-lying excited state $|E\rangle$ which we assume also to be a singlet; E lies above G by an energy Δ_z, and between these two states there exists an electronic matrix element $\langle E|J_z|G\rangle = \alpha_z$. In general there will also be matrix elements of J_x, J_y between $|G\rangle$ and other excited states, but we assume that these have energies so high that their admixtures to $|G\rangle$ can be neglected. This procedure gives a simple set of relations (see appendix) involving just the one electronic matrix element α_z, and we shall be concerned only with magnetic fields applied along the z axis, an axis which is determined by the ligand field and fixed in the crystal. We assume necessarily that this axis is parallel for all ions.

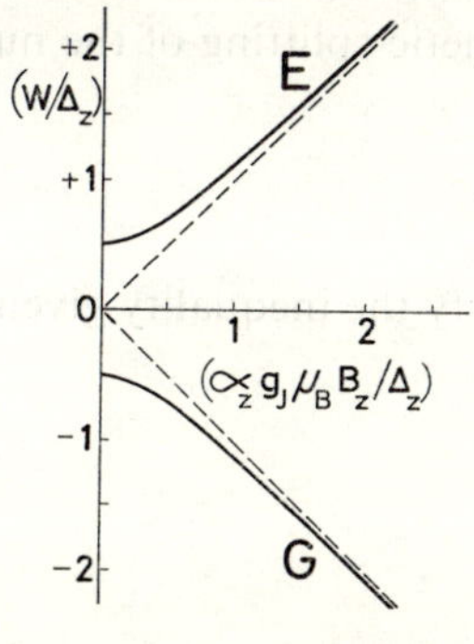

Fig. 1. Energy of two singlet levels with an initial splitting Δ_z, when a magnetic field B_z is applied (in reduced units).

The behaviour of the energy levels in a magnetic field B_z is shown in fig. 1. In the region where $(\alpha_z g_J \mu_B B_z) \ll \Delta_z$, we have a quadratic Zeeman effect, and at temperatures such that only the ground state is occupied each ion acquires an induced electronic magnetic moment

$$m_z^E = a_z(g_J \mu_B)^2 B_z, \tag{2}$$

where

$$a_z = 2\alpha_z^2/\Delta_z. \tag{3}$$

The electronic susceptibility is temperature independent and has the single component

$$\chi_z^{\mathrm{E}} = a_z N(g_J \mu_{\mathrm{B}})^2. \tag{4}$$

The value of α_z may vary widely, and we look for its maximum permissible value. This arises in the special case of a pair of states

$$\begin{aligned} |E\rangle &= 2^{-\frac{1}{2}}\{|J_z = +J\rangle + |J_z = -J\rangle\}, \\ |G\rangle &= 2^{-\frac{1}{2}}\{|J_z = +J\rangle - |J_z = -J\rangle\}, \end{aligned} \tag{5}$$

for which $\langle E|J_z|G\rangle = \alpha_z = J$, while the corresponding matrix elements of J_x, J_y are zero. To obtain numerical values we arbitrarily assume that $\Delta_z = 10$ K; with $\alpha_z = J$ this gives the values of a_z listed in table II, and since

$$\chi_z^{\mathrm{E}} = \tfrac{3}{40}(g_J J)^2 \text{ per gram ion} \tag{6}$$

the values of the electronic susceptibility are larger than those of a gram ion of, say, a nickel salt at 1 K.

When the ion acquires an electronic magnetic moment, a large magnetic field B_{E} is set up at the nucleus through the action of the magnetic hyperfine interaction. This field is proportional to the electronic moment and hence is determined by the external magnetic field. The magnetic splitting of the nuclear energy levels may be written as

$$W_{\mathrm{N}} = -g_I \mu_{\mathrm{B}} I_z(B_z + B_{\mathrm{E}}). \tag{7}$$

For small values of B_z which satisfy the inequality given earlier, B_{E} is proportional to B_z, so that

$$W_{\mathrm{N}} = -g_I \mu_{\mathrm{B}} I_z B_z(1 + K_z), \tag{8}$$

where

$$K_z = a_z(g_J A_J/g_I) \tag{9}$$

is the factor by which the nuclear g-factor is enhanced. Effectively the z component of the nuclear moment becomes

$$m_z^{\mathrm{N}} = g_I \mu_{\mathrm{B}} I_z(1 + K_z) \tag{10}$$

and when $K_z \gg 1$, the value for $I_z = I$ is

$$m_z^{\mathrm{N}} = a_z g_J A_J I. \tag{11}$$

The values of this quantity, given in table II, approach, and in one case exceed, a Bohr magneton.

TABLE II

Values of various parameters, assuming $a_z = 2\alpha_z^2/\Delta_z$ with $\alpha_z = J$ and $\Delta_z = 10$ K. K_z is the nuclear enhancement factor in low fields and the last column gives the effective nuclear moment

Ion	J	a_z (deg K)$^{-1}$	JA_J (mK)	$K_z = a_z(g_J A_J/g_I)$	$a_z g_J A_J I$ (Bohr magneton)
Pr^{3+}	4	3.2	+210	145	0.336
Tb^{3+}	6	7.2	+153	379	0.413
Ho^{3+}	8	12.8	+312	995	2.18
Tm^{3+}	6	7.2	−113	623	−0.078

The enhancement factors K_z are also given in table II. Since, in our approximation, the nuclear g factor perpendicular to the z axis is only g_I, the nuclear susceptibility is highly anisotropic. Parallel to the z axis it is increased by a factor $(1 + K_z)^2$, so that it may be orders of magnitude larger than the unenhanced nuclear susceptibility. It follows Curie's law down to temperatures where kT is of the same order as the enhanced nuclear interactions discussed in section 4.

3. *Enhanced nuclear cooling.* In the process of magnetic cooling the first step is isothermal magnetization in a large external magnetic field. For our purpose this needs to be so large that $(\alpha_z g_J \mu_B B_z) \gg \Delta_z$; this means that in fig. 1 we have reached the region where the energy levels are diverging almost linearly with B_z, and the electronic Zeeman splitting is virtually independent of the initial splitting Δ_z. In practice this may not require more than a few tesla, directed in our example along the z axis. The magnetic nuclear Zeeman splitting is given by eq. (7) or, more precisely, by eq. (A.10). It follows from eq. (A.11) that B_E, the magnetic field at the nucleus generated by the electrons, reaches a limiting value just equal to that given by the hyperfine interaction when the full electronic magnetic moment of the ground state is achieved. In our example this corresponds to that for a level with $|J_z| = J$, and the values of B_E are given in table III. Obviously these are enormous compared with any possible value of B_z, so that the latter may be ignored. The splitting between successive nuclear levels is just (JA_J), whose values in thermal units are given in table II. It is clear that by magnetization at a temperature of say 50 mK, a very large fraction of the nuclear entropy can be removed, and this is confirmed by table III. For comparison, figures are given also for the entropy removed from copper nuclei in an external field of 8 T at the lower temperature of 10 mK. The gain is enormous, but there is a price to be paid: the temperature reached on demagnetization to zero applied field is not in the region of micro-

TABLE III

Values of the maximum electronic magnetic field B_E at the nucleus, and the entropy removed. For the lanthanons, $x = JA_J/kT$, with $T = 50$ mK. For copper, a field of 8 tesla at $T = 10$ mK is assumed [8])

Ion	I	B_E (tesla)	x	Entropy (S/R) fraction removed	Entropy (S/R) total
Pr^{3+}	5/2	337	4.19	96 %	1.792
Tb^{3+}	3/2	314	3.05	86 %	1.386
Ho^{3+}	7/2	740	6.22	99 %	2.079
Tm^{3+}	1/2	662	2.27	55 %	0.693
Cu	3/2	(8)	0.43	10 %	1.386

degrees kelvin, as in a true nuclear cooling experiment, but in the region of millidegrees. This temperature is of course of the same order as that where the nuclear susceptibility departs from Curie's law, and is therefore determined mainly by the enhanced nuclear interactions which we now consider.

4. *Enhanced nuclear interactions*. Ordinarily, interactions between nuclei are very small, but we are dealing with nuclear lambs dressed in electronic wolves' clothing. As a result, the nuclear interactions may be greatly enhanced. We consider first the interactions between neighbouring nuclei.

The simplest nuclear interaction is the dipole–dipole interaction between neighbouring nuclei, which is increased by a factor $(1 + K_z)^2$ for the z components of the nuclear dipole moments. In our example we can neglect the x, y components which are not enhanced, giving the simple hamiltonian

$$\mathscr{H}_{ij} = (1 + K_z)^2 g_I^2 \mu_B^2 r^{-3}(1 - 3\cos^2\theta) I_{iz} I_{jz}, \tag{12}$$

where θ is the angle between the z axis and the line joining ions i, j whose separation is r.

Under the influence of the nuclear magnetic moment, the electron shells around each nucleus are partly polarized in directions parallel to the nuclear moments. If between the electron shells on neighbouring ions i, j there is anisotropic exchange interaction which can be written as

$$\mathscr{H}_E = (J_i \cdot \mathscr{J}_{ij}^E \cdot J_j) \tag{13}$$

then matrix elements of the form

$$(A_J)_i (I_i \cdot J_i)(J_i \cdot \mathscr{J}_{ij}^E \cdot J_j)(A_J)_j (J_j \cdot I_j) \tag{14}$$

give rise to a nuclear exchange hamiltonian of the form

$$\mathscr{H}_N = (I_i \cdot \mathscr{J}_{ij}^N \cdot I_j) \tag{15}$$

whose z component is

$$(\mathscr{J}_{ij}^N)_z I_{iz} I_{jz} = (a_z A_J)_i (a_z A_J)_j (\mathscr{J}_{ij}^E)_z I_{iz} I_{jz}\,. \tag{16}$$

The nuclear exchange interaction in our example will be highly anisotropic even if the electronic exchange is isotropic, being an Ising type interaction involving only the z components, as in the dipole–dipole interaction (12). For a pair of ^{165}Ho ions, with the parameters assumed above, $(a_z A_J)^2 = 0.25$, showing that the effective nuclear exchange interaction may be only one order of magnitude smaller than the electronic exchange interaction. In metals this may predominate over the enhanced nuclear dipole–dipole interaction, since for a pair of ^{165}Ho ions, 5 A apart, the coefficient of $I_{iz}I_{jz}$ in (12) is only some -5 mK even with maximum enhancement.

Apart from interactions between ions, there is within each ion a "pseudo-quadrupole" interaction

$$P_z\{I_z^2 - \tfrac{1}{3}I(I+1)\}, \tag{17}$$

where from eq. (A.9),

$$P_z = -\tfrac{1}{2}a_z A_J^2\,. \tag{18}$$

This is a second-order effect of the magnetic hyperfine interaction which must be added to the true quadrupole interactions. In our example of ^{165}Ho, eq. (18) seems likely to be the predominating effect, with P_z about -10 mK (see table 4) compared with $+3$ mK for the true interaction with the 4f electrons, but the contribution from the ligand field cannot be estimated without knowing the crystal structure.

TABLE IV

Values of the pseudo-nuclear quadrupole-splitting parameter $P_z = -\frac{1}{2}a_z A_J{}^2$. The last column gives the overall splitting of the nuclear levels

Ion	I	P_z (mK)	$P_z(I^2-\frac{1}{4})$ (mK)
Pr^{3+}	3/2	−4.41	− 26.5
Tb^{3+}	3/2	−2.34	− 4.6
Ho^{3+}	7/2	−9.73	−117
Tm^{3+}	1/2	—	—

The thermal effects of these various interactions may be judged in a first approximation by comparing their contributions to the high-temperature tail of the specific heat. We have

$$CT^2/R = \frac{1}{2}\left\{\frac{I(I+1)}{3k}\right\}^2 \sum_{j>i} (\mathscr{I}^{\mathrm{N}}_{ij})^2_z + \frac{1}{45k^2} P_z^2 I(I+1)(2I-1)(2I+3), \quad (19)$$

where $(\mathscr{I}^{\mathrm{N}}_{ij})_z$ is now the numerical sum of the two terms in (12) and (16). It turns out that the second term of the right-hand side of eq. (19), with $P_z = -10$ mK, gives a contribution rather larger than the first term if only dipole–dipole interaction is included. Since we have Kramers' degeneracy in the nuclear spin system, the quadrupole interaction cannot remove all the degeneracy in the nuclear levels; this must occur through the internuclear interactions, but in our simplified model we have a purely Ising-type interaction for which it is difficult to predict where this would occur.

5. *Some other possibilities.* We now consider some cases where the lowest electronic energy levels produced by the action of the ligand field are quite different. Of particular interest is the set of levels shown in fig. 2(a), use of which should make it possible to reach much lower temperatures through enhanced nuclear cooling.

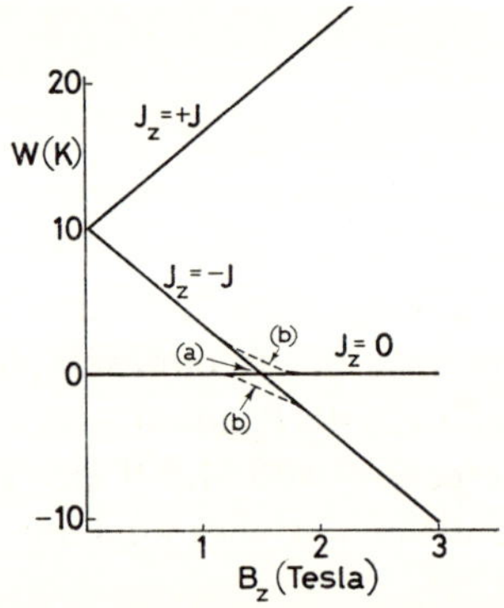

Fig. 2. Splitting in a magnetic field B_z of three levels, $|J_z = 0\rangle$ and $|J_z = \pm J\rangle$. (a) The levels $J_z = 0$ and $-J$ cross if no matrix elements exist between them. (b) These levels follow the broken lines, converging but not crossing, if there is a small component of B perpendicular to the z axis.

In a ligand field of axial symmetry the ground state could be the electronic singlet state $|J_z = 0\rangle$, but with the doublet $|J_z = \pm J\rangle$ only a few degrees higher in energy. If a large magnetic field is applied along the symmetry axis, the state $|J_z = -J\rangle$ can be made to cross the state $|J_z = 0\rangle$, thus becoming the new ground state and possessing a large hyperfine interaction which gives a splitting JA_J of the nuclear levels. For the ion Ho^{3+}, a field of 2 tesla is sufficient to reduce the energy of the state $|J_z = -J\rangle$ by some 14 K, and an isothermal magnetization at 50 mK would remove the nuclear entropy to the extent given in table III.

On reducing the applied field to the point where the levels $J_z = -J$ and $J_z = 0$ cross, the electronic entropy (and hence also the nuclear entropy in an adiabatic process) depends on the extent to which the populations of the two electronic levels become equalized. Transitions between states with such different values of J_z have a low probability, and at first sight it might be thought that on demagnetizing further the system would remain in the $J_z = -J$ state, which is now an excited state so that the electronic system is at a negative temperature. In practice this is unlikely to occur, since a component of the applied field normal to the z axis will admix (to a small extent) all states of different J_z, but with the same value of I_z, so that the levels do not truly cross, but approach and diverge as indicated in fig. 2(b). Then, provided that demagnetization can proceed in such a way that the system always remains in the lowest electronic state, we should return at zero field to a state which is accurately described as $|J_z = 0\rangle$. For this state the enhanced nuclear interactions are small provided that the electronic states $|J_z = \pm 1\rangle$ lie much higher in energy, and the temperature reached on demagnetization should be correspondingly lower.

A somewhat different situation occurs if the ground state is $|J_z = 0\rangle$ and the nearby doublet is $|J_z = \pm 1\rangle$, as in fig. 3, which shows also the nuclear splitting for $I = \frac{1}{2}$. In this case the states $|J_z, I_z\rangle$ equal to $|-1, +\frac{1}{2}\rangle$ and $|0, -\frac{1}{2}\rangle$ are admixed by the hyperfine interaction and cannot cross. Thus the level (a), which is described approximately by $|-1, +\frac{1}{2}\rangle$ in a strong applied field and by $|0, -\frac{1}{2}\rangle$ in a weak field, is always the lowest level when A_J is positive. If in a strong field nearly all the nuclear entropy is removed, then this is the only level with an appreciable population. On demagnetization we return to the situation where the

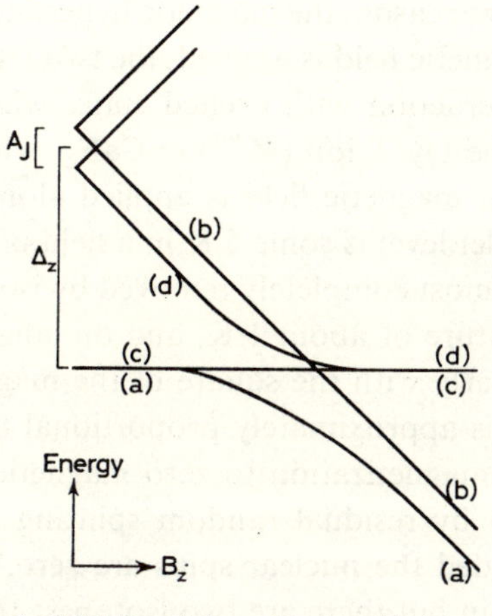

Fig. 3. Splitting in a magnetic field B_z of three levels with $|J_z = 0\rangle$ and $|J_z = \pm 1\rangle$. Interaction is included with a nuclear spin $I = \frac{1}{2}$, through a term $A_J(\boldsymbol{J} \cdot \boldsymbol{I})$ with a positive value of A_J.

electronic state is $|J_z = 0\rangle$. The effective nuclear temperature depends on the extent to which the populations become equalized for the states (a), (c) which are degenerate in zero field, where they are approximately $|0, -\frac{1}{2}\rangle$ and $|0, +\frac{1}{2}\rangle$.

The nuclear interactions are not so small as in the preceding example where the low-lying electronic doublet is $|J_z = \pm J\rangle$ with $J > 1$. There exist matrix elements $\langle J_z = \pm 1 | J_x, J_y | J_z = 0\rangle = \frac{1}{2}\{J(J+1)\}^{\frac{1}{2}}$ which give rise to enhanced nuclear interactions for the x, y components of the magnetic dipole and exchange interactions. Thus these interactions must again be highly anisotropic, since their z components are not enhanced. Also, for $I > \frac{1}{2}$, there will be a pseudo-nuclear electric quadrupole interaction of the form (17), but with a positive sign for P_z.

In the examples discussed hitherto the ions must be in a ligand field of axial symmetry to produce the electronic level splittings which have been assumed. The nuclear effects must similarly have axial symmetry, and we have seen that they are likely to be highly anisotropic. In contrast, for ions in ligand fields of cubic symmetry, the susceptibility and the enhancement factors must be isotropic. The electronic states are complicated admixtures of various values of J_z, and the quantities α, K (where we may now drop the subscripts) are not so large as for the special cases assumed above. Nevertheless a good fraction of the nuclear entropy can be removed under favourable circumstances, and the fact that the nuclear electric quadrupole interaction must be zero in a singlet electronic state means that on demagnetization the temperature reached is controlled solely by the interactions between the nuclear spins.

For ions with $J = 4$, 6 and 8, a cubic ligand field produces splittings into 4, 6 and 7 levels, respectively. In all, only four of these are singlet levels (Γ_1 or Γ_2), but there are also four doublet levels (denoted by the symbol Γ_3), which have some curious properties. They are "non-magnetic"; that is, neither state has a permanent electronic magnetic moment because all matrix elements of J_x, J_y, J_z within the doublet are zero. For the same reason, the magnetic hyperfine interaction within the doublet is zero. When a magnetic field is applied, the two levels split apart through a second-order Zeeman interaction with excited states which is different for the two levels. An example is the Dy^{2+} ion ($4f^{10}$) in CaF_2, whose lowest eight levels are shown in fig. 4. When a magnetic field is applied along a four-fold axis, the splitting of the lowest doublet level is some 5 K in a field of 2 tesla. The electronic entropy of $R \log 2$ can be almost completely removed by isothermal magnetization in such a field at a temperature of about 1 K, and on adiabatic demagnetization the temperature will fall nearly with the square of the magnetic field because the splitting of the Γ_3 doublet is approximately proportional to H^2. This is a purely electronic effect, and on demagnetization to zero magnetic field the temperature reached will be determined by residual random splitting of the doublet due to strains in the crystal, provided the nuclear spins are zero. For dysprosium 56 % of the isotopes have zero spin but there are two isotopes, 161 and 163 which have $I = \frac{5}{2}$. In zero magnetic field there will be a nuclear electric quadrupole interaction

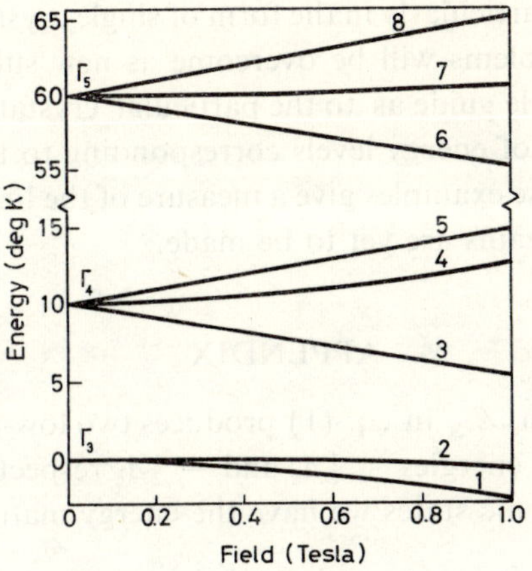

Fig. 4. Effect of a magnetic field (parallel to a four-fold axis) on Dy^{2+} ($4f^{10}$, $J = 8$) in CaF_2, showing the second-order Zeeman splitting of the lowest doublet through interaction with levels of the two excited triplets (after ref. 10).

of an unusual kind [Abragam and Bleaney[9]), chap. 18.6]. For an electronic doublet with $I = \frac{5}{2}$ we have altogether 12 states, which in a purely cubic field split into two doublets and two quartets. This may be blurred by the strain splitting of the electronic doublet, but the work of Mergerian *et al.*[10]) suggests this is not large. The main problem in this particular substance is conversion of the excess of Dy^{3+} ions into Dy^{2+} ions, but this would not arise for a Γ_3 doublet of a tripositive ion. Such a doublet occurs once each for $J = 4$ and $J = 6$, and twice for $J = 8$, as shown in table V.

TABLE V

Splitting of $J = 4, 6, 8$ into singlet, doublet and triplet levels under the action of a cubic ligand field

	Singlets	Doublets	Triplets
$J = 4$	Γ_1	Γ_3	$\Gamma_4 + \Gamma_5$
$J = 6$	$\Gamma_1 + \Gamma_2$	Γ_3	$\Gamma_4 + 2\Gamma_5$
$J = 8$	Γ_1	$2\Gamma_3$	$2\Gamma_4 + 2\Gamma_5$

5. *Conclusion.* Electronic magnetic cooling was achieved experimentally some ten years after it was first suggested, while nuclear cooling took nearly twenty years. Enhanced nuclear cooling was suggested theoretically by Al'tshuler[5]), and has been explored experimentally in the pioneer work of Andres and Bucher[6, 7]). Their work has used intermetallic compounds of the lanthanides, where the conduction electrons shorten the nuclear relaxation times but also introduce exchange interactions. Such compounds are often difficult to produce with a controlled

chemical composition, particularly in the form of single crystals. We may anticipate that these technical problems will be overcome as new substances are tried, but unfortunately there is little guide as to the particular crystal structure which might produce the special sets of energy levels corresponding to the examples discussed above. Nevertheless, these examples give a measure of the limits of the method, and show that considerable gains are yet to be made.

APPENDIX

If the ligand field term $\mathscr{H}_X$ in eq. (1) produces two low-lying electronic singlet states, $|E\rangle$ and $|G\rangle$ with energies $+\frac{1}{2}\Delta_z$ and $-\frac{1}{2}\Delta_z$ respectively, then, neglecting $\mathscr{H}_Q$ and all other electronic states we have the energy matrix

$$\begin{array}{c|cc|} E & +\frac{1}{2}\Delta_z - g_I\mu_B B_z I_z & \alpha_z(g_J\mu_B B_z + A_J I_z) \\ G & \alpha_z(g_J\mu_B B_z + A_J I_z) & -\frac{1}{2}\Delta_z - g_I\mu_B B_z I_z \end{array}, \tag{A.1}$$

where I_z is not an operator but simply denotes the nuclear magnetic quantum number. The energy levels are

$$W_{\pm} = -g_I\mu_B B_z I_z \pm \tfrac{1}{2}\Delta_z \sec\theta, \tag{A.2}$$

where

$$\tan\theta = 2\alpha_z(g_J\mu_B B_z + A_J I_z)/\Delta_z. \tag{A.3}$$

In the ground state the net magnetic moment has the component

$$m_z = -\delta W/\delta B_z = g_I\mu_B I_z + \alpha_z g_J\mu_B \sin\theta, \tag{A.4}$$

where the first term is the projection of the nuclear moment while the second contains both the induced electronic moment and the enhanced nuclear moment.

When θ is so small that $\sin\theta$ can be replaced by θ, we have approximately

$$m_z = g_I\mu_B I_z(1 + K_z) + a_z(g_J\mu_B)^2 B_z, \tag{A.5}$$

where

$$a_z = 2\alpha_z^2/\Delta_z. \tag{A.6}$$

The last term in (A.5) is the induced electronic magnetic moment and the first term the enhanced nuclear magnetic moment. The nuclear enhancement factor K_z is given by

$$K_z = a_z g_J A_J/g_I \tag{A.7}$$

$$= 2a_z g_J \mu_B^2\langle J||N||J\rangle\langle r^{-3}\rangle, \tag{A.8}$$

where the symbols are those used by Abragam and Bleaney[9]), and it follows from eq. (A.8) that K_z is always positive.

When B_z is zero, θ is small provided that the hyperfine interaction is small compared with Δ_z, and the lower energy level can be written as

$$W_- = -\tfrac{1}{2}\Delta_z - (\alpha_z^2 A_J^2/\Delta_z)I_z^2 = -\tfrac{1}{2}\Delta_z - \tfrac{1}{2}a_z A_J^2 I_z^2, \tag{A.9}$$

where the last term is the "Pseudo-nuclear electric quadrupole interaction". This must be added to the true nuclear electric-quadrupole interaction with the electric-field gradient both from the 4f electrons and from the ligand field with the appropriate Sternheimer factors.

When a very strong external magnetic field is applied, it is convenient to rewrite (A.2) in the form

$$W_- = -g_I \mu_B B_z I_z - \alpha_z(g_J \mu_B B_z + A_J I_z) \operatorname{cosec} \theta \tag{A.10}$$

and when $\operatorname{cosec} \theta \to 1$ (the strong-field limit) the nuclear splitting is given by

$$W_N = -g_I \mu_B B_z I_z - \alpha_z A_J I_z \tag{A.11}$$

showing that the enhanced magnetic nuclear interaction reaches a limit set by the hyperfine structure. The electronic Zeeman energy is given by the second term in (A.10); for $\operatorname{cosec} \theta = 1$ this becomes simply $-\alpha_z g_J \mu_B B_z$ corresponding to the asymptotic straight line in fig. 1.

REFERENCES

1) Debye, P., Ann. Physik **81** (1926) 1184.
2) Giauque, W. F., J. Amer. Chem. Soc. **49** (1927) 1864, 1870.
3) Gorter, C. J., Phys. Z. **35** (1934) 923.
4) Kurti, N. and Simon, F. E., Proc. Roy. Soc. **A149** (1935) 152.
5) Al'tshuler, S. A., Soviet Physics – JETP Letters **3** (1966) 112.
6) Andres, K. and Bucher, E., Phys. Rev. Letters **21** (1968) 1221, **22** (1969) 600, **24** (1970) 1181.
7) Bucher, E., Andres, K., Maita, J. P., Cooper, A. S. and Longinotti, L. D., J. Phys. (Supplement) **32** (1970) C1-114.
8) Symko, O. G., J. low Temp. Phys. **1** (1969) 451.
9) Abragam, A. and Bleaney, B., Electron Paramagnetic Resonance, Clarendon Press (Oxford, 1969).
10) Mergerian, D., Harrop, I. H., Stombler, M. P. and Krikorian, K. C., Phys. Rev. **153** (1967) 349.

Physica **69** (1973) 330–335 © *North-Holland Publishing Co.*

SUR LA RÉPARTITION ENTRE ÉMISSION LUMINEUSE SPONTANÉE ET ÉMISSION LUMINEUSE INDUITE

A. KASTLER

Laboratoire de Physique de l'Ecole Normale Supérieure, Paris, France

Reçu le 24 mai 1973

Résumé

Dans un mémoire fondamental paru en 1917, Einstein avait montré que l'émission de rayonnement par un atome fait entrer en jeu deux processus différents d'émission, l'émission spontanée et l'émission induite. Il avait montré qu'on retrouve ainsi d'une manière particulièrement simple la relation de Planck qui décrit le rayonnement d'une cavité en équilibre thermique avec la matière (rayonnement du corps noir).

Dans la suite, on a considéré les deux processus comme entièrement indépendants, et dans ces conditions l'intensité du rayonnement spontané ne doit pas être influencée par la présence auprès de l'atome de la densité de radiation qui provoque l'émission induite. En analysant le processus d'échange d'énergie entre l'atome et les oscillateurs harmoniques du vide qui représentent les modes d'ondes stationnaires d'une cavité (ou les cellules de l'espace des phases), l'auteur donne une nouvelle définition des deux processus de rayonnement qui semble indiquer que ces processus pourraient être interdépendants.

1. *Les relations d'Einstein.* En 1917, Einstein[1]) avait établi la distinction entre émission spontanée et émission induite de rayonnement par les atomes. L'émission spontanée est une émission ayant des caractères d'incohérence et possédant des directions d'émission indépendantes des directions des radiations présentes auprès de l'atome tandis que l'émission induite est l'équivalent d'une absorption négative et renforce le rayonnement inducteur. En désignant par $E_2 - E_1 = h\nu$ l'intervalle d'énergie entre deux niveaux atomiques, le niveau inférieur E_1 et le niveau supérieur E_2, en appelant N_1 et N_2 les populations respectives de ces niveaux et $\rho_\nu = \mathrm{d}\rho/\mathrm{d}\nu$ la densité spectrale d'énergie de l'intervalle de fréquence ν à $\nu + \mathrm{d}\nu$ près de l'atome, les nombres de photons absorbés et émis par unité de temps sont donnés par les relations:

$$I_\mathrm{a} = N_1 B_{12} \rho_\nu \quad \text{et} \quad I_\mathrm{e} = N_2 (A_{21} + B_{21} \rho_\nu). \tag{1}$$

A l'équilibre thermique la relation de Boltzmann détermine le rapport des populations des niveaux atomiques:

$$\frac{N_2/g_2}{N_1/g_1} = e^{-h\nu/kT} = e^{-\sigma} \quad \text{en posant} \quad \sigma = \frac{h\nu}{kT}, \tag{2}$$

g_2 et g_1 désignant les poids statistiques (ou les degrés de dégénérescence) des deux niveaux E_2 et E_1.

La relation qu'on tire de ces formules pour ρ_ν à l'équilibre thermique doit s'identifier avec la relation de Planck, ce qui exige que

$$B_{12} = \frac{g_2}{g_1} B_{21} \quad \text{et} \quad \frac{A_{21}}{B_{21}} = \frac{8\pi\nu^2}{c^3} h\nu. \tag{3}$$

Nous poserons dans la suite $A_{21} = A$ et $B_{21} = B$. Le coefficient A a les dimensions de l'inverse d'un temps et s'identifie avec la durée de vie moyenne du niveau supérieur E_2 lorsque la transition $E_2 \to E_1$ est l'unique transition partant du niveau supérieur E_2 vers le bas.

2. *Les modes d'ondes stationnaires du rayonnement.* Le rayonnement électromagnétique dans une cavité se répartit, comme Lord Rayleigh[2]) et Jeans[3]) l'ont montré, entre un nombre fini de "modes d'ondes stationnaires". Ce nombre, par unité de volume, et dans l'unité d'intervalle de fréquence $\Delta\nu = 1$ au voisinage de la fréquence ν est donné par

$$g = 8\pi\nu^2/c^3. \tag{4}$$

Si nous désignons par $\bar{n}$ le nombre moyen de photons par mode et par $\bar{E}$ l'énergie moyenne de radiation contenue dans un mode, soit $\bar{E} = \bar{n}h\nu$, nous pouvons écrire

$$\rho_\nu = g\bar{E} = (8\pi\nu^2/c^3)\bar{E} \tag{5}$$

(relation qui a été utilisée par Planck pour établir sa formule). Cette relation est équivalente à

$$\rho_\nu = (8\pi\nu^2/c^3)h\nu \cdot \bar{n}. \tag{6}$$

Confrontant (6) avec (3), nous pouvons en déduire que

$$B\rho_\nu = A\bar{n}. \tag{7}$$

Les relations d'Einstein régissant l'absorption et l'émission de rayonnement par un atome se mettent donc sous la forme simple:

$$I_a = (g_2/g_1)N_1 A\bar{n}, \tag{8}$$

$$I_e = N_2 A(1 + \bar{n}). \tag{9}$$

Dans la relation (9) on a coutume de considérer le terme

$$I_s = N_2 A \cdot 1 \tag{10}$$

comme l'intensité d'émission spontanée et le terme

$$I_i = N_2 \cdot A \cdot \bar{n} \tag{11}$$

comme l'intensité d'émission induite.

La relation donnant ρ_ν à l'équilibre thermique ($N_2/N_1 = e^{-\sigma}$) se met alors sous la forme, équivalente à la relation de Planck:

$$\bar{n} = (e^\sigma - 1)^{-1}, \tag{12}$$

mais nous devons remarquer que cette relation ne dépend que de la valeur de la somme $I_e = I_s + I_i$ et non de la manière dont cette somme I_e se répartit entre I_s et I_i.

3. *L'oscillateur harmonique du vide.* Les "modes d'ondes stationnaires" d'une cavité peuvent être identifiés avec les "cellules de l'espace des phases" comme l'a fait Bose[4]). Chacun des modes peut être représenté par un "oscillateur harmoni-

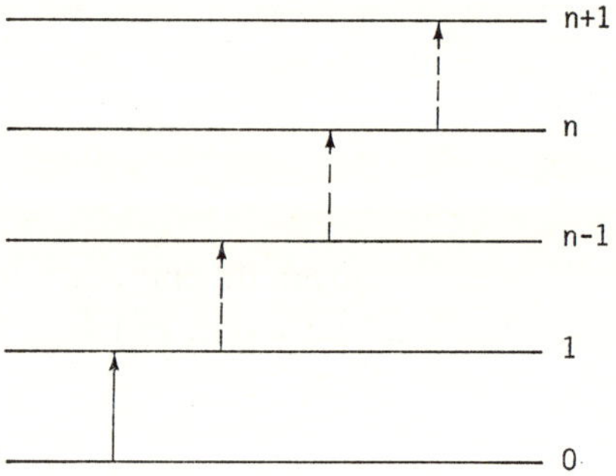

Fig. 1.

que" possédant un nombre infini de niveaux équidistants d'énergie $E_n = (n + \frac{1}{2})h\nu$ [réf. 5]. Un processus d'absorption d'un photon par un atome correspond à une transition d'émission $n \to n - 1$ de l'oscillateur du vide, transition à laquelle la mécanique quantique affecte une amplitude de probabilité

$$a_{n \to n-1} \sim n^{\frac{1}{2}}. \tag{13}$$

De la même façon, un processus d'émission de l'atome s'identifie avec une transition d'absorption de l'oscillateur du vide, transition affectée d'une amplitude de probabilité

$$a_{n \to n+1} \sim (n + 1)^{\frac{1}{2}}. \tag{14}$$

(Les signes $\sim$ signifiant "proportionnelle à".)

Les intensités correspondantes (nombre de photons échangés par unité de temps) sont proportionnelles aux carrés des amplitudes de probabilité, c'est à dire à n pour l'intensité de la transition $n \to n - 1$ à partir du niveau E_n de l'oscillateur, et à $(n + 1)$ pour l'intensité de la transition $n \to n + 1$ à partir du même niveau E_n.

Si l'on veut aboutir aux formules (10) et (11) pour les intensités d'émission spontanée et d'émission induite de l'atome, il faut admettre que dans chaque processus élémentaire $n \to n + 1$ de l'oscillateur du vide il y a bipartition entre émission induite (terme n) et émission spontanée (terme 1).

4. *Nouvelle définition des émissions spontanées et induites.* Une telle manière de voir nous paraît peu naturelle. Chaque processus $n \to n + 1$ de l'oscillateur, affecté d'une amplitude de probabilité proportionnelle à $(n + 1)^{\frac{1}{2}}$ forme un tout indissociable qui doit donner lieu à l'émission d'un rayonnement homogène. Il nous paraît plus naturel de proposer les définitions suivantes pour les deux espèces d'émission:

– Une émission spontanée de l'atome est une émission que se fait dans une cellule *vide* de l'espace des phases. Il lui correspond la transition $0 \to 1$ de l'oscillateur du vide.

– Une émission induite de l'atome est une émission vers une cellule de l'espace des phases qui contient des photons. Il lui correspond l'ensemble des transitions $n \to n + 1$ de l'oscillateur du vide pour lesquelles $n \neq 0$.

Si l'on adopte cette manière de voir, on obtient pour un rayonnement d'équilibre thermique (rayonnement gaussien) les expressions suivantes pour les intensités des deux types d'émission *:

$$I_s = N_2 A \frac{1}{1 + \bar{n}}, \tag{15}$$

$$I_i = N_2 A \left(\bar{n} + \frac{\bar{n}}{1 + \bar{n}}\right). \tag{16}$$

Ces relations diffèrent des relations (10) et (11), mais l'intensité d'émission totale, égale à la somme:

$$I_e = I_s + I_i = NA(1 + \bar{n}) \tag{17}$$

est la même que précédemment et les conditions d'équilibre entre rayonnement et matière restent les mêmes.

Si les formules (15) et (16) représentent effectivement les valeurs des deux types d'émission, de caractères différents, il en résulte des conséquences physiques importantes: l'émission spontanée n'est pas un processus indépendant de la présence de

* Voir appendice.

rayonnement auprès de l'atome. Elle ne peut avoir lieu que dans les cellules de l'espace des phases restées vides. Lorsque de telles cellules contiennent des photons, elle est réduite au bénéfice de l'émission induite. Pour une occupation faible des cellules ($\bar{n} \ll 1$), l'intensité d'émission induite dans ces cellules est le double de celle donnée par les formules d'Einstein.

APPENDICE

A l'équilibre thermique, la répartition des photons entre les g oscillateurs du vide de fréquence ν est régie par la relation de Boltzmann:

$$g_n = g_0 \exp(-nh\nu/kT) = g_0 \, \mathrm{e}^{-n\sigma},$$

g_n étant le nombre d'oscillateurs à l'état n (nombre de cellules de l'espace des phases contenant n photons).
D'où

$$g = \sum_{n=0}^{\infty} g_n = g_0(1 - \mathrm{e}^{-\sigma})^{-1}, \quad \text{ou} \quad g_0 = g(1 - \mathrm{e}^{-\sigma}),$$

$$g_n = g(1 - \mathrm{e}^{-\sigma})\mathrm{e}^{-n\sigma}.$$

Le nombre moyen de photons par oscillateur $\bar{n}$ est défini par

$$\bar{n} = \sum_{n=0}^{\infty} n g_n / \sum g_n .$$

Si nous posons

$$y = \sum_{n=0}^{\infty} \mathrm{e}^{-n\sigma} = (1 - \mathrm{e}^{-\sigma})^{-1}$$

nous avons

$$-\mathrm{d}y/\mathrm{d}\sigma = + \sum_{n=0}^{\infty} n \, \mathrm{e}^{-n\sigma} = \mathrm{e}^{-\sigma}(1 - \mathrm{e}^{-\sigma})^{-2}.$$

D'où

$$\sum_{n=0}^{\infty} n g_n = g(\mathrm{e}^{\sigma} - 1)^{-1} \quad \text{et} \quad \bar{n} = (\mathrm{e}^{\sigma} - 1)^{-1}.$$

Nous retrouvons ainsi la formule (12) équivalente à la relation de Planck, et nous en tirons $\mathrm{e}^{-\sigma} = \bar{n}/(1 + \bar{n})$. K étant une constante à déterminer, nous pouvons écrire, pour la probabilité d'émission spontanée de l'atome (transition $0 \to 1$ de l'oscillateur du vide):

$$I_s = Kg_0 \cdot 1 = Kg(1 - e^{-\sigma}) = Kg \frac{1}{1 + \bar{n}}$$

et pour la probabilité d'émission induite:

$$I_i = K \sum_{n=1}^{\infty} g_n(n + 1) = Kg(1 - e^{-\sigma}) \sum_{n-1}^{\infty} (n + 1) e^{-n\sigma}.$$

Cette dernière somme se calcule ainsément en la décomposant en ces deux termes:

$$\sum_{n=1}^{\infty} e^{-n\sigma} = e^{-\sigma}(1 - e^{-\sigma})^{-1} \quad \text{et} \quad \sum_{n=1}^{\infty} n\,e^{-n\sigma} = e^{-\sigma}(1 - e^{-\sigma})^{-2}.$$

Il vient

$$I_i = Kg(e^{-\sigma} + (e^{\sigma} - i)^{-1}) = Kg \left(\bar{n} + \frac{\bar{n}}{1 + \bar{n}} \right).$$

Il en résulte que

$$I_e = I_s + I_i = Kg(1 + \bar{n}).$$

La confrontation de cette dernière relation avec (9) montre qu'il faut poser $Kg = N_2 A$.

RÉFÉRENCES

1) Einstein, A., Phys. Z. **18** (1917) 121.
2) Lord Rayleigh, Phil. Mag. **49** (1900) 539 et Nature **72** (1905) 243.
3) Jeans, J., Nature **72** (1905) 293.
4) Bose, S. N., Z. Phys. **26** (1924) 178.
5) Debye, P., Ann. Physik **33** (1910) 1427.

Physica **69** (1973) 336–340 © *North-Holland Publishing Co.*

FIELD-DEPENDENT "KORRINGA" RELAXATION OF PROTONS IN ZrH_2

A. E. ZWEERS, H. B. BROM and W. J. HUISKAMP

Kamerlingh Onnes Laboratorium der Rijksuniversiteit Leiden, Leiden, Nederland

(Communication No. 403*d*)

Received 15 June 1973

Synopsis

The proton spin-lattice relaxation rate (T_{1n}^{-1}) in the transition metal hydride ZrH_2 is determined in the temperature (T) range 40 mK $\leq T \leq$ 1 K and at magnetic fields (H) between 1 kOe and 9.5 kOe. At fixed magnetic field the product $T_{1n}T$ is found to be constant, suggesting a Korringa-like relaxation process. However, T_{1n} depends strongly on the magnetic-field strength. In the measured field region T_{1n} is approximately proportional to H^3.

1. *Introduction.* The possibility of polarizing nuclear spins was suggested in 1935 by Gorter[1]) and by Kurti and Simon[2]). This suggestion was based on the property that atomic nuclei have magnetic moments, associated with the nuclear spin, *I*, and further on the experimental demonstration in the same year that ultralow temperatures could be reached by adiabatic demagnetization.

Today this so-called brute-force method lies within the scope of realization. Superconducting coils produce fields of about 100 kOe, while temperatures below 10 mK can be obtained by ^{3}He–^{4}He dilution refrigerators. However, in order to orient protons serious problems arise still, because the thermal contact of the proton spins with the lattice at low temperatures is usually quite small. Hence several other techniques, *e.g.*, dynamic polarization[3, 4]) and nuclear refrigeration (ref. [3, 5]) are used, which circumvent the thermal-equilibrium problem. One of the motivations for the present investigation was the metal-like character of hydrogen in the transition-metal hydrides, which could possibly result in a Korringa-like proton-relaxation process and which is presumably far more effective than the relaxation processes[6]) in the dilute paramagnetic crystals used in the above-mentioned polarization schemes.

The physical properties of the transition-metal hydrides, particularly those concerning the influence of the hydrogenic s electron on the electronic bands of the transition metal, are not well understood. In ZrH_2 several authors[7, 8]) have found

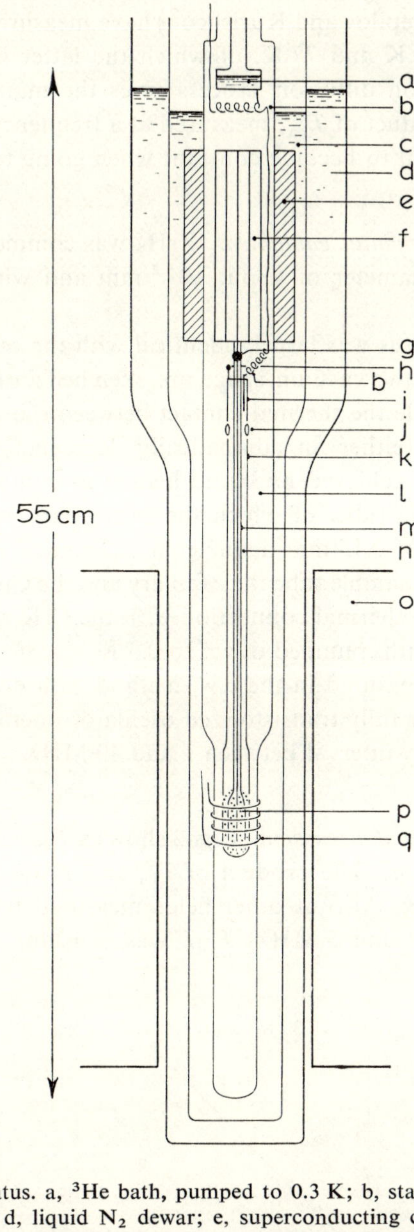

Fig. 1. Cryogenic apparatus. a, ^3He bath, pumped to 0.3 K; b, stainless-steel capillary; c, ^4He bath, pumped to 1.0 K; d, liquid N_2 dewar; e, superconducting coil magnet; f, cooling salt; g, carbon resistance thermometer; h, heater; i, Cu upper wall of the sample tube; j, copper-glass junction; k, pyrex lower wall of the sample tube; l, vacuum space; m, bundle of Cu wires from the cooling salt; n, sample tube; o, magnet; p, sample; q, NMR coil.

evidence that the hydrogen atoms lose their valence electron when diffusing in the Zr metal, affecting both the transition metal and proton spin–lattice relaxation rate[9,10]). Khodosov, Shepilov and Kurishco[7]) have measured T_{1n} in the temperature range between 720 K and 77 K, of which the latter is below the diffusion regime, where the proton diffusion process gives the main contribution to the relaxation rate. The product of T_{1n}, measured at a frequency of 24 MHz, and the temperature T was found to become constant when going to lower temperatures.

2. *Sample and experimental equipment.* ZrH_2 was commercially obtained as a powder with a grain diameter of about 10^{-2} mm and with a purity degree of 99.5 %.

The cryogenic apparatus was largely identical with the one described earlier[6]). The helium dewar and the vacuum space are sketched in fig. 1. As cooling salt we used CrK alum, while the thermal contact between the ZrH_2 powder and the temperature reservoirs (either an adiabatically demagnetized cooling salt or a pumped ^{3}He bath) was achieved by liquid helium as contact agent. He gas was condensed in the sample tube, of which the lower part was glass-walled, *via* a stainless-steel capillary of 0.15 mm diameter with length 2 × 30 cm. In the closed copper upper part of the sample tube the capillary and the Cu bundle of the cooling salt are soldered. Before thermal connection with the CrK alum the capillary was precooled by the ^{3}He bath, pumped down to 0.3 K.

NMR signals were measured in the c.w. method with double T bridges and a marginal oscillator. This fully transistorized oscillator operates at r.f. levels down to 0.1 mV in a frequency interval between 1 and 40 MHz.

3. *Experimental data and discussion.* Fig. 2 shows a T_{1n} *vs.* T plot at a frequency $\nu = 30$ MHz ($H = 7$ kOe). The product of T_{1n} and T was found to be constant between 40 mK and 1 K. Also at other fields measured between 9.5 kOe and 1 kOe (40, 30, 20, 15, 10 and 5 MHz) $T_{1n}T$ was constant, but the value of the

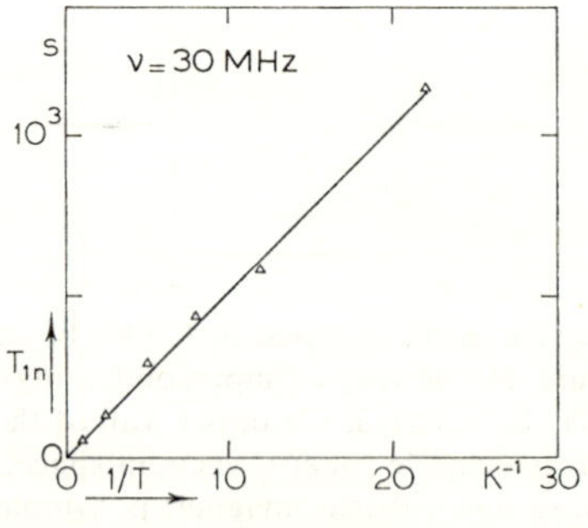

Fig. 2. T_{1n} plotted *versus* $1/T$ at $\nu = 30$ MHz. The drawn line corresponds to a constant value of the product $T_{1n}T$.

product appeared to be strongly field dependent. An illustration is given in fig. 3, which shows the field dependence of T_{1n} at a temperature $T = 0.1$ K.

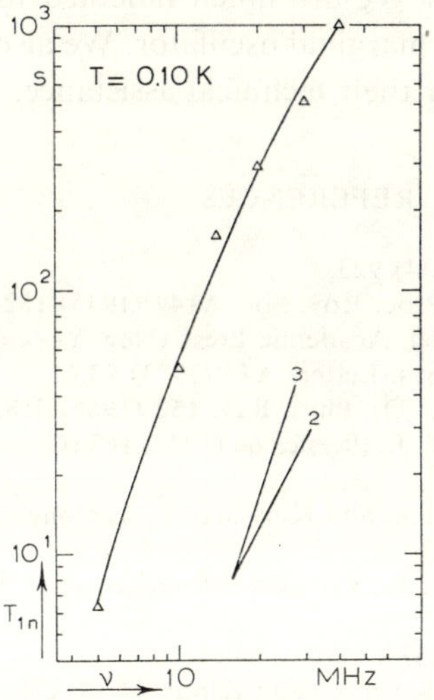

Fig. 3. T_{1n} plotted *versus* ν at $T = 0.1$ K on logarithmic scale. The drawn curve corresponds approximately to $T_{1n} \propto \nu^3$.

The $T_{1n}T$ value at $\nu = 24$ MHz as determined by Khodosov *et al.*[7]), namely $T_{1n}T = 53$ Ks, agrees very well with our result. So, it is unlikely that impurities cause the anomalous field dependence of the "Korringa constant". Further measurements on other hydrides of transition metals will be examined in the near future to clarify the relaxation mechanism(s) involved. It may be mentioned that at $\nu = 5$ MHz even at the lower temperatures variations in temperature were almost instantaneously followed by changes in the NMR signal. From these observations we estimate that the time necessary for establishing thermal equilibrium between cooling salt and sample is less than one second. This demonstrates that the contact-agent properties of liquid ^{4}He are excellent, as already argued by Vilches and Wheatley[11]). Therefore it was also possible to perform relaxation measurements in the following way. After the establishment of thermal equilibrium between the proton spins and the lattice, a heat pulse was applied to the sample, and subsequently the temperature was held constant by continuous heating. Thereafter the decay of the NMR signal was recorded.

Summarizing, the proton spins in ZrH_2 show a rather unexpected strong-field dependence of the nuclear relaxation time at low temperatures. Furthermore at these temperatures below 1 K liquid ^{4}He appears to be very suitable as contact agent for NMR measurements on powders.

Acknowledgments. This investigation is part of the research programme of the "Stichting voor Fundamenteel Onderzoek der Materie (F.O.M.)" which is financially supported by the "Nederlandse Organisatie voor Zuiver Wetenschappelijk Onderzoek (Z.W.O.)". We are much indebted to Mr. R. Hulstman, who designed and constructed the marginal oscillator. We also thank Mr. J. van Weesel and Mr. J. van der Waals for their technical assistance.

REFERENCES

1) Gorter, C. J., Phys. Z. **35** (1934) 923.
2) Kurti, N. and Simon, F. E., Proc. Roy. Soc. **A149** (1935) 152.
3) Daniels, J. M., Oriented Nuclei, Academic Press (New York and London, 1965).
4) Borghini, M. and Udo, F., Phys. Letters **A43** (1973) 93.
5) Langley, K. H. and Jeffries, C. D., Phys. Rev. **152** (1966) 358.
6) Brom, H. B. and Huiskamp, W. J., Physica **60** (1972) 163 (Commun. Kamerlingh Onnes Lab., Leiden No. 391*a*).
7) Khodosov, E. F., Shepilov, N. A. and Kurishco, V. I., Congrès International "L'Hydrogène dans les Métaux", Paris 1972.
8) Engel, N. N. and Johnston, J. E., Congrès International "L'Hydrogène dans les Métaux", Paris 1972.
9) Schreiber, D. S., Phys. Rev. **137A** (1965) 860.
10) Ehrenfreund, E., Weger, M., Korn, C. and Zamir, D., J. Chem. Phys. **50** (1969) 1907.
11) Vilches, O. E. and Wheatley, J. C., Rev. Sci. Instrum. **37** (1966) 819.

Physica **69** (1973) 341–353 © *North-Holland Publishing Co.*

A HIGH-FIELD PHASE TRANSITION IN THE LINEAR CHAIN COMPOUND $CuSO_4 \cdot 5H_2O$

M. W. VAN TOL* and N. J. POULIS

Kamerlingh Onnes Laboratorium der Rijksuniversiteit Leiden, Leiden, Nederland
(Communication No. 403*e*)

Received 4 July 1973

Synopsis

Cupric sulphate pentahydrate contains two nearly independent magnetic systems, originating in the two unequivalent Cu^{2+} ions in the unit cell. One of these systems can be described as one-dimensional chain of spins $S = \frac{1}{2}$ with an antiferromagnetic Heisenberg interaction $J/k = -3.0$ K. The weak coupling between the chains gives rise to a phase transition at about 0.1 K in the field interval between 3 kOe and 38 kOe. This phase transition has been detected by nuclear magnetic resonance and by specific-heat experiments. The results of these measurements are discussed and a tentative theory is developed to explain the nature of the transition.

1. *Introduction.* The relative ease with which cupric sulphate pentahydrate can be obtained as large single crystals is not the only reason for its importance and its long history in crystallography and solid-state physics. Especially the measurements of the past two or three decades prove that this compound is a very special specimen from the magnetic point of view. From the early publications we mention the measurement of the magnetic moment of the Cu^{2+} ion by De Haas and Gorter[1]) and the determination of the magnetic axes of the single crystal by Mookherji *et al.*[2]). In 1948, a single crystal of cupric sulphate pentahydrate was the first magnetic solid in which nuclear magnetic resonance was performed by Bloembergen[3]) and Poulis[4]). From this time on, cupric sulphate has been on the research programme of the Kamerlingh Onnes Laboratory and investigations by means of various methods were carried out. The experiments of Miedema, Van Kempen, Haseda and Huiskamp[5]) indicated the existence of two nearly independent magnetic systems, corresponding to the two unequivalent Cu^{2+} ions in the unit cell. One system was supposed to have relatively strong exchange interactions extending in one dimension, which was assumed to cause short-range order in linear chains at a temperature of about 1 K. The other system should have much weaker inter-

* Present address: Philips Research Laboratories, Eindhoven, The Netherlands.

actions and behave like an almost ideal paramagnetic system at temperatures down to 0.1 K. Nuclear magnetic resonance (NMR) experiments by Wittekoek and Poulis[6, 7]) confirmed this hypothesis and proved that the ions at (0, 0, 0) constitute the linear-chain system, while the paramagnetic ions are situated at ($\frac{1}{2}$, $\frac{1}{2}$, 0). Their NMR experiments also allowed the accurate determination of the interaction J within the chains, the Curie–Weiss constant θ_p of the paramagnetic system and the interaction J_{12} between the two systems. Apart from these data, which are gathered in table I, many new ideas on the behaviour of antiferromagnetic linear chain (ALC) systems were obtained.

TABLE I

	a (Å)	b (Å)	c (Å)	α (deg)	β (deg)	γ (deg)	$-J/k$ (K)	θ_p (K)	J_{12}/k (K)
$CuSO_4 \cdot 5H_2O$	6.14	10.74	5.99	82.3	107.4	102.7	3.0	0.02	0.10
$CuSeO_4 \cdot 5H_2O$	6.23	10.87	6.08	82.2	107.1	102.8	1.7	0.05	0.07

Parallel with the experiments reported before, considerable interest in the theory of ALC systems arose from the basic publication by Bethe[9]) in 1931, in which the eigenstates of the hamiltonian

$$\mathscr{H} = -J\sum_{i=1}^{N} \boldsymbol{S}_i \cdot \boldsymbol{S}_{i+1} \quad (\boldsymbol{S}_{N+1} \equiv \boldsymbol{S}_1), \tag{1}$$

were considered. Without trying to be complete, we mention the calculation of the ground-state energy in the limit $N \to \infty$ by Hulthén[10]), the zero-temperature magnetization isotherm by Griffiths[11]) and the partition function by Inawashiro and Katsura[12]).

Although an ideal one-dimensional spin system of the type described by eq. (1) does not possess a phase transition, it seemed reasonable to expect that a two- or three-dimensional system of weakly coupled chains would do. Since the experimental evidence on cupric sulphate (and on the isomorphic selenate) shows that the (0, 0, 0) ions in these compounds behave like such a system, we decided to search for such a phase transition. The paramagnetic ions at ($\frac{1}{2}$, $\frac{1}{2}$, 0) formed, in a certain way, an extra complication which we expected to overcome by saturating their magnetization by the application of a high magnetic field at a sufficiently low temperature.

The next two sections present the experimental proof of the existence of a phase transition by NMR and specific-heat measurements, respectively. In the last section a tentative though far from complete theory is presented, which might form the starting point for a satisfactory explanation of the observed facts.

2. *Nuclear magnetic resonance.* The magnetization isotherms of a linear-chain compound exhibit their typical character most clearly at temperatures $T \ll |J/k|$ as illustrated in fig. 6 of ref. 12. The zero-temperature isotherm represents a nearly linear relationship between the magnetization M and the external field H for small values of H. With increasing field, the derivative dM/dH gradually increases until it reaches infinity at $H_0 = 2|J/g\beta|$. Above this field the magnetization remains constant at its saturation value. According to calculations of Inawashiro and Katsura[12]) the isotherms at $T \ll |J/k|$ follow the zero-temperature curve closely, except in the near vicinity of H_0, where the sharp edge is rounded off.

In order to obtain the magnetization of the linear-chain system separately from that of the paramagnetic ions, proton magnetic resonance was used to discriminate between the contributions of the two systems in cupric sulphate. In a well chosen orientation of the external field with respect to the crystalline axes, four resonance lines are clearly separated from the rest of the spectrum while one of these lines is the most sensitive one to the ALC magnetization. The application of a high magnetic field simplifies the discrimination between the two subsystems further. When the external field is large compared to the internal field at the proton position due to the Cu^{2+} ions, the shift Δ of a resonance line is to a good approximation proportional to the projection of the internal field on the direction of the external field.

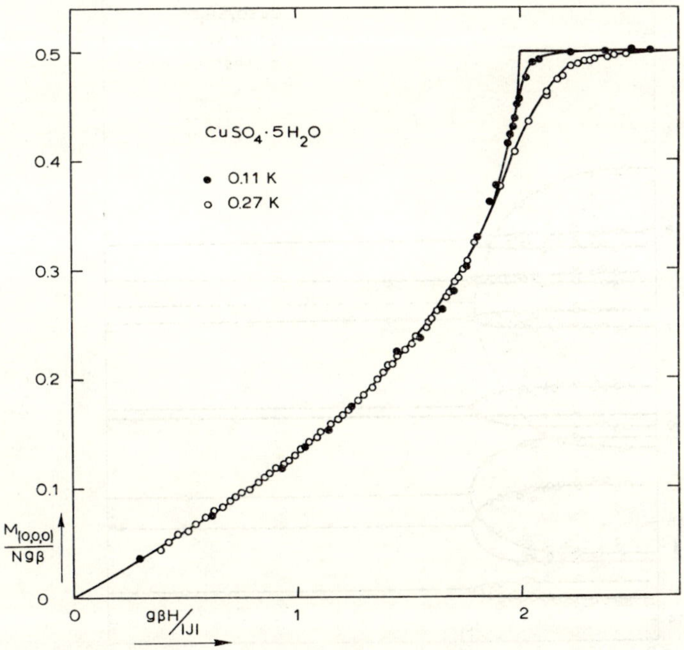

Fig. 1. Magnetization of the linear-chain system in cupric sulphate pentahydrate *versus* field at 0.11 K and 0.27 K. Drawn curves represent the theoretical curves according to refs. 11 and 12, corrected for interchain interaction.

In this case the study of only two resonance lines is sufficient to obtain the magnetizations of the two subsystems separately.

The magnetization of the ALC system obtained in this way is shown on a reduced scale in fig. 1 for temperatures of 0.11 K and 0.27 K. The drawn lines in this figure represent Griffiths's[11]) curve for $T = 0$ and the isotherms for 0.11 K and 0.27 K according to Katsura and Inawashiro[12]), corrected for interchain interaction. This interaction J' has been accounted for *via* a simple molecular-field approximation in which the external field H has been replaced by the effective field

$$H_{\text{eff}} = H + qJ'/g\beta\langle S^z_{\text{ALC}}\rangle,$$

where q represents the number of neighbouring chains in the crystal. The value of qJ'/k from the fitting of Griffiths's zero-temperature isotherm to the experimental data amounts to -0.14 (± 0.03) K. This small value, compared to $J/k = -3$ K,

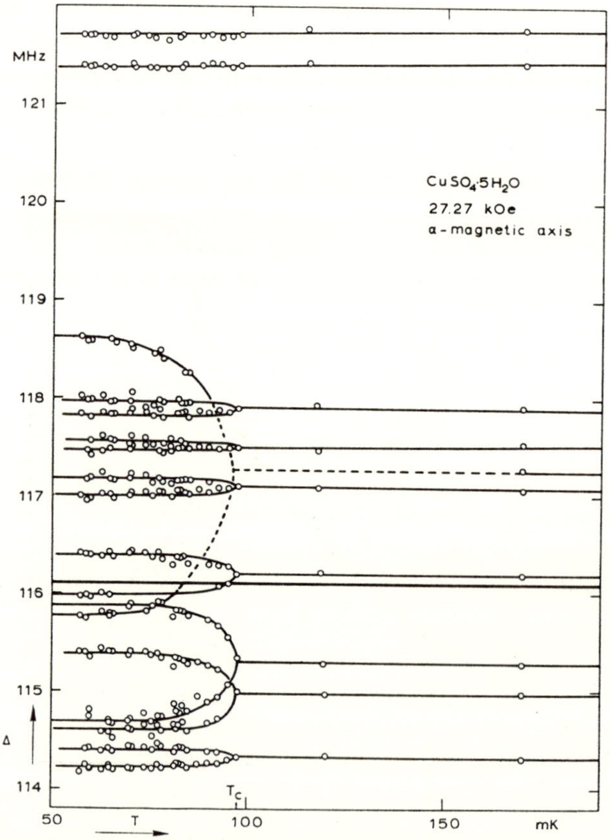

Fig. 2. Resonance frequencies for the ten proton lines in cupric sulphate *versus* temperature. The external field is directed parallel to the α magnetic axis.

ascertains that the (0, 0, 0) ions in cupric sulphate are a very good example of a lattice of weakly coupled antiferromagnetic chains.

In search for possible cooperative effects due to the interchain interaction J' we explored the temperature range below 0.3 K in external fields of such a magnitude that the magnetization of the paramagnetic system was saturated. An example of these measurements is given in fig. 2, where the resonance frequencies of the various protons in the unit cell are plotted against the temperature T in a field of 27.3 kOe. Above 98 mK the resonance frequencies are independent of the temperature, as was expected from the experimental magnetization isotherms given in fig. 1. Below this temperature the resonance lines split and the frequency difference of each pair of "components" shows the characteristic temperature dependence of a spontaneous magnetization. As has been argued elsewhere[13]), the splitting $\nu^+ - \nu^-$ is a direct measure of the difference in the two sublattice magnetizations.

Calculations of the splitting in which the Cu^{2+} ions are represented by point dipoles show that the measured splitting is compatible with the assumption that the components of the sublattice magnetization perpendicular to the external field are temperature dependent while the parallel components are not. The relatively small temperature range in which the splittings have been measured allows only a rough estimate of the spontaneous perpendicular magnetization $M_\perp$ at zero temperature, which yields a value of about one third of the magnetization M_z parallel to the external field.

The relative magnitudes of the line splittings of the different protons in the unit cell prove unambiguously that the canting of the spins below the transition temperature occurs in the linear-chain system only. In lower fields, where the magnetization of the paramagnetic system is not entirely saturated, complications are to be expected and the canted ALC spins seem to induce also a canting of the paramagnetic spins.

3. *Specific heat.* The heat capacity C_H of cupric sulphate will contain contributions of both the paramagnetic and the antiferromagnetic chain system. When the paramagnetic ions are regarded as free spins, the energy-level separation of $g\beta H$ induced by the external field H will cause a contribution to the specific heat of the Schottky type. The maximum of 0.22 R of this contribution occurs at a temperature $T_{max} = 0.42\, g\beta H/k$. The expression for T_{max} shows that at temperatures of the order of the transition temperature T_c, which is about 0.1 K, the paramagnetic system will only contribute appreciably to the specific heat in relatively low fields. The expected slight deviations of the C_H *vs.* T curve from the pure Schottky shape, due to the interactions within the paramagnetic system and to the "cross interaction" J_{12} between the two systems, will be left out of discussion because of their relative unimportance.

At the transition temperature T_c the contribution of the antiferromagnetic linear chains to the specific heat is expected to show the λ anomaly typical for phase transitions of the second kind. However, the area under the peak should be small, since most of the entropy of the chains has already been removed above 1 K. Because the maximum of the specific heat of the paramagnetic system shifts to lower temperatures with decreasing external field, the anomaly caused by the ALC system at T_c will be superposed on the well-known Schottky curve in low fields. An example of this situation is given in fig. 3, which shows the specific heat capacity of $CuSO_4 \cdot 5H_2O$ in a field of 2.91 kOe. A sharp peak is clearly visible although it is small compared to the contribution of the paramagnetic system.

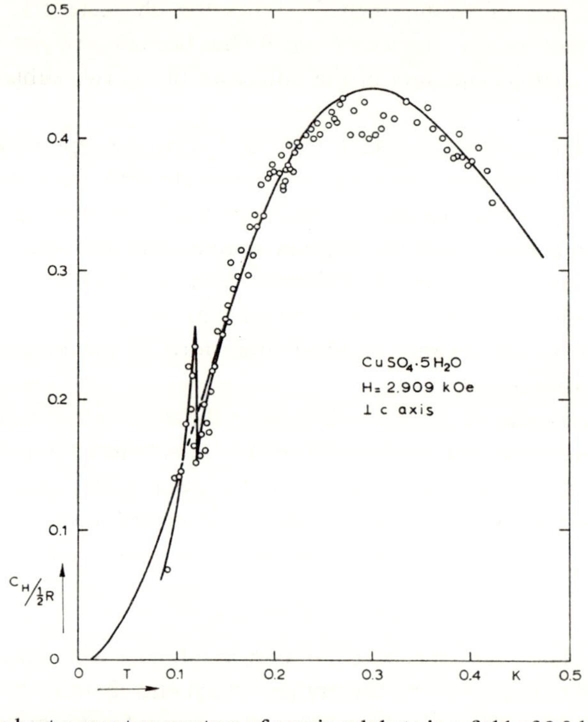

Fig. 3. Specific heat *versus* temperature of cupric sulphate in a field of 2.9 kOe. The drawn curve represents the calculated Schottky anomaly originating in the paramagnetic system.

The drawn curve represents the Schottky specific heat calculated from $C_H/\frac{1}{2}R = (\Delta/2kT)^2 \cosh^{-2}(\Delta/2kT)$, with $\Delta = g\beta H$. At still lower fields the broad maximum of the Schottky curve shifts to still lower temperatures, thus inhibiting the detection of the small linear-chain peak.

In high fields the contribution of the paramagnetic system to the specific heat is small at the transition temperature, because $T_c \ll T_{max}$. Since this contribution is well-known and small enough to be corrected for, measurement of the specific heat in high magnetic fields yields the amount of entropy S_c involved in the phase

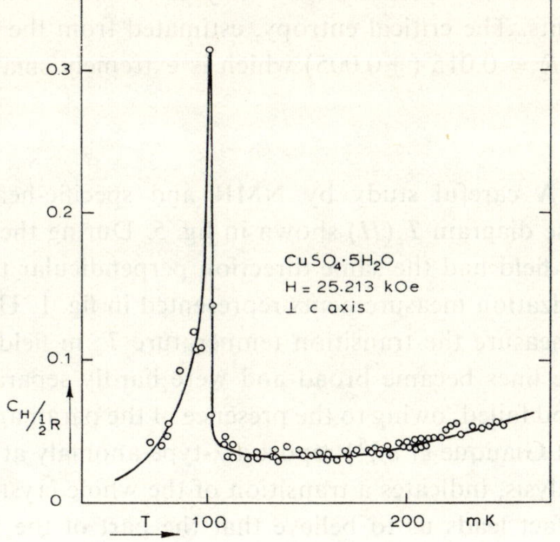

Fig. 4. Specific heat of cupric sulphate in a field of 25.2 kOe. The drawn curve is for visual aid only.

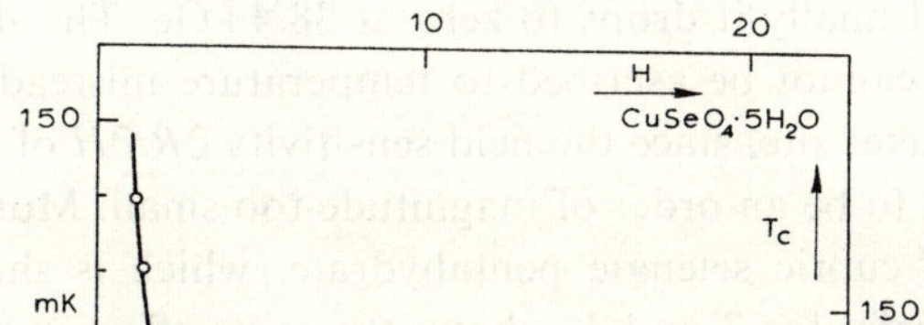

Fig. 5. Phase-boundary curve $T_c(H)$ for cupric sulphate (open symbols). Black dots indicate the transition temperature of cupric selenate and refer to the upper and right scales.

transition of the linear-chain system. Fig. 4 may serve as an example of these high-field measurements. The critical entropy, estimated from the area under the peak, amounts to $S_c/R = 0.015\ (\pm 0.005)$ which is extremely small compared to $\frac{1}{2}\ln 2$.

4. *Phase diagram.* A careful study by NMR and specific-heat experiments finally led to the phase diagram $T_c(H)$ shown in fig. 5. During these experiments the external magnetic field had the same direction perpendicular to the c axis as applied in the magnetization measurements represented in fig. 1. Unfortunately it was not possible to measure the transition temperature T_c in fields below 2 kOe because the resonance lines became broad and were hardly separable while also the specific-heat method failed, owing to the presence of the paramagnetic Schottky anomaly. In zero field Giauque *et al.*[8]) report a λ-type anomaly at 35 mK which, according to their analysis, indicates a transition of the whole crystal to the ferromagnetic state. This fact leads us to believe that the part of the phase diagram below about 10 kOe is not representative of the ordering of a system consisting of weakly coupled linear chains only.

Above 10 kOe T_c increases slightly with increasing field, it reaches a maximum at about 30 kOe and finally it drops to zero at 38.4 kOe. The slight rise between 10 kOe and 30 kOe cannot be ascribed to temperature misreadings due to stray field at the thermometer site, since the field sensitivity $\partial R/\partial H$ of the Speer resistor thermometer proved to be an order of magnitude too small. Moreover, the transition temperature of cupric selenate pentahydrate, which is shown in the same figure on different scales for T and H, shows the same effect in about half the external field. As already mentioned, the intrachain interactions J of sulphate and selenate differ by a factor 1.73. Therefore the field scale in fig. 5 for the selenate has been multiplied by 1.73. When the temperature scale for the selenate is multiplied by 0.83, the measured transition temperatures of cupric selenate coincide over the whole field interval with the curve drawn through the cupric sulphate points. Apart from the remarkably good agreement between the results on both compounds, this indicates that the interchain interactions J' differ by a factor 0.83. The interchain coupling of cupric sulphate being determined from the magnetization measurements as $qJ'/k = 0.14\ (\pm 0.03)$ K, a value of $qJ'/k = 0.17(\pm 0.04)$ results for the selenate.

5. *Theory.* The main theme of this section will be to show that in the presence of an external magnetic field a system of weakly coupled chains of spins with antiferromagnetic Heisenberg interaction may exhibit a transition to a state in which the transverse components of the individual spins have long-range ordering. For that purpose a theory will be set up which starts from the exact description of a single chain and introduces the interchain interaction by means of the molecular-

field theory. The isolated chain will be represented by the hamiltonian with periodic boundary conditions

$$\mathcal{H} = -J\sum_{i=1}^{N} \boldsymbol{S}_i \cdot \boldsymbol{S}_{i+1} - g\beta H \sum_{i=1}^{N} S_i^Z \quad (\boldsymbol{S}_{N+1} \equiv \boldsymbol{S}_1), \tag{2}$$

as proposed by Bethe[9]). Since the interchain interaction J' has been assumed to be much weaker than the intrachain interaction J, appreciable cooperative effects will only occur at temperatures $T \ll |J/k|$. We assume that at these temperatures only the lowest few energy levels of the chains will be important. We consider in particular the states with minimal energy for various values of the external field. These states belong to a subclass C^* of the class of bound states C introduced by Bethe[9]). All states in C^* are nondegenerate[14]) so they can be denoted by the quantum number m for the total spin in the z direction only. The asterisk within the brackets $|{}^*m\rangle$ in the notation indicates that $|{}^*m\rangle$ belongs to the class C^* of lowest-energy states. The energy-level diagram of a ring of eight spins as given by Bonner and Fisher[15]) shows, that when $|{}^*m\rangle$ is the ground state of the chain in a certain external field the first excited state will be either $|{}^*m-1\rangle$ or $|{}^*m+1\rangle$.

The interchain interaction is introduced as a perturbation with the simplest possible form, *i.e.*, by a hamiltonian

$$\mathcal{H}' = -J'\sum_{\alpha=1}^{q} \sum_{i=1}^{N} \boldsymbol{S}_i \cdot \boldsymbol{S}_{i\alpha}, \tag{3}$$

where $\boldsymbol{S}_{i\alpha}$ represents the ith spin in the αth neighbour chain. Since for any value of the external field H both the ground state and the first excited state belong to the class C^*, the matrix elements of $\mathcal{H}'$ connecting the states in C^* will be assumed to play a very important part in the phase transition. In order to get some insight in these elements, the perturbation (3) is replaced by its molecular-field equivalent

$$\mathcal{H}' = -qJ'\sum_{i} \boldsymbol{S}_i \cdot \langle \boldsymbol{S}_{i\alpha} \rangle, \tag{4}$$

where q represents the number of neighbouring chains and $\langle \boldsymbol{S}_{i\alpha} \rangle$ is the expectation value of spin i in chain α. Because of the presence of the magnetic field H in the z direction the terms $\langle \boldsymbol{S}_{i\alpha} \rangle$ will contain a large part $\langle S_\alpha^z \rangle$ that is independent of the position i in the neighbour chains. The part of the perturbation (4) which contains $\langle S_\alpha^z \rangle$ commutes with the unperturbed hamiltonian (2), so that its overall effect can be represented by an effective field

$$H_{\text{eff}} = H + qJ'\langle S_\alpha^z \rangle / g\beta. \tag{5}$$

The remaining part of the perturbation depends on the position i, so that the off-diagonal matrix elements between the lowest two levels read

$$\mathcal{H}'_{m,m\pm 1} = -qJ'\langle {}^*m| \sum_{i=1}^{N} (S_i^x \langle S_{i\alpha}^x \rangle + S_i^y \langle S_{i\alpha}^y \rangle) |{}^*m \pm 1\rangle. \tag{6}$$

Here we have used the fact that an operator like $\sum_i S_i^z(\langle S_{i\alpha}^z\rangle - \langle S_\alpha^z\rangle)$ cannot give a contribution to the off-diagonal elements. A straightforward calculation[16]) shows that under an operator T that describes the translation of the chain over one lattice position, all the states $|{*m}\rangle$ behave as $T|{*m}\rangle = (-1)^m|{*m}\rangle$. Therefore, the only operators which give nonzero contributions to the matrix elements (6) are those which are multiplied by -1 under this translation. They are

$$\mathscr{H}'_{m,m\pm1} = -qJ'\langle\sigma_\alpha^{x,y}\rangle\langle{*m}|\sum_i(-1)^i S_i^{x,y}|{*m}\pm1\rangle, \tag{7}$$

where $\langle\sigma_\alpha^{x,y}\rangle = N^{-1}\langle\sum_{i=1}^N(-1)^i S_\alpha^{x,y}\rangle$ is the mean value of the ordering of the spins in the neighbouring chains. From this equation we may expect that in the case of a phase transition the perpendicular spin components will have long-range ordering. It is further clear, that the transition temperature T_c depends on the external field through the numbers m and $m\pm1$ that indicate the lowest two states. A very rough estimate of this dependence can be obtained by neglecting all energy levels of the chain except the lowest two. In an external field H_m of such a magnitude that the total magnetization per (unperturbed) chain $\langle\sum_i S_i^z\rangle$ equals $m+\frac{1}{2}$ at $T = 0$, only the energy levels $|{*m}\rangle$ and $|{*m+1}\rangle$ will be considered. Using the same reasoning as in ref. 17 each chain may be represented by an effective spin S' with components

$$\begin{aligned} S'_x &= \tfrac{1}{2}(\mathscr{H}'_{m,m\pm1})^{-1}\sum_{i=1}^N(-1)^i S_i^x, \\ S'_y &= \tfrac{1}{2}(\mathscr{H}'_{m,m+1})^{-1}\sum_{i=1}^N(-1)^i S_i^y, \\ S'_z &= -(m+\tfrac{1}{2}) + \sum_{i=1}^N S_i^z. \end{aligned} \tag{8}$$

In this representation the hamiltonian (2) with perturbation (4) is replaced by

$$\mathscr{H} + \mathscr{H}' = -g\beta(H - H_m)S'_z + \eta(\langle S'_{\alpha x}\rangle S'_x + \langle S'_{\alpha y}\rangle S'_y), \tag{9}$$

in which $\eta = 4|qJ'|(\mathscr{H}_{m,m+1})^2/N$ and $\langle S'_{\alpha x}\rangle$ and $\langle S'_{\alpha y}\rangle$ are the expectation values of the effective spins in the neighbour chain α. This equation, in which the spin-independent term has been neglected, is formally equal to the hamiltonian of a spin $S' = \frac{1}{2}$ in a field with components

$$H_x = \eta\langle S'_{\alpha x}\rangle, \quad H_y = \eta\langle S'_{\alpha y}\rangle, \quad H_z = g\beta(H - H'_m). \tag{10}$$

The eigenvalues of eq. (9) and the free energy F of an assembly of N' spins S' are easily calculated:

$$\begin{aligned} F &= N'(-kT\ln z + \tfrac{1}{2}\eta\langle S'_\perp\rangle^2), \\ z &= 2\cosh\{[g^2\beta^2(H - H_m)^2\langle S'_z\rangle^2 + \eta^2\langle S'_\perp\rangle^2]^{\frac{1}{2}}/2kT\}, \end{aligned} \tag{11}$$

in which $\langle S'_\perp \rangle = (\langle S'_x \rangle^2 + \langle S'_y \rangle^2)^{\frac{1}{2}}$ represents the perpendicular spin component. The value of $\langle S'_\perp \rangle$ is determined by minimizing the free energy F and can, in the special case that $H = H_m$, be solved from

$$\langle S'_\perp \rangle = \tfrac{1}{2} \tanh (\eta \langle S'_\perp \rangle / 2kT). \tag{12}$$

The transition temperature T_c at $H = H_m$ follows immediately from the coincidence of the three roots of eq. (12):

$$kT_c = \eta/4 = |qJ'|(\mathscr{H}'_{m,m+1})^2/N. \tag{13}$$

The quantity $|qJ'|$ can be obtained from measurements of the magnetization and application of eq. (5), while the shape of the phase boundary depends entirely on the coefficients $\mathscr{H}'_{m,m+1}$. Although these coefficients have not yet been obtained for infinite ($N \to \infty$) chains, a first approximation is provided by their values in finite rings. The results of straightforward calculations from the exact wave functions in rings of 6, 8, 10 and 12 spins are summarized in table II and plotted against the appropriate values of H_m in fig. 6. Although the transition temperatures could be calculated as a function of H also for values of H different from H_m, we restricted ourselves to the values $T_c(H_m)$, and for each value of N we drew a smooth curve through these points [this curve is different from the actual $T_c(H)$ which has a number of N minima]. It is assumed that the transition temperature

TABLE II

The calculated matrix elements $\mathscr{H}'_{m,m+1}$ for rings with 6, 8, 10 and 12 spins

N	m	H_m	$\mathscr{H}'_{m,m+1}$	$(\mathscr{H}'_{m,m+1})^2/N$
6	0	0.68 474	+2.97 359	1.47 371
	1	1.61 803	−2.89 443	1.39 629
	2	2.00 000	+2.44 949	1.00 000
8	0	0.52 267	−3.52 828	1.55 609
	1	1.32 648	+3.54 705	1.57 270
	2	1.80 194	−3.39 711	1.44 255
	3	2.00 000	+2.82 843	1.00 000
10	0	0.42 324	+4.01 632	1.61 308
	1	1.11 628	−4.08 686	1.67 024
	2	1.59 655	+4.06 717	1.65 419
	3	1.87 939	−3.83 918	1.47 393
	4	2.00 000	+3.16 228	1.00 000
12	0	0.35 584	−4.45 817	1.65 628
	1	0.96 101	+4.55 940	1.73 234
	2	1.41 879	−4.61 230	1.77 277
	3	1.73 275	+4.35 635	1.71 487
	4	1.91 899	−4.23 724	1.49 619
	5	2.00 000	+3.46 410	1.00 000

in the thermodynamic limit ($N \to \infty$) can be obtained by extrapolating these smooth curves. As a result of these calculations the transition temperature T_c increases slightly with increasing external field up to about $H = \frac{3}{4} H_0$. At higher fields T_c decreases and finally drops sharply at $H = H_0 = 2|J/g\beta|$.

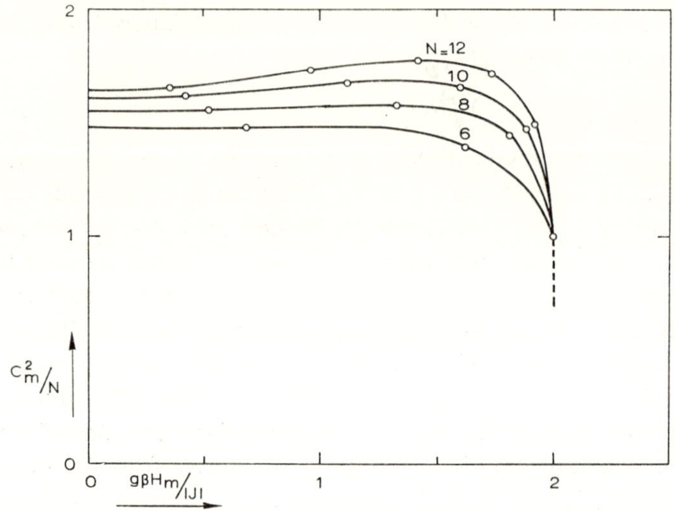

Fig. 6. Values of the coefficients $(\mathscr{H}'_{m,m+1})^2/N$ *versus* H_m as calculated for rings of 6, 8, 10 and 12 spins.

The theory sketched above is subjected to serious criticism, especially since our assumption that only the lowest two levels are important leads to an incorrect result for the entropy in the thermodynamic limit $N \to \infty$. However, we believe that the matrix elements $\mathscr{H}'_{m,m+1}$ may be important in the explanation of the phase transition, especially because of the resemblance between the rather peculiar behaviour of our theoretical results and the measured phase boundary in cupric sulphate pentahydrate.

Acknowledgements. The authors wish to thank Dr. H. W. Capel for his valuable advise and for reading the manuscript. The help of Mr. K. M. Diederix during the experiments is highly appreciated. This investigation is part of the research programme of the "Stichting voor Fundamenteel Onderzoek der Materie (F.O.M.)" which is financially supported by the "Nederlandse organisatie voor Zuiver Wetenschappelijk Onderzoek (Z.W.O.)".

REFERENCES

1) De Haas, W. J. and Gorter, C. J., Commun. Phys. Lab., Leiden No 210*d* (1930).
2) Krishnan, K. S. and Mookherji, A., Phys. Rev. **50** (1936) 860.

3) Bloembergen, N., Physica **16** (1950) 95.
4) Poulis, N. J., Physica **17** (1951) 392.
5) Miedema, A. R., Van Kempen, H., Haseda, T. and Huiskamp, W. J., Physica **28** (1962) 119 (Commun. Kamerlingh Onnes Lab., Leiden No. 331*a*).
6) Wittekoek, S., Poulis, N. J. and Miedema, A. R., Physica **30** (1964) 1051.
7) Wittekoek, S. and Poulis, N. J., Physica **32** (1966) 693.
8) Giauque, W. F., Fisher, R. A., Hornung, E. W. and Brodale, G. E., J. chem. Phys. **53** (1970) 3733.
9) Bethe, H. A., Z. Phys. **71** (1931) 205.
10) Hulthén, L., Ark. Mat. Astron. Fys. **26A** (1938) 11.
11) Griffiths, R. B., Phys. Rev. **133** (1964) A768.
12) Inawashiro, S. and Katsura, S., Phys. Rev. **140** (1965) A 892.
13) Van Tol, M. W., Diederix, K. M. and Poulis, N. J., Physica **64** (1973) 363.
14) "Mathematical Physics in One Dimension" p. 481, E. Lieb and D. Mattis, eds., Academic Press (New York, 1966).
15) Bonner, J. C. and Fisher, M. E., Proc. Phys. Soc. **80** (1962) 508.
16) Van Tol, M. W., thesis Leiden, 1972. See also: Des Cloizeaux, J. and Pearson, J. J., Phys. Rev. **128** (1962) 2131.
17) Tachiki, M. and Yamada, T., J. Phys. Soc. Japan **28** (1970) 1413.
Also: Suppl. Progr. theor. Phys. **46** (1970) 291.

ANALYTIC SUBJECT INDEX